# Enterprise Health Information Management and Data Governance

**Merida L. Johns, PhD, RHIA**

*ISBN: 978-1-58426-155-1*
*AHIMA Product No.: AB104213*

*AHIMA Staff:*
Megan Grennan, Production Development Editor
Leslie Kadlec, MA, RHIA, Director, HIM Practice Excellence, Technical Editor
Jason O. Malley, Vice President, Business and Innovation
Diana Warner, MS, RHIA, CHPS, FAHIMA, Director, HIM Practice Excellence, Technical Editor
Caitlin Wilson, Assistant Editor
Pamela Woolf, Director of Publications



For more information, including updates, about AHIMA Press publications, visit
http://www.ahima.org/publications/updates.aspx

*American Health Information Management Association*
*233 North Michigan Avenue, 21st Floor*
*Chicago, Illinois 60601-5809*

*ahima.org*

# Brief Table of Contents


About the Author . . . xiii

Preface . . . xv

Acknowledgements . . . xix

Introduction: Data and Information Governance . . . xxi

**Part I The Enterprise Solution** **1**

Chapter 1 The Transforming World of Health Information . . . 3

Chapter 2 History of Health Information Systems . . . 21

Chapter 3 Electronic Health Information Systems . . . 45

Chapter 4 The Enterprise Solution: A Modern Model of HIM Practice . . . 61

**Part II The Collaborative Domains** **77**

Chapter 5 Data Governance . . . 79

Chapter 6 Data Architecture Management . . . 105

Chapter 7 Metadata Management . . . 143

Chapter 8 Master Data Management . . . 171

Chapter 9 Enterprise Content and Record Management . . . 189

Chapter 10 Data Security Management . . . 207

Chapter 11 Business Intelligence and Big Data . . . 229

Chapter 12 Data Quality Management . . . 247

Chapter 13 Terminology and Classification Systems Management . . . 267

**Part III Epilogue** **293**

Chapter 14 EIM in Action . . . 295

Appendix A. The Health Insurance Portability and Accountability Act . . . 303

# Detailed Table of Contents


About the Author . . . xiii

Preface . . . xv

Acknowledgements . . . xix

Introduction: Data and Information Governance . . . xxi

**Part I The Enterprise Solution** 1

Chapter 1 The Transforming World of Health Information . . . 3
The Case for an Enterprise Solution . . . 3
Definition of Health Information . . . 6
Data Flow and Information Retrieval Complexity . . . 7
Health Information Content . . . 12
*Clinical Documentation* . . . *12*
*Legal and Administrative Documentation* . . . *13*
Uses and Users of Health Information . . . 15
*Uses of Health Information* . . . *16*
*Users of Health Information* . . . *17*

Chapter 2 History of Health Information Systems . . . 21
Health Information Systems: The Evolutionary Path . . . 21
*Systems Approach* . . . *22*
*Evolution of Health Information Systems* . . . *25*
Paper-Based Systems . . . 25
Electronic-Based Systems . . . 27
*The 1960s-1970's: The Beginning Decades* . . . *28*
*The 1980s: Deployment of Departmental and Functional Systems* . . . *29*
*The 1990s: Electronic Health Record Vision and Rise of the Hybrid Environment* . . . *29*
The Hybrid Environment . . . 31
The New Millennium: Safety Concerns, Cost Reduction, Improved Efficiency . . . 32
History of Management and Governance of Health Information Systems . . . 36
Electronic Health Record . . . 37
*IOM Vision* . . . *37*
*Breaking Down Organization Data Silos* . . . *38*
*Beyond the Organization* . . . *39*

Chapter 3 Electronic Health Information Systems . . . 45
Clinical Information Systems . . . 46
*Anesthesia Information Management System* . . . *47*
*Automated Patient Identification and Bar Coding* . . . *47*
*Clinical Data Repository* . . . *47*
*Computerized Physician/Provider Order Entry* . . . *47*
*Critical Care Information Systems* . . . *48*
*Dietary Department and Management Systems* . . . *48*
*Electronic Document Management Systems* . . . *49*
*Emergency Department Systems* . . . *49*

*Laboratory Information Systems* . . . 49
*Medication Administration Systems* . . . 50
*Medication Reconciliation Systems* . . . 50
*Monitoring Systems* . . . 50
*Nursing Information Systems* . . . 50
*Operating Room Management Systems* . . . 50
*Patient Care Pathways* . . . 51
*Pharmacy Information Systems* . . . 51
*Real Time Locator Systems* . . . 51
*Radiology Information Systems* . . . 51
*Radiology Picture Archiving and Communication Systems* . . . 52
*Results Reporting, Retrieval, and Management* . . . 52
Administrative Information Systems . . . 52
*Registration-Admission-Discharge-Transfer Systems* . . . 53
*Automated Diagnostic Coding* . . . 54
*Bed Management* . . . 54
*Business Intelligence Management* . . . 54
*Financial Information Systems* . . . 54
*Inpatient Scheduling Systems* . . . 54
*Master Patient Index* . . . 55
*Record Completion Management* . . . 55
*Request for and Release of Health Information Management* . . . 56
*Workforce Management* . . . 56
System Interoperability . . . 56
*Levels of Interoperability* . . . 56
*Interfaces* . . . 57
*Computer Networks* . . . 57

Chapter 4 The Enterprise Solution: A Modern Model of HIM Practice . . . 61
Traditional HIM Practice . . . 62
A Contemporary Model of Practice . . . 63
*Domains of Practice* . . . 63
*EHIM Domains* . . . 66
Data Life Cycle Management . . . 66
Data Architecture Management . . . 67
Metadata Management . . . 68
Master Data Management . . . 68
Content and Record Management . . . 69
Data Security Management . . . 69
Information Intelligence and Big Data . . . 69
Data Quality Management . . . 70
Terminology and Classification Management . . . 70
Data Governance . . . 70
*EIM Organization and Structure* . . . 71
*EIM Benefits* . . . 72

**Part II The Collaborative Domains** 77

Chapter 5 Data Governance . . . 79
Data Governance Definitions and Concepts . . . 80
The Case for Data Governance . . . 81
Data Governance Frameworks and Methodologies . . . 82
*Method for an Integrated Knowledge Environment (MIKE2.0)* . . . 82
Sponsorship and Scope . . . 83

Governance Organization . . . 83
Governance Policies . . . 84
Governance Processes . . . 85
Data Investigation and Monitoring . . . 85
Technology and Architecture . . . 85
*Data Governance Institute Framework . . . 85*
Rules and Rules of Engagement . . . 85
*Mission . . . 85*
*Goals, Governance Metrics and Success Measures, and Funding Strategies . . . 86*
*Data Rules and Definitions . . . 86*
*Decision Rights . . . 86*
*Accountabilities . . . 86*
*Controls . . . 86*
People and Organizational Bodies . . . 87
*Data Stakeholders . . . 87*
*Data Stewards . . . 87*
*Data Governance Office (DGO) . . . 88*
Data Governance Processes . . . 88
DGI Data Governance Life Cycle . . . 88
*Value Statement Development . . . 88*
*Program Roadmap Preparation . . . 89*
*Plan and Fund the DG Program . . . 89*
*Design, Deploy, and Govern the DG Program . . . 89*
*Data Management Association Framework . . . 90*
*IBM Data Governance Council Framework and Maturity Model . . . 92*
*Oracle Best Practices in Data Governance Framework . . . 93*
*Khatri and Brown DG Framework . . . 94*
*Framework for Corporate Data Quality Management . . . 95*
*Contingency Approach to Data Governance . . . 96*
*Non-healthcare DG Implementation Cases . . . 98*
Case of BT: Data Quality Focus . . . 98
Case of Deutsche Telekom: Data Quality Focus . . . 98
Interpretations of BT and Deutsche Telekom Cases . . . 99
*DG in the Healthcare Sector . . . 99*
Case of Medco Health Solutions . . . 99

Chapter 6 Data Architecture Management . . . 105
Life Cycles for Managing Systems Development . . . 106
Systems Development Life Cycle . . . 107
System Initiation . . . 108
SDLC Development Methods . . . 109
*The Waterfall Method . . . 109*
*Parallel Method . . . 110*
*Validation and Verification Model . . . 110*
*Rapid Application Development Methods . . . 112*
Iterative Method . . . 112
Prototyping . . . 112
Spiral Method . . . 113
Agile Development . . . 113
Requirements Analysis . . . 114
*Requirements Gathering Techniques . . . 115*
Document Analysis . . . 115
Observation . . . 115
Interviewing . . . 115
Joint Application Development . . . 116
Requirements Analysis Outputs . . . 117

Data Architecture Documentation Techniques and Tools . . . 117
*Use Cases* . . . *117*
*Data Flow Diagrams* . . . *120*
DFD Components . . . 121
Data Flow Diagram Example . . . 121
*Data Models* . . . *125*
Database Structures . . . 125
*Flat File Structure* . . . *125*
*Hierarchical Structure* . . . *126*
*Network Structure* . . . *126*
*Relational Structure* . . . *127*
*Object-Oriented Structure* . . . *128*
*Data Modeling* . . . *130*
Components of an Entity Relationship Diagram . . . 130
Conceptual, Logical, and Physical Data Modeling . . . 131
*Conceptual Data Model* . . . *131*
*Logical Data Model* . . . *132*
*Physical Data Model* . . . *133*
*CASE Tools* . . . *135*
*Data Dictionary* . . . *135*
Applying Data Governance . . . 138

Chapter 7 Metadata Management . . . 143
Metadata Purpose and Types . . . 145
*Technical Metadata* . . . *145*
*Business Metadata* . . . *146*
*Benefits of Metadata Management* . . . *148*
Identifying Metadata . . . 149
*Existing Sources of Metadata* . . . *150*
*Data Life Cycle and Metadata* . . . *153*
*Metadata Schemas* . . . *155*
Dublin Core Schema . . . 156
Continuity of Care Record (CCR) . . . 157
*CCR Syntax and Encoding* . . . *159*
Managing Metadata . . . 161
*Metadata Planning* . . . *161*
*Using and Developing Metadata Schema* . . . *162*
*Metadata Repository Options and Management* . . . *163*
Metadata Repository Approaches . . . 163
Respository Management . . . 165
*Metadata Quality* . . . *166*
Applying Data Governance . . . 167

Chapter 8 Master Data Management . . . 171
Master and Reference Data Concepts . . . 172
*Master Data* . . . *172*
*Reference Data* . . . *173*
Master and Reference Data Management . . . 174
*Identifying Master Data* . . . *175*
*Profiling and Cleansing Master Data* . . . *176*
*Data Matching* . . . *177*
Deterministic Matching . . . 178
Matching with Standardization Rules . . . 178
Probabilistic Matching . . . 178
Steps in Record Matching . . . 179
*Identify Attributes for Matching* . . . *179*

*Identify the Framework for Matching* ... *179*
*Define Thresholds* ... *180*
Data Validation and Remediation ... 180
Ongoing Surveillance ... 180
*Technical Management* ... *182*
Consolidated Hub Implementation ... 183
Registry Hub Implementation ... 183
Coexistence Implementation ... 183
Transaction Hub Implementation ... 183
Applying Data Governance ... 184

Chapter 9 Enterprise Content and Record Management ... 189
Concepts of Enterprise Content and Record Management ... 190
*Records* ... *190*
*Documents* ... *191*
*Content* ... *191*
Document, Record, and Content Management ... 192
*The Continuum of Document, Record, and Content Management* ... *193*
Content Management Tools ... 196
*Collaboration Content Management* ... *196*
*Digital Asset Management* ... *197*
*Web Content Management* ... *197*
Content Management Classification Alternatives ... 197
*Taxonomies* ... *197*
*Thesauri* ... *199*
Ontologies ... 200
*Metadata* ... *200*
Content Life Cycle Management ... 201
Applying Data Governance ... 202

Chapter 10 Data Security Management ... 207
Key Terms in Healthcare Data Security ... 208
Access and Use of Patient Data ... 208
Data Security Breaches ... 209
Security Concepts ... 210
*Protecting Data Privacy* ... *211*
*Ensuring Data Integrity* ... *211*
*Ensuring Data Availability* ... *212*
Security Threats ... 212
*Threats Caused by People* ... *212*
*Threats Caused by Environmental, Hardware, or Software Factors* ... *213*
The Health Insurance Portability and Accountability Act ... 214
Developing a Data Security Program ... 216
*Security Organization* ... *217*
*Security Plan* ... *217*
Evaluation of Information Assets ... 218
Evaluation of Security Risk and Vulnerability ... 219
Protection, Detection, and Response ... 221
*Awareness Training – Operational Control* ... *221*
*Risk Management Program – Management Control* ... *221*
*Incident Detection – Technical Control* ... *221*
*Incident Response Plan and Procedures – Operational Control* ... *222*
*Access Controls – Technical Control* ... *222*
*Physical Controls – Operational Control* ... *222*
*Administrative Controls – Management Control* ... *222*
*Software Application Controls – Technical Control* ... *222*

*Network Controls – Technical Control* . . . 222
*Business Continuity Plan – Operational Control* . . . 223
*Data Quality Control Processes – Operational Control* . . . 223
Applying Data Governance . . . 224

Chapter 11 Business Intelligence and Big Data . . . 229
Data and Healthcare Organizations . . . 230
*Primary Data Sources* . . . 231
Clinical Primary Data . . . 231
Administrative and Operational Primary Data . . . 232
*Secondary Data Sources* . . . 232
Internal Secondary Data . . . 232
External Secondary Data . . . 233
Data for Decisions . . . 234
*Decision Making Levels* . . . 235
*Access and Reporting* . . . 236
*Analytic Approaches* . . . 237
Business Intelligence Maturity Models . . . 238
Business Intelligence Data Life Cycle . . . 239
*Data Acquisition* . . . 239
*Data Cleansing and Transformation* . . . 240
*Data Integration* . . . 240
*Data Reduction* . . . 241
*Data Repositories* . . . 241
Business Intelligence Architecture . . . 242
Applying Data Governance . . . 243

Chapter 12 Data Quality Management . . . 247
The State of Data Quality . . . 248
Data Quality Dimensions . . . 249
Methods for Data Quality Management and Assessment . . . 252
*AHIMA Data Quality Management Model* . . . 252
Framework . . . 252
Key Processes . . . 253
Measurement . . . 256
Implementation . . . 257
Governance . . . 257
*Canadian Institute for Health Information Data Quality Framework* . . . 257
Framework . . . 258
Key Processes . . . 258
Measurement . . . 259
Implementation . . . 259
Governance . . . 259
*GS1 Data Quality Framework 3.0* . . . 259
Framework . . . 260
Key Processes . . . 260
Measurement . . . 261
Implementation . . . 261
Governance . . . 261
Applying Data Governance . . . 262

Chapter 13 Terminology and Classification Systems Management . . . 267
Terminologies and Classifications in Healthcare . . . 268
History of Terminology and Classification Systems . . . 268
Terminologies and Classifications Used for Administrative and Statistical Reporting . . . 271
*International Classification of Diseases, Ninth Revision, Clinical Modification* . . . 272

*International Classification of Diseases, Tenth Revision, Clinical Modification/ Procedure Coding System* . . . 272
*Current Procedural Terminology* . . . 273
*Healthcare Common Procedure Coding System* . . . 273
*National Drug Codes* . . . 274
Other Terminologies and Classifications . . . 274
*Systematized Nomenclature of Medicine Clinical Terms* . . . 274
*Logical Observation Identifiers, Names and Codes* . . . 274
Terminology and Classification Challenges . . . 275
Data Set Standards . . . 277
*Uniform Hospital Discharge Data Set* . . . 278
*Uniform Ambulatory Care Data Set* . . . 280
Interoperability and Data Interchange Standards . . . 281
*Standards for Interoperability* . . . 282
Data Mapping . . . 283
*Data Mapping Principles* . . . 284
*Equivalence Ratings* . . . 286
Applying Data Governance . . . 288

**Part III Epilogue** **293**

Chapter 14 EIM in Action . . . 295
Retreat Planning . . . 296
*Retreat Participants* . . . 296
*Retreat Facilitator* . . . 296
*Retreat Setup* . . . 296
*Retreat Preparation* . . . 297
Retreat Agenda . . . 298
Summary of the Retreat . . . 300

Appendix A. The Health Insurance Portability and Accountability Act . . . 303

Glossary . . . 315

Index . . . 333

# About the Author

Merida L. Johns, PhD, RHIA, has more than 40 years of health information management experience on national and international levels and is a noted author and presenter in the field. She has over 50 published articles and has authored several books and book chapters in health information management and healthcare informatics. Dr. Johns holds B.A. and B.S. degrees from Seattle University, a Master's in Community Services Administration from Alfred University, New York, and a PhD from The Ohio State University.

She began her career in 1973 and held the positions of Director of Quality Assurance, Assistant, and Director of Medical Record Departments. Dr. Johns held tenured positions at The Ohio State University and the University of Alabama at Birmingham where in 1991 she was the founding director of the nation's first Master's Program in Health Informatics for the training of healthcare CIOs.

Dr. Johns held numerous elected and appointed professional positions with AHIMA, AMIA, CAHIIM, HIMSS, professional state associations, and non-profit community groups. She served as AHIMA's president in 1997 and received three AHIMA national honors including Professional Achievement, Champion, and Distinguished member awards. Most recently, in 2013, she received the Illinois Health Information Management Association's Professional Achievement Award.

Currently, Dr. Johns heads up The Monarch Center for Women's Leadership Development, a company she founded that helps women help themselves fulfill their leadership and economic potential through leadership coaching and workshops.

# Preface

Call it a data deluge, data explosion, data overload, or data revolution: the twenty-first century is the data century. Digital data growth rates are increasing at a phenomenal pace for most businesses. A recent study finds digital data more than doubling every two years. In 2011, the amount of data created and replicated was projected to surpass 1.8 trillion gigabytes of data. This is a growth factor of nine times since the data phenomenon study began in 2005 (Gantz and Reinsel 2011). How can we conceptualize this amount of data? Picture a stack of DVDs the equivalent of 480,000 miles high. That equals almost 20 trips around the circumference of the earth, or a trip to the moon and back!

This textbook tackles how healthcare organizations can manage their data in this era of dramatic data explosion and growing deployment of information technologies.

## The Data Challenge

Today, individuals create data as personal e-mail, social media, digital pictures, videos, word-processed documents, and online transactions. Business enterprises that employ enterprise resource management (ERM) systems, customer relationship management (CRM) systems, and sophisticated business intelligence (BI) solutions are markedly increasing the amount of data captured and stored about customers, products, processes, suppliers, partners, and competitors. Furthermore, regulatory requirements play a role in the data deluge. Legislation, such as the Sarbanes-Oxley Act and the Health Insurance Portability and Accountability Act (HIPAA), requires companies to maintain more data for longer periods of time. Technological advances add to the data avalanche, making it possible to store data for longer periods of time.

Just like other industries, healthcare is experiencing massive data growth. Industry experts anticipate the volume of data to grow by 25 – 50 percent annually as a result of electronic health records (EHRs) deployment, sophisticated monitoring and imaging technologies, new advances in medicine such as genomics, implementation of new information technologies, and legislative mandates (BridgeHead Software 2010).

Increasingly, data challenges in healthcare extend to both the management of internal enterprise data and the management of external data. More and more, healthcare is focused on health and wellness, federal mandates that improve the experience of care and the health of the population, and reducing per capita costs of healthcare. As a result, enterprises need to incorporate and manage data generated from external sources and have the capability to interchange data with a variety of providers, state and federal agencies, and others associated with the delivery and payment of healthcare services and the management of population health. All of these factors create complex and challenging data management issues.

Like companies in other industries, healthcare enterprises including hospitals, clinics, and physician practices, suffer from data quality problems. Data quality issues can be symptoms of a plethora of other problems. To remedy and prevent these causes, become more strategically and operationally effective, make more informed decisions, offer better services, and improve patient care and outcomes, healthcare organizations must take a 180-degree turn in the way they view and manage their data. The drivers and imperatives for better information, such as a more competitive marketplace and a growing demand for accountability, are reaching a crescendo. Healthcare organizations, large and small, must understand their sustainability and future viability relies on the quality of their data and how they manage this resource on an enterprise-wide basis.

## Data Management Challenges

Establishing an enterprise-wide data management program is no small feat. There are several reasons why organizations encounter difficulty in launching an organization-wide program. One reason is that managing data and information as organizational assets is a relatively new concept for many businesses, including healthcare.

The concept of data as an asset is difficult to grasp, and until recently most business college courses have not treated the management of data in the same way as other assets like people, buildings, and equipment. A healthcare organization, for example, understands that magnetic resonance imaging machines, monitoring devices, and buildings are assets; these are tangible things they can see and feel. But data are different. People can't touch or visualize data in the same way as for other assets. Consequently, organizations do not place the same weight on data as they do on workforce, financial, and material assets. In healthcare, return on investment (ROI) does not necessarily play out the same way as in other businesses. Other industries measure ROI in terms of increasing revenue. In those industries, the business case for data management is that it helps to grow revenue through better leverage of customer relations by improving customer retention, reducing attrition rates, and increasing operational efficiency. In healthcare, the object is to keep patients healthy, reduce unnecessary and duplicative tests and medication administration, and shorten patient stays. This means providing better healthcare does not necessarily result in increased revenue. ROI calculation is not as tangible in a bottom line perspective in healthcare as in other industries, so healthcare organizations must use other measures to make the business case for enterprise information management (EIM). This textbook strives to arm the reader with a strong case for EIM.

## Health Information Management: The Enterprise Solution

Like other industry data and information management specialists, information technology and the information economy are drastically transforming the roles and functions of health information management (HIM) professionals. Because data management in a digital era is a new and developing discipline in healthcare and other industries, the concepts and practices in data management are dynamic and evolving. Consequently, there are a myriad of different terms, definitions, and models of practice that have been developed to describe the discipline. Unfortunately, there is no precise and agreed-upon definition or description of the totality of functions that encompass data and information management. Even professional associations in the domain are not synchronized in how they define the evolving discipline. However, the majority of worldwide industries are in agreement that data in today's world are a critical element of the twenty-first century economy and must be treated as a tangible enterprise asset.

The primary purpose of this textbook is to provide the foundation and guide for the roles, functions, and practices that healthcare organizations must embrace for successfully managing healthcare data in a digital era. This book takes an integrative approach to the traditional roles of HIM, offering challenging opportunities for enriching the practice domain and leveraging the benefits of quality data for the healthcare sector. A primary feature of this textbook is providing the context in which health information exists, taking a systems view of how people, processes, technology, and the content of data are intermingled, related, and dependent on one another. Whenever possible, the text differentiates between data and information using the customary distinction that data are raw facts, the input into an information system, while information provides meaning to data, derived from data processing, and is the output of an information system. For a full explanation, see the Introduction to this text.

However, in real-life application, such distinctions may become unclear and there often are areas of overlapping management functions among these. Since the quality dimensions of data directly impact the usefulness and quality of information, the text advocates that data management is a critical and associated component of information management and thus places it under the umbrella of EIM.

The intent of the book is not to prescribe a specific roadmap for EIM. Instead, it provides a framework and logical structure to help students understand the components of HIM in a digital era and to provide them with opportunities to develop the necessary skills for performing functions associated with these components.

While there are many definitions proposed for HIM, the premise of this text is that it is defined as:

> *The systematic study and practice of the planning, organization, and coordination of healthcare information focusing on how it is structured and designed, captured, stored, disseminated, used, disposed, and kept reliable and secure. Encompassing people, processes, technology, and content, the purpose of the discipline is to manage information as an asset, ensuring that its value is identified and leveraged to its fullest for all stakeholders across the healthcare environment.*

At the heart of the definition is that health information is an asset, and should be managed so that its value is exploited for the benefit and interests of all stakeholders. This text takes the position that in the digital era, the scope of HIM practice goes beyond traditional information management tasks. The text builds an argument for a new model of HIM practice that incorporates enterprise data management and its governance.

Although HIM can and should encompass more than digital media, this textbook concentrates on electronic HIM. It does not explore the technical application of clinical vocabularies and classification systems for coding or healthcare reimbursement methods, areas that traditionally are considered within the practice of HIM professionals.

# Organization

The text is divided into three parts plus appendices:

Part I provides foundational material about the complexities of data flow, the evolution of healthcare information systems, concepts of EIM, and the content, context, uses, and users of health information. Chapter 1 presents the narrative, Exploring Enterprise Information Management: The St. Rita's Healthcare System Case Study, used throughout the book to illustrate current data issues and how HIM professionals can resolve them. Students can use chapters 1, 2, and 3 either as a review for those who have an understanding of healthcare data and information system concepts, or as an introduction for students who have not had previous coursework in these subjects. Chapter 4 completes the introductory material with an in-depth treatment of EIM.

Part II is a series of chapters on each of the core EIM domains and associated practices. While the functions of information management may be carried out in a department or business unit context, their best leverage and benefits are realized when they are coordinated on an enterprise level. The explored enterprise functions include data governance, data architecture, metadata management, master data management, enterprise content and record management, data security management, business intelligence and big data, data quality management, and terminology and classification systems management.

Part III, chapter 14, provides an opportunity for students to experience how a project effort comes to a conclusion and to join the EIM team in making decisions about the road ahead for St. Rita's by critiquing a draft version of the EIM final report. This chapter can be used as either a simulation or the foundation for a rigorous class discussion.

# Features

## Exploring Enterprise Information Management: The St. Rita's Healthcare System Case Study

Introduced in chapter 1 and carried throughout the text as a boxed narrative, the case study for St. Rita's Healthcare System brings a real-world perspective to student learning. A case study approach introduces, coordinates, and explores the concepts and interrelationships of EIM and data governance. The St. Rita's Healthcare System case study brings to life and clarifies key textual concepts through the interactions, discussions, problem-solving efforts, and decisions made by the recurring cast of characters on the EIM team at St. Rita's Healthcare System. It includes many of the challenges that most healthcare organizations now face, and that students will encounter in the HIM workplace. All characters and the St. Rita's Healthcare System appearing in this work are fictitious. Any resemblance to real persons or places, living or dead, is purely coincidental.

## Part of the Team: Topics for Discussion and Action

Students are invited to be a part of the St. Rita's case study through a set of activities at the end of each chapter. Part of the Team exercises are designed to get students involved in simulated activities that provide assistance to the St. Rita's case study.

## Advanced Concepts

A set of advanced exercises, called Advanced Concepts, is provided for in-depth analysis and study. These exercises and activities are designed for senior baccalaureate- and graduate-level students.

## Learning Objectives, Figures, Tables, and Key Terms

Each chapter contains learning objectives that call out the main concepts and are in accordance with Bloom's Taxonomy. An abundant number of figures and tables are included throughout the book as a pedagogical tool to explain and reinforce key concepts. Key terms appear throughout the text in bold font.

## Chapter 14, EIM in Action

Chapter 14, EIM in Action, functions as a culminating and summative activity that integrates the knowledge and perspectives of the previous chapters and concludes the St. Rita's Healthcare System Case Study. Students are invited to participate in a simulated proposal development effort to establish an EIM division for St. Rita's Healthcare System. The final proposal developed by the St. Rita's EIM team is provided in the student workbook that accompanies this text. This chapter can be used either as a simulation for a class exercise or as the foundation for a rigorous discussion.

## Student Workbook

The student workbook contains the following information to help students develop further EIM knowledge and skills:

- Additional learning objectives for each chapter
- List of key terms
- The Practice Side, real life cases that augment the theory and application provided in the related chapter
- Application exercises provide opportunities to further explore the content in each chapter
- Review questions for each chapter, aimed at higher levels of cognitive reasoning

## Instructor's Manual

An instructor's manual is available that serves as an instructional guide for each chapter. It includes the following:

- A high-level overview for each chapter
- Additional learning objectives for each chapter
- Glossary of key terms
- Suggested instructional methods
- Suggested projects
- PowerPoint slide decks for each chapter

## References

Bridgehead Software. 2010 (July). Report: The BridgeHead Software International 2010 Data Management Healthcheck Survey. http://www.bridgeheadsoftware.com/uploads/BH_Rpt_Data_management_survey_results_US_Letter.pdf.

Gantz, J. and D. Reinsel. 2011 (June). Extracting Value from Chaos. IDC. http://www.emc.com/collateral/analyst-reports/idc-extracting-value-from-chaos-ar.pdf.

# Acknowledgements

This book is dedicated, with gratitude, to Mary Alice Hanken, PhD, RHIA; Gretchen Murphy, MEd, RHIA, FAHIMA; Kathleen Waters, RHIA; and in memory of Eileen O'Donnell, MBA, MEd, RHIA, pathfinders who guided the HIM profession into the digital era, and who were my first HIM mentors and role models; and in the memory of health informaticians Frederick Ostroy, PhD and Terrel W. Herzig, whose passion for doing the right thing provided the North Star for writing this text.

Special acknowledgement to my colleagues Gary Davis, MSHI; J. Michael Hardin, PhD; Gretchen Murphy, MEd, RHIA, FAHIMA; and Shelia Searson, CIPP whose insights and critique added perspective and quality to the text. To Megan Grennan and Pamela Woolf, for their help polishing a diamond in the rough and whose perseverance and belief in the text turned dream into reality.

---

AHIMA Press would like to thank Deborah K. Green, RHIA, MBA and Sofia Empel, PhD, CRM, IGP for their review and feedback for this book.

# Introduction

## Data and Information Governance

Vendors, consultants, and others in the health information management (HIM) industry sometimes use data governance (DG) and information governance (IG) interchangeably. However, they are not the same thing (Dimick 2013). Using the terms interchangeably not only obscures the important differences between the two, but adds confusion in the industry and marketplace. The intent of this introduction is to provide clarity between the purpose of and the functions performed by both.

## Data, Information, Knowledge, and the Wisdom Pyramid

Understanding the distinction between DG and IG begins with examining the difference between the governed assets: namely data and information. The data, information, knowledge, and wisdom (DIKW) hierarchy best illustrates the differences (figure 1). References to the DIKW hierarchy in knowledge management and information science literature first appeared in the 1980s and are the essentials of computer, information and library sciences (Bernstein 2011). In the DIKW hierarchy, data are facts that have no relation to any other fact or event. For example, "The blood pressure readings are 138/80, 140/82, and 138/80" has no particular meaning other than the recording of three facts or events. When a fact is related to some other data, however, the relationship forms a piece of information. For example, if the blood pressure readings are related to being Mr. Smith's, then the data are transformed into information. Likewise, if the blood pressure readings are related to specific dates and times, this becomes a piece of information. Mr. Smith's blood pressure readings over time represent a pattern of values that are above the blood pressure normal range, indicating a possible pre-hypertension stage, and represent knowledge and a move up the DIKW hierarchy.

Figure 1. DIKW pyramid

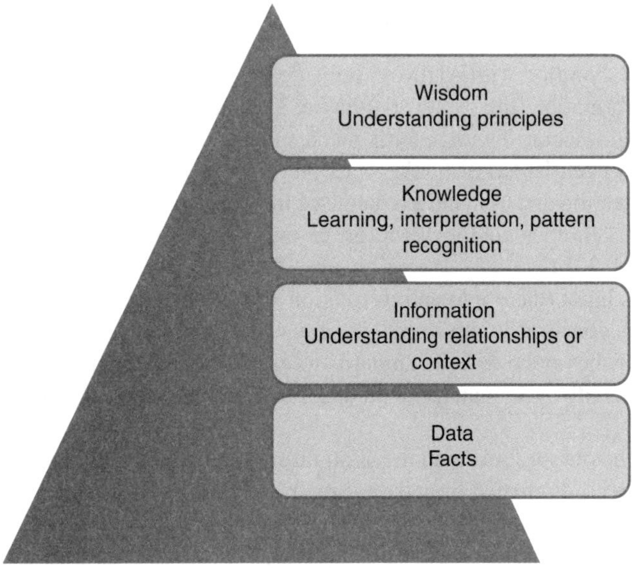

©Merida L. Johns

Successively higher levels in the DIKW pyramid are dependent on the levels below. There is a direct relationship between data and information. The quality of information positively correlates to the quality of the data which compose the information. Unavailable, incorrect, or incomplete data adversely affect the quality of the information. In the blood pressure example above, missing, incomplete, or incorrect data would negatively affect the information provided to the physician about Mr. Smith.

While a relationship exists between data and information, it is evident they are not the same thing. Consequently, the governance of each would be expected to be different (Kooper et al. 2011).

## Distinctions Between Data and Information Governance

**Governance** is generally defined as the establishment of policies and the continual monitoring of their proper implementation for managing organization assets to enhance the prosperity and viability of the organization (Business Dictionary). Essentially, governance is a process with an enforcement component (Ladley 2012). Governance is an enterprise activity. Both DG and IG exercise authority across the entire organization. In both, the governance power is vested in a top organizational authority, and governance is executed through a framework of policies, standards, rules, and decision rights and is implemented by means of a formal structure of assigned roles, responsibilities, and accountabilities.

Use of the term data governance traces back to the 1990s, when organizations began to realize the value of data expanded beyond its use in operational transactions and extended to decision support functions (Chen 2010). To support analysis and decision making, organizations consolidated data, usually by using data warehouse technology. Data warehouses made consolidation technologically possible, but they could not guarantee data quality. It became evident that organizations needed policies and standards to ensure data across the organization were consistently defined, structured, accurate, and current before being loaded into a data warehouse. Over the past two decades, **data governance** has broadened from the governance of structured data for data warehousing purposes. As discussed in chapter 5, DG is now viewed to include oversight of data in any format, including structured and unstructured data (DAMA 2010). DG is an enterprise-wide function for defining, implementing, and enforcing policies and standards for all enterprise data (Chen 2010).

Where DG focuses on data assets, IG is traditionally defined in terms of records management, privacy regulation, information security, data flows, and ownership (Economist Intelligence Unit 2008). IG emerged scientifically in 2004 as a framework to support the work of the National Health Service (NHS) on security and confidentiality of healthcare information and how patient identifiable information can be used. The NHS framework is based on the concepts that information should be secure and confidential, obtained fairly and efficiently, recorded accurately and reliably, used effectively and ethically, and shared lawfully and appropriately (Donaldson and Walker 2004). The Sedona Conference has a corresponding view of IG, defining it as an organization's coordinated approach to satisfy legal and compliance requirements while managing risks and optimizing value (The Sedona Conference 2013). In a benchmarking study of IG in healthcare carried out in collaboration with AHIMA, IG is defined as "a comprehensive platform for the effective and efficient management of the information [life cycle]" (Cohasset Associates and AHIMA 2014, 12). This definition appears in line with traditional functions associated with records management.

An evolving view of IG, however, is that it should focus on the proper use and application of information, concerned with the seeking and finding, creation and use, and exchange of information. This viewpoint seeks to optimize the value of information to all concerned stakeholders and views information, which is interpreted data, as an intangible asset unlike technology or data (Kooper et al. 2011).

In DG, the asset governed is input (data) into an information system. Data can be in multiple forms form such as text, video, or audio. DG is typically concerned with oversight of data quality and how data are defined, captured, structured, stored, and retrieved and establishes policies and standards to execute its oversight or governance in these areas. These encompass functions such as data life cycle management, data modeling, metadata management, master data management, and data security, among others.

In IG the asset governed is the output (information) of an information system. IG focuses on the control and use of the actual documents, reports, and records created from data (Smallwood 2013). IG policies are typically concerned with how information is used, shared, and analyzed by the organization. It includes policies, procedures, and standards concerned with information confidentiality, regulatory compliance, and ethical information use. Examples of common IG standards and policies relate to information release, regulatory compliance for documentation, information retention and disposal, and controls that minimize misinformation, disinformation, and error. Figure 2 illustrates some of the distinctions between DG and IG functions.

Figure 2. Comparison of DG and IG functions

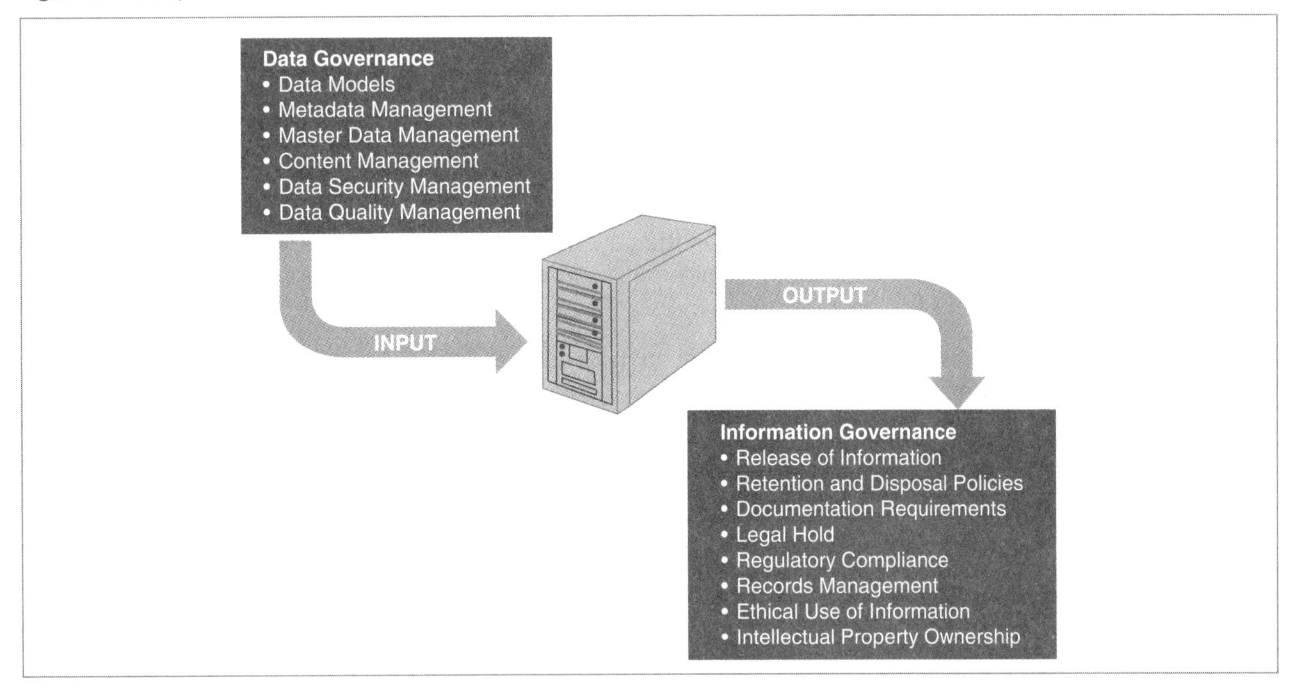




Similar distinctions between DG and IG have been made in reviewing HIM baccalaureate degree competencies and domains. Here, DG is defined in relation to data management functions concerned with reliability, validity, and interoperability of data, and IG is defined in relation to functions concerned with release of information and appropriate interpretation of analytics (Reinhart-Thompson and White 2014). In the HIM curriculum, domains concerned with data content, structure, standards, and analytics are associated with DG, whereas domains related to information protection, compliance, and leadership are associated with IG.

Human and physical resources are critical business assets, but they are different from one another. No company would govern its human capital using the same strategies, policies, procedures, and standards as it would to govern its physical plant. Likewise, data and information are both critical assets and, while related, they are not the same. Businesses must give due attention to DG and IG, requiring governance policies, standards, and organizational structures that uniquely sustain the business value and purposes of each (Nadhan 2014).

## References

Bernstein, J. H. 2011. The data-information-knowledge-wisdom hierarchy and its antithesis. *NASKO, 2*(1): 68–75. https://journals.lib.washington.edu/index.php/nasko/article/viewFile/12806/11288.

Business Dictionary. n.d. http://www.businessdictionary.com/definition/governance.html.

Chen, W. 2010. A Brief History of Data Governance. Kalido Conversations. http://blog.kalido.com/a-brief-history-of-data-governance/.

DAMA. 2010. *The DAMA Guide to the Data Management Body of Knowledge*. Bradley Beach, NY: Technics Publications LLC.

Dimick, C. 2013. Governance apples and oranges: Differences exist between information governance, data governance, and IT governance. *Journal of AHIMA* 84(11): 60–62.

Donaldson, A. and P. Walker. 2004. Information governance—A view from the NHS. *International Journal of Medical Informatics* 73(3): 281–284.

Economist Intelligence Unit. 2008. The future of enterprise information governance: A report from the Economist Intelligence Unit.

London: The Economist Intelligence Unit Limited. https://c.ymcdn.com/sites/www.simnet.org/resource/group/0F59E34E-CD05-4889-AAD6-7C2891934489/the_economist.pdf.

Kooper, M.N., R. Maes, and R. Lindgreen. 2011. On the governance of information: Introducing a new concept of governance to support the management of information. *International Journal of Information Management* 31(3): 195–200.

Ladley, J. 2012. *Data Governance How to Design, Deploy and Sustain an Effective Data Governance Program.* Waltham: Morgan Kaufmann.

Nadhan, E.G. 2014 (January 22). Information governance is more than just data governance. Blog post on Enterprise CIO Forum. http://www.enterprisecioforum.com/en/blogs/enadhan/information-governance-more-just-data-go.

Reinhart-Thompson and L.S. White. 2014. Integrating Data and Information Governance Throughout the HIM Curriculum. 2014 Assembly on Education Symposium, Chicago, IL.

Smallwood, R.F. 2013. *Managing Electronic Records: Methods, Best Practices, and Technologies.* Hoboken: John Wiley & Sons, Inc.

The Sedona Conference. 2013 (December 5). Webinar: Commentary on Information Governance.

# Part I

# The Enterprise Solution

Chapter 1

# The Transforming World of Health Information

Why should organizations be concerned with treating health information as an enterprise asset? Health information is the life blood of the health services industry. Without healthcare information, it would be almost impossible to treat patients, reimburse healthcare providers, receive service from public health agencies, conduct research, develop pharmaceuticals, and make healthcare policy decisions. The list of people, agencies, companies, and industries that rely on healthcare information is nearly exhaustive. Healthcare services and related industries would essentially cease to operate without access to healthcare information. If these examples are not sufficiently convincing, then consider the following:

- In 2009, the US Legislature passed the Health Information Technology for Economic and Clinical Health (HITECH) Act, which mandates the Office of the National Coordinator for Health Information Technology to build an interoperable, private, and secure nationwide health information system and support the widespread, meaningful use of health information technology in the United States. The HITECH Act seeks to improve healthcare delivery and patient care through investments in health information technology.
- Healthcare spending is dramatically increasing as a percentage of the US gross domestic product (GDP). In 2009 and 2010, healthcare spending was 17.9 percent of the GDP (Kaiser Family Foundation 2012). Deployment of information systems and related technologies is anticipated to reduce healthcare costs (Girosi et al 2005). Some studies suggest the United States could save as much as $80 billion annually in healthcare spending by implementing information technology and appropriate use of the technology by all providers (Congressional Budget Office 2008, 8).
- Improvement in the quality and delivery of health information has been associated with improved decision making, reduced medical errors, and better healthcare efficiency, effectiveness, and care processes (Buntin 2011).

The quality and usefulness of information depends upon the degree of quality of the data used by end users to create the information. The common adage "garbage in, garbage out" applies to the relationship between data and information. Thus, there are several risks of not managing data as an asset and ensuring its quality, security, and ease of use. These risks include: endangered quality of information, threatened patient safety, potential increase in costs and inefficiencies, and hindered clinical research, effective administrative, and clinical decision making.

## The Case for an Enterprise Solution

The case for an enterprise solution for managing data and information as enterprise assets is compelling and supported by multiple government and business reports and studies. The case for St. Rita's health system is presented below. While this is a fictional case, the information management issues and challenges facing healthcare enterprises from hospitals, clinics, and physician office practices are real. St. Rita's and its associated data concerns are used throughout the text to introduce **enterprise information management** (EIM) and **data governance** (DG) concepts and to examine how approaches can be applied to alleviate data quality issues. EIM is the set of functions used by organizations to plan, organize, and coordinate people, processes, technology, and content for managing information as a corporate asset that ensures data quality, safety, and ease of use. DG is a specific EIM function that supports coordination among all other EIM functions by establishing data standards, policies, procedures, and accountabilities that span the entire organization.

Throughout the textbook, we follow the St. Rita's team as they come to grips with data issues and establish an enterprise-wide health information management (HIM) and DG program that seeks to reduce data redundancy and improve the quality, security, and ease of use of information. As a future or current HIM practitioner, you will face similar challenges; the journey with the St. Rita's team will help you confront these.

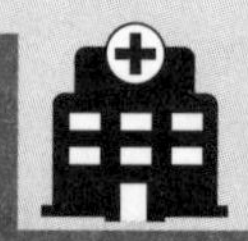

## The Health and Well-being of Enterprise Information Management: The St. Rita's Healthcare System Case Study

### The St. Rita's Dilemma

"We have a catastrophe in data and information management here at St. Rita's," said Joan Morton, the new chief information officer (CIO) at St. Rita's heathcare system. "I'm concerned about the data integrity issues that I've uncovered in my short time here at St. Rita's. Just to name a few of the problems, we have duplicate data in the master patient index(MPI), reports whose statistics don't coincide with each other, and a lack of documentation standards. I need a team of people who can sort out the root causes and determine the feasibility of developing an enterprise division that ensures the integrity of our data. We need these problems fixed as soon as possible if we want to complete the migration from our legacy databases to a new electronic health record (EHR), participate in the state health information exchange (HIE), and meet regulatory requirements," Joan continued as she addressed a new interdisciplinary team she formed to tackle these data issues. "I'd like to know if you think we are in as bad a shape as I've described," she queried the team.

Denise was the first to offer an opinion. As an HIM professional, she knew the problems all too well. "We have mounds of duplicate data," she began. "We also have issues with incomplete data. For example, one review of our data showed that 9 percent of blood pressure recordings were incomplete, leading to less than optimal care. Our master files for patients, providers, and suppliers have duplicate data. This means we have to identify the correct record and then purge the duplicate data which takes time and is expensive. Duplicate data also cause problems in locating the right records with the right information and slows down business processes. Worse yet, in the case of the patient index, it can potentially cause harm to patients," Denise concluded in an animated fashion.

Bob and Linda immediately agreed. Linda, a decision support specialist and Bob, a business analyst, knew these problems all too well. Each day on the front lines, they struggled to rectify data errors they encountered in the reports they both generated.

"Frequently," Linda said, "we find data discrepancies due to data and document management systems that are not integrated with each other. These 'data silos' cause a major problem because the system of record (SOR) may be difficult to identify."

"And from my experience," Bob added, "we made poor decisions because of bad data. Some of our decisions in procurement of materials, for example, have been way off due to bad data. Many times we have inventory that exceeds our needs and other times not enough to meet our needs."

"What frustrates me," began Val, a long-time project manager at St. Rita's, "is that there is no process control for database design, data development, or data management here. Every department has its own silo of data and development methods. There's no coordination of database development, no consistent roadmap for ensuring data integrity. We need an organizational plan that standardizes processes, sets up protocols, and institutes audit procedures that will ensure data integrity and security in all of our database and data efforts."

"And database design is dependent on good processes that identify work flows so the systems we design support the work of the end users," added Shirlee, a clinical analyst and former director of radiation therapy. "Too many times I've seen information systems become a hindrance instead of a support," she emphasized.

As a systems analyst and interface engineer, Monte had an extraordinary background in data exchange issues and saw the results of data exchange problems every day. "I concur about all of these issues," he added. "What adds to the mix of the data problems at St. Rita's are data exchange issues. We don't have streamlined systems that allow us to exchange data from one application to another, as Linda has noted. Efficient exchange is predicated on having good data models and systems design processes, neither of which we have now." The team offered additional insights about the state of data management at St. Rita's and were in agreement that the issues were severe and needed to be addressed in a coordinated and collaborative fashion.

"My objective is to ensure that data are treated as a corporate asset and to improve their reusability, accessibility, and quality," Joan stated. "I've brought you together as a team because you all have worked at St. Rita's and understand our institution's culture. I also know that you are skilled, smart, determined, have an excellent background in health information technology and management, and a can-do attitude," Joan emphasized. "We don't have to build the Starship Enterprise right away, but a good start on a rocket booster is where I'd like to see things take off. My instinct is that we need an office for EIM whose goals are to reduce data redundance and improve data quality, security, and ease of access. What I want is top-notch data stewardship. But this idea needs verification. I'm designating you as the EIM team to investigate the feasibility of this idea and, if realistic, identify how we might get such an effort off the ground. Your charge is to study the problems, recommend new ideas and improvements, and develop an action plan to achieve these."

Joan made a strong case. It was true that St. Rita's needed to look at managing data as an enterprise asset and establish a central point of leadership to lead the effort. The information systems department was excellent from a technical perspective, but they had never addressed data management from a business perspective. In fact, they viewed data administration solely as a database administration function. Furthermore, the skills in HIM had not been leveraged by St. Rita's on an enterprise-wide level. While there was a corporate HIM department, its emphasis was on operational rather than strategic aspects of information management.

The new EIM team did not know what other institutions were doing in EIM. Joan said that lack of an enterprise focus on data and information management was a problem across all industries, so the team knew that others must be working to solve the very problems Joan was talking about.

Although the selected team members had a good background in project planning, information technology, clinical practice, and HIM, they knew it would be necessary to study to become knowledgeable on the newest ideas in EIM. The wheel should not be reinvented, the EIM team agreed. Joan also mentioned "data stewardship." The team needed to figure out what she meant by data stewardship and what its relationship was with EIM. The team knew that they had a lot of work ahead of them to answer all of Joan's questions.

Joan was a dynamic personality and had a number of quick results during her brief tenure at St. Rita's. Her personable manner and integrity put her in a good position within the executive and the medical staff ranks. Her technical know-how made big bonus points with the information systems department directors. And, her ability to see the big picture was what the executives wanted; a rare combination in any one person. While she had a vision for the future, she needed to delegate the nuts and bolts of putting it all together. The EIM team knew that Joan had a reputation for surrounding herself with good content experts. They knew that Joan wanted them as part of the bigger team to make her vision a reality.

### Taking Action

The next day, the EIM team convened their first meeting. Val was appointed by Joan as the EIM team leader. Val's experience as a project manager provided her with the skills needed to head up such a big effort.

The team devoted a large portion of the first meeting to examining the charge Joan had given them. From their discussion, the team developed a charter that defined the ground rules for team operation and identified the project goals, deliverables, and scope (a copy of the team charter is available in the accompanying student manual).

After their initial meeting, the EIM team moved forward quickly. Potentially developing a new EIM office meant real leadership: setting a vision, articulating it, and then selling it not only to the information systems department, but also to the organization at large. What would the EIM mission be? What would the scope of EIM and its functions be? Would EIM be a separate office or division or more of a matrix configuration? How would the EIM office mesh with other organizational units? Specifically, what were the process models, audit controls, standards, and prototypes they needed to develop?

The team understood that Joan expected a global picture, but also recognized that specifics were just as critical. They knew that Joan wanted an executive briefing on the EIM function as the team's deliverable that included a specific proposal about how this concept could work at St. Rita's. The proposal would answer these questions as well as others they would discover as they proceeded with their charge. The proposal would be big picture in narrative, but heavy on appendices to clarify the new EIM role at St. Rita's and would include:

- Background on EIM (current trends and thinking on the organization of a data management division)
- Situational analysis of St. Rita's data issues
- Rationale for pursing EIM at St. Rita's, a citation of problems at St. Rita's, and a plan for how establishing an EIM office could solve the current data crisis
- Structural organization and fit of EIM at St. Rita's
- EIM mission
- EIM functions and scope
- EIM five-year plan

The team recognized that understanding the nature of health information and data flow was a crucial component in establishing a successful EIM program. They needed to know how to define health information and understand how the various components of the data and information flow affect the organization, individuals within the organization, and stakeholders outside the organization. One of the first items the team undertook was a discussion on the nature of health information and the complexity of data flow.

## Definition of Health Information

Depending upon the context, health information has different definitions. *Health information* can be defined as information about diseases, conditions, and wellness issues (MedlinePlus 2013). In this context, health information is found in authoritative sources such as books, journals, pamphlets, and other materials. The National Library of Medicine (NLM), for instance, is the world's largest source for these materials, containing over 170 million items related to biomedical, health sciences, and health and healthcare topics. Given the above definition, The National Health Information Center (NHIC) is another example of a health information source. Through resources such as the Health Information Resource Database and the Health Finder website, the NHIC puts health professionals and consumers in touch with over 1,000 organizations that provide information about illness, diseases, wellness, health services, and tools for healthy living.

However, the definition of health information within the healthcare delivery context differs from those above of the NLM and NHIC. For example, the definition of health information provided in the Health Insurance Portability and Accountability Act (HIPAA) refers to health information as:

> Any information whether oral or recorded in any form or medium, that: (1) Is created or received by a healthcare provider, health plan, public health authority, employer, life insurer, school or university, or healthcare clearinghouse; and (2) Relates to the past, present, or future physical or mental health or condition of an individual; the provision of healthcare to an individual; or the past, present, or future payment for the provision of healthcare to an individual. (45 CFR 160.103)

Although not specifically defining health information, the Institutes of Medicine (IOM) provides several definitions that help clarify the meaning of health information with regard to patient health information:

- Patient record: Repository of information about a single patient. This information is generated by healthcare professionals as a direct result of interaction with a patient, with individuals who have personal knowledge of the patient, or with both.
- Computer-based patient record: An electronic patient record that resides in a system specifically designed to support users by providing accessibility to complete and accurate data, alerts, reminders, clinical decision support systems, links to medical knowledge, and other aids.
- Primary patient record: Used by healthcare professionals while providing patient care services to review patient data or document their own observations, actions, or instructions.
- Secondary patient record: Derived from the primary record and contains selected data elements to aid nonclinical users (for example, persons not involved in direct patient care) in supporting, evaluating, or advancing patient care. Patient care support refers to administration, regulation, and payment functions. Patient care evaluation refers to quality assurance, utilization review, and medical or legal audits. Patient care advancement refers to research. These records are often combined to form what the committee terms a secondary database (for example, an insurance claims database) (Dick, et al 1997 55–56).

Besides the IOM definitions, there are differing meanings for terms used to describe health records in electronic format. For example, the terms *electronic medical record*, *computer-based patient record*, *electronic health record*, and *personal health record* are often used interchangeably. To alleviate confusion among the use of terms and provide a consistent language that could support a system of public policies, private development, and outreach and educational initiatives for development and deployment of an electronic health information infrastructure, the National Alliance for Health Information Technology released a report defining key terms related to health information technology support. The following key terms are defined and used throughout this text:

- **Electronic medical record (EMR)**: An electronic record of health-related information on an individual that can be created, gathered, managed, and consulted by authorized clinicians and staff within one healthcare organization.
- **Electronic health record (EHR)**: An electronic record of health-related information on an individual that conforms to nationally recognized interoperability standards and that can be created, managed, and consulted by authorized clinicians and staff across more than one healthcare organization.
- **Personal health record (PHR)**: An electronic record of health-related information on an individual that conforms to nationally recognized interoperability standards and that can be drawn from multiple sources while being managed, shared, and controlled by the individual (National Alliance for Health Information Technology April 20, 2008, 16, 17, 19).

## Data Flow and Information Retrieval Complexity

The steady stream of data, multiple decision makers, complexity of decisions, and numerous contact points make HIM challenging. To understand the complexity, take a look at an example of the data flow and information retrieval for a patient making an appointment with her physician at a local clinic in figure 1.1.

Figure 1.1. Appointment scheduling example

Vicki Smith wants to make an appointment to see her primary care physician (PCP) at the local family practice clinic. When she calls the clinic, the receptionist retrieves Vicki's demographic and insurance information stored in the electronic registration system. The data that was used by the receptionist to produce this information was gathered by the office staff at Vicki's first visit to her PCP. Over the phone, the receptionist must verify Vicki's demographic and insurance information and update the data, if needed. The receptionist checks the electronic appointment system to see what appointment times are available, and then schedules Vicki for an appointment with her PCP.



At first glance, figure 1.1 might look like a fairly simple transaction. But to complete the appointment request, several items of relevant, useful, and accurate information must be accessible to the receptionist. For example, data that must be available to generate the information needed for the appointment request is depicted in table 1.1.

Table 1.1. Example of data for an appointment request

| Data | Description |
|---|---|
| Patient Basic Demographic Data:<br>• Last, first, and middle name<br>• Date of birth<br>• Gender<br>• Marital status<br>• Medical record number (unique identifier)<br>• Social security number | Basic demographic data are the keys to identifying and linking information about that individual and are stored in multiple databases. If these data are incorrect, information needed for patient care may not be retrieved, duplicate records may be created, or data may be matched to the wrong person, all of which lead to clinical information fragmentation and patient safety concerns. |
| Patient Additional Demographic Data:<br>• Current home street address, city, state, and zip code<br>• Current home, work, and cell phone numbers<br>• Message phone number<br>• Current e-mail addresses<br>• Language spoken at home<br>• Emergency contact phone number<br>• Guarantor phone number | These data are a second level of personal identification and are needed so the clinic or provider can contact the patient. Incorrect data could hinder pertinent follow-up information or contact and could lead to patient care or safety issues. |
| Provider Data:<br>• Last, first, and middle name of the provider<br>• Provider credentials | The receptionist requires these data to identify the correct PCP, link the data to the correct patient, and find the available appointment dates and times. |
| Primary Insurance Coverage:<br>• Insurance company<br>• Plan type<br>• Group number<br>• Effective date<br>• Expiration date<br>• Plan name<br>• Policy number<br>• Relationship to holder<br>• Employer name<br>• Other health benefit plan | These data are essential in determining the insurance coverage and linking this information to the patient, provider, and visit. Incorrect data prevents timely and accurate reimbursement to the clinic. |
| Appointment Data:<br>• Reason for visit<br>• Provider-booked appointments<br>• Provider-available appointments<br>• Appointment type | These data are required to establish the patient's reason for a visit to the clinic (for example, follow-up care, complete physical, blood pressure check), to determine PCP availability, and to allocate appropriate time for the visit. |



An error in any of the data listed in table 1.1 could potentially cause patient safety risks, adversely impact reimbursement, create operational inefficiencies, increase costs, unfavorably impact patient outcome statistics, or result in poor customer service and satisfaction. A patient safety risk could result if the receptionist did not accurately identify Vicki Smith and created a duplicate record or matched her with a patient with a similar name. In these cases, correct information concerning Vicki Smith's previous medical history and treatment would not be available to the PCP to make treatment decisions. Incorrect contact information for follow up purposes could potentially result in liability risks. If the receptionist documents the wrong phone number or e-mail, she could release confidential information to persons not entitled to it. Personal health information is protected under federal regulation, such as the HIPAA, and communication of this type of information to someone other than the patient may result in fines, required notitication of breaches to affected individuals, or other action. Inaccurate insurance information may result in insufficient co-payment at the time of visit, or could hold up reimbursement, unnecessarily causing cash flow and other financial issues for the clinic. Consequently, ensuring that data are managed accurately must be made a top priority for both patient care and business reasons.

The information flow is further examined when Vicki Smith arrives for her clinic appointment (figure 1.2).

Figure 1.2. Example of outpatient visit data and information flow

When Vicki Smith arrives for her appointment, the nurse gathers and records basic medical information for Vicki's EHR. This includes Vicki's vital signs such as blood pressure, temperature, pulse, respirations, height, and weight.

Before seeing Vicki, her PCP reviews her medical history, results of previous tests and examinations that are available in the clinic's EHR system, and retrieves the new information just documented by the nurse. During Vicki's appointment, the PCP collects additional information from her about her current medical complaints, updates her medical history, and performs a physical examination. The PCP records all of these new data in the clinic's EHR system.

The PCP orders three laboratory tests and a mammogram, fills out two prescriptions for medication, and orders a consultation by another physician to follow up on Vicki's current medical problems. Because the clinic's EHR system can exchange data, the clinic electronically sends the orders and prescriptions to the laboratory, radiology department, and pharmacy, and sends the request for consultation to the consultant.

After Vicki's visit is complete, the clinic electronically sends data about the duration, type of visit, and Vicki's diagnosis and treatment to the insurance carrier for reimbursement. When the laboratory and radiology department complete the tests and exams, they send the results electronically to the clinic. The consultant's report is also electronically sent, when she completes it.

The PCP follows up with Vicki by e-mail regarding the test and exam results and provides additional information for care and treatment. Because the clinic has a patient portal to a PHR, Vicki can view the results of her laboratory tests and mammogram exam.



Considering the contact points, information sources, and data flows from the appointment request through visit completion and follow-up, the complexity of data and information management is extensive. Figure 1.3 provides an example of the typical data flows that might occur for an outpatient visit such as Vicki's.

Figure 1.3. Clinic appointment and visit data flow

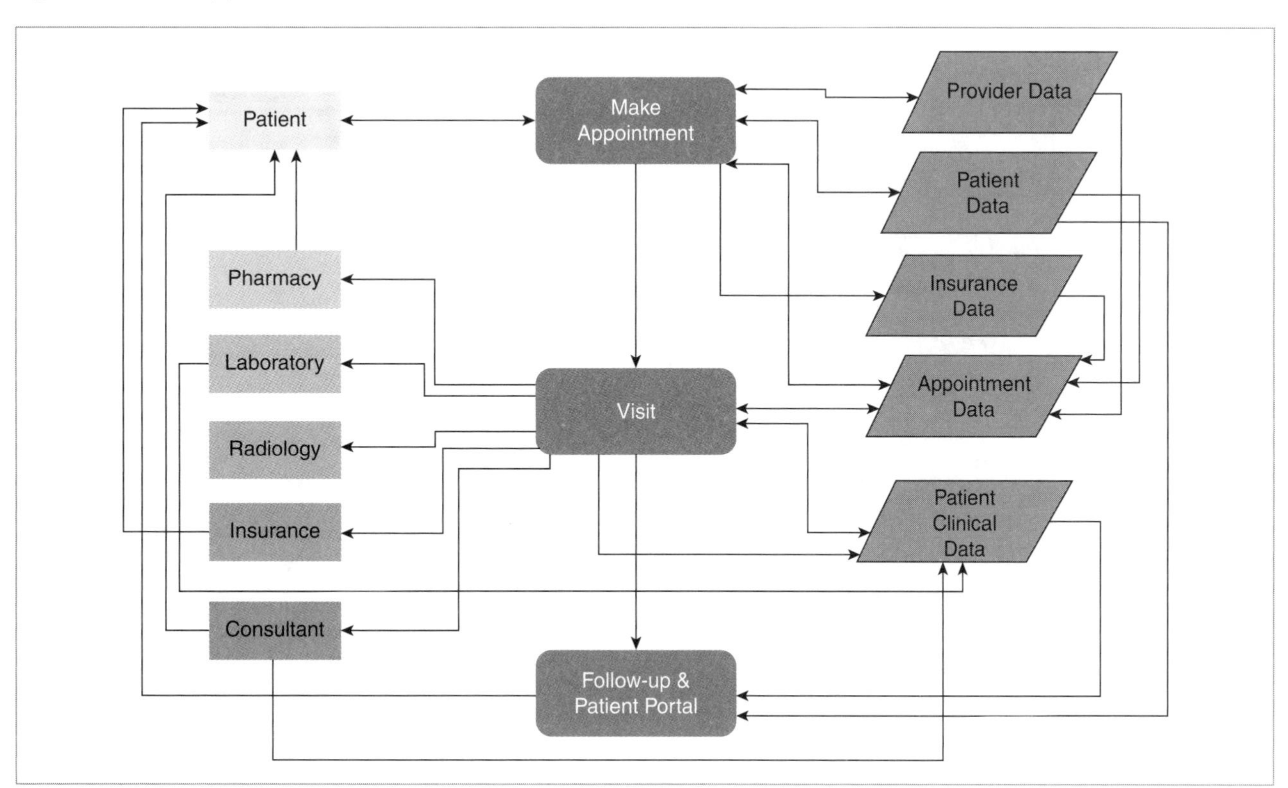

Extrapolating this scenario to a hospital stay, in which the patient receives more tests, treatments, and is cared for by numerous providers, the data flows and contact points become even more voluminous and complex. If the entirety of healthcare delivery is considered, including outpatient, inpatient, long-term care, rehabilitative care, and intersections with public health and secondary users such as insurance companies, then the elaborate information flow becomes even more evident. At any point in the healthcare delivery process, data error may occur. Poorly designed information systems, equipment and software failure, transmission errors, human error, poor process, and inadequate data management are among the contributors.

Communication flow outside the organization can introduce more opportunities for data error. Figure 1.4 provides a representation of what these external data flows might look like across multiple organizations, agencies, and the continuum of the healthcare system. Here, data are shared among different providers, payers, accreditors, and research and care review organizations. No matter their source, data errors can contribute to poor medical decisions, patient outcomes, research, and healthcare policy development.

To help improve communication among all providers in the healthcare delivery system, initiatives are underway to better provide the ability to share patient information through state **health information exchanges** (HIEs). A federal-state collaboration, the purpose of HIEs is to enable and expand the secure electronic movement and use of health information among organizations using nationally recognized standards (HHS 2011). Sharing and using healthcare information among providers improves the quality and efficiency of healthcare. Through HIEs, an individual's health data would be accessible to a patient care provider irrespective of the site of the provision of care. For example, if a patient was seen in the emergency department (ED) of a hospital, but normally received care at a clinic in another town, the physician in the ED would be able to access the patient's pertinent medical data from the clinic's EHR system. Figure 1.5 depicts an HIE showing how hospitals, clinics, free-standing laboratories, public health agencies, and others would share information.

Because HIEs are based on the exchange or access of data from provider EHR systems, their success ultimately rests on the quality of data contained in the participating organizations' individual EHR systems. This is yet another rationale for implementation of robust EIM programs.

Figure 1.4. Healthcare data information flow across users

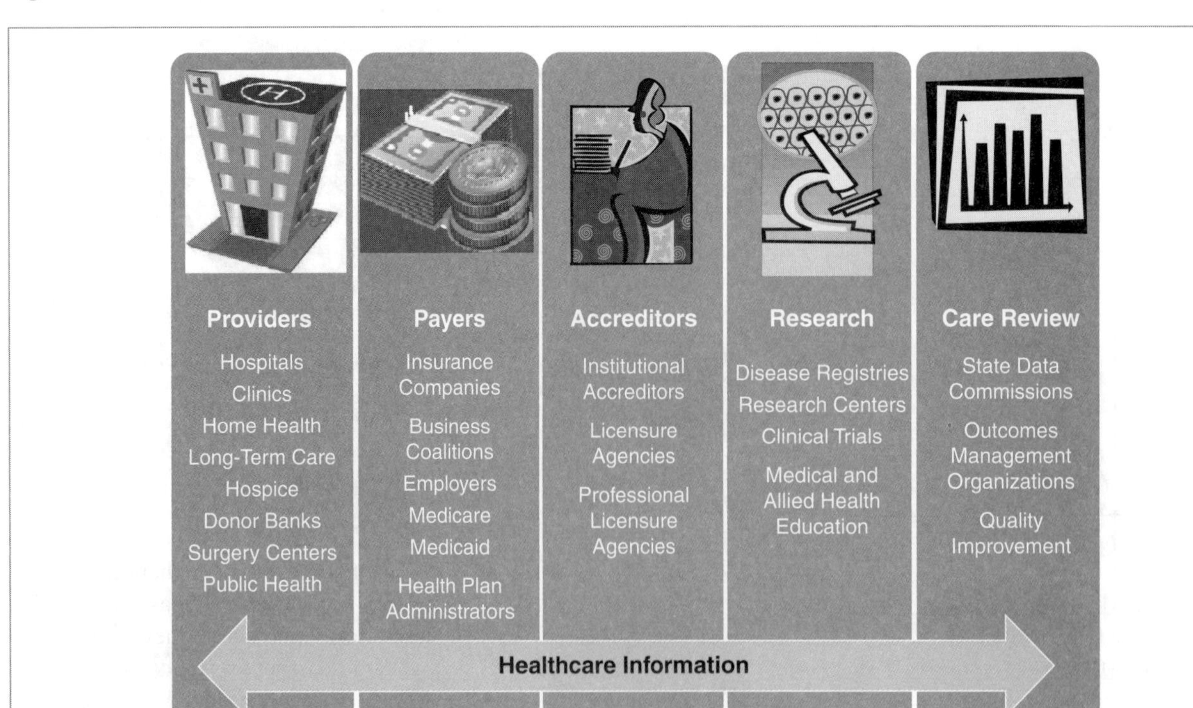

Figure 1.5. Example of health information exchange

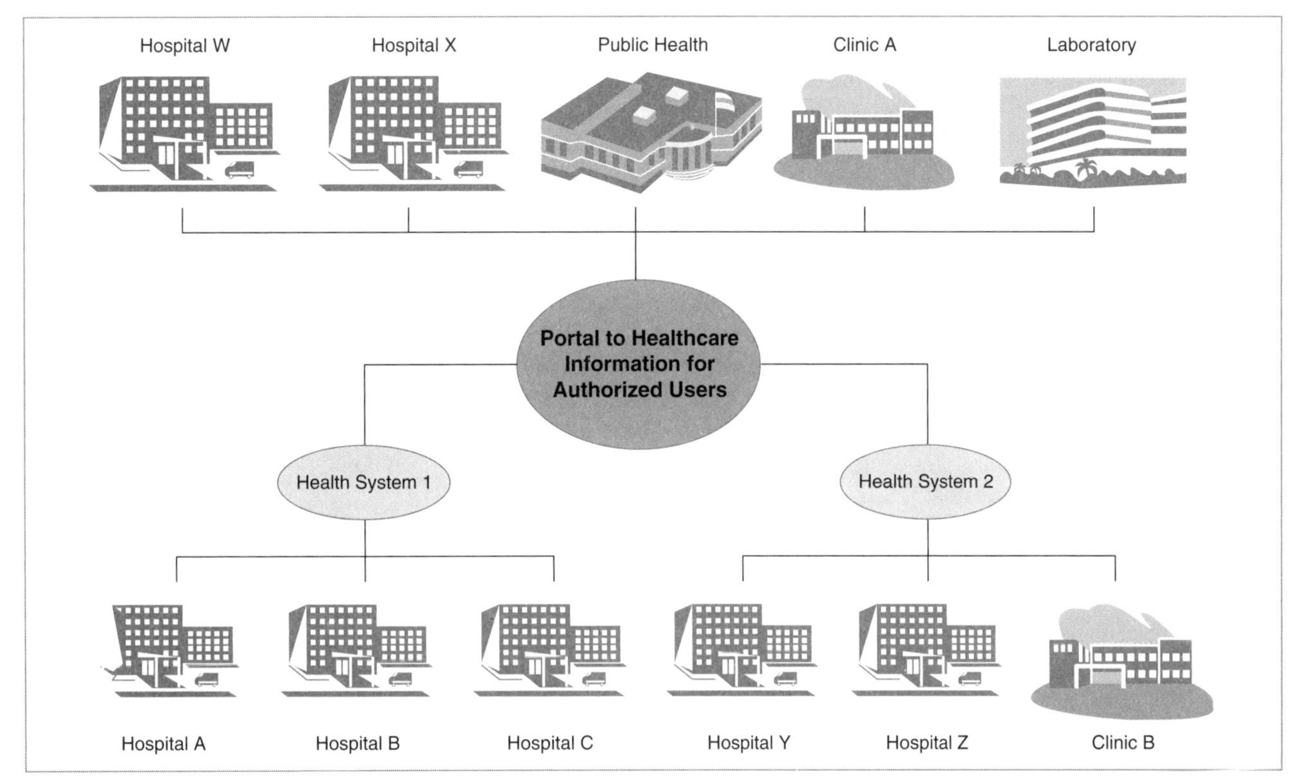




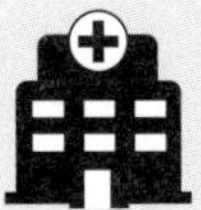

## *The St. Rita's Healthcare System Case Study*

One of Joan Morton's charges to the EIM team was to determine the scope of an EIM program at St. Rita's. Having been a program manager, Val knew that determining scope is a critical element for the success of any program. Considering this, Val put the EIM program scope on the agenda as the main discussion point of an initial team meeting. "What should be the scope of information and data included in a healthcare organization's EIM program?" Val prompted the team. "Should it be limited to healthcare data and information? Or, should EIM include administrative, clinical, legal, and all other types of data and information?"

"Well, the 'E' in EIM stands for enterprise," responded Shirlee. "That would imply a program that encompasses all types of data and information, not just clinical."

Denise agreed with Shirlee's assessment and added: "There is a dependency between clinical and other types of data. For example, if registration data aren't correct, this impacts data in the clinical system downstream and ultimately affects the quality of the information that is retrieved. It's like thowing a pebble into a pond. A ripple effect is created that goes across all data,"

"Hmm," mused Monte. "Including all data sounds like a huge effort. Do we even understand the amount and categories of data we have? I know that I don't know that."

"And," interjected Bob, "What are others doing with EIM program implementation? Are there liabilities in a broad or narrow scope? And, does St. Rita's have the resources to support a broad scope?" he asked.

The team made a list of these concerns and determined they needed more information before they could make a thoughtful decision about EIM program scope. They believed sorting out these issues was fundamental to a successful EIM program. Shirlee and Denise volunteered to outline the type of data considered clinical, administrative, and legal, and Monte offered to investigate best practices in determining EIM program scope. They would present their findings at the next team meeting.

# Health Information Content

While health information is broadly defined in this chapter, knowledge about the specific content (data) that composes the information is important in establishing an EIM and DG program. EIM encompasses people, processes, technology, and content. It is concerned with the people and processes that generate and use information, the technologies that capture, store, and disseminate information, and focuses on the content of the information which is composed of data and their context.

Often, the terms data and information are mistakenly used interchangeably. However, there is a distinction between data and information. **Data** are raw facts. For example, the numbers 120 and 80 are data, or raw facts. The letters E, M, and G are also data. We do not know what these numbers and letters mean without a context. Data become **information** when we place them within a context, process, summarize, organize, and analyze them. To transform these data into information, we could say that Mrs. Jones' blood pressure was 120/80 or that Mr. Block's electromyogram (EMG) was normal. In these instances, the raw facts are placed into a specific context that provides meaning, becoming information.

The success of an EIM and DG program, of which the purpose is to reduce data redundancy and improve the quality, security, and ease of access of information, depends both on the data and the integrity of the processes that transform the data into information. Thus, knowing the health information content, which is composed of data and their context, is essential for any health professional.

What constitutes health data and information depends on the healthcare delivery setting. For example, an acute care hospital patient record will contain different information than an outpatient clinic or a public health clinic. Clinics do not record intensive care unit (ICU) monitoring information. However, ICU information would be a normal piece of documentation in an acute care hospital patient record.

Nevertheless, there are similarities among all settings in the data that they capture and maintain. Documentation best practices are the same no matter what the setting. For instance, hospitals, clinics, and physician practices would normally retain a patient's history, physical examinations, laboratory tests, and reports of x-ray examinations. Documentation best practices would require the responsible practitioner to sign and date each report, exam, or notation in all healthcare facilities, regardless of the healthcare setting. In most cases regardless of setting, we can categorize health information as clinical, administrative, or legal documentation. The following sections expand upon each of these information sets.

## Clinical Documentation

The primary purpose of **clinical documentation** is to provide a detailed account of pertinent facts, findings, and observations relating to a patient's health history, examinations, tests, treatments, procedures, and supportive care. Clinical documentation is a primary communication tool among healthcare providers and facilitates the planning and management of an individual's treatment and care over a lifetime. Besides supporting direct patient care, clinical documentation is an important resource for evaluating the appropriateness, adequacy, and outcomes of healthcare delivery and patient care. Healthcare professionals use clinical data for research, quality assessment, and utilization management of healthcare services, and also frequently report it to external accrediting, licensing, and federal agencies to serve these purposes. For example, federal law requires acute care facilities to submit a patient-specific list of data items called the Uniform Hospital Discharge Data Set (UHDDS) for any patient in a federal health program (for example, Medicare and Medicaid). Likewise, long-term care facilities must submit a uniform set of demographic and clinical data called the Minimum Data Set for Long Term Care Version 2.0 (MDS 2.0) for Medicare and Medicaid nursing home residents.

The need for precise, complete, and accurate clinical documentation is vital to substantiate that reimbursement claims are valid and correct. Third-party payers (such as insurers, Medicare, and Medicaid) require evidence that the services delivered by providers are consistent with what the organization has billed and with the individual's insurance coverage. Moreover, healthcare professionals use clinical documentation for risk management purposes to improve patient care and safety and to corroborate the delivery of care and services, thereby protecting the interests of patients, providers, and healthcare institutions in legal matters.

To ensure that clinical documentation meets its intended purposes, healthcare professionals must follow best practices in documentation. Omitting items such as patient identification, dates, times, signatures, and precise clinical notes makes it difficult to substantiate what care the patient received, hampers appropriate reimbursement, and may be problematic in malpractice or other litigation. Regardless of the documentation medium and format (for example, paper or electronic), following documentation best practices is essential. See figure 1.6 for an example of documentation best practices.

Figure 1.6. Example of clinical documentation best practices

**Clinical Documentation Best Practices**

- Establish documentation policies and guidelines that ensure uniformity of both content and format of the patient record in compliance with governmental, regulatory, accreditation, industry standards, and organizational policies—including those for accuracy, completeness, timeliness, and copy functionality—and should apply to paper and electronic formats.
- Organize the patient record to facilitate data retrieval and compilation.
- Allow only persons authorized by the hospital's policies to document in the patient record. This information should be recorded in the medical staff rules and regulations or the hospital's administrative policies.
- Specify in hospital policies or medical staff rules and regulations who may receive and transcribe a physician's verbal orders.
- Require patient record entries to be documented at the time the treatment they describe is rendered.
- Require authors of all entries to be clearly identifiable with names and credentials.
- Stipulate abbreviations and symbols in the patient record to be permitted only when approved according to hospital and medical staff bylaws, rules, and regulations.
- Specify all entries in the patient records are to be permanent. Documentation in paper medium must be made in black or blue ink.
- In electronic records, limitations of copy functionality must include measures such as
  - Clearly labeling the information as copied from another source
  - Limiting the ability for data to be copied and pasted from other systems
  - Limiting the ability of onc author to copy from another author's documentation
  - Allowing a provider to mark specific results as reviewed
  - Allowing only key, pre-defined elements of reports and results to be copied or imported
  - The ability to monitor a clinician's use of copy and paste
- Require documentation associated with the patient to whom it pertains. In paper medium, patient identification, including name and health record number, must appear on every page or document associated with the patient. In electronic medium, safeguards, such as alerts or prompts, must be in place that notify the user when the potential for an incorrect association exists.
- Electronic entries shall be individually authenticated by use of user identification and password.
- Documentation errors shall only be made in the following way:
  - Errors in documentation in paper media: So that the original entry is not obliterated, a single line shall be drawn through the error, labeled as an error, the correction made as a notatin with the time and date the correction was made and signature and credentials of the individual makine the correction. No white-out, erasure, or eradiction is permitted.
  - Errors in documentation in electronic media: Shall be made only through an amendment to the document or entry.

Source: Adapted from Smith 2001 and AHIMA 2013.

## Legal and Administrative Documentation

To carry out customary practices and operations, healthcare delivery organizations must collect and maintain various types of data. Some of these data may be prescribed by accrediting bodies, law, or regulation, or required for administrative functions. These normally include consents, authorizations, and acknowledgements. For example, institutions obtain a written patient consent for treatment, operations, and procedures for legal purposes. To comply with HIPAA regulations, organizations receive a patient's signed acknowledgement of the receipt of the notice of privacy practices document. Authorizations for permission to release information are also obtained in certain circumstances.

**Administrative data** that is collected by the organization or other entities includes demographic, emergency contact, and insurance information as well as personal property checklists. Death certificates may be included for patients who have expired during hospitalization.

Figure 1.7 provides an inventory of healthcare and administrative documentation that is normally maintained in an acute-care setting. This inventory would be consistent with the documentation practices at St. Rita's. Descriptions and examples of many of these reports are available in paper and electronic format in the student ancillaries for this book.

Figure 1.7. Inventory of health information documentation

| Inventory of Health Information Documentation | |
|---|---|
| **Clinical Information** | |
| Problem List | Laboratory Reports |
| Emergency Department Admission | Chemistry |
| Emergency Department Clinical Record | Histology |
| Emergency Department Physician Notes | Immunology |
| Emergency Department Nursing Record | Microbiology |
| Ambulance/EMT Documentation | Pathology/Cytology |
| Referral Information | Hematology |
| History and Physical Examination | Blood Gasses |
| Consultation Report | Blood Bank Record |
| Physician Progress Notes | Transfusion Record |
| Nursing Progress Notes | Autopsy Reports |
| Nursing Assessments | Outside Reference Lab Reports |
| Flowsheets | Radiology Reports |
| Medication Administration (MAR) | X-Ray |
| IV Administration and Therapy | Nuclear Medicine |
| Acute Hemodialysis | CAT Scan |
| Intake and Output | Ultrasound |
| Pain Management | Magnetic Resonance Imaging (MRI) |
| Heparin Drip | Other Imaging Reports |
| Five Minute Check Report | Diagnostic Reports |
| Diabetic Record | EKG/ECG |
| Chemotherapy | Cardiac Stress Tests |
| Ancillary Progress Notes | Telemetry Monitoring |
| Case Manager | Pulmonary Studies |
| Continued Stay Review | Vascular Lab Studies |
| Physical Therapy | Audiology |
| Occupational Therapy | EEG |
| Social Work | EMG |
| Nutrition | Other Non-Invasive Reports |
| Respiratory Care | Labor, Delivery, and Newborn Records |
| Care Plan Documentation | Other Documentation |
| Observation Documentation | |
| ICU Documentation | |

(continued)

Figure 1.7. Continued

| Clinical Information | |
|---|---|
| Admission Orders | Resuscitation Data Record |
| Physician Orders | Cardiopulmonary Arrest Record |
| Operative Procedures | Restraint/Seclusion Record |
| Preoperative Assessments | Discharge Summary |
| Preoperative Checklists | Discharge Instructions |
| Anesthesia Documentation | Patient Discharge Plan |
| Operative Reports | Report of Death |
| Post-operative Documentation | Face Sheet |
| **Authorizations, Consents, and Other Legal Documents** | |
| Acknowledgement of HIPAA Privacy Notice | Consents: |
| Acknowledgement of Patient's Rights | Intensive Care |
| Authorization for Disclosures | Obstetrical Care |
| Advance Directive | Chemotherapy |
| Consent to Treatment | Operation and Procedure |
| **Administrative** | |
| Registration Form | Death Certificate Copy |
| Financial Information | |
| Personal Items Checklist | |
| Questionnaires | |



## Uses and Users of Health Information

The purpose of EIM is to meet the needs of all stakeholders in the organization for available, secure, and quality information. However, the scale of EIM implementation varies across organizations, given the size, resources, and experience of the organization. The EIM effort should apply to all organization information assets including health, management, administrative, and research data. Implementing a broad EIM program encompassing all information assets is difficult to complete on a short-term basis. EIM implementation is usually an iterative process that begins with a single focus and continually expands. Since St. Rita's current business imperative was deployment of an EHR system, the team thought that EIM efforts should focus on health information and closely related administrative information assets. Once established for these information assets, the program would be scaled up by the organization to include all other information assets.

### *The St. Rita's Healthcare System Case Study*

The St. Rita's team knew from their initial study that if the EIM and data governance program was to succeed, they had to understand the information environment the program was intended to address. "Content and context go together," Val said to the team.

"That is a spot-on observation," added Monte. "I've seen many systems that were technically superb but failed because they did not adequately support the work of the end users. In fact, I've heard several complaints about current administrative and clinical systems because of this very reason."

Due to the importance of understanding both content and context of any information system, the team studied the uses and users of health information. At the conclusion, they agreed that the primary objective of all EIM and DG programs is to meet the needs of the uses and users of health information.

## Uses of Health Information

The primary purpose for the collection, maintenance, and use of health information is to benefit the patient by supporting delivery of patient care and related services. Specifically, we can categorize the **primary uses of health information** contained in a patient record as shown in figure 1.8.

Figure 1.8. Primary uses of healthcare information

**Patient uses**
Patients use health information in communication with healthcare providers and to participate in self-management of their own care. For example, patients with hypertension may maintain a log of their blood pressure readings and provide these to their physician. Patients also use their health information to reconcile and verify billing for their healthcare services. More recently, patients are documenting and maintaining their health information in PRHs.

**Patient care delivery uses**
Health professionals use health information to describe signs, symptoms, and diseases and their causes to support the diagnosis and treatment of patients. They use it for communication among healthcare providers as well as a communication tool to support continuity of care across healthcare institutions.

**Patient care management uses**
Health professionals use health information in aggregate to improve patient care and its delivery. They accomplish this by documenting the characteristics of the population served by an institution (case-mix), health delivery practices, utilization of services, and the outcomes of patient care to help manage risk and accomplish quality improvement.

**Patient care support uses**
To allocate resources appropriately, such as healthcare staff, beds, and equipment, organizations rely on analysis of health information. For example, to staff the hospital with the appropriate mix of individuals to support the care of its patients, an organization needs to know the diagnoses and severity of illness of its patients. By analyzing patient health data in aggregate, organizations analyze trends in patient volume, demographics, diagnoses, care, and outcomes to more effectively develop forecasts and assess workloads.

**Business and legal uses**
Health information is essential in determining charges, preparing a bill, or submitting insurance claims for services provided. With the implementation of prospective payment systems (PPS) and other third-party reimbursement programs, health information is essential to receive appropriate reimbursement and to adjudicate insurance claims. Institutions also use health information to report, assess, and manage costs. Documentation of health information becomes an organization's business of record and thus the organization uses it to provide legal evidence of services and care provided.

Source: Adapted from Dick, et al. 1997.

**Secondary uses of health information** are not directly related to a specific encounter, but are used by organizations, state and federal agencies, accreditation and licensing bodies, educational and research institutions, and others to "influence the environment in which patient care is provided," and include education, research, regulation, and policy making (Dick, et al. 1997, 78). Figure 1.9 provides an overview of these uses.

Figure 1.9. Secondary uses of healthcare information

**Education uses**
Institutions use health information to assist in teaching medical, nursing, allied health, and other professional students who are training to work in healthcare fields. They also use health information to further the education of current health providers and others through educational opportunities such as formal meetings of medical professionals that discuss or evaluate clinical cases and to prepare presentations on clinical care at professional meetings.

**Accreditation, licensure, regulation, and legal uses**
Healthcare organizations undergo various mandatory and voluntary review processes. In order to operate, hospitals and nursing care facilities, for example, must meet mandatory regulatory standards that are legislated by the state in which they are located. In addition to mandatory regulation, healthcare facilities often elect to undergo voluntary accreditation by recognized accreditation agencies. Voluntary accreditation groups establish guidelines and standards for the operation and management of healthcare facilities and care outcomes. Both licensure and accreditation agencies require healthcare organizations to submit health information for review to determine if they are meeting safety, operations, and quality of care standards. Furthermore, health information may be used as evidence in civil and criminal legal proceedings.

**Research uses**
Health information plays an essential role in medical research. Such information assists in conducting clinical research to study the mechanisms of human disease, therapies, and interventions for disease. Health researchers use health information in clinical trials to answer specific questions about the biomedical or behavioral interventions of new or known drugs, treatments, or devices. In addition to these, they use health information to study outcomes and cost-effectiveness of care and develop disease, immunization, and other registries and databases.

**Public health uses**
Health institutions and providers report health information to public health agencies to help identify threats to the health and safety of individuals and to the public at large. This includes information that helps public health agencies prevent or control disease, injury, or disability.

**Policy-making uses**
Federal, state, and local governments use aggregate health information for policy-making purposes to improve the health and well-being of its citizens. For example, state governments use aggregate information to substantiate the need for additional healthcare facilities in a particular region. National government may use aggregate health information to determine quality of care measures using data sets collected from hospitals, home health, and long-term care facilities.

Source: Adapted from Dick, et al. 1997.

## Users of Health Information

Figure 1.4 portrays the flow of healthcare information across the healthcare system. The IOM identified seven broad categories of health information users:

- Healthcare delivery organizations such as hospitals, physician offices, and clinics
- Quality management and monitoring organizations and companies such as those providing services for utilization management, quality of care review, and case management
- Companies providing reimbursement services such as claims management, insurers, and benefits management
- Organizations or agencies involved in healthcare research or data collection
- Educational institutions for the training of healthcare professionals and other related disciplines
- Healthcare accreditation agencies and policy-making bodies, organizations, and agencies (Dick, et al. 1997, 79)

Such a disparate array of health information users has several implications from an EIM perspective. One of the most basic of these is the challenge of exchanging and using information among various entities that have different electronic information systems. The ability to exchange data in a meaningful way requires the development and implementation of electronic exchange standards (chapter 12) that every electronic information system uses. A second issue deals with privacy and security. One example is the act of sharing individually identifiable data with another organization and ensuring that these data are protected from tampering or inappropriate use. A third concern involves tracking data flow from one entity to another and maintaining appropriate records about who received what information and when. Another challenge is ensuring that data updated in an originating entity's database are automatically updated in a downstream system of another entity.

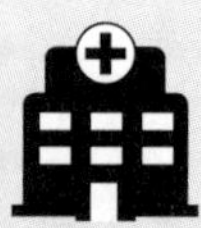

## *The St. Rita's Healthcare System Case Study*

At their next meeting, the EIM team combined all the information they collected about health information uses and users. The primary purpose of the meeting was to come to a consensus about the starting point for the EIM program at St. Rita's. "We should target initial efforts to the internal users of health information," offered Linda.

"I would agree with that assessment," Shirlee responded. "Those on the front lines need to have the right information at the right time for both patient care delivery and administrative purposes. And, the benefits of good data for internal users will flow to external users as well."

"Those are great points," agreed Val. "But how do we deal with healthcare information exchange, which is also a primary goal for St. Rita's?" she asked.

"If we look carefully, healthcare information exchange is embedded within the definition of the EHR," interjected Monte. "In order to have a functioning EHR," he continued, "the focus needs to be on meeting internal needs first, but the end goal should be that quality data are appropriately made available by using recognized standards for data exchange. This will ensure that clinicians and staff can use information across more than one healthcare organization."

Given their discussion, the EIM team came to the consensus that the full spectrum of EHR functionality must be the goal pursued by St. Rita's. By focusing on the needs of internal users as a first priority with an eye toward data exchange, external users would be downstream beneficiaries of EIM efforts.

## Part of the Team: Discussion and Action

The following topics are discussion items and actions that the EIM team would feasibly address. If you were part of the EIM team, what would you contribute to these discussions and action determinations?

1. The EIM team made the decision that EIM should include healthcare and administrative data. Do you believe this was a prudent choice? Why or why not? What would you have contributed to the discussion?
2. The EIM team agreed that meeting internal user needs first was a priority of EIM efforts and that external users would benefit from these efforts. The team, however, provided no specifics about this. If you were part of the team, what specific benefits for external users could you list that would back up the team's decision?

## Advanced Concepts

The chapter makes several assumptions about the positive impact on healthcare delivery that the use of health information technology would make. As more and more resources are put into the implementation of healthcare technology, are these assumptions holding up? Part of the EIM team's effort is to show evidence of the benefits of healthcare information technology in support of an EIM program. Given this, research the following:

1. The Congressional Budget Office cites studies suggesting the United States could save up to $80 billion annually in healthcare spending by implementing information technology and appropriate use by all providers (Congressional Budget Office 2008, 8). Is this a realistic projection? Are there data today that confirm or refute these projections?
2. Healthcare information technology has been promoted by researchers, the government, and others as increasing the quality of patient care. How is this assumption supported? Provide a list and a synopsis of five studies that have researched this assumption. Include an evaluation of the strength of each of these from a methodological perspective. What conclusions can you draw?

## References

AHIMA. 2013. Practice Brief: Assessing and improving EHR data quality (Updated). *Journal of AHIMA* 84(2): 48–53 [expanded online version].

Buntin, M.B., M.F. Burke, M.C. Hoaglin, D. Blumenthal. 2011. The benefits of health information technology: A review of recent literature shows predominantly positive results. *Health Affairs* 30 (3): 464–471.

Congressional Budget Office. 2008 (May). Evidence on the Costs and Benefits of Health Information Technology. http://www.cbo.gov/ftpdocs/91xx/doc9168/05-20-HealthIT.pdf.

DAMA. 2010. *Guide to Data Management Body of Knowledge.* Bradley Beach: Technics Publications.

Dick, R.S., E.B. Steen, and D.E. Detmer, eds. 1997. *The Computer-Based Patient Record: An Essential Technology for Health Care,* rev. ed. Washington, DC: National Academies Press. http://books.nap.edu/openbook.php?record_id=5306&page=R1.

45 CFR 160.103: Health Insurance Portability and Accountability Act of 1996.

Girosi, F., R. Meili and R. Scoville. 2005. *Extrapolating Evidence of Health Information Technology Savings and Costs.* Santa Monica, CA: RAND Corporation. http://www.rand.org/content/dam/rand/pubs/monographs/2005/RAND_MG410.pdf.

Kaiser Family Foundation 2012 (May 1). Health Care Costs: A Primer. http://kff.org/health-costs/report/health-care-costs-a-primer/.

MedlinePlus. 2013. http://www.nlm.nih.gov/medlineplus/aboutmedlineplus.html.

National Alliance for Health Information Technology and the Department of Health and Human Resources. 2008 (April 20). Report to the Office of the National Coordinator for Health Information Technology on defining key health information technology terms. https://www.nachc.com/client/Key%20HIT%20Terms%20Definitions%20Final_April_2008.pdf.

Shortliffe, E.H. and L.E. Perreault. 2000. Medical Informatics: Computer applications in healthcare, 2nd ed. Edited by G. Wiederhold, and L.M. Fagan. New York: Springer-Verlag.

Smith, C. 2001. Practice Brief: Documentation requirements for the acute care inpatient record. *Journal of AHIMA* 72(3): 56A–56-G).

US Department of Health and Human Services. 2011. The Office of the National Coordinator for Health Information Technology State Health Information Exchange Program. http://www.healthit.gov/policy-researchers-implementers/state-health-information-exchange.

# Chapter 2

# History of Health Information Systems

"Those who don't know history are destined to repeat it." A famous quote by Edmund Burke could directly apply to healthcare information systems today. Knowing past efforts, successes, and failures in healthcare information systems and learning from them is important for the advancement of the field. Unfortunately, the repetition of the same or similar mistakes over the past few decades has been one reason for arresting the progress in meeting the benefit expectations of electronic health records (EHRs). Consider, for example, the following specific EHR-related errors that research studies have documented:

- Allowable medication cannot be ordered because it is not included in the pick-list drop-down box
- Incorrect defaults for drug dosage
- Two action buttons with the same label but different functionality
- Incorrect policy allows hard-stops on clinical alerts causing delays in needed therapy
- Data entry screen does not provide all pertinent information to perform task (Sittig and Singh 2011)

By knowing and applying lessons from the past, healthcare organizations could have prevented these errors. The focus of this chapter is to traverse the historical and evolutionary path of health information systems, highlight important constructs and concepts in information technology development and deployment, and identify how the challenges of the past can inform a new generation of health information management (HIM) professionals in facing and solving the challenges of the present and future. Specifically, this chapter covers topics that help you to:

- Explain the evolution of health information systems development
- Evaluate the degree that health information management and governance practices meet industry needs
- Apply systems theory to health information systems
- Explain key functions in health information systems
- Summarize the vision and future of EHRs

## Health Information Systems: The Evolutionary Path

In problem solving, understanding the context, history, and how others solved problems in the past, either successfully or unsuccessfully, is crucial to good decision-making outcomes in the present. Similarly, in developing and implementing healthcare information systems, understanding the context of a problem, and knowing how someone solved a problem determines how well you can resolve similar and new problems. The following sections discuss systems theory and provide a framework for understanding the context in which information systems development and implementation occur. This section explores the history of healthcare information systems, providing examples of how health professionals have solved problems and resultant consequences that have led to issues similar to those facing St. Rita's.

### The St. Rita's Healthcare System Case Study

The St. Rita's EIM team knew they were stepping into a complex environment and the keys to the data challenges facing St. Rita's lay, to a large extent, in studying the context and history of how St. Rita's got to its present situation.

"Why do information silos exist at St. Rita's? And why is there no consistent roadmap for ensuring data integrity or standardization across the enterprise?" Bob asked at an early morning team meeting.

Val was the first to respond. "Until recently, data has never been thought of as a corporate asset. In the past, the technology and data primarily supported operations and tactical decision making, like admitting a patient or determining how many beds were available. Because of this, data silos functioned perfectly well. Technology now is more sophisticated and gives us the ability to amass, manipulate, and analyze large amounts of data. To do this, however, requires data standardization across the enterprise."

"Hmm," Shirlee mused. "That explanation helps me see the bigger picture. Knowing the history and context really does explain how things have gotten where they are now," Shirlee added.

The EIM team suspected that if they studied the history of healthcare information systems, the answers to Bob's questions would become clear and would help them understand the reasons for St. Rita's data issues. It would also provide insights about how to implement the EIM and DG program at St. Rita's. Understanding an organization's culture and history is a key factor in successfully transitioning to new ways of thinking, the team concluded. To begin to unravel the current data situation at St. Rita's, the team decided to study how information systems and their management had evolved over time.

## Systems Approach

The foundational term in "health information system" is the word "system." Knowing the nature of systems is essential to understanding how they impact an organization. A **system** can be defined as a group of elements that interact with each other through defined relationships to achieve a common goal or objective. Sometimes these elements are systems themselves and are referred to as **subsystems**, or systems within systems. Systems function in an external environment and need to be dynamic to accommodate change. For example, the human body is made up of component parts, or subsystems. Among these are respiratory, circulatory, integumentary, and neurological subsystems. Each subsystem interacts with other subsystems through predefined relationships. As a whole, they are dynamic and adjust to changing environments. Take for instance, environmental temperature. When the temperature outside is hot, the body subsystems react through a variety of predetermined biochemical and other processes to accommodate the elevated environmental temperature and to achieve a common goal of maintaining a constant level of body temperature. Any change in one subsystem affects other subsystems and can potentially affect the stability of the entire system. Thus, a system can further be defined as a group of components that:

- Influence each other
- Interact through defined relationships
- Work toward accomplishing a common goal
- Adapt and respond to environmental changes

Figure 2.1 provides a visual representation of a system.

An **information system** exists in an external environment and consists of subsystems that work toward a common goal. In a big picture perspective, the subsystems include people, processes, technologies, and data. Each of these influences other subsystems and interacts through defined relationships to work toward achieving a common goal. An information system must be able to adapt to environmental changes, for example, increased usage or increased data volume. Figure 2.2 depicts these features of an information system.

Figure 2.1. System components

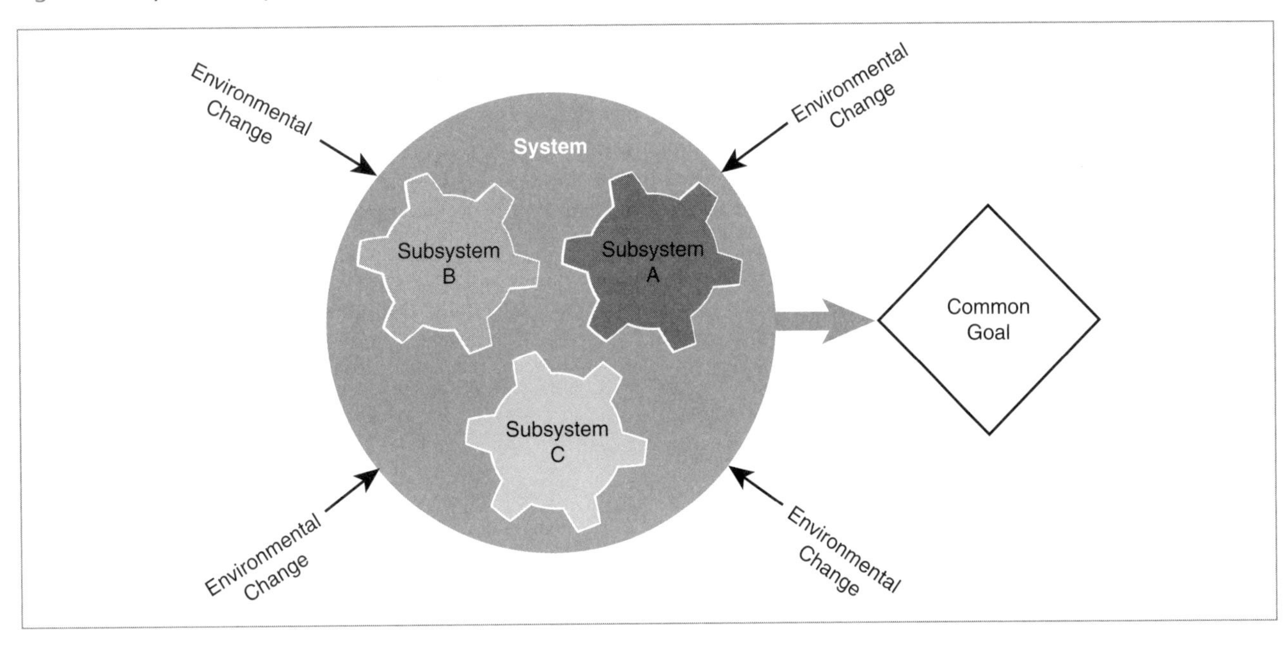


©Merida L. Johns

Figure 2.2. Information system components

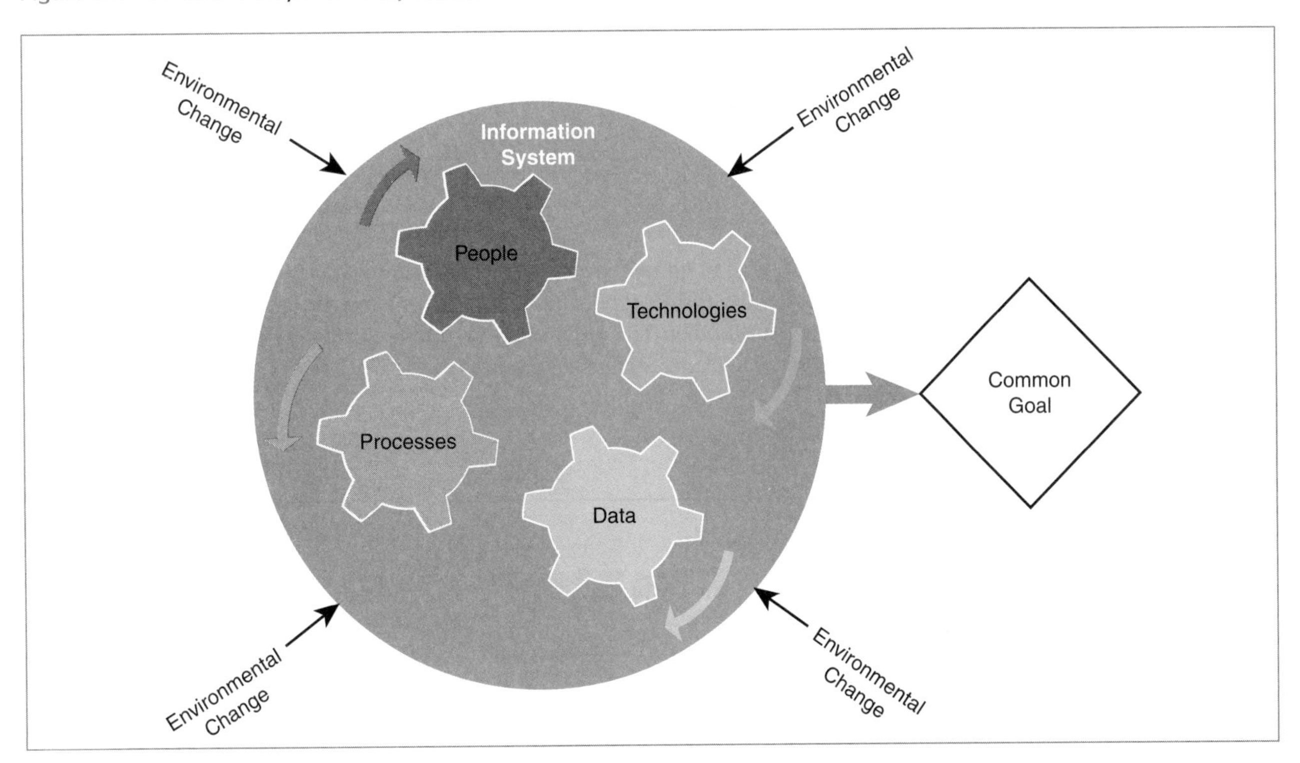


©Merida L. Johns

A system functions by accepting input, transforming the input, and producing an output. A system also relies on a feedback loop that influences future input. In an information system, input, output, and the feedback loop consist of data. These form the basis for the system's operation. **Input** initiates action by the system; **feedback** is a control mechanism that, acting on input, allows for self-correction or maintenance; and **output** is the end product of system processes. Take, for example, an order entry system in an EHR system. The goal of the system is to accept physician orders (input) for medication or diagnostic tests, alert physicians if they are ordering the proper medication dosage (feedback), process the physician orders, and produce an output, such as a request to the pharmacy for a specific medication, or a request to the laboratory to perform a specific test. In this example, an order entry system is composed of:

- **People** including nurses, physicians, laboratory technicians, and pharmacists
- **Data** about the type and amount of medication or diagnostic test the physician ordered
- **Processes** that include entering the data in a specified format and transforming the data into specific requests
- **Technology** including software and hardware devices used to accept input, transform the data, and produce the output, which, in this case, are physician orders

Predefined interactions and relationships between the people, processes, data, and technology cause the information system to function. Figure 2.3 portrays an order entry system for medication orders.

Figure 2.3. Order entry system

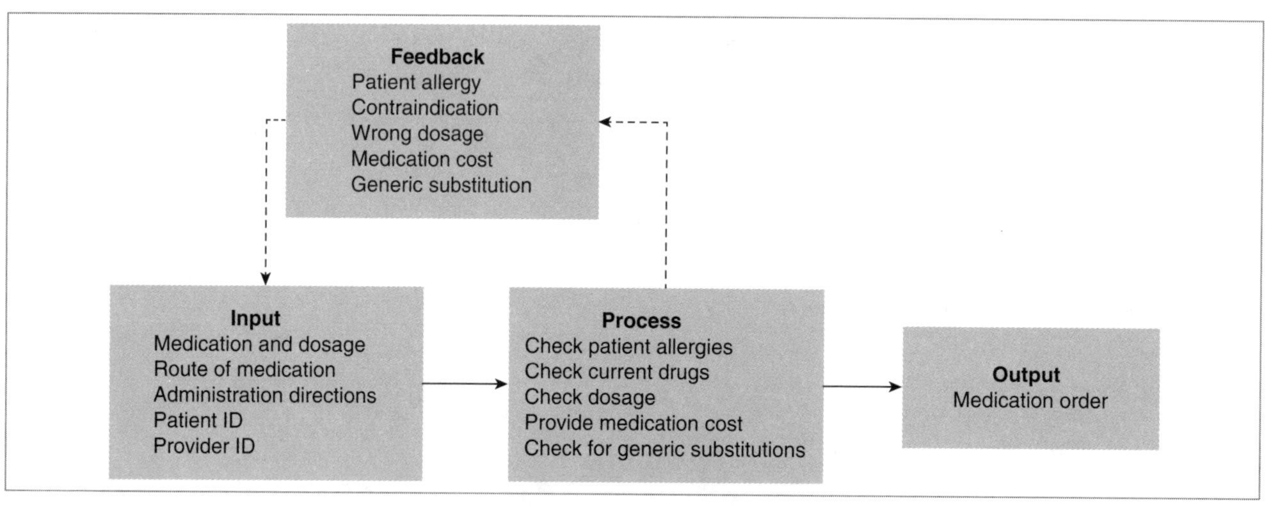


©Merida L. Johns

You can also view the order entry system described in figure 2.3 as a subsystem within an organization's EHR. An EHR is composed of many subsystems such as order entry, results reporting, laboratory, pharmacy, nursing, and radiology. In figure 2.4, the subsystems interact and influence each other. The order entry system collects the physician order data and passes these to the laboratory, radiology, and pharmacy subsystems in a predefined format. Each of those subsystems takes

Figure 2.4. Example of EHR subsystem interaction

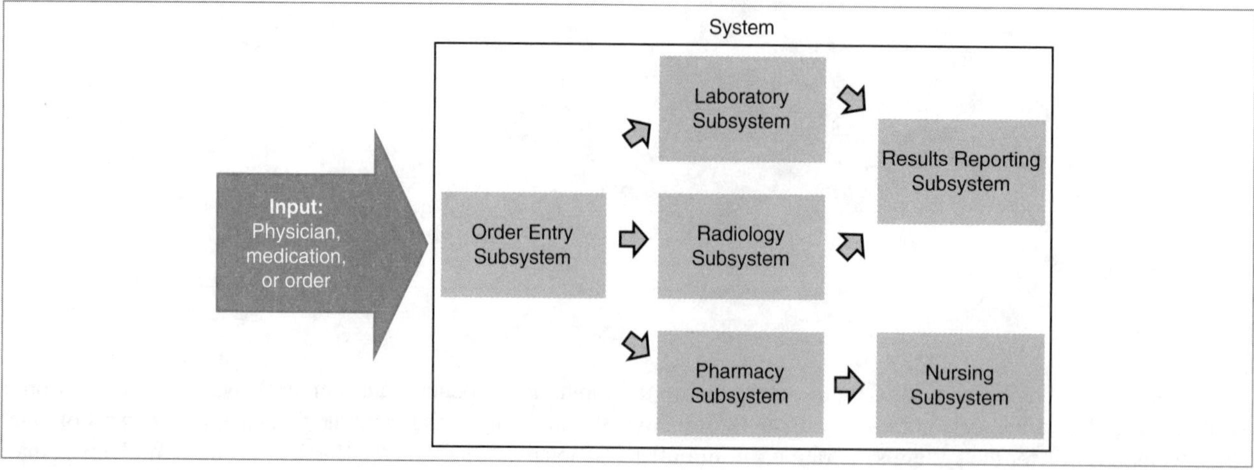


©Merida L. Johns

these data and processes the orders. The pharmacy dispenses the right medication for delivery to the nursing care unit. The nursing staff documents the administration of the medication in the nursing subsystem. The clinical laboratory collects the required specimen, completes the correct test, and reports the test results to the physician through the results reporting subsystem. The radiology department receives the physician order, completes the appropriate diagnostic exam, and reports the findings to the physician through the results reporting subsystem. Note that the output of the order entry subsystem serves as the input to the pharmacy, radiology, and laboratory subsystems. All of these subsystems and their data comprise part of the EHR system.

A problem or change in any one subsystem can impact other subsystems and ultimately, the total EHR system. For instance, if a data element, such as an identification number, is changed during a system upgrade from four to six characters in length in one subsystem, the other subsystems cannot accommodate the data because the data element length is too long. Information systems can provide unlimited benefits to an organization if they are well developed, integrated, and managed to meet the tasks to be performed in meeting the needs of the organization.

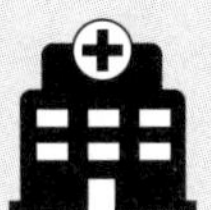

### The St. Rita's Healthcare System Case Study

The St. Rita's team acknowledged that a systems viewpoint was vital in establishing an EIM and DG program. In developing standards, policies, and procedures for an enterprise-wide program, the team knew they had to be sensitive to the effects these may have on the organization's information subsystems. They would measure the success of the EIM program in terms of how well it supported end user tasks in meeting the needs of the organization.

## Evolution of Health Information Systems

Healthcare information systems have evolved to support the delivery of both healthcare and administrative functions. A useful way of studying the evolution is to use a data-information-knowledge model that evolves from the simplest to most complex information systems. Data are facts, images, or sounds that convey no particular meaning, such as the number 70. **Information** moves beyond data and consists of sets of data that are related and have been placed in context, are filtered, manipulated, or formatted in some way and are useful to a particular task. Reporting that Mrs. Jones' fasting glucose is 70 mg/dL is a piece of information because the data 70 is related to mg/dL fasting glucose and to Mrs. Jones. **Knowledge** consists of a combination of rules, relationships, ideas, and experiences applied to information. For example, a rule for a normal glucose range may be 70–99 mg/dL. Applying this knowledge to Mrs. Jones' fasting glucose of 79 mg/dL would result in concluding that her fasting glucose was normal. Figure 2.5 displays a comparison between data, information, and knowledge and accompanying sophistication in the development and management of these between paper and electronic information systems.

The data-information-knowledge model is useful in assessing the advancement of healthcare information systems. In early applications the emphasis was on turning data into information. This resulted in the development of specific applications such as laboratory, pharmacy, and radiology systems. These applications were frequently not integrated with each other and resulted in what is commonly referred to as data silos. Today, the emphasis is increasingly on making knowledge an integral part of EHR systems. For this to occur, however, healthcare organizations must integrate data across applications. As information systems become more complex, their development and management also become more complicated and mature. This is the tension point that St. Rita's is facing. The next sections of this chapter explore the development and management of healthcare information systems from the simplest paper-based systems to the more complex knowledge-based systems.

### Paper-Based Systems

The beginning of the evolution of health information systems in the United States began with the first systematic efforts by the American College of Surgeons (ACS) in 1919 to establish hospital standards. The ACS **Hospital Standardization**

Figure 2.5. Comparison of data, information, and knowledge systems

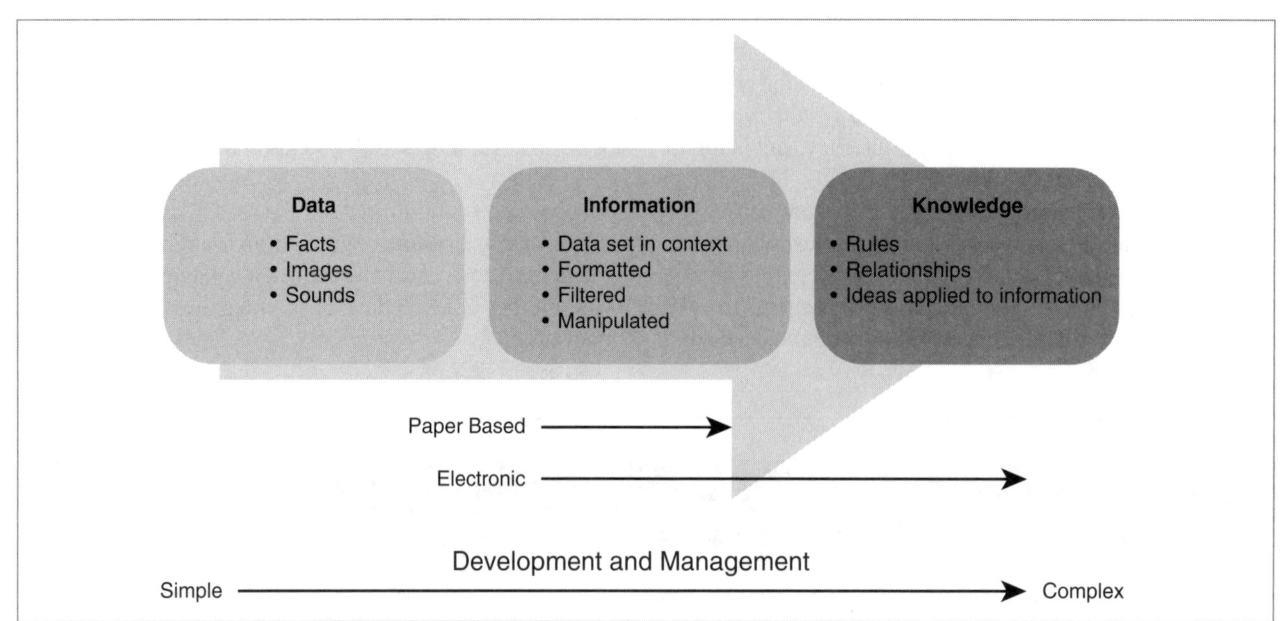


©Merida L. Johns

**Program** laid the groundwork for today's hospital standardization and accreditation programs, such as the Joint Commission. Prior to this time, the creation and management of hospital medical records were the responsibility of the physician. Unless the physician was interested in medical research, the medical records in the early 20th century were "practically worthless" (Huffman 1941, 101).

The impetus for the Hospital Standardization Program by the ACS was to raise the standards of surgery by requiring minimum quality standards for hospitals. The appalling state of hospital medical records and the related patient safety and quality of care issues prompted the newly formed ACS to begin development of hospital standards in 1913. The ACS adopted the first standards at the end of 1919. Of the five standards, one specifically required hospitals to maintain complete and accurate medical records for each patient (American College of Surgeons 2011).

To meet the medical record standard, hospitals had to establish procedures and processes for the maintenance, storage, and access to medical records. In addition, staff was hired to manage these early information systems, and the job position of medical record clerk was established.

A review of figure 1.7 (chapter 1) shows that today's best practices for paper-based and electronic records essentially retains the broad components that were first enumerated in the ACS 1919 Standards. The management of paper-based systems has traditionally focused on controlling objects such as records, reports, and forms rather than on the information contained in these objects. The principal tasks include record storage, record tracking, forms development and control, release of healthcare information, and compilation of documentation by healthcare providers into categorized and organized individual patient records. These tasks ensure that specific documentation (such as operative report, physician orders, physician notes, medical history, and physical exam) are appropriately included in a patient's record, but do not necessarily focus on the quality of data within the reports.

While today's HIM environment is moving away from paper-based information systems, many of the foundational processes are still essential in an electronic environment. For example, each patient must have a unique identifier that is key to locating and retrieving all of the patient's health information. In both paper and electronic worlds, this is referred to as the **medical or health record number**.

Organization policy and government, accrediting, licensing, and other agencies require specific documentation to be maintained, whether in a paper or electronic environment. For example, a patient who undergoes surgery must have a pre-operative anesthesia evaluation, an intraoperative anesthesia report, a post-operative anesthesia evaluation, an operative report, and a pathology report if tissue was removed. Each of these reports has specific content requirements. For instance, among other items, the intraoperative report must include the name of the person administering the anesthesia, premedication, type and amount of anesthesia administered, and induction methods.

Figure 2.6 provides a list of the management tasks traditionally performed for paper systems and compares these to those that healthcare organizations should incorporate into an EIM program for EHR systems.

Figure 2.6. Typical information management tasks in paper and electronic systems

| Management Requirement | Paper-based System | Electronic System |
|---|---|---|
| **Unique patient identifier** | ✓ | ✓ |
| **Maintenance of clinical information**<br>• **Input**<br>• **Assembly**<br>• **Storage**<br>• **Deficiency analysis**<br>• **Retrieval** | ✓ | ✓ |
| **Maintenance of administrative information**<br>• **Input**<br>• **Assembly**<br>• **Storage**<br>• **Retrieval** | ✓ | ✓ |
| **Maintenance of authorizations, consents** | ✓ | ✓ |
| **Access controls** | ✓ | ✓ |
| **Release of information** | ✓ | ✓ |
| **Tracking access and release of information** | ✓ | ✓ |
| **Forms design** | ✓ | |
| **Template/Screen design** | | ✓ |
| **Records retention** | ✓ | ✓ |
| **Records disposition** | ✓ | ✓ |



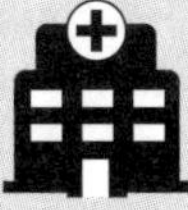

### *The St. Rita's Healthcare System Case Study*

The EIM team wondered how much of St. Rita's health information was in paper format. The team would need to find this out and determine if the EIM and data governance (DG) program should encompass both paper and electronic worlds. From the comparison of the traditional paper-based information system practices to those required in an electronic world, the EIM team knew that while many of the functions are the same, the way they are performed are dramatically different. Therefore the move to EIM would likely necessitate organizational and cultural changes for St. Rita's.

## Electronic-Based Systems

In many respects, the history of adoption of information systems in healthcare follows a pathway similar to other industries. Implementation in other industries was based on a synergy among compelling external and internal factors. This included advances in information and business technologies, growth in competitive and global markets, desire to reduce costs and increase productivity and profits, need for better and faster information, increased complexity in the product development life cycle, and recognition of information as a business asset.

In healthcare, the factors were analogous to those in other industries and included, among others, the advancement of information technologies, development of sophisticated biomedical technologies, expanded knowledge of the diagnosis and treatment of disease, greater complexity in healthcare delivery, increased consumer knowledge and expectations, government financing of healthcare delivery, and the need for more efficient and cost-effective healthcare delivery.

The implementation of federal healthcare financing through Medicare, a more competitive managed-care marketplace, and the associated pressures to lower healthcare costs and increase quality of care have been influential factors in hospital information technology (HIT) adoption (Borzekowski 2002). The incentives attached to Medicare reimbursement appear to be one of the primary drivers for the adoption of HIT by hospitals and individual providers today.

**The 1960s-1970's: The Beginning Decades**

By 1968, almost 24 percent of hospitals in the United States had adopted some type of HIT (Borzekowski 2002). The scope of adoption focused primarily on administrative and financial information and corresponded to what was occurring in other industries. These systems usually supported accounting functions such as accounts payable and receivable, and payroll; staff management such as staff scheduling and employee time and attendance tracking; patient administrative functions such as patient registration, admission, discharge, transfer (R-ADT); and systems that supported diagnostic and procedure coding for the collection of statistical data used in patient care and outcome and research analysis. During this time, the sophistication level of software applications and computer technology restricted systems to supporting transaction processing. Little was available to support more data-intensive analytical processing. Moreover, there was little or no ability to exchange data among systems. This led to the creation of data silos resulting in data duplication and data quality issues that remain problematic for hospitals today, including St. Rita's.

Hospitals primarily had three system choices during this period: in-house development, shared data processing services, and turnkey systems. **In-house systems** were designed, developed, operated, and supported by a hospital onsite staff. Typically, main-frame based systems, they were located in larger hospital facilities, frequently university-related, that had the staff and financial resources available to maintain such systems.

Shared software and data processing services were one alternative to in-house systems. **Shared services** usually included software applications developed by the vendor and operated on hardware at the vendor site. Software applications and hardware were shared by multiple hospitals, thus reducing the costs for all hospitals involved. The hospital and the vendor site communicated through telephone lines or, in less sophisticated systems, by paper forms. Shared systems were, in concept, the forerunner of cloud computing with similar concerns involving data security, maintenance, and other issues that are the same today.

In the latter part of the 1970s, turnkey systems were introduced. **Turnkey** systems usually consisted of software applications developed by a vendor which were then installed on a computer system located at the hospital site. They were called turnkey systems because the vendor staff performed the development and maintenance, and hospitals could just about "turn the key" and begin system operation. Hospital onsite staff was responsible for day-to-day operation of turnkey systems and there was little if any modification or customization ability. Turnkey systems coincided with the introduction of mini-computers which were smaller, less expensive, and sometimes more powerful than mainframe computers. Consequently, these systems provided smaller hospitals the opportunity to obtain electronic systems due to lower price points and the reduced need for a large information systems (IS) staff. Turnkey systems remain a popular choice today for small hospitals, physician practices, and clinics.

Although financial and administrative systems were the principal emphasis for HIT adoption during this era, there were also several clinical and medical decision-making models that were developed. These early and innovative systems demonstrated the potential benefits of HIT by improving efficiency of the delivery and quality of patient care. Many of these development efforts were supported by government funds through agencies such as the Agency for Healthcare Research and Quality. Among these HIT models included the following:

- The multiphasic screening health examination system spearheaded by Dr. Morris Collen at Kaiser Permanente
- The Problem-Oriented Medical Information System (PROMIS) championed by Dr. Lawrence Weed
- Computer-based interactive consultation programs that assisted physicians in the diagnosis and treatment of disease states such as electrolyte and acid-based disorders pioneered by Dr. Howard Bleich
- The Computer Stored Ambulatory Care Record (COSTAR) directed by Dr. Octo Barnett
- The Health Evaluation through Logical Processing (HELP) system led by Dr. Homer Warner at LDS Hospital
- The Regenstrief Medical Record System (RMRS) led by Dr. Clement McDonald and Dr. William Tierney
- Technicon Medical Information System at El Camino Hospital
- MYCIN expert system spearheaded by Dr. Ted Shortliffe at Stanford University (Fitzmaurice, Adams, and Eisenberg 2002 and Blois and Shortliffe 1990)

These pioneering systems provided the rich foundational work that contributed to today's healthcare information systems. As an illustration, Dr. Collen's multiphasic health screening, a forerunner of today's preventative medicine, consisted of a series of procedures and tests that screened for conditions such as heart disease, diabetes, and cancer. Automation of the multiphasic screening program provided data for large-scale population research, which demonstrated the value of large database automation in providing analytic and predictive statistics for healthcare. Another example from these pioneering efforts, a legacy of the work of Dr. Lawrence Weed and the PROMIS, is the maintenance of a problem list now required by federal regulation for each patient's EHR. And the Technicon Medical Information System was an early model of an attempt to integrate systems and computerize order entry. Each of these systems has provided a legacy of knowledge and experimentation that provides the framework for today's systems.

### The 1980s: Deployment of Departmental and Functional Systems

During the 1980s, there was a continuing focus on developing more sophisticated financial and administrative information systems. Part of this was influenced by the prospective payment system, introduced by Medicare, that reimbursed hospitals a pre-determined amount based on a patient's diagnosis, the procedures the provider performed, and certain complications arising during hospitalization. This reimbursement system was called **diagnosis-related groups (DRGs)**.

To collect reimbursement, hospitals had to submit *International Classification of Diseases, Ninth Revision, Clinical Modification* (ICD-9-CM) diagnostic and procedure codes along with patient demographic data that were subjected to complex algorithms that determined the reimbursement rate. It became essential that financial and diagnostic coded data be merged together, and that these data be accurate and complete. Automated assisted coding applications quickly developed and were implemented by hospitals to help ensure the accuracy of coded data, as well as to expedite the billing process. Implementation of the DRG-based reimbursement system had a snowball effect and became more important as Medicaid state programs and private insurers began to reimburse hospitals under managed care arrangements with preset payment amounts and implement utilization review of services.

Coincidentally, **integrated delivery systems** (IDS) began to emerge at this time to provide more efficient and effective care, reduce costs, and provide better outcomes. An IDS is an organizational arrangement of a network of health providers that may include hospitals, physicians, and a **health maintenance organization** (HMO) that provides coordinated services along the continuum of care from ambulatory, acute, and long-term care and may extend across a geographical region. Information sharing among providers is vital to provide a continuum of care. Thus, these arrangements were yet another driver for development of better clinical and administrative information systems.

Departmental clinical and administrative applications began to appear with the growing presence and maturity of mini-computers. Among these were laboratory, radiology, dietary, and pharmacy clinical systems and administrative systems for such functions as human resources, materials management, tracking paper-based health records, and diagnostic coding. These standalone systems were efficient in supporting the tasks of individual departments, but did not necessarily integrate or even interface easily with each other or the hospital R-ADT or financial functions. This phenomenon, often called a **best-of-breed system**, led to separate databases that were developed and managed independently. The cautions from the 1970s about standalone systems and issues of data redundancy and data quality were not regarded. Thus, best-of-breed systems resulted in silos of disconnected, duplicated, and inconsistent data across the various systems. Microcomputers and associated software and databases made it easy for departments to purchase or create simple applications but also fueled data proliferation and decentralization of data management. All of these factors led to data definition problems and data redundancy, accuracy, and security issues. In most cases, hospitals had no central authority for the management of data throughout the enterprise.

### The 1990s: Electronic Health Record Vision and Rise of the Hybrid Environment

Technological advances and continued cost, efficiency, and quality drivers pressed health information systems into the beginning of a new era. The need for integrated information systems that could reduce data redundancy, increase data quality, and provide decision-making capabilities was in demand as healthcare delivery and the marketplace became more complex. Technological advancements in local and wide area networks, data repositories, decision support systems, and standards development for health record content and information interchange such as Health Level Seven (HL7) created an environment that enabled movement toward more integrated systems.

In 1991, an IOM seminal work provided the vision for a computer-based patient record (Dick et al. 1991). This report outlined the benefits and framework for computer-based record systems that could improve patient care. It helped to push to the forefront the need for a longitudinal "electronic patient record that resides in a system specifically designed to support users by providing accessibility to complete and accurate data, alerts, reminders, clinical decision support systems, links to medical knowledge, and other aids" (IOM 1991, 11). The report's 12 recommendations stand the test of time, and are just as applicable in the new millennium as they were when IOM created them.

The IOM report emphasized that **computer-based patient record** (CPR) systems were not a distinct product healthcare organizations could purchase off the shelf. Rather, the CPR was a concept of maintaining health-related and patient-related data electronically and relied on multiple data sources and technologies to ensure that end users could access complete and accurate data, and be provided with alerts, reminders, clinical decision support, and links to medical knowledge. For example, direct patient care data may be stored on multiple clinical systems both internal and external to an organization. Information to aid clinicians in decision support may reside in bibliographic databases such as Medline, and information that tracks the performance of health providers may reside in specialized data warehouses (chapter 9). The significant idea, however, is that information and communication technologies and software that work together integrate and support all of these data sources to provide accurate, complete, and timely information to all stakeholders. Importantly, organizations across the healthcare sector would use the information byproducts of CPRs in the assessment and management of population health, in research for tracking the performance of healthcare providers, by consumers for participating in their own healthcare decisions, and to help inform healthcare policy decisions.

A second edition of the IOM report appeared in 1997 and corresponded with the midpoint of the target date set in the original report for achieving widespread implementation of CPRs by 2007. A commentary in the second edition provided the sense of urgency for the development and adoption of CPRs:

> Until CPR use becomes the norm for all practitioners across all provider settings as recommended in the original report, we will continue to lack the tools needed to manage the quality and costs of healthcare, the scientific basis for healthcare will continue to be undermined, and the dramatic transformation of healthcare so urgently required will be impeded. Thus, a major challenge facing us is to determine how to advance from where we are to where we need to be with respect to the development and diffusion of CPRs. (IOM 1997, vii)

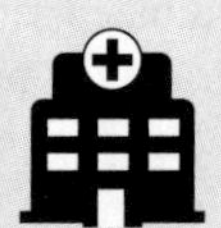

## The St. Rita's Healthcare System Case Study

Studying the history of electronic information systems helped the EIM team understand that St. Rita's data problems were not unique. St. Rita's path correlated with the general history of information technology adoption that the team uncovered. St. Rita's had silos of data and data quality issues because it implemented separate departmental systems over time. The team recognized that management, organizational, and cultural barriers would likely challenge EIM implementation. "Organizational change," said Val at a team meeting, "usually involves a perceived or real threat by some stakeholders such as fear of losing employment, disruption of regular routines, investing time and energy in learning new processes, or change in job status."

"So changing from departmental and best-of-breed systems to a more centralized information management structure such as EIM may prove threatening to some departments," Shirlee added. "I can also see that collaborating with other organizations that are potential competitors may constitute a political barrier," Linda observed.

"And relocating to another department may cause a sense of loss of community," Denise suggested. The team concluded that managing all of these aspects of change must be a big part of their plan to an EIM migration. The success of EIM at St. Rita's would be as much about these types of organizational, cultural, and political issues as it was about the technology.

"You realize there are systems in between paper and electronic," Val continued. "The evolution of electronic health information systems includes a hybrid world where organizations find themselves jumping the crevasse between paper and electronic worlds. Many hospitals envision living in a combination, or hybrid, record world using both paper and electronic media for some time to come," she added.

"This sounds like it could be a real coordination challenge," Linda reflected.

"I believe it might be," Val responded. "Before we can identify the boundaries of an EIM and DG program at St. Rita's we need to know the subsystems that make up the entirety of the health information system, including existing paper, electronic, and hybrid subsystems," said Monte.

The team's discussion turned to listing the issues that might likely exist in a hybrid environment and the impact of these from an EIM perspective. They decided to confirm their suspicions by finding out what normally constituted a hybrid environment. Information from surveying the literature would help the team set the scope of the EIM and DG program later on.

## The Hybrid Environment

Achieving the CPR vision during the 1990s was beyond the capability of virtually all healthcare organizations. The US Department of Defense and the US Veterans Administration were able to advance their efforts in developing the vision of a CPR system. In part, this was due to the confidentiality and security regulations that had been in place inside the government since the late 1970s, availability of funding for the effort, and access to staff and advanced technologies necessary to develop the type of complex applications required by a CPR system. Only a few major private sector organizations launched large scale efforts (Berner, Ditmer, and Simborg 2005).

The reasons for this were varied. First, a fully functional EHR depends upon the ability to exchange and preferably integrate data from a variety of data sources. Standards for data content and data interchange were in the beginning stages of development and there was no consistent way to organize, represent, or encode clinical data so interchanging systems could accept and understand it.

Second, the content of health information is an intricate mixture of text, images, video, and sound. Coupled with complex and varied decision-making and service delivery processes, systems were difficult to develop. Unlike a manufacturing line or an accounting transaction, many unpredictable factors influence medical decision making and patient care. Designs other industries use, such as structured data entry using drop-down boxes and menus, do not necessarily accommodate the nuances and differences among patients or the medical decision-making process (Ash et al. 2004). While the inability of vendors to provide a fully functional system that mirrored the IOM vision constituted a major barrier, hospitals and other healthcare delivery organizations were slow to adopt portions of a total EHR system.

Third, healthcare organizations often cited system cost as a barrier. A computer physician order entry (CPOE) system was estimated to cost approximately $8 million for a 500-bed hospital, and a bar coding identification system estimate was $1 million for an average hospital (Medicare Payment Advisory Commission 2004, 167). Costs go beyond purchase and initial implementation. Continued maintenance, training, and update costs also figured into the hesitancy to adopt HIT. Many organizations believed it was difficult to quantify benefits of HIT and had difficulty proving return on investment. Other barriers included the challenge of fitting the technology into workflow processes, the general reluctance of clinicians to accept HIT, and the lack of interoperability among systems (Medicare Payment Advisory Commission 2004).

In addition to these barriers, maintaining the confidentiality, privacy, and security of electronic personal health information was also a concern. Until the implementation of the Health Insurance Portability and Accountability Act (HIPAA) in 2003, personal health information privacy and security safeguards rested with state law. As a result, protection relied on a patchwork of laws that were not uniformly consistent among states and did not provide the same level of protections. HIPAA legislation provided the first national privacy and security requirements for personal health information whether a healthcare organization maintained it electronically or in other media.

Due to these factors, healthcare organizations during the 1990s and early 2000s moved to an "in-between" option of part paper and part electronic medical record, referred to as a **hybrid record**. The hybrid record continues into the second decade of the millennium as a method to reach the vision of the CPR. The mixture of electronic and paper varies from facility to facility. For instance, one hospital may have laboratory and radiology reports stored electronically while maintaining all other content in paper format. Often, facilities will scan paper documents such as physician and nursing notes, consents, and authorizations and store these in electronic document management (EDM) systems (chapter 9). The scanned documents stored in EDMs should be linked to electronic data, such as electronic tests and other reports, so that all of the patient's data are available electronically. Scanning paper documents does not meet the fully functional vision of an EHR because individual data elements from scanned material cannot be retrieved, aggregated, or manipulated by healthcare professionals and others for patient care and other purposes. However, the combination of scanned documents linked with electronic data does provide a better opportunity for improved information access.

For a variety of reasons, hybrid records present many management challenges. For one, there must be a system in place to identify the location of the health information. Is the information in paper, scanned, or electronic format? Can authorized persons easily access it when and where they need it?

For another, there must be a process in place that links paper, scanned, and electronic documents and associated information so that a clinician has complete and accurate data available when needed. From a legal perspective, organizations must address several issues. They will need to develop privacy and security procedures for the different types of media. They must also implement processes that ensure that addendums or corrections can be made, and that the most updated versions of these are easily identified and can be accessed from an EDM system. Furthermore, for legal purposes, the source of each report must be identified.

## The New Millennium: Safety Concerns, Cost Reduction, Improved Efficiency

During the first few years of the new millennium, there was an accelerated push by the federal government for adoption of HIT. The government and non-profit organizaitons released several reports that supported the benefits of HIT.

In 2000, an IOM report galvanized the momentum for healthcare information technology adoption. The report estimated that 98,000 patient deaths occur each year due to medical errors. It also focused on systems theory as an explanation for human error in which error occurs when systems or their subsystems fail. The report highlighted several ways healthcare organizations could incorporate information technologies into systems to prevent human error, for example:

- Using order entry systems that provide real-time alerts if a medication order is out of range for weight or age, or is contraindicated
- Using bar coding for positive identification and detection of misidentified patients, records, and so forth
- Using "hear back" for oral orders and instructions, for example, having a pharmacist repeat a phoned-in prescription to the caller
- Monitoring vital signs, blood levels, and other laboratory values for patients receiving hazardous drugs (IOM 2000, 175)

In 2001, the National Committee on Vital and Health Statistics (NCVHS) issued a report that detailed a strategy and 27 recommendations for building a national health information infrastructure (NHII). The first of its recommendations proposed establishing a senior level position, reporting directly to the Secretary of Health and Human Services, to "provide strategic national leadership for development of the NHII and set the agenda for NHII investments, policymaking, and integration with ongoing health and healthcare activities inside and outside of government" (NCVHS 2001, 39). The NCVHS believed that many elements were in place that supported an NHII, such as EHR and digital imaging applications and technical pieces like the World Wide Web, e-mail, search engines, and encryption. However, the NCVHS felt too many of these were proprietary, fragmented, and incomplete and that coordination was essential if appropriate, adequate, and timely information and knowledge sharing was to be made available for the best possible decision making in all areas of healthcare delivery. This report laid the foundation for the establishment of the Office of the National Coordinator for Health Information Technology (ONC).

In 2004, the IOM Committee on Data Standards for Patient Safety called for healthcare organizations to adopt information technology that would collect and share essential health information on patients and their care (Aspden et al. 2004, 1). The committee's report relied in part on the NCVHS 2001 work and outlined a plan for development of a NHII to "provide immediate access to complete patient information and decision support tools for clinicians and their patients and to capture patient safety information as a by-product of care, and use this information to design even safer delivery systems" (Aspden, et al. 2004, 1).

Achieving these goals depended upon the establishment of an NHII as defined by the NCHVS in 2001 and consisting "of a set of values, practices and relationships, laws and regulations, health data standards, technologies, and systems and applications that support all facets of individual health, healthcare delivery, and public health" (Aspden et al. 2004, 46). To build the NHII and improve safety and quality of care, the IOM report concluded that healthcare providers must invest in EHR systems that could capture patient and other clinical data and interact with decision support systems. In a previous report, this committee outlined the functionalities and capabilities that such EHR systems should include (National Research Council 2003, 7–11). Table 2.1 includes a summary of these.

By presidential executive order in 2004, the Office of the ONC was created to help spur widespread adoption of interoperable EHRs within 10 years. During its initial years, the ONC's efforts concentrated on defining and establishing a national agenda for health information exchange (HIE) by designing and evaluating standards-based prototype architectures, which are models of technology architectures based on standards that allow different systems to operate together and exchange data. Key partners in the ONC's endeavors to establish an NHII included the Healthcare Information Technology Standards Panel (HITSP), the Certification Commission for Healthcare Information Technology (CCHIT), the Health Information Security and Privacy Collaboration (HISPC), and the NCVHS.

Table 2.1. EHR system core functionalities

| Functionality | Capability |
|---|---|
| Health information and data | Capture and display patient data through well-designed interfaces. |
| Results management | Manage results of tests and procedures for quicker provider access and to allow for quicker recognition and treatment of medical problems, reduce duplication of tests and procedures, and improve care coordination among providers. |
| Order entry or management | Capture and process physician orders to improve workflow, reduce lost orders and ambiguities, generate related orders automatically, monitor for duplicate orders, reduce the time to fill orders, and increase clinician productivity. |
| Decision support | Provide computerized decision support to enhance clinical performance in prescribing of drugs, diagnosis and management, and detection of adverse events and disease outbreaks. |
| Electronic communication and connectivity | Provide efficient communication and connectivity for creating and populating EHRs, communication and integration tools, and telehealth systems. |
| Patient support | Provide patient support for participation in his or her own healthcare including patient education, home monitoring systems, and communication with providers. |
| Administrative processes | Support administrative processes such as scheduling admissions, procedures, and visits; billing and claims management; validation of insurance eligibility; and identification of eligible individuals for clinical trials or chronic disease management programs. |
| Reporting and population health management | Facilitate reporting and population health management by accessing and producing required data for public and private sector reporting at the federal, state, and local levels for patient safety and quality, as well as for public health. |

Source: Adapted from IOM 2004.

In 2004, the ONC awarded $22.6 million in contracts to nine HIEs to begin trial implementations of a national health information network (NHIN). This collective group worked to establish specifications and exchange patient data in a secure environment. By 2009, they placed work products such as interface and data specifications, testing materials, and trust agreements in the public domain.

These trial implementations were a major step forward in modernizing healthcare delivery in the United States through the use of information technology. In 2010, the ONC announced availability of State Health Information Exchange (State HIE) Cooperative Agreement awards and gave awards to 56 entities including states and eligible territories. These awards funded states' efforts to rapidly build their capacity for exchanging health information within and across state lines.

With just 15 percent of non-federal acute care hospitals in the United States estimated to have implemented a basic EHR in 2010, the 10-year goal of wide-spread HIT adoption set down in 2004 was far from realized (ONC May 2014). The Health Information Technology for Economic and Clinical Health (HITECH) Act, passed in 2009, authorized the Department of Health and Human Services (HHS) to establish programs to improve healthcare quality, safety, and efficiency through the promotion of HIT and provided an infusion of incentives for hospitals and eligible professionals (EP), such as physicians and chiropractors, to adopt HIT in hopes of substantially increasing the percentage of basic EHR adoption by 2015. Under HITECH, qualifying providers, hospitals, and critical access hospitals (CAHs) can receive incentives for adopting HIT and meeting specified objectives through the use of that technology. The incentives appeared to help boost EHR adoption with 59.4 percent of non-federal acute care facilities having adopted a basic EHR by 2013 (ONC May 2014).

To qualify for incentive payments, eligible hospitals and providers must adopt, implement, upgrade, or successfully demonstrate that they meet meaningful use criteria by using certified EHR technology. The key conditions include "meaningful use criteria" and "certified EHR technology." A **certified EHR technology** is a technology that an ONC Authorized Testing and Certification Body (ATCB) has tested and certified. The ONC maintains a comprehensive listing of complete EHRs and EHR modules available on its website.

**Meaningful use** (MU) criteria are specific objectives and measures that all EPs and hospitals must meet to show they are using EHRs in meaningful ways that positively affect the care of their patients. There are three stages of criteria with each successive stage using information technologies in increasingly sophisticated ways. Stage one criteria, which began in 2011, focused on capturing health information in a standardized format and using that information to track key clinical conditions, communicating that information for care coordination, and initiating the reporting of clinical quality measures and public health information.

Stage two MU criteria focuses on a more rigorous HIE. It broadens the scope and sophistication of the use of HIT and includes the use of technologies for disease management, clinical decision support, medication management support for patient access to their health information, transitions in care, quality measurement and research, and bidirectional communication with public health agencies.

Stage three criteria moves forward in achieving the ultimate goals of MU by centering on achieving improvements in quality, safety, and efficiency, concentrating on decision support for national high priority conditions, patient access to self-management tools, access to comprehensive patient data, and improving population health outcomes (Centers for Medicare and Medicaid Services 2010).

There are three parts to the criteria for each stage of MU. These include a core set of objectives, a menu set of objectives or measures, and clinical quality measures. There are different core objectives and menu sets for EPs and hospitals. For Stage one, MU-eligible hospitals and CAHs have to meet all core objectives and five out of ten from the menu set objectives. Eligible professionals must meet all core objectives for eligible providers and five out of ten from the menu set objectives. As part of meeting one of the MU core measures, EPs and eligible hospitals must report on clinical quality measures in order to successfully attest to MU and receive an incentive payment. Table 2.2 shows stage one MU core measures for eligible hospitals. A comparison between Stage one and Stage two MU core objectives for eligible hospitals is available on the Centers for Medicare and Medicaid (CMS) website.

Table 2.2. **Stage one meaningful use core measures – eligible hospitals**

| Objective | Measure | Exclusion |
|---|---|---|
| (1) Use computerized provider order entry (CPOE) for medication orders directly entered by any licensed healthcare professional who can enter orders into the health record per state, local, and professional guidelines. | Licensed healthcare professionals order at least one medication using CPOE for more than 30 percent of all unique patients with at least one medication in their medication list admitted to the eligible hospital's or CAH's inpatient or emergency department (POS 21 or 23).<br>Optional Alternate: More than 30 percent of medication orders created by authorized providers of the eligible hospital's or CAH's inpatient or emergency department (POS 21 or 23) during the EHR reporting period are recorded using CPOE. | No Exclusion |
| (2) Implement drug-drug and drug-allergy interaction checks. | The eligible hospital or CAH has enabled this functionality for the entire EHR reporting period. | No exclusion |
| (3) Maintain an up-to-date problem list of current and active diagnoses. | Healthcare professionals record at least one entry or an indication as structured data that they know of no problems for more than 80 percent of all unique patients admitted to the eligible hospital's or CAH's inpatient or emergency department (POS 21 or 23). | No exclusion |
| (4) Maintain active medication list. | Healthcare professionals record at least one entry (or an indication that the patient is not currently prescribed any medication) as structured data for more than 80 percent of all unique patients admitted to the eligible hospital's or CAH's inpatient or emergency department (POS 21 or 23). | No exclusion |
| (5) Maintain active medication allergy list. | Healthcare professionals record at least one entry (or an indication that the patient has no known medication allergies) as structured data for more than 80 percent of all unique patients admitted to the eligible hospital's or CAH's inpatient or emergency department (POS 21 or 23). | No exclusion |

(continued)

Table 2.2. Stage one meaningful use core measures – eligible hospitals (*Continued*)

| Objective | Measure | Exclusion |
|---|---|---|
| (6) Record all of the following demographics:<br>(A) Preferred language<br>(B) Gender<br>(C) Race<br>(D) Ethnicity<br>(E) Date of birth<br>(F) Date and preliminary cause of death in the event of mortality in the eligible hospital or CAH. | Health professionals record demographics as structured data for more than 50 percent of all unique patients admitted to the eligible hospital's or CAH's inpatient or emergency department (POS 21 or 23). | No exclusion |
| (7) Record and chart changes in the following vital signs:<br>(A) Height<br>(B) Weight<br>(C) Blood pressure<br>(D) Calculate and display body mass index (BMI)<br>(E) Plot and display growth charts for children 2–20 years, including BMI | For more than 50 percent of all unique patients age two and over admitted to the eligible hospital's or CAH's inpatient or emergency department (POS 21 or 23), healthcare professionals record height, weight, and blood pressure as structured data.<br>**New Measure:** For healthcare professionals to record blood pressure(for patients age three and over only) and height and weight (for all ages) of more than 50 percent of all unique patients admitted to the eligible hospital's or CAH's inpatient or emergency department (POS 21 or 23) as structured data during the EHR-reporting period. | No exclusion |
| (8) Record smoking status for patients 13 years old or older. | Healthcare professionals record the smoking status of more than 50 percent of all unique patients 13 years old or older admitted to the eligible hospital's inpatient or emergency department (POS 21 or 23) as structured data. | Any eligible hospital or CAH that admits no patients 13 years or older to their inpatient or emergency department (POS 21 or 23). |
| (9) Report hospital clinical quality measures to CMS. | Successfully report to CMS hospital clinical quality measures selected by CMS in the manner specified by CMS. | No exclusion |
| (10) Implement one clinical decision support rule related to a high priority hospital condition along with the ability to track compliance with that rule. | Implement one clinical decision support rule. | No exclusion |
| (11) Provide patients with an electronic copy of their health information (including diagnostic test results, problem list, medication lists, medication allergies, discharge summary, and procedures) upon request. | Personnel in the eligible hospital or CAH (POS 21 or 23) provide more than 50 percent of all patients in the inpatient or emergency departments with an electronic copy of their requested health information within three business days. | Any eligible hospital or CAH that has no requests from patients or their agents for an electronic copy of patient health information during the EHR-reporting period. |
| (12) Provide patients with an electronic copy of their discharge instructions at time of discharge, upon request. | More than 50 percent of all patients who are discharged from an eligible hospital or CAH's inpatient or emergency department (POS 21 or 23) and who request an electronic copy of their discharge instructions receive it. | Any eligible hospital or CAH that has no requests from patients or their agents for an electronic copy of the discharge instructions during the EHR-reporting period. |
| (13) Protect electronic health information created or maintained by the certified EHR technology through the implementation of appropriate technical capabilities. | Conduct or review a security risk analysis in accordance with the requirements under 45 CFR 164.308(a)(1) and implement security updates as necessary and correct identified security deficiencies as part of its risk management process. | No exclusion |

Source: CMS 2010.

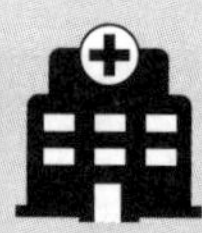

## The St. Rita's Healthcare System Case Study

Val was overwhelmed by the amount of material the team had gathered on government efforts to encourage HIT adoption. "I think, though, we've only scratched the surface," she said to her team members. Bob agreed and pointed out that the team still needed to review additional work by the ONC on standards and certification requirements for EHRs.

"We haven't touched anything at all on content or exchange standards, not to mention legal issues and regulatory requirements," Denise said.

"And the whole area of EIM components and how EIM is implemented needs to be delved into," Monte reminded the group.

The team arranged an hour meeting to set out its strategy for moving forward. They knew that studying the events and trends in HIT was important to their effort. They needed to be sure they were on target with the foundational knowledge before they attempted developing an EIM and DG plan. They decided the next step was to understand how healthcare organizations had traditionally managed HIT. This would give them a baseline to assess an organizational fit for the EIM and DG program, help determine its structure, and identify key players that should be part of the EIM and DG process at St. Rita's. They concluded that the next effort should be a comprehensive overview of the typical clinical and administrative information systems. This information would be useful later on when an inventory of St. Rita's information systems would likely be conducted.

# History of Management and Governance of Health Information Systems

Just nine years after the ACS implement the Hospital Standardization Program in 1919, the Association of Record Librarians of North America (ARLNA) was formed by a group of 35 members of the Club of Record Clerks meeting at the Hospital Standardization Conference in Boston in 1928. Under its auspices, the formation of a prescribed course of study and curriculum was developed and the first college and hospital-based programs for medical record librarians were approved in 1934. The ARLNA established a Board of Registration in 1933 that developed and administered a qualifying certification examination in medical record librarianship. The ARLNA was the predecessor of today's American Health Information Management Association (AHIMA). The primary responsibility for the management of health information essentially fell to this new group of professionals and lasted well into the late 1970s. As information technologies were gradually introduced into healthcare facilities in the 1970s and 1980s, the responsibility for management of the health information system became a shared responsibility, principally between the medical record department and the IS department.

Just as technology and standards development advanced in the 1980s, organizational structures for the management of health information matured. Industries outside of healthcare established executive level positions for the management of information technology and systems. Other industries had embraced **information resources management** (IRM) for nearly two decades, but the concept of managing information as a resource and integrating all information processes and computer, communication, office automation, distributed processing technologies, and selection, implementation and operation of computer systems under a senior-level officer was new to healthcare.

Until this time, IT was usually managed at a departmental level and frequently reported to the chief financial officer (CFO). IT was typically responsible for the operation and maintenance of automated systems including financial, administrative, and R-ADT. During the 1980s, health organizations maintained the bulk of clinical information in paper medical records. Clinical reports from standalone electronic systems, such as clinical laboratory, were usually printed on paper medium and placed by unit clerks in the permanent paper medical record. The medical record department was responsible for the compilation, filing, storage, tracking, and retrieval of medical records as well as maintenance of the organization's master patient index. This organizational structure often inhibited an enterprise-wide view of information technology use. Furthermore, departmental functional systems such as clinical laboratory or radiology maintained their own oversight, thus causing even more fragmentation in data management practices and information communication across the enterprise.

The **chief information officer** (CIO) position began to emerge in healthcare in the late 1980s and early part of the next decade and was a critical turning point in the management of healthcare information systems because of its alignment with the concept that information is a corporate asset and should be managed strategically at an executive level. The CIO is normally responsible for setting the IT vision and leadership and oversees strategic planning, implementation, and operation of enterprise information resources. Many times, however, the title "CIO" was assumed by an IT director but the responsibilities for IT remained at a departmental level and the function still reported to the CFO rather than the **chief executive officer** (CEO) of the organization. It was not until the mid-1990s and early into the next decade that the role of the CIO matured in healthcare organizations as a senior executive-level position.

In the 1990s, the medical record department often reported to the CFO rather than an operations or other executive. This transition was due to the increasing emphasis on revenue cycle management with DRG implementation. The medical record department was a key player in this cycle, which was usually responsible for diagnostic and procedural coding and DRG assignment, upon which reimbursement was usually based for Medicare and Medicaid patients.

Throughout the late 1990s and first decade of the millennium, the medical record department more and more frequently reported directly to the CIO as the position gained more prominence in healthcare facilities. In 1992, the College of Healthcare Information Management Executives (CHIME) was established with the goals of serving the professional development needs of healthcare CIOs and advocating the more effective use of information management within healthcare (CHIME 2014). The establishment of a professional organization helped to elevate the prominence and importance of enterprise information management by advocating for and advancing the role of CIOs in healthcare. Coincidentally, during the 1990s the name of the medical record department gradually transitioned to the "health information department" in most facilities. This was due in part to the recognition that the management of medical records was expanding to the broader role of health information management as information technology matured in healthcare facilities.

In the early years, the CIO was responsible for IT, telecommunications, management engineering, and to a lesser extent, medical records (Johns 1991). However, by the second decade of the 2000s, the management portfolios of healthcare CIOs expanded as IT touched almost every area of the organization. Among areas reporting to the CIO included biomedical engineering, supply chain management, HIM, and process and performance improvement (Hagland 2010).

## Electronic Health Record

Like any system, the EHR is greater than the sum of its parts. The EHR is not something that is purchased off-the-shelf. Instead, an EHR is a combination and coordination of applications and technologies that are designed to capture and share health information beyond the walls of an organization (Garrett and Sneidman 2011). As noted earlier, the IOM laid out the vision of an EHR in 1991 and was subsequently enhanced by the federal government (Amatayakul 2012). This section describes the IOM vision and how it is being furthered today.

### IOM Vision

The IOM believed that "CPRs are a key infrastructural requirement to support the information management needs of physicians, other health professionals, and a variety of other legitimate users of aggregated patient information" (IOM 1997, xi). Elaborating further, the IOM Report explains the vision of the CPR:

> One must be careful when describing a "CPR market," not to tether the concept to a single, static idea whose incarnation can be purchased "off-the-shelf." In some sense, it is precisely the static nature of the paper-based record that has been such a great burden to the practice of medicine. Instead, a CPR system is a constantly evolving concept whose value and function is expected to grow with the constantly changing demands of the healthcare environment and the improving technology upon which the system is built. (IOM 1997, 6)

The CPR vision was not an automated paper record. Rather, the following five hallmarks demonstrated the expansiveness of the CPR vision:

- Integrated view of patient data
- Access to knowledge resources
- Physician order entry and clinician data entry
- Integrated communications support
- Clinical decision support (IOM 1997, 6)

The IOM's vision has stood the test of time, and various terms have appeared, attempting to describe the concept. As discussed in chapter 1, due to lack of standard definitions and concerns about marketplace confusion, the ONC developed standard definitions for EMR and EHR in 2008. These are the terms and common definitions that are in use today that, taken together, represent the scope of the IOM's initial vision and have essentially replaced the term "CPR."

## Breaking Down Organization Data Silos

Every organization implements an EMR differently. Some organizations have implemented best-of-breed systems, which are often offered by a vendor who has a focused product line and whose system is designed to excel in a specific area, such as a laboratory information system, radiology information system, or other system. Best-of-breed systems are usually chosen because they offer extensive functionality and specialized features that best meet the needs of a clinical department or functional area. Traditionally, data sharing among best-of-breed systems has been challenging and has led to data silos. With the adoption of interchange standards such as **HL7** and others, and with the use of clinical data repositories, data sharing among best-of-breed systems is becoming easier. Besides data integration issues, each best-of-breed system uses a different user interface, making it challenging for end users to learn the nuances of inputting and retrieving data from every system.

In implementing an EMR, other organizations have chosen to select an **integrated solution** from a single vendor. In this arrangement, one vendor provides multiple clinical and administrative applications (for example, laboratory, pharmacy, radiology, CPOE, R-ADT) that use a common database and have a consistent user interface. From a data integration perspective, these systems are attractive; however, the functionality of each application may not adequately meet the needs of each department or business area. In other words, single vendor integrated solutions may handle several applications very well, but fall short of the ideal capabilities in others. Ideally, the system should be designed with the end user's needs in mind. However, with single vendor solutions, the organization frequently has to perform business process redesign to accommodate the information system.

On the surface, it may appear that a single vendor integrated solution is the best choice. However, a single vendor integrated solution has its pros and cons. Integrated solutions may initially cost less, and require less end user training and continuing technical support and maintenance. If problems arise with the system, the organization only needs to negotiate with one vendor. Once in a relationship with a single solution vendor, however, it may be difficult for the organization to leverage negotiation of costs for system changes or upgrades. And if the relationship becomes totally unsatisfactory, changing to a new vendor is a formidable endeavor because the organization will need to replace the entire enterprise system.

Best-of-breed solutions provide better functionality, but pose maintenance and data quality issues. The more complex and numerous the interfaces are among systems, the greater the probability of error introduction. The less consistent the end user interfaces are among systems, the greater the training needs and the potential for data entry error. Organizations must review best-of-breed vs. integrated solutions with the following criterion in mind: How well does the product meet the organization's functional, informational, and technical needs (English 2003)?

An in-between option is called **best of suite**. In this option, an organization chooses multiple core vendors for related functions. For example, a group of related clinical applications may be from one vendor, financials from another vendor, and supply chain management from another vendor. While this arrangement reduces the number of potential vendors, there still exist data silos and quality issues.

In attempting to reach the IOM vision, but keep best-of-breed systems, organizations are looking toward **clinical data repository** (CDR) technology that is able to unify data from various organization source systems through special software called connectivity engines that collects data from one system and sends it to another. An **enterprise MPI** (EMPI) is a connectivity engine that is incorporated into an application that identifies and consolidates records for each patient. Organizations can customize the user interface so there is consistency for input and data retrieval throughout the system. Depending on the vendor, users can personalize screen views to display, drill-down, compare, and perform other data manipulations. Thus, CDR technology allows organizations to leverage their existing information infrastructure and maintain best-of-breed systems, while integrating data from multiple sources.

## Beyond the Organization

An EMR limits data flow to within the organization, and does not build a 21st century health information system capable of supporting longitudinal patient care or delivering a comprehensive, knowledge-based system that provides information to policy makers. To improve patient care and outcomes, deliver more effective and efficient services, and share information and knowledge with patients, consumers, healthcare and public health professionals, public agencies, and other stakeholders, an EHR system must ensure secure, reliable, consistent, accurate, and appropriate information flow among decision makers across institutions. The EHR fulfills these requirements because its boundaries "are built not around the organization documenting the information but around the patient and his or her health-related information" (National Alliance for Health Information Technology 2008, 17).

Interoperability is a key factor for EHR implementation. In healthcare, **interoperability** is defined as "the ability of different information technology systems and software applications to communicate, to exchange data accurately, effectively and consistently, and to use the information that has been changed" (National Alliance for Health Information Technology 2008, 10). National standards that support interoperability are needed to create, transmit, store, and manage health-related data. There are a number of types of standards that must work together to support the EHR. Among these standards are those that

- Identify and define the components that are supported by an EHR
- Identify the data elements, attributes, values, and definitions that are included in the EHR
- Provide protocols of how the data elements transmit from one computer to another
- Provide standardized ways of data representation, such as diagnostic coding systems

To help facilitate interoperable EHRs, two initiatives were launched by the ONC: development of an NHIN and development of certification criteria for an EHR inspection process.

The NHIN is a set of standards, services, and policies that enable professionals to securely exchange health information over the Internet. The NHIN will support appropriate use of healthcare information for population health purposes (for example, public health). The NHIN is dependent upon the availability of healthcare information through EHR systems. The ONC is primarily focused on coordinating efforts for development of the NHIN through the sponsorship of several programs, described below.

To help ensure that EHR products meet functional, content, and technological standards, AHIMA, the Healthcare Information Management and Systems Society (HIMSS) and the National Alliance for Health Information Technology (The Alliance) initially funded and established the **Certification Commission for Health Information Technology** (CCHIT) in 2004. In 2005, the HHS awarded CCHIT a three-year contract to develop and evaluate certification criteria and an inspection process for EHRs and their associated computer networks.

In 2010, the ONC named CCHIT as an **ONC Authorized Testing and Certification Body** (ONC-ATCB) for certifying EHR products capable of meeting meaningful use criteria. Ambulatory, inpatient, emergency department, behavioral health, long-term and post-acute care EHRs, and e-prescribing are products certified by CCHIT. As of 2014, there are five other organizations designated as an ONC-ATCB with varying scopes of authorization. These include Surescripts, LLC; ICSA Labs; SLI Global Solutions; InforGard Laboratories, Inc.; and Drummand Group, Inc.

HIMSS Analytics, a not-for-profit subsidiary of HIMSS, developed an EMR Adoption Model to track EMR adoption progress at hospitals and health systems (although the model is titled "EMR," the seventh stage of the model includes EHR interoperability functionality). HIMSS Analytics tracks data about adoption practices among various types of hospitals and provides comparisons and other statistics that can trend hospital adoption rates. Table 2.3 provides a summary of EMR capabilities for each stage (HIMSS Analytics).

Table 2.4 displays the adoption rate for EHRs for 2013 using the HIMSS Analytics model as a guide. These data suggest that most hospitals are at Stage 3. However, only 1.1 percent, or about 58 out of of 5,310 hospitals have achieved the IOM vision.

Table 2.3. Summary of stage capabilities of HIMSS Analytics EMR Adoption

| Stage | Capabilities |
|---|---|
| Stage 0 | • Three key ancillary systems, laboratory, pharmacy, and radiology not implemented |
| Stage 1 | • Three key ancillary systems, laboratory, pharmacy, and radiology installed |
| Stage 2 | • Key ancillary systems feed data to a CDR<br>• Physicians can access and review all orders and results<br>• CDR contains a controlled vocabulary<br>• CDR has rudimentary conflict checking via clinical decision support |
| Stage 3 | • Nursing, clinical documentation is implemented and integrated with the CDR for at least one inpatient service<br>• Electronic medication administration record application (MAR) is implemented<br>• First level clinical decision support is implemented to error check with order entry such as drug/drug, drug/food, drug/lab conflict<br>• Medical image access from Picture, Archiving and Communication (PAC) system is available to physicians outside of the Radiology department via organization's intranet |
| Stage 4 | • CPOE added to nursing and DCR environment<br>• Second level of clinical decision support implemented related to evidence based medicine protocols |
| Stage 5 | • Closed loop medication administration with bar coded unit dose medications<br>• eMAR and bar coding or RFID are implemented and integrated with CPOE and pharmacy<br>• The healthcare provider verifies the "five rights" (for example, right patient, right time and frequency, right medication, right dose, and right route) bedside with bar code scanning on unit dose and patient ID |
| Stage 6 | • Full physician documentation with structured templates and discrete data are implemented for at least one inpatient care service (for example, progress and consult notes, discharge summaries, problem list, and diagnosis list maintenance)<br>• Level 3 clinical decision support related to protocols and outcomes in form of variance and compliance alerts implemented<br>• Full complement of PACS systems provides medical images to physician via intranet and displaces all film-based images |
| Stage 7 | • Providers no longer use paper charts to deliver and mange patient care<br>• EMR has a mixture of discrete data, document images, and medical images<br>• Data warehousing implemented to analyze patterns of clinical data<br>• Clinical data can be shared via standardized electronic transactions with those authorized to treat a patient (for example, hospitals and ambulatory care clinics) or HIEs, payers, and patients<br>• Summary data continuity for all services (such as, inpatient, outpatient, ED, and ambulatory care clinics) |

Source: HIMSS Analytics 2011.

Table 2.4. Percentage of hospitals at each stage of adoption – fourth quarter, 2013

| Stage | Percentage of hospitals at each stage of adoption – fourth quarter, 2013 |
|---|---|
| Stage 0 | 5.8% |
| Stage 1 | 3.3% |
| Stage 2 | 7.6% |
| Stage 3 | 30.3% |

(continued)

Table 2.4. Percentage of hospitals at each stage of adoption - fourth quarter, 2013 (*Continued*)

| Stage | Percentage of hospitals at each stage of adoption – fourth quarter, 2013 |
|---|---|
| Stage 4 | 15.5% |
| Stage 5 | 22% |
| Stage 6 | 12.5% |
| Stage 7 | 2.9% |

Source: HIMSS Analytics 2011.

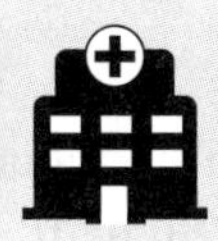

## *The St. Rita's Healthcare System Case Study*

The EIM team members were serious as they reviewed the data from their research at their team meeting. Opening the discussion, Shirlee said, "Now I think I'm beginning to understand the nature of the problems we have. Our history here at St. Rita's closely follows the path almost all other hospitals have taken with implementation of best-of-breed systems, many of which don't interface, manage technology as opposed to information, focus on short-term solutions, and are department-centric instead of patient-centric."

"What catches my attention," Val said, "is the notion of a patient-centric view. St. Rita's mission is to deliver quality patient care; our customer is the patient. System design that meets our organization's mission and our strategic goals will ultimately meet the needs of the end users."

The EIM team continued their discussion, mulling over the path that St. Rita's took. "You're right about how focusing on short-term solutions yields short-term results," Monte said. "We need a system for the future; one that is flexible and supports a longitudinal view of the individual. We need a change of approach to data and information management at St. Rita's. We need a strategy that maximizes our data asset, engages the entire organization in shared responsibility, and provides a centralized point of leadership," Monte continued.

The team was energized to embark on solving St. Rita's data problems. As the team reviewed the materials they had gathered, including a preliminary inventory of applications installed at St. Rita's, they concluded that the health system was only at Stage 2 of the HIMSS Analytics Model. Granted, some applications such as medication administration and nursing documentation were at Stage 3, there still was a long way to go with decision support and Radiology PACs. The team knew there was an enormous amount of work to do.

"To get our arms around this situation, we need a model that will help us tackle every data issue," said Val.

Linda considered what Val just said. "One of our biggest hurdles will be our organizational culture," Linda said. "Before we can sell the EIM concept to others in the organization, we have to have a convincing story that depicts how EIM benefits everyone," she added.

Everyone was in agreement. The next step was to outline the functions of EIM and develop an easily understood graphic showing the power of EIM in moving the organization forward in achieving the EHR.

## Part of the Team: Topics for Discussion and Action

The following topics are discussion items and actions that the EIM team would feasibly address. If you were part of the EIM team, what would you contribute to these discussions and action determinations?

1. Describe the systems concept in evaluating an information system. Explain why the use of this concept is or is not important in moving St. Rita's toward the EHR.
2. What do you believe were the major drivers in the evolution toward the EHR? Are these the same drivers that are fueling the momentum for the EHR today? How are these drivers going to impact the work of the EIM team?

3. Assess the characteristics of an EHR that make it more than automation of a paper health record. Prepare a list of these characteristics the EIM team could use in assessing their progress in achieving the IOM vision.
4. Do you agree with Shirlee that best-of-breed system implementation was a significant contributor to the data problems at St. Rita's? Elaborate on what you would add to this discussion if you were on the EIM team.
5. Assess the challenges facing St. Rita's in achieving the IOM's vision of an EHR. Prioritize these from least to most challenging and prepare an outline of your rationale for the EIM team.
6. Construct a two-dimensional model of an EHR the EIM team could use to communicate the vision of the EHR to hospital executives and middle management.

## Advanced Concepts

This chapter provided an overview of some of the major issues concerning the history of HIT adoption, the external and internal forces moving transformation of health information from paper to automation, and a glimpse at the challenges facing St. Rita's in successfully tackling its data issues. The following are advanced exercises for those who want to prepare for real world situations by expanding their understanding and knowledge base about these topics.

1. The IOM issued several reports that raised the visibility of EHR benefits and accelerated the adoption of HIT. Read the following reports and synthesize the elements each report has in common. From your synthesis, construct a conceptual framework that could be used by the EIM team for describing an EHR.
   - **IOM 1997**—The Computer-Based Patient Record: An Essential Technology for Healthcare, rev. ed. http://www.nap.edu/openbook.php?record_id=5306&page=R1.
   - **IOM 2003**—Key Capabilities of an Electronic Health Record System: Letter Report. http://books.nap.edu/openbook.php?record_id=10863&page=430#p2000a02b9970430001.
   - **IOM 2004**—Patient Safety Achieving a New Standard for Care http://www.iom.edu/Reports/2003/Patient-Safety-Achieving-a-New-Standard-for-Care.aspx.
2. In the article, *Three Decades of Research on Computer Applications in Healthcare Medical Informatics Support at the Agency for Healthcare Research and Quality*, testimony to the foundational and important contributions made by early pioneers in health information systems is provided. Investigate each of the systems discussed and evaluate each one's contribution to the current status of the EHR today. http://jamia.bmj.com/content/9/2/144
3. The EIM team knows they must present a convincing rationale for an EIM program. Develop a simple diagram that shows the power of EIM in moving St. Rita's forward in achieving the vision of the EHR.

## References

Amatayakul, M. 2012. *Electronic Health Records: A Practical Guide for Professionals and Organizations.* 5th ed. Chicago: AHIMA Press.

Aspden, P., J. Corrigan, J. Wolcott, and S. Erickson, eds. Committee on Data Standards for Patient Safety. 2004. *Patient Safety: Achieving a New Standard for Care.* Washington, D.C.: National Academies Press.

American College of Surgeons. 2011. The 1919 minimum standard document. http://www.facs.org/archives/minimumhighlight.html.

American Hospital Association. 2011. Interview of Chantal Worzala by MDNewsNetwork. September 1, 2011. http://www.youtube.com/watch?v=3ClawyBtXQk.

Ash, J., M. Berg, E. Coiera. 2004. Some unintended consequences of information technology in health care: The nature of patient care information system-related errors. *Journal of American Medical Informatics Association.* 11(2): 104–112. doi: 10.1197/jamia.M1471 http://www.ncbi.nlm.nih.gov/pmc/articles/PMC353015/.

Berner, E.S., D.E. Detmer, and D. Simborg. 2005. Will the Wave Finally Break? A Brief View of the Adoption of Electronic Medical Records in the United States. *Journal of American Medical Informatics Association.* 12(1): 3-7. doi: 10.1197/jamia.M1664.

Borzekowski, R. 2002. Healthcare Finance and The Early Adoption of Hospital Information Systems. FEDS Working Paper No. 2002-41. http://papers.ssrn.com/sol3/papers.cfm?abstract_id=337960.

Centers for Medicare and Medicaid Services. 2010. CMS Finalizes Definition of Meaningful Use and Certified Electronic Health Record (EHR) Technology. http://www.cms.gov/Newsroom/MediaReleaseDatabase/Fact-sheets/2010-Fact-sheets-items/2010-07-163.html?DLPage=1&DLFilter=CMS&DLSort=0&DLSortDir=descending.

CHIME. 2014. History of CHIME. http://www.cio-chime.org/chime/about/history.asp?

English, L. 2003. How best-of-breed software selection causes IQ problems. Information Management. http://www.information-management.com/issues/20031001/7434-1.html.

Fitzmaurice, M.J., K. Adams, and J.M. Eisenberg. 2002. Three decades of research on computer applications in healthcare medical informatics support at the agency for healthcare research and quality. *Journal of the American Medical Informatics Association.* (2): 144-160. http://jamia.bmj.com/content/9/2/144 doi: 10.1197/jamia.M0867.

Fonkych, K. and R. Taylor. 2005. *The State and Pattern of Health Information Technology Adoption.* Santa Monica: RAND Corporation. http://www.rand.org/pubs/monographs/MG409.html.

Garrett, P., J. Seidman. 2011. (January 4). Health IT Buzz. EMR vs EHR: What is the difference? http://www.healthit.gov/buzz-blog/electronic-health-and-medical-records/emr-vs-ehr-difference/.

Hagland, M. Healthcare Informatics. 2010. (March 27). Expanding Universes. http://www.healthcare-informatics.com/ME2/dirmod.asp?sid=&nm=&type=Publishing&mod=Publications%3A%3AArticle&mid=8F3A7027421841978F18BE895F87F791&tier=4&id=89289070F2274D459E5698E1394B2D4F.

HIMSS Analytics. 2011. EMR Adoption Model. http://www.himssanalytics.org/hc_providers/emr_adoption.asp.

HIMSS. 2008. Healthcare integration and connectivity: Results of a survey by the enterprise information systems steering committee. http://www.himss.org/files/himssorg/content/files/integrationconnectivitysurvey.pdf.

HIMSS Analytics. 2014. Electronic Medical Record Adoption Model. http://www.himssanalytics.org/emram/emram.aspx.

Huffman, E. K. 1941. Requirements and advantages of registration for medical record librarians. *Bulletin of the American Association of Medical Record Librarians.*

Institute of Medicine. 1991. *The Computer-Based Patient Record: An Essential Technology for Healthcare.* Edited by R.S. Dick and E.B. Steen. Washington, DC: National Academies Press.

Institute of Medicine. 1997. *The Computer-Based Patient Record: An Essential Technology for Healthcare,* rev. ed. Edited by R.S. Dick, E.B. Steen, and D.E. Detmer. Washington, DC: National Academies Press. http://www.nap.edu/openbook.php?record_id=5306&page=R1.

Institute of Medicine. 2000. *To Err is Human: Building a Safer Health System.* Washington, D.C: National Academies Press.

Institute of Medicine, Committee on Data Standards for Patient Safety, and Board on Health Care Services. 2004. Key Capabilities of an Electronic Health Record System: Letter Report. *Appendix E in Patient Safety: Achieving a New Standard for Care.* Washington, DC: The National Academies Press. http://books.nap.edu/openbook.php?record_id=10863&page=430#p2000a02b9970430001.

Johns, M.L. *Relationship of Functions Performed by Hospital Chief Information Officers and Organization, Job, and Person-Related Characteristics* [PhD dissertation.] Columbus, OH: Ohio State University; 1991.

Medicare Payment Advisory Commission. 2004 Report to Congress: New Approaches in Medicare. http://www.medpac.gov/documents/reports/June04_Entire_Report.pdf?sfvrsn=0.

National Alliance for Health Information Technology. April 20, 2008. Report to the Office of the National Coordinator for Health Information Technology on defining key health information technology terms. *Department of Health and Human Resources.* https://www.nachc.com/client/Key%20HIT%20Terms%20Definitions%20Final_April_2008.pdf.

National Committee on Vital and Health Statistics. 2001. Information for Health: A Strategy for Building the National Health Information Infrastructure. http://aspe.hhs.gov/sp/nhii/documents/NHIIReport2001/.

Charles, D., M. Gabriel, M.F. Furukawa. May 2014. Adoption of electronic health record systems among U.S. non-federal acute care hospitals: 2008–2013. ONC Data Brief No. 16. http://www.healthit.gov/sites/default/files/oncdatabrief16.pdf.

Sittig, D.F., B.L. Hazlehurst, J.H.H. Jimison, and M.C. Hornbrook. 2002. A clinical information system research landscape. *The Permanente Journal* 6(2): 62–68. https://www.thepermanentejournal.org/files/Spring2002/landscape.pdf.

Sittig, D. and H. Singh. 2011. Defining health information technology-related errors: New developments since to err is human. *Archives of Internal Medicine.* 2011 July 25; 171(14): 1281–1284. http://www.ncbi.nlm.nih.gov/pmc/articles/PMC3677061/pdf/nihms476207.pdf.

Wager, K., F.W. Lee, and J.P. Glaser. 2009. *Health Care Information Systems: A Practical Approach for Health Care Management.* 2nd ed. San Francisco: Jossey-Bass.

# Chapter 3

# Electronic Health Information Systems

Electronic health information systems are complex networks frequently consisting of hundreds and even thousands of computer applications with thousands of inputs, processes, and outputs performed daily. Best practices dictate that organizations should maintain an inventory of all installed and approved computer applications and hardware they use. Ensuring compatibility among applications, safeguarding data, complying with software licenses requirements, responding to software audits, ensuring continuity, and protecting software and hardware assets are just a few reasons organizations should maintain such an inventory. Software inventory and discovery tools are often used by information systems professionals to identify hardware and software used across an organization and their configurations. Even with automated tools, inventories of software and hardware may be incomplete.

Effectively applying enterprise information management (EIM) practices requires a complete accounting of applications and an understanding of the purpose, input, processes, and output of each. This chapter provides an overview of topics that will help you to:

- Compare and contrast the clinical and administrative applications that are usually part of the application portfolio of a healthcare organization
- Describe system interoperability concepts and practices
- Evaluate an organization's application portfolio using a systems approach

## *The St. Rita's Healthcare System Case Study*

Following the study of health information technology (HIT) evolution, the EIM team began to create an outline of the typical clinical and administrative applications included in an electronic health information system. "This outline will prove valuable in helping us eventually complete an inventory of systems at St. Rita's," Val said.

"I understand," said Bob, "that some facilities don't have a complete inventory of systems. That seems impossible to believe, but it certainly is something that we should investigate at St. Rita's." The team agreed and got down to work to develop an annotated list of the most common information systems in the healthcare environment.

# Clinical Information Systems

A **clinical information system (CIS)** has been variously defined. The IOM defined a CIS as "dedicated to collecting, storing, manipulating, and making available clinical information important to the delivery of patient care" (Dick et al. 1997). An expansion of this definition describes a CIS as a:

> ...Collection of various information technology applications that provides a centralized repository of information related to patient care across distributed locations. This repository represents the patient's history of illnesses and interactions with providers by encoding knowledge capable of helping clinicians decide about the patient's condition, treatment options, and wellness activities. The repository also encodes the status of decisions, actions underway for those decisions, and relevant information that can help in performing those actions. The database could also hold other information about the patient, including genetic, environmental, and social contexts. (Sittig, Hazlehurst, Palen, Hsu, Jimison, and Hornbrook 2002, 62)

There are many benefits of a CIS. Primary among these is providing access to organized, complete, and legible patient information in a timely manner to professionals who need it for healthcare delivery purposes. Healthcare professionals, researchers and others also credit the CIS for improving patient safety and outcomes, reducing costs, and improving operations and efficiency. Other benefits include

- Accessing the medical literature to support diagnosis and treatment
- Aggregating patient data for decision making
- Providing automatic warnings or suggestions when the patient's data satisfy certain logical rules
- Providing critiques to clinicians when ordering therapies or diagnostic tests
- Providing access to clinical guidelines for standards of care
- Providing clinical decision support in diagnosis or analyzing tradeoffs and the likelihood of alternative outcomes (Sittig 2002)

This CIS definition is very broad. There is no one specified inventory of a CIS that fits all hospitals or healthcare organizations. The elements comprising a CIS vary among organizations depending upon their needs, the organization's capability to use information technology (IT) resources, and what vendors the organization selects. For instance, a CIS at one hospital may include laboratory, radiology, and pharmacy systems supported by computerized provider order entry (CPOE). At another hospital, a CIS may contain these elements as well as a nursing information system. Furthermore, the terminology used to describe the components within a CIS differs from facility to facility. For example, Hospital A's nursing information system may include patient charting, staff scheduling, and decision support, while Hospital B's nursing information system may include only patient charting. Complicating terminology issues further, some equate a CIS to an organization's electronic health record (EHR). Irrespective of the terminology used, organizations must maintain an inventory of all applications for the reasons cited earlier. Some of these applications are defined below in alphabetical order.

## The St. Rita's Healthcare System Case Study

"Where should be begin?" asked Shirlee at the next team meeting. "I know that St. Rita's must have hundreds, maybe thousands, of applications. How do we narrow down this process?" she continued.

"Why don't we begin by looking at what the industry considers to be the typical clinical applications," Monte offered. "Our IT department, like most other IT departments, uses software asset management tools, a special type of software, that captures an inventory of every software application running on any hardware device connected to a computer network at St. Rita's. We can get a list from the IT department and see what clinical applications are installed at St. Rita's," Monte suggested.

"That sounds like a good idea," offered Val. "What about developing a preliminary list of CIS subsystems that we consider fundamental to any CIS and provide a summary of each system? We know the list would need to be expanded and additionally defined. And, we might need to delve further and identify subsystem components. For example, what does the nursing information system at St. Rita's include? What are the specific functions of the pharmacy management system?" Val continued. The team agreed with this approach, and Shirlee and Monte offered to develop an annotated list of the fundamental CIS subsystems.

## Anesthesia Information Management System

The primary purpose of an **anesthesia information management system (AIMS)** is to automate the capture, storage, and presentation of data during the intraoperative period. For example, data on the type of anesthesia the healthcare professional administered, patient's vital signs while under anesthesia, and data output from monitors used during the operative period. Many systems have additional functionality to handle pre- and post-operative patient-related information and are able to incorporate decision support capabilities. The functions available depend upon the type of product the organization purchased. Robust systems provide information that professionals can use for management, quality improvement, reporting quality measures, and research purposes.

## Automated Patient Identification and Bar Coding

This automated patient identification and bar coding technology is also referred to as bar code point of care (BPOC). This type of **bar code point of care** (BPOC) system enables the use of bar code technology for identifying any individual or object. In the clinical setting, healthcare professionals use it for medication administration, transfusions, specimen collection and diagnostics, point-of-care testing, and patient charges. Patients receive a bar-coded identification wrist band on admission. Healthcare workers have a bar-coded identification badge. To illustrate the application for medication administration, caregivers scan their identification badge to log into the system and then scan the patient's identification band to access patient data. The caregiver then scans the bar-coded medication to verify drug, dose, administration time, and route, and that they are administering it to the correct patient. The caregiver records all data associated with the medication administration in the medication administration record (MAR). Similar processes are used for for collecting laboratory specimens, transfusion administration, and point-of-care testing.

## Clinical Data Repository

A **clinical data repository (CDR)** is a real-time database that updates data immediately when it it is entered by a person, directly from a device or in another manner. A CDR consolidates data from different clinical source systems (for example, laboratory, pharmacy, and radiology) within an organization to present a unified view of a single patient's data. The CDR is the backbone of the electronic medical record (EMR). It provides user access to current patient data and allows direct data input by clinicians. In addition to discrete data, a CDR can store images of paper documents and clinical images, such as those from picture archiving and communication systems (PACS) (addressed below). Customary data types stored in a CDR include clinical laboratory test results, pharmacy information, radiology reports and images, pathology reports, diagnostic codes, and narrative reports (for example, operation, history, physical exam, and discharge summaries).

## Computerized Physician/Provider Order Entry

**Computerized physician/provider order entry (CPOE)** systems allow licensed individuals, and those with ordering privileges, to directly enter medical orders such as medications, tests, and treatments. The system electronically routes orders to the appropriate departments and individuals for completion. There is a range of decision support capabilities in many CPOE systems such as alerts for drug-drug contraindications, drug overdoses or patient allergies, or other physiologic contraindications. Ideally, CPOE systems integrate with other clinical subsystems and knowledge sources that assist the physician or healthcare provider with selecting tests or procedures and the right medication, dosage, route, and administration time frame. Figure 3.1 provides an example of an order entry screen.

Figure 3.1. Example of order entry screen

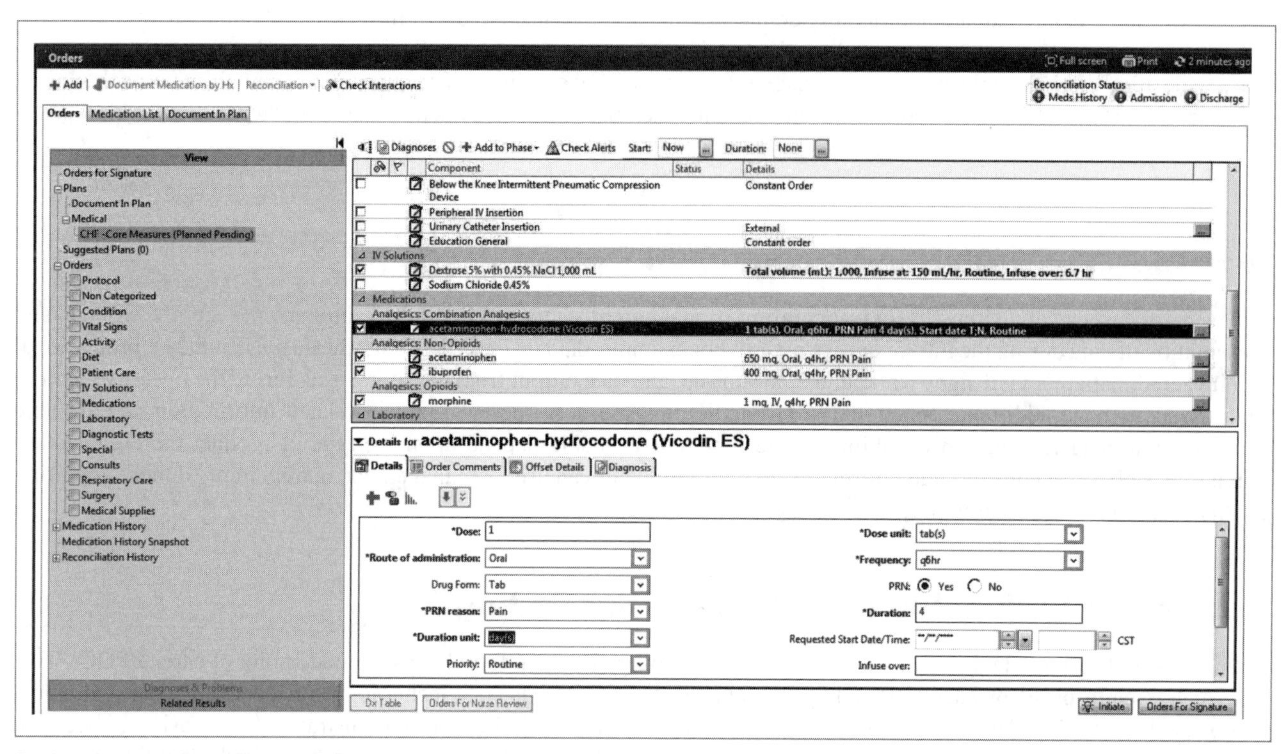




## Critical Care Information Systems

**Critical care information systems (CCIS)** provide intensive care units (ICU) with automated documentation for collection, management, and display of patient information. These systems allow direct documentation input by ICU caregivers and can include patient assessment, treatment plans, caregiver notes, and flow sheets. A CCIS usually integrates with monitoring devices, thus providing critical physiologic data accessible to caregivers. The vendor or organization information systems staff may build alerts and other decision-supporting functions such as quality of care guidelines into the CCIS and customize the unit or specific patient situation. The CCIS integrates with other CIS subsystems, such as clinical laboratory and pharmacy, and data are usually presented in a number of ways, including graphs and flow charts. Some CCIS's integrate all caregiver notes including intensivists, nurses, and disciplinary therapists. A strength of CCIS's is that the organization can use data collected to report quality measures for regulatory compliance and quality of care improvement.

More recently, healthcare organizations are implementing electronic-ICU systems (e-ICU) that are a type of telemedicine application. These systems have a central command center made up of a network of cameras, monitors and two-way communication links. The command center allows intensivists and ICU nurses to make virtual patient rounds, remotely monitoring a patient's condition, checking vital signs, and communicating with hospital personnel.

## Dietary Department and Management Systems

**Dietary department and management systems** support patient nutritional assessment and management, and data related to diet meal orders, cancellations and reorders, menu development, patient menu choice, and meal tracking and delivery. Integration with other CIS components such as Registration-Admission, Discharge, Transfer (R-ADT) and order entry is important. For example, integration with an R-ADT system allows the dietary department to deliver a meal to the correct patient's room, and integration with the order entry system allows a physician's diet order to be directly transferred to the dietary system so there are fewer delays and less opportunity for error. Data from the system may also support other department administrative functions. For example, a purchasing management system, when integrated with a dietary management system, can track food inventory. This system can automatically and regularly order food when food inventories deplete to pre-specified levels. When synchronized with data from R-ADT systems that provide patient census data, staff scheduling management systems can aid in the assignment of appropriate numbers and types of dietary staff. Dietary department and management systems produce administrative reports such as numbers of meals served, types of meals served, and cost and other production reports.

## Electronic Document Management Systems

**Electronic document management systems** (EDM) are often called an EHR bridge technology because they are an initial step to converting paper documentation into a digital format. The primary function of an EDM system is to electronically scan paper documents, creating a digital image which can be indexed and stored by the system for retrieval and viewing by end users. Content such as history, physical exams, operative reports, radiology reports, and discharge summaries from a transcription system are electronically transmitted into an EDM system, indexed, and stored. These systems may also include workflow technology that automatically identifies tasks to be performed for preparing and scanning documents and ensures that processes are carried out in the correct sequence and within specific time parameters. Healthcare organizations frequently use EDM systems to support a hybrid health record environment.

## Emergency Department Systems

An **emergency department information system** (EDIS) provides management and operational tools to improve emergency department (ED) performance. Features of many EDISs include patient registration, central visualization screen for patient management, management of patient flow, monitoring patient movement throughout the ED, reporting ED room status, managing requests, and notifications for patient beds and resources. Some EDISs use real time locator systems (RTLS) for tracking patients. An EDIS provides capabilities for clinical documentation by physicians, nurses, and other caregivers. The EDIS normally will have bidirectional interfaces with other subsystems such as CPOE, master patient index, R-ADT, laboratory, pharmacy, and radiology. EDIS data are used for administrative functions such as monitoring quality of care and charge capture.

## Laboratory Information Systems

**Laboratory information systems** (LIS) support a variety of administrative and operational functions of anatomical pathology and clinical laboratory departments including workflow automation, financial and management reporting, and quality assurance. Clinical laboratories usually have several different functional areas. These normally include clinical chemistry, hematology, clinical microbiology, cytology, surgical pathology, and blood banking. Each of these specialties has its own functions and many LIS vendors have specific applications to meet the needs of each. The basic functions an LIS performs include patient and specimen identification, specimen tracking, results reporting, quality control, management reporting, and inventory control. LIS should include instrument interfaces as well as CPOE and results reporting interfaces. Figure 3.2 is an example of an electronic lab report.

Figure 3.2. Electronic lab report

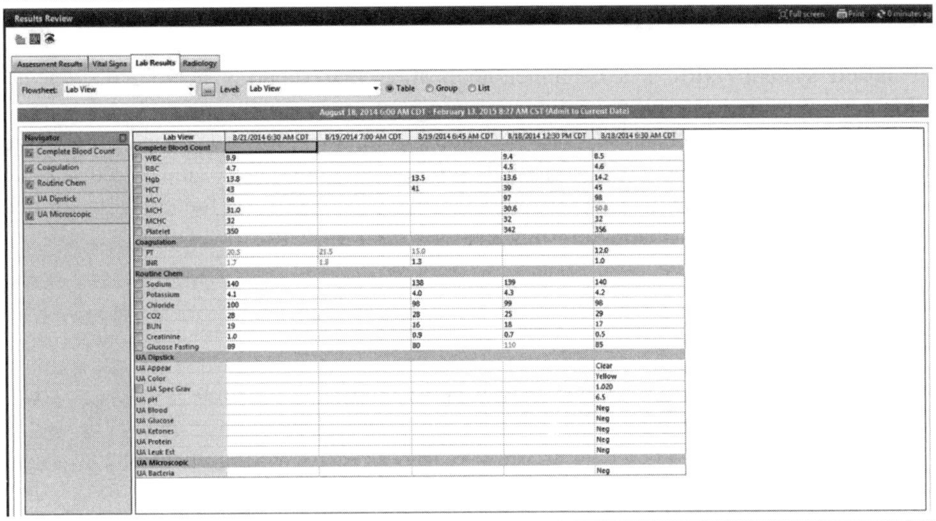

Results Review

Assessment Results | Vital Signs | Lab Results | Radiology

Flowsheet: Lab View | Level: Lab View | Table | Group | List

August 18, 2014 6:00 AM CDT - February 13, 2015 8:27 AM CST (Admit to Current Date)

Navigator: Complete Blood Count; Coagulation; Routine Chem; UA Dipstick; UA Microscopic

| Lab View | 8/21/2014 6:30 AM CDT | 8/19/2014 7:00 AM CDT | 8/19/2014 6:45 AM CDT | 8/18/2014 12:30 PM CDT | 8/18/2014 6:30 AM CDT |
|---|---|---|---|---|---|
| **Complete Blood Count** | | | | | |
| WBC | 8.9 | | | 9.4 | 8.5 |
| RBC | 4.7 | | | 4.5 | 4.6 |
| Hgb | 13.8 | | 13.5 | 13.6 | 14.2 |
| HCT | 43 | | 41 | 39 | 45 |
| MCV | 98 | | | 97 | 98 |
| MCH | 31.0 | | | 30.6 | 30.8 |
| MCHC | 32 | | | 32 | 32 |
| Platelet | 350 | | | 342 | 356 |
| **Coagulation** | | | | | |
| PT | 20.5 | 21.5 | 15.0 | | 12.0 |
| INR | 1.7 | 1.8 | 1.3 | | 1.0 |
| **Routine Chem** | | | | | |
| Sodium | 140 | | 138 | 139 | 140 |
| Potassium | 4.1 | | 4.0 | 4.3 | 4.2 |
| Chloride | 100 | | 98 | 99 | 98 |
| CO2 | 28 | | 28 | 25 | 29 |
| BUN | 19 | | 16 | 18 | 17 |
| Creatinine | 1.0 | | 0.9 | 0.7 | 0.5 |
| Glucose Fasting | 89 | | 80 | 110 | 85 |
| **UA Dipstick** | | | | | |
| UA Appear | | | | | Clear |
| UA Color | | | | | Yellow |
| UA Spec Grav | | | | | 1.020 |
| UA pH | | | | | 6.5 |
| UA Blood | | | | | Neg |
| UA Glucose | | | | | Neg |
| UA Ketones | | | | | Neg |
| UA Protein | | | | | Neg |
| UA Leuk Est | | | | | Neg |
| **UA Microscopic** | | | | | |
| UA Bacteria | | | | | Neg |

## Medication Administration Systems

Caregivers use **medication administration systems** (MAS) to support the administration of medication to patients. MASs are supported by bar coding technology. Caregivers use a point-of-care electronic device to scan the patient's bar-coded identification band and bar-coded medication to ensure the medication complies with the physician order and that the caregiver administers the right drug in the right dose, by the right route, and at the correct time. Built-in decision support features check for patient allergies, drug-drug, and drug-lab interactions. The MAS automatically documents medication administration in an electronic **medication administration record** (MAR). Medication administration systems must interface with subsystems such as CPOE, master patient index, and other patient documentation.

## Medication Reconciliation Systems

A **medication reconciliation system** helps manage the coordination of drugs for a patient across the continuum of care to avoid medication discrepancies. At admission, a current list of medications the patient is taking is entered into the system. The list may be obtained from the physician, patient, an electronic prescription history system, or other source and is entered manually by a designated hospital caregiver or electronically from an electronic source. From this list, the physician verifies which drugs the patient should continue and which new medications, if any, the physician needs to order through a CPOE system. During hospitalization, the medication reconciliation system tracks new drug orders, and if the patient is transferred to a different level of care within the facility, the physician verifies the current medication regimen. When the physician discharges the patient, the physician reconciles medications pre-hospitalization and during hospitalization, and the system produces a post-hospitalization list of medications. Some systems incorporate e-prescribing systems so post-discharge medications orders are electronically transferred to a pharmacy of the patient's choice.

## Monitoring Systems

Monitoring systems (for example, infusion or ventilators) are typically associated with intensive care and other critical care areas such as surgical suites, EDs, and recovery units. **Monitoring systems** provide periodic or continuous observation of the patient or physiological functions in guiding decisions of therapeutic interventions. Patient monitors store patient data, provide data electronically to life-support equipment, perform complex data analysis, and provide noise and text alerts to potentially life-threatening conditions to caregivers. With some systems, alerts can be programmed, installed, and provided to caregivers on mobile devices such as wireless phones, laptop computers, specially-designed personal digital assistants (PDAs), and pagers. Many of these systems retain audit trails of events and how caregivers handled them.

## Nursing Information Systems

A **nursing information system** (NIS) is a computer application that supports nursing documentation for patient assessment, development of patient care plans, and documenting patient care delivery. NISs are usually integrated with other clinical information subsystems, such as CPOEs, so that information is organized and users can easily retrieve it. NISs usually include decision support features that include prompts and reminders, guides to disease linkages between signs or symptoms, and access to online medical resources. Many systems provide functionality for documenting at the patient bedside by using terminals called computers on wheels (COWs) or PDAs.

## Operating Room Management Systems

**Operating room management systems,** sometimes called perioperative information systems, provide coordination of human and material resources during pre-operative, intra-operative, and post-operative phases of care. Depending upon the solution, they can support clinical documentation, tracking patient status, staffing management, equipment allocation and tracking, scheduling operating room suites, and coordinating patient flow throughout the perioperative period. Systems may also capture charges for supplies, operating room, and anesthesia time, among other charges. Similar to other clinical subsystems, operating room management systems may integrate with several other subsystems. For example, these might include instrument management systems (IMS) that provide information related to instruments, instrument sets, and tray inventories used for operative procedures. They may also integrate with tracking systems that manage the chain of custody of biologicals and non-biologicals used by the operative team during an operative procedure such as blood products, allograft tissues, and implants. Data byproducts of operating room management systems can be used by the organization for quality of care and efficiency improvements.

## Patient Care Pathways

**Clinical care pathways** are multidisciplinary, structured care plans that healthcare professionals use to implement clinical guidelines and protocols for a specific patient group, usually based on diagnosis or surgical procedure. A detailed sequence of events provides steps for managing the care of the patient and includes goals, treatments, medications, tests, monitoring, and other interventions. When integrated with other clinical subsystems such as a CPOE, nursing documentation, and clinical laboratory, healthcare professionals can effectively monitor each step in the pathway.

## Pharmacy Information Systems

**Pharmacy information systems** should integrate with CPOE and medication administration systems and should access patient demographic and key clinical information. Once an authorized healthcare professional enters a medication order in a CPOE, the pharmacy immediately receives it. These systems provide online verification work lists that allow pharmacists to review, verify, and fill incoming orders. Decision support capabilities provide contraindication information. Some systems integrate with automated dispensing stations. Administrative functions common with these systems include inventory management and stock requisition, financial reporting, and a variety of quality management reporting features.

## Real Time Locator Systems

**Real time locator systems** (RTLS) use wireless technology that identifies, determines, and tracks the location of equipment, materials, and personnel, and, in the case of healthcare patients, throughout a building or healthcare complex. The system works by placing RTLS tags on a movable object, such as wheel chairs and portable IV pumps, or on an identification badge or wrist band in the case of an individual or patient. Although technologies such as infrared and ultrasound can also be used, the underlying technology on the RTLS tag is usually radio frequency, referred to as radio frequency identification (RFID). Typically, fixed points throughout a building or complex are fitted with sensors that can read data from the RTLS tag. As an object or individual fitted with an RTLS tag passes through the fixed points, the system tracks its movement. Depending upon the technology used, RTLS tags can be passive, semi-passive, or active. Semi-passive and active tags are powered by batteries. Passive tags track assets and people as they pass through specific areas. Active tags not only track assets or individuals but also are able to identify their location at any time.

Specific examples in healthcare include RTLS wrist band identification that can track patients transferred to ancillary departments for tests and procedures. Healthcare organizations also use RTLS tags to locate and route movable medical equipment and monitor the time caregivers are in a patient's room, or are providing care to a patient. More recently, RFIDs and RTLSs have been implemented in hospital "smart rooms" that provide humidity and temperature control status, bed rail status, and verification of devices associated with a specific patient.

## Radiology Information Systems

Like other departmental systems, **radiology information systems** (RIS) support workflow of departmental functions and communication within and outside the radiology department. Specific administration functions that this system may support include workflow management, materials management, charge capture, and management reporting. RISs usually include patient scheduling, patient tracking, and results reporting. Other features of an RIS may include digital transcription for report documentation by manual or voice recognition, means and integrated document management, and image scanning.

## Radiology Picture Archiving and Communication Systems

A radiology **picture archiving and communication system** (PACS) is a medical imaging technology that provides storage and access to images from various modalities such as x-ray computed tomography (CT), magnetic resonance imaging (MRI), positron emission tomography (PET), mammograms, and digital radiography. PACS eliminates the need to manually file, retrieve, or transport physical films. PACS images are stored and transferred by the system using the Digital Imaging and Communications in Medicine (DICOM) standard. Some PACS also accommodate storage of non-image data documents that use standard formats such as the Portable Document Format (PDF). Using a secured network, images can be transmitted by the system to workstations for retrieval and reviewing. PACS should be integrated with other CIS and administrative subsystems such as the master patient index (MPI).

## Results Reporting, Retrieval, and Management

**Results reporting**, often referred to as results retrieval, provides the functionality to retrieve patient data and principally retrieve laboratory reports and diagnostic studies such as radiology reports. Less sophisticated systems allow look-up of data from one ancillary or source system at a time, for example, viewing only clinical laboratory results. However, the technology has evolved, and more state-of-the-art systems allow a user to access patient data from multiple source systems at the same time via one interface. The display properties vary among systems and some allow the end user to manipulate data for graphing or comparison purposes among the data from multiple source systems. This functionality is usually referred to as results management.

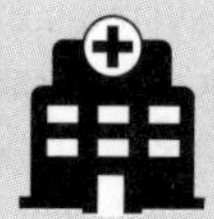

### The St. Rita's Healthcare System Case Study

"That's a long list of clinical systems," said Denise when the EIM team reconvened to review what Shirlee and Monte had gathered so far. "Do you think these represent all of the systems at St. Rita's?" she asked.

"I think we have identified some of the most common systems, but I doubt that this is an exhaustive list," said Shirlee.

"I am beginning to see how important it is to use a systems approach in viewing these clinical systems," Linda remarked. "What happens in the CPOE subsystem clearly affects multiple other subsystems. And, the quality of the data for the medication reconciliation system is plainly affected by the quality of data that is input into the nursing information system when the patient is admitted to a nursing unit."

"You're right," concurred Monte. "Data quality begins with data input. I'm afraid we haven't been as diligent in designing the front end of our systems carefully enough to ensure good data input or support the tasks of the end user."

The EIM team spent additional time developing a draft template they could use to inventory the clinical systems at St. Rita's. They then moved forward to identify what constituted administrative information systems and how the function of these might influence the clinical systems they had just listed.

# Administrative Information Systems

**Administrative information systems** are a suite of applications that support organizational strategic and operational management. Many of these systems could be referred to as dual purpose because they provide support for both administrative and clinical functions. For example, data from the master patient index is required for billing purposes as well as being the key locator and identification for all patient-specific data in a clinical information system. Data from many source clinical systems feed administrative systems. For example, automated diagnostic coding relies on accessing data from the patient's clinical record about the patient's diagnosis, procedures, and other interventions. Business intelligence functions depend on access to clinical information, including clinical process improvement. Consequently, a firm division line between administrative and clinical systems is arbitrary.

From a systems perspective, administrative and clinical information systems are subsystems of the organization's total information system. Thus, each of these systems will likely influence the functions of other subsystems within the total organizational information systems space. For instance, a data error in the master patient index administrative system could be transmitted throughout all the clinical subsystems, resulting in patient identification errors and feasibility adversely affecting patient care.

The following is a list and brief description of customary applications within administrative information systems.

## Registration-Admission-Discharge-Transfer Systems

**Registration-admission-discharge-transfer (R-ADT)** systems (also called patient management) are one of the backbone applications of a healthcare organization's information system. These systems capture patient demographic, insurance, and other administrative data at the time of registration or admission. The R-ADT system tracks the movement of patients when there is an intra-facility transfer from one care area to another during hospitalization, and identifies the date and time that physicians discharge patients. Data from R-ADT systems are used by the healthcare organization to calculate statistics such as patient length of stay, average length of stay during a period of time, and hospital percentage of occupancy. They also produce statistics about care unit utilization and other data for utilization review. Almost all other major clinical and administrative systems rely on the data in the R-ADT system. Figure 3.3 is an example of a data input screen for an R-ADT system.

Figure 3.3. Sample data input screen for R-ADT system

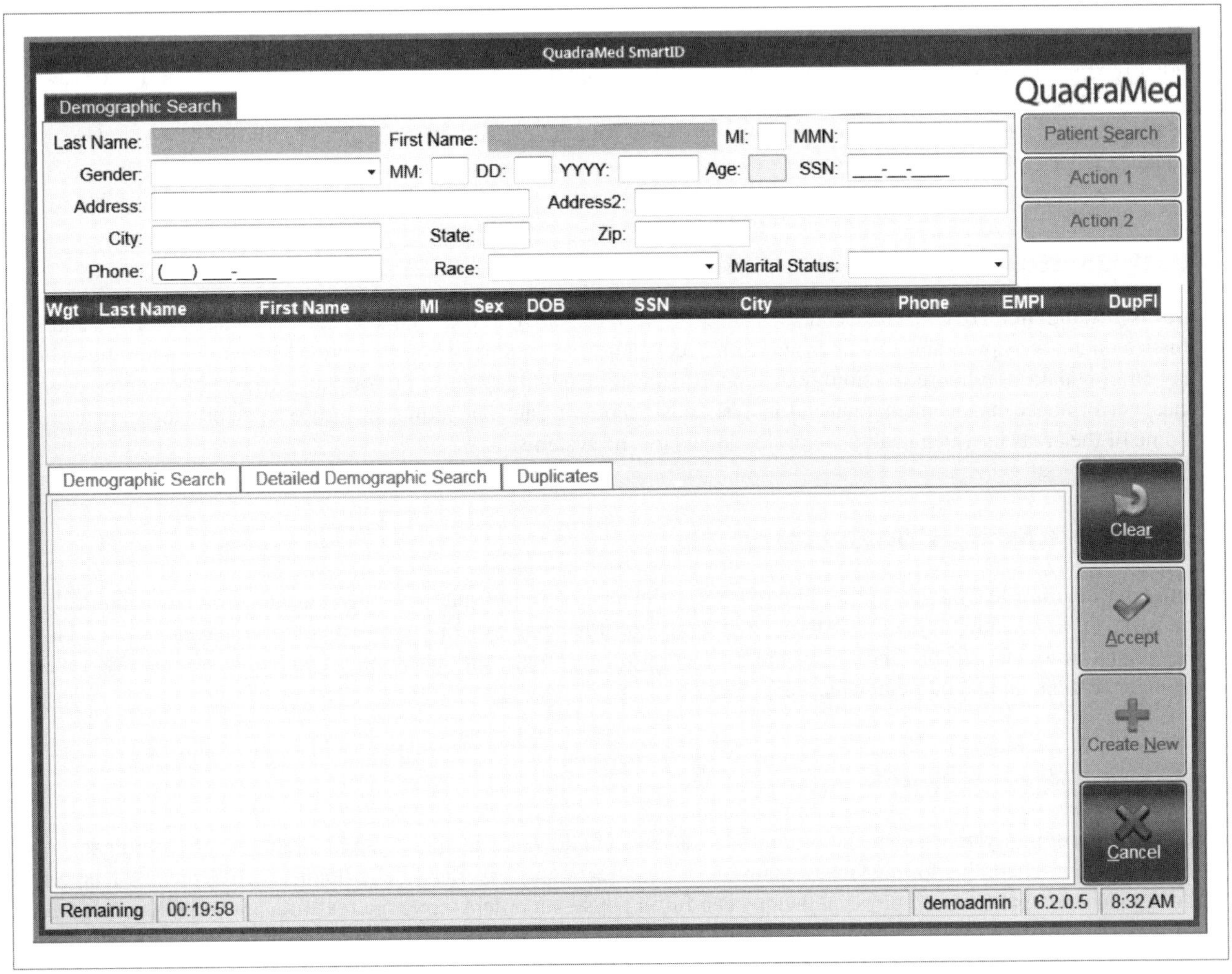

## Automated Diagnostic Coding

Hospitals and other healthcare organizations are required by Medicare and other third party payers to submit diagnostic and procedure codes for reimbursement purposes. These codes (for example, ICD-10-CM and CPT) provide a standardized method for classifying morbidity and mortality information. In the 1980s, automated tools were introduced by vendors to help make the assignment of codes more efficient and increase coding quality. Today, the amount of support provided by automated coding tools varies substantially. Some tools simply allow coders to manually input codes and then the system performs a series of edit checks based on classification rules to help ensure that code assignment is correct. Other tools using heuristic logic may also assign a diagnostic-related-group (DRG), based on diagnosis and procedure codes, which billing departments use for invoicing purposes. Increasingly, these systems are becoming more sophisticated and include natural language processing for reading and interpreting digital information. Such systems pull data from various clinical systems and automatically suggest the correct code assignment. These more advanced systems are commonly called computer-assisted-coding (CAC). Many of these systems transfer data to financial systems for bill and invoice preparation. Data from these systems also track coder productivity and assist with workflow analysis.

## Bed Management

**Bed management systems** automate the process of assigning a patient to a specific hospital care unit, taking into consideration all of the services required to support the patient's condition during hospitalization. Features of these systems include tracking bed inventory, categorizing bed requests, managing patient queues, and managing environmental services for room preparation. The system uses real-time electronic dashboards to relay information about bed status, matching patient characteristics to available beds and appropriate staffing. Bed management systems also produce administrative reports to help evaluate the efficiency of workflow and bed assignment. Reduced wait times for the admission of ED and surgery patients, reduced dietary and pharmaceutical costs due to the elimination of food trays and pharmaceuticals being delivered to empty beds, and increased effectiveness of discharged services are among the benefits documented by using bed management systems (Boyer 2002).

## Business Intelligence Management

**Business intelligence** (BI) systems collect data from various subsystems, both clinical and administrative, and use sophisticated analysis programs to analyze performance against key indicators or measures. Depending upon the system, it may employ data warehouse technology to support data storage and organization for data retrieval of complex queries. Clinical performance management, financial analysis, cost accounting and budgeting, and process performance management are some of the areas in which healthcare professionals use BI systems.

## Financial Information Systems

**Financial information systems** are an umbrella of a financial systems suite and rely on data from both clinical and administrative information systems. Among the types of financial systems are patient and payer billing, claims management, accounts payable and receivable, collection monitoring, staff scheduling, budgeting, accounting, revenue cycle management, and facility maintenance.

## Inpatient Scheduling Systems

**Inpatient scheduling systems**, sometimes referred to as inpatient flow management systems, support care coordination and manage inpatient scheduling for diagnostic exams, tests, and treatments. Ancillary departments such as dietary, laboratory, radiology, and occupational and physical therapy can fulfill physician orders through a real-time integrated system whose benefits result in reducing test and exam delays and conflicts. Ideally, these systems should incorporate or integrate with other systems such as patient transport and departmental systems.

## Master Patient Index

The **master patient index (MPI),** sometimes referred to as a master person index, is a mainstay of an EIM. The MPI assigns a unique patient identifier (often referred to as a medical or health record number) to a patient and is a permanent identifier for each patient who receives services at a healthcare facility. A unit numbering system is usually used by the MPI in which a patient maintains the same medical record number irrespective of the number of admissions or service encounters. This facilitates managing a patient's multiple encounters as a "unit" over the course of a lifetime. The unique identifier maps to other source systems and is a key to identifying data about a patient's multiple hospitalizations or encounters from many data sources (like clinical and administrative systems). The MPI contains a subset of information that identifies the patient such as name, date of birth, gender, and address, and is considered the "system of record" for patient identification. Increasingly, these systems use sophisticated matching algorithms to ensure that duplicate health records are not created for the same patient or to detect identity fraud. When an MPI is developed for an entire enterprise that has multiple facilities or groups, it is usually referred to an **enterprise master patient index** or (EMPI). Figure 3.4 is an example of a patient name search of an MPI.

Figure 3.4. Example of an MPI screen

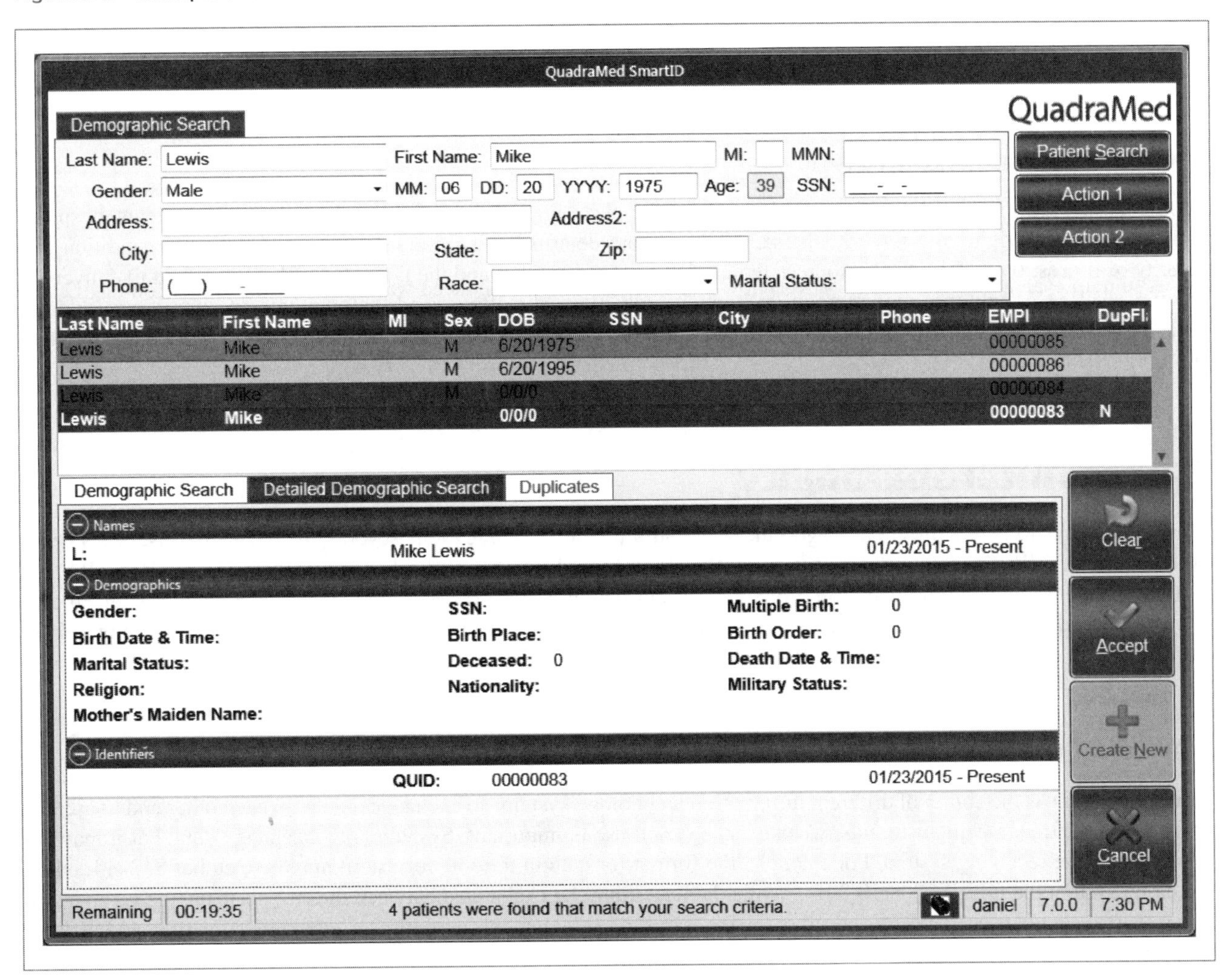


©Merida L. Johns

## Record Completion Management

In hospitals, the HIM department is usually responsible for reviewing each patient's health record at the time of discharge to ensure that all documentation and reports by physicians and other staff concerning the patient's stay are included in the record. Once HIM personnel review the record, they flag any deficiencies they find. Examples of deficiencies include missing or incomplete reports or signatures. **Record completion management** systems automate managing workflow, routing deficiency notices to the correct clinician for completion, and tracking record deficiencies and their completion. Data from these systems support administrative analysis of record deficiencies and workflow.

### Request for and Release of Health Information Management

Health Insurance Portability and Accountability Act (HIPAA) federal regulations provide patients the right to request access to and receive copies of their health record (some limitations apply). Patients also have a right to an accounting of certain disclosures of their health information to third parties. HIPAA regulations require healthcare organizations to meet these requests within certain time frames. Thus, a healthcare facility must maintain an ongoing record of patient requests for their information as well as an accounting of certain disclosures. Automated **request for and release of health information management** systems support the capture of data that tracks disclosure of health information (what information and to whom it was disclosed) and monitors and tracks requests from patients for their own information to ensure timely compliance with federal regulations. Many of these systems can integrate with a document management system so scanned copies of requests and other correspondence can be captured and stored within the system. These systems may also include a module to handle billing and collections for production of paper copies of the health record.

### Workforce Management

From a human resource perspective, hospitals are very complex organizations. To provide services for patients, hospitals must assemble the right workforce skill mix. Many factors determine this mix, including the patient's condition and severity of illness, type of medical resources required to treat the patient, and the type of staff best prepared to deliver the specific services. **Workforce management systems** usually support staffing needs assessments and workforce balance, capacity planning, and clinical staff scheduling. These systems generate various administrative reports to determine future appropriate staffing levels.

## System Interoperability

Not having ways to communicate among clinical and administrative applications severely restricts their usefulness. For example, if the MPI does not exchange a patient's health record number and other identifying data with the R-ADT system, then these data would need to be recollected and reentered into the R-ADT system. This would result in data duplication and could introduce data errors. Therefore, developing ways of electronically communicating among these applications is essential.

### Levels of Interoperability

**Interoperability** is the ability of different information technology systems to exchange data with each other and to use that data (HIMSS 2013). Distinguishing between exchange and use is important. Systems may exchange data, but it may not be usable by the receiving system. For example, the format for date in the source system may be October 8, 2014, but in the target system the format is 08/10/2014. While the data might be exchanged between the two systems, the receiving or target system cannot use it. Considering all of the thousands of data elements systems use, accomplishing the two functions of interoperability—exchange and use—is a complex undertaking. Therefore, interoperability relies on the development of special software called interfaces. These interfaces must use agreed upon standards for data transport, terminology, and structure (Fridsma 2013). There are three levels of interoperability in healthcare systems:

- Foundational interoperability allows one system to exchange data with another, but the target system cannot interpret the data. It is the lowest level of operability.
- Structural interoperability allows one system to exchange data with another system in a common data format and structure and retains the identification of the data. For example, transferring lab test results from one system to

another preserves the identification of the test and its measurements. Structural interoperability is an intermediate level of operability.

- Semantic interoperability allows the exchange of data in a standard format and preserves its meaning by adding metadata and linking each data element to a controlled vocabulary. This allows the target system to interpret and use the exchanged data. For example, the data field "Gender" would be associated with a controlled vocabulary and interpreted to mean the same thing in both the source and target systems. Semantic interoperability is the highest level of interoperability (HIMSS 2013).

## Interfaces

To accomplish interoperability at any level, information systems professionals usually develop interfaces among systems. **Interfaces** are specialized software that allow computer systems to communicate with each other and are developed as point-to-point interfaces by computer programmers or by using an interface engine. A **point-to-point interface** is developed to permit communication between two systems. Given the magnitude of separate clinical and administrative systems, developing interfaces using a point-to-point strategy would be an enormous undertaking. For example, a separate interface would need to be developed between the R-ADT system and every other system requiring the use of a patient's health record number. That may entail development of several hundred interfaces.

Interface engines are frequently used by organizations to address the problem of construction and maintenance of hundreds of interfaces. An **interface engine** is a software program that simplifies the development and management of interfaces by acting as a hub for data exchange. Interface engines receive and exchange messages, provide message management and verification, and perform mapping, translation, and modification of data, if needed. For example, an interface engine used in healthcare may be able to accept and send messages in standard formats such as HL7, LOINC, XML, and CVS and may use a variety of transport methods such as HTTP, HTTPS, PDF, and FTP.

## Computer Networks

In addition to interfaces, interoperability is also dependent upon an infrastructure of computer networks. A **computer network** is a communication network consisting of a transmitter that sends data, a receiver that receives data, and a medium that connects the transmitter and receiver and provides the pathway for the transmission of the data. The medium often is a cable that connects computers, database servers, and workstations, although wireless networks are common as well. Data communication involves transferring information in binary form, which is the electronic equivalent of ones and zeros. In addition to computers, a network can incorporate a variety of computer devices (called nodes) such as printers, fax modems, scanners, phones, and other devices.

Network computers can be either clients or servers. A **client computer** accesses shared resources. A **server computer** provides a variety of shared resources to other computers. In the case of clinical and administrative applications, data that multiple applications or computers use is usually stored and managed in database systems on a server computer. There are a variety of configurations that organizations use for a network infrastructure. The most common include the bus, ring, star, and mesh topologies.

The **bus topology** is an older configuration where each computer connects to a common backbone or trunk through some kind of connector. This configuration works best with a limited number of devices, and while inexpensive to implement, a major disadvantage is that the central cable is a single point of failure. If this cable fails for any reason then the entire network goes down. In a **star topology,** each device connects to a central hub. All of the data on the network has to pass through the hub which then forwards it to the correct destination. Like the bus topology, the star topology has a single point of failure, which is the hub. If the hub fails then the entire network is compromised. In the **ring topology** each device connects to the network in a closed loop or ring. A unique address identifies each machine. The signal passes through each device connected to the ring in one direction. Ring topology usually uses a token-passing scheme where the message being passed from one device to another is inserted in the token and passed from one device to another until it reaches its destination. This topology works well for small networks and can flexibly add new devices to the network. A downfall of ring topology is that the failure of one device will cause the entire network to go down. The **mesh topology** combines the best characteristics of the bus, ring, and star topologies. In this topology, each device is interconnected to each other. If one device fails, the network will not go down. The World Wide Web is the most well-known example of a mesh topology.

## The St. Rita's Healthcare System Case Study

Shirlee and Monte delivered their presentation on administrative information systems to the EIM team. "I was never aware of all the different administrative systems that keep St. Rita's running. I knew about the MPI but never thought about applications like bed scheduling systems," remarked Bob at the end of the presentation.

"What struck me is that so many of the clinical applications are dependent upon the administrative systems and vice versa," Denise added. "An error in one system can potentially pass through to all other applications."

"That's right," Linda joined in. "But I now understand how difficult it is to integrate all of these systems and the reasons why we have so many data silos at St. Rita's. I can't imagine the time it takes for our IT staff to develop all the computer interfaces needed so that data can be exchanged easily."

"Your assessment is correct," Monte replied. "And when there are no standards for data exchange or for naming and formatting data elements among systems, developing interfaces becomes a nightmare. A good EIM and DG program would help to reduce or eliminate problems like these," he added with conviction.

Val thanked Shirlee and Monte for their thorough work and then led the team in a discussion of next steps. The team concluded that a top priority of any EIM program is developing and maintaining a complete inventory of information system applications and documenting what data from each application are used by other applications. The team noted these priorities and determined that they now had the background to fully explore the components of an EIM program and how it might help St. Rita's manage all of the diverse administrative and clinical applications.

## Part of the Team: Topics for Discussion and Action

The following topics are discussion items and actions the EIM team would feasibly address. If you were part of the EIM team, what would you contribute to these discussions and action determinations?

1. Shirlee and Monte assembled a lengthy list of clinical and administrative applications, but are these the usual systems installed at most acute care facilities? To determine this, interview the HIM directors of two or three acute care facilities. Go over Shirlee and Monte's list with them and confirm whether or not the facility has these applications installed. What do your results show? Were Shirlee and Monte on target with their list? Did you discover additional applications that acute care facilities commonly implement or ones from the list that they did not implement?
2. Monte mentioned to the EIM team that there are software asset management tools that identify and prepare an inventory of the applications that run on an organization's networks. Is Monte correct that these tools are regularly used by healthcare IT departments? To follow up on Monte's assertion, interview two or three IT directors at acute care facilities to determine if they use such tools and their opinion of the usefulness of these tools. You can use the interview matrix below as a sample to conduct your interviews.

| Interview question | Hospital A | Hospital B | Hospital C |
|---|---|---|---|
| Do you currently use a software asset management tool to gather an inventory of all of your software applications? | | | |
| If you do, who is the vendor of the tool? | | | |
| Is the tool effective? If not, what are some problems? | | | |
| If you do not use such a tool, how is your inventory of applications developed and maintained? | | | |

## Advanced Concepts

1. HIMSS Analytics provides a comprehensive overview of over 100 HIT applications divided into the following four categories: Applications of EMRAN (Electronic Medical Record), Operations applications, Clinical Services applications, and Support Services applications (HIMSS 2014). Review this list and see if the applications appear in the list developed by Shirlee and Monte. Take a deep dive into one of the four categories and prepare an annotated list of each type of application and determine market penetration by searching the HIMSS Analytics site and other sites. Use the template below to compile your data. The HIMSS HTP Research Report may be useful in completing this activity (HIMSS 2013). What implications can you draw from your results? How should St. Rita's be benchmarking itself against the HIT application category you have studied and the other three categories?

| Application | Overview of Purpose and Functions | Key Vendors | Market Penetration |
|---|---|---|---|
| | | | |
| | | | |
| | | | |
| | | | |
| | | | |
| | | | |

## References


Boyer, E.R. 2002. A new approach to acute care hospital bed management. 2003 Esri International User Conference. http://training.esri.com/bibliography/index.cfm?event=general.recorddetail&id=28483.

Dick, R.S., E.B. Steen, and D.E. Detmer, eds. 1997. *The Computer-Based Patient Record: An Essential Technology for Health Care*, rev. ed. Washington, DC: National Academies Press. http://books.nap.edu/openbook.php?record_id=5306&page=R1.

Fridsma, D. 2013. Interoperability vs. Health Information Exchange: Setting the Record Straight. January 9. http://www.healthit.gov/buzz-blog/meaningful-use/interoperability-health-information-exchange-setting-record-straight/.

HIMSS. August 2013. HTP healthcare transformation project buying patterns of US hospitals. http://apps.himss.org/transformation/docs/HTP_ResearchReport_August2013.pdf.

HIMSS. 2014. Essentials of the U.S. hospital IT market. http://www.himssanalytics.org/docs/Essentials%20Sell%20Sheet%209th%20Edition%202.pdf.

Sittig, D.F., B.L. Hazlehurst, J. Hsu, H. Jimison, and M.C. Hornbrook. 2002. A clinical information system research landscape. *The Permanente Journal* 6(2): 62–68. https://www.thepermanentejournal.org/files/PDF/Spring2002.pdf#page=64.

Chapter 4

# The Enterprise Solution: A Modern Model of HIM Practice

Call it enterprise information management (EIM), enterprise data management (EDM), or data administration (DA), the concept is the same: managing data as an enterprise asset. This text uses the term "enterprise information management" in preference to other terms for several reasons, one of which is that EIM is the continuum of the traditional work performed by health information managers. Therefore, maintaining the same terminology offers consistency in the context of the health information management (HIM) profession.

While data are the building blocks of information, the scope of HIM professional practice encompasses, but also goes beyond, data. HIM professionals are concerned with not only data issues but also with patterns, trends, and relationships among data. For example, an accounting of disclosures of a patient's health information deals with relationships among data and retrieval of not just data but information. Understanding the business meaning of data elements, the format in which data are presented, and the relevance of data in any given situation are part of information management, which is increasingly central to the work of HIM professionals. Extending the traditional tasks of HIM practice from a departmental to an enterprise focus drives the profession to embrace modern methods of information management practice.

The HIM profession has significant expertise and tradition in all aspects of HIM. HIM professionals have raised themselves to the challenge of evolution time after time as external and internal forces changed the dynamics of HIM. Today the profession must take a radical turn in how it views its role and uses its knowledge and skill base in support of a new era of digital information management. This chapter covers topics that will help you to:

- Analyze the historical context of HIM
- Compare and contrast traditional and new models of professional HIM practice
- Construct a new view and model of HIM appropriate for the current environment

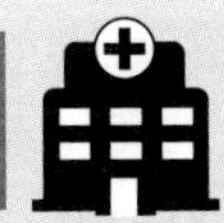

## The St. Rita's Healthcare System Case Study

"One of the first things we need to understand is how the management of digital data is different from management of paper records," said Val as she convened the Monday morning meeting of the EIM task force.

"Are the processes really that different?" quipped Bob. "Basically isn't it just a change in mindset?" The rest of the team pondered Bob's statement.

"I think there is a big difference between managing the two," Denise stated. "Just the processes for gathering data for the electronic record would be fundamentally different, not to mention how we would exchange the information itself," she continued.

The team continued to debate the similarities and differences between managing paper records versus digital data.

"Well, the central question still stands," said Val. "Before we move forward, we have to do our due diligence and identify precisely if differences exist at St. Rita's and if so, how these affect management of the information resource." Val went to the white board and with the help of the team outlined the two principal questions the team must answer: 1) What is traditional HIM practice? And, 2) What type of practice (traditional or otherwise) is needed to manage information in a digital environment? With their task identified, the team went to work to get the answers. The following is what they found out.

# Traditional HIM Practice

Beginning in 1928 and extending through the rest of the century, HIM tasks were traditionally departmentally focused and concerned with the management of objects more than data and information. A review of the American Health Information Management Association (AHIMA) 1984 and 1990 practice standards indicate most tasks involved planning, developing, and implementing systems designed to control, monitor, or track the quantity of record content, flow, storage and retrieval, or data on departmental personnel productivity (Johns 1991). These activities centered on the paper medical record with emphasis on identifying the presence or absence of documents and signatures as opposed to ensuring the appropriateness, quality, timeliness, or completeness of the information within the documents and its usefulness in decision support. Such tasks included, for example, record storage and retrieval, forms control, record tracking, locating missing reports, control of release of information and coding final diagnoses and procedures as they appeared on the face sheet of the health record. Confirming the professional name of the medical record librarian or administrator, HIM practice was geared toward a librarianship or custodial role.

Managing paper records principally involves controlling physical objects that contain data. The format of data collection is managed through forms design and control. In the paper environment, the focus is on capturing and storing data such as urinalysis, complete blood count, chest x-ray, and history or physical exam reports that reside in a discrete place (a paper document). Each report has a descriptive title and is further identified by a unique qualifier such as a patient health record number. The collection of documents associated with each patient is compiled in a physical file (record) which is identified by a unique qualifier, usually the patient health record number. Management of data in paper systems is usually limited to ensuring documents assembled in a file are correctly matched with the record unique identifier and that providers have signed and dated entries in the documents. A signature characteristic of paper records is that data are confined to a physical object. For example, the data associated with a urinalysis, a complete blood count, or a physical examination report are not integrated together for easy analysis (such as in a graph). Basically, the data are "trapped" within the physical object. This feature makes information comparison and dissemination challenging because the records are usually confined to one or only a few physical locations. This impedes timely information retrieval. For example, if a physician is documenting in a paper record, another care provider cannot use the record nor can anyone else access it for administrative purposes, such as coding. Figure 4.1 provides a schematic of the functions and tasks of HIM practice in a paper environment. The traditional bedrock of HIM practice focus has been on people, process, and documents.

Figure 4.1. Traditional model of HIM practice

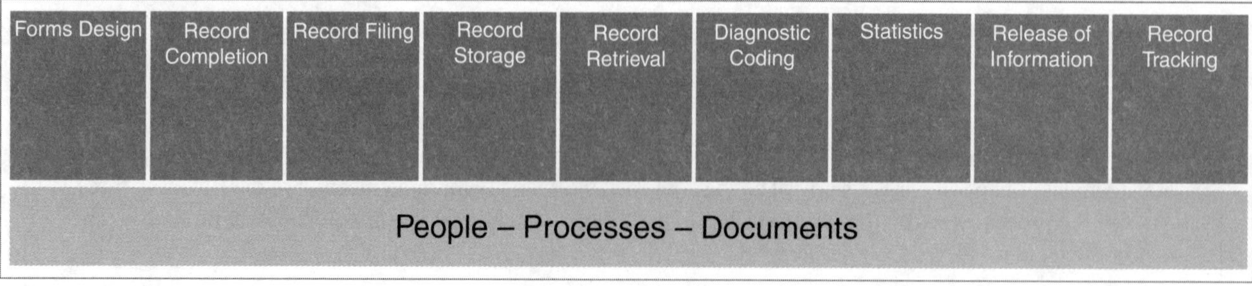


©Merida L. Johns

HIM practice in the electronic world, however, must focus on the management of data rather than the management of physical objects. Electronic data are located in databases, digital documents, or digital media (such as images or audio) and multiple users can share and use them for many purposes at the same time. For instance, data in the MPI may be stored in one data base, but users can share the data with all clinical and administrative applications for unique person identification purposes. Management of data versus management of physical records is what dramatically changes the practice of HIM in today's environment.

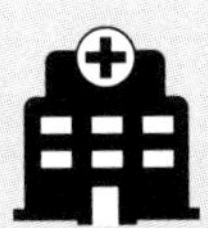

**The St. Rita's Healthcare System Case Study**

"Wow!" said Bob when the team came together a couple of days later for a brief follow-up. "I'll be the first to agree that managing digital data is way different than managing paper records." Bob argued that they needed a new model of HIM practice at St. Rita's. "We need a contemporary model of practice that moves HIM from paper records management to an electronic record and information management environment," he stated. "Both paper and electronic records involve data capture, and the management of both also encompasses storage, retrieval, and information dissemination functions. While each includes these functions, the knowledge, skills, processes, and technology by which electronic records and the information contained therein are managed are dramatically different from those of paper records management. Managing electronic records requires a 180-degree turn in how we view and actually perform HIM practice," Bob reasoned.

"You sure did take an about-face," said Shirlee, "and I couldn't agree with you more."

"What would a new model of practice look like?" queried Linda.

The team tossed around several ideas, wrote them on sticky notes, and arranged them on the white board. They reviewed the AHIMA Core Model, the Data Management Association model, and other HIM models (detailed below). The team then took all of these and began developing a contemporary model of HIM practice that would accurately reflect the needs of today's information management.

# A Contemporary Model of Practice

The new millennium requires a different set of tasks and supporting skills for managing health information that is systems-based with an enterprise-and-beyond perspective. External and internal forces have increased the dependence of healthcare enterprises on information in order to operate and manage their organizations, justify costs, prove quality, and remain competitive. Furthermore, the healthcare delivery system is equally dependent on information for the same reasons. The increasing information dependence has heightened the role and status of information technology and the management of information. It has also highlighted the need for transformation in information management functions. Organizations can no longer afford data to be trapped within single documents and files or in singular locations. The traditional tasks performed by health information managers are not sufficient to support the current complex and competitive environment. An entirely new group of information management functions is essential to meet today's needs. The following sections describe these functions, called domains of practice.

## Domains of Practice

Coinciding with advances in technology and needs of the healthcare industry is a progressive line of thinking of what should constitute a contemporary model of information management practice. HIM should encompass a collection of information service tasks within the domains of data capture, data retrieval, data analysis, and information dissemination (Johns 1991). These service tasks were consolidated in an enhanced model consisting of four domains of practice: information engineering, information retrieval, information analysis, and policy development (Johns 1997). More recently, in 2011, AHIMA incorporated these service tasks as the foundation for its new view of HIM and Core Model of Practice (figure 4.2). Considering the escalation of information dependence and technology sophistication, the domains of information engineering, retrieval, analysis, and policy development provide the basis for an expanded contemporary

Figure 4.2. AHIMA core model of HIM practice

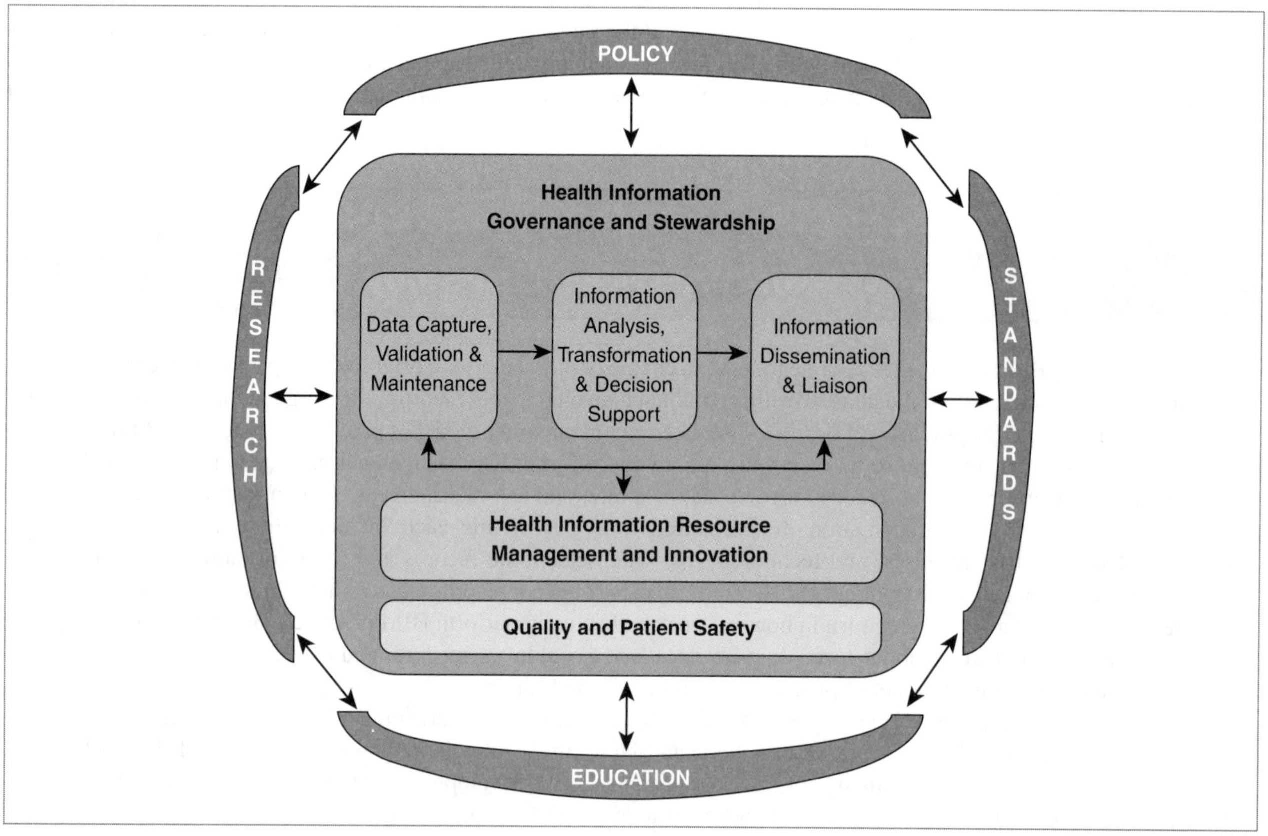

Source: AHIMA 2011.

model that incorporates modern terminology, practice, and interdisciplinary theory. This theory is called **enterprise health information management (EHIM)**.

The EHIM model (figure 4.3) combines previous contributions to the field of information management. This includes the perspective that information management includes planning for information systems and management of both people and technology, which we commonly refer to as **information resources management (IRM)** (Synnot 1981). The EHIM model incorporates the perspective that information management is primarily concerned with characteristics such as information ownership, content, quality, and appropriateness and suggests information management is primarily concerned with information as an asset (Schneyman 1985).

Building on these frames of reference, the EHIM model is forward-thinking and includes current thought from discipline experts on data quality, data governance (DG), master data management, HIM, EIM, from professional organizations such as the Data Management Association (DAMA) and AHIMA, and from others such as the Data Governance Institute and The Method for an Integrated Knowledge Environment. In particular, the DAMA model provides a comprehensive view of EIM functions, albeit calling it data management, and includes facets of all the other models. The DAMA model includes the following domains which become the basis for the St. Rita's EHIM model:

- Data governance
- Data life cycle management
- Data architecture management
- Data warehousing and business intelligence management
- Data quality management
- Metadata management
- Data security management
- Data development
- Data operations management
- Reference and master data management
- Document and content management

Figure 4.3. EHIM model of HIM practice

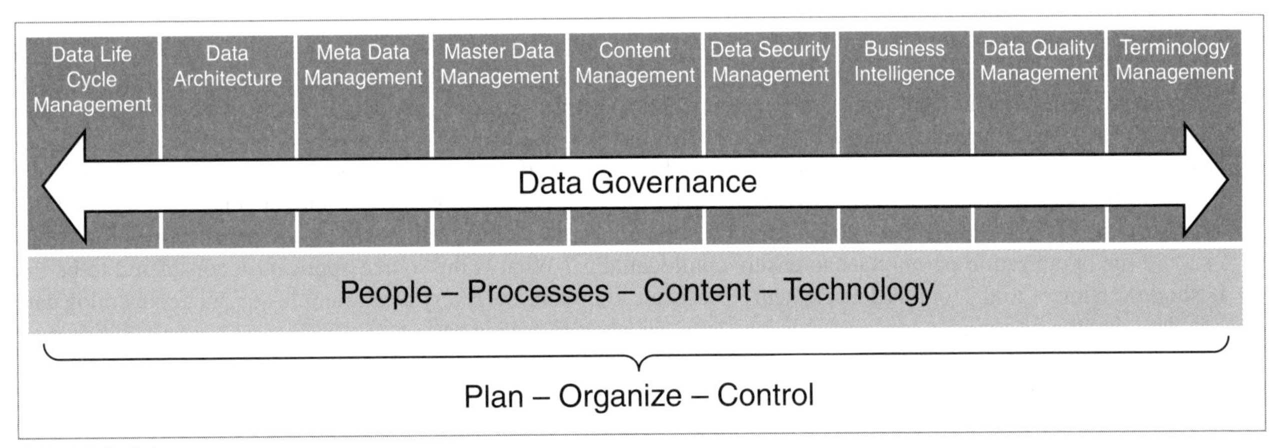


©Merida L. Johns

Figure 4.3 depicts EHIM from a systems perspective, showing that the synergy among people, processes, technology, and content is the foundation or core of EHIM practice. The practice consists of a set of domains that organizations use to plan, organize, and coordinate to produce equilibrium and value to all the domains. While the functions of planning, organizing, and controlling exist in both paper and electronic worlds, what organizations plan for, how they organize the functions, and how they control the functions are dramatically different. The EHIM model uses the following domains from the DAMA model: DG, data architecture management, business intelligence, data quality management, metadata management, data security management, master data management, and content management. The EHIM model also adds data life cycle management and terminology management domains.

In chapter 2, we described an information system (figure 2.1) as being composed of a group of components that includes people, processes, technologies, and data (content). These components influence each other and interact through defined relationships to work toward achieving a common goal. To manage an information system's data and resulting information, all of these components or subsystems and their interactions must be taken into account. Consider the following questions for an R-ADT application.

- *People: Who are the people involved in capturing and using the R-ADT system?* At first glance, one might say the users include registration clerks, caregivers, and patient-care support staff who need to know when a patient is admitted and discharged, and the patient's location in the hospital while hospitalized. There are, however, others who are dependent upon the data in an R-ADT system. For example, administrative staff requires output from the R-ADT system to process patient bills. Departmental and senior level management use R-ADT system data to assess occupancy rates, average length of stay, and combine these with other information to determine trends. Outside agencies, such as Medicare and accreditation and licensure bodies rely on R-ADT system data for assessing compliance with quality and other criteria. Healthcare policy and planning agencies use R-ADT application data for developing health policy. These are a few examples of the parties who depend on R-ADT data and whose needs one should consider when designing the application.
- *Processes: What are the processes that the R-ADT application supports?* The obvious answer is that the application supports the registration, admission, discharge, and transfer of a patient within a hospital. Beyond these, almost any process that requires patient identification or location depends on R-ADT data: the clinical laboratory needs to know the identity and location of a patient in the hospital to collect blood and other specimens, the housekeeping staff needs to know when a patient has vacated a room in order to prepare the room for the next patient, and the dietary department needs to know how many meals to prepare and to whom the meals should be delivered. The list of processes supported by the R-ADT is almost exhaustive and each of these processes in turn includes several discrete tasks that one must consider when designing the application. Information managers need to know the inputs and outputs of each process and how they are interconnected.
- *Technology: What technologies does the R-ADT application require?* It requires software, hardware, and communications technologies. More specifically, information managers need to know what technologies and software the application needs to capture, store, share, and disseminate the data. For instance, do the master data for patients reside in a clinical data repository? If not, where do they reside? How are they communicated to applications such as a laboratory information system or a radiology information system?

- *Content: What data do the processes need for support, how do the data flow within each process, and how do data flow among all the processes as a whole?* Information managers need to identify the specific data elements the application requires, such as patient last, first, and middle names; patient date of birth; patient gender; and patient home address. Information managers must define each of these data elements as to its length, type (numeric or character), default value, and other characteristics. For example, is patient gender represented by a numeric value such as "1" or "2," by a character value such as "M" or "F," or a text string such as "male" or "female?" Should there be more than two values for gender to adequately define a patient population? Is the organization using the data element "patient gender" in applications other than the R-ADT system? If so, how is patient gender defined in those applications? Is "patient gender" considered a confidential data element? If so, what type of security protections should the organization put in place to ensure confidentiality? What is the source application considered to be the "single version of truth" for this data element? These questions address a very small sample of issues concerning data content that the information manager must tackle on an enterprise-wide basis.

The R-ADT example above is a simple illustration of the interconnectedness of people, processes, technology, and content. At its very core, EHIM is concerned with the synergy among these components and how the components must harmoniously and effectively work together to capture, store, and disseminate the right information to the right person at the right time. HIM in the next decade and beyond must incorporate all of these components in its professional practice and focus on their synergy as the above R-ADT example illustrates.

While each EHIM domain stands on its own, there is also dependency among them. Each domain affects others. If one domain is not optimally executed, this adversely affects the performance of other domains. The interconnectivity among the domains means EHIM must be viewed as a total package of activities necessary for achieving data quality.

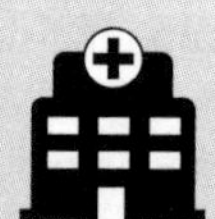

### The St. Rita's Healthcare System Case Study

Joan Morton listened intently to the preliminary report of the EIM team. Joan was impressed with the team's research and was intrigued with the EHIM model. "OK," she said to the team. "This is a good first concept. Now I need specifics. First, I want an overview of the functions of each domain and a description of how the functions of each domain will help fix St. Rita's data quality problems. Second, I want options for putting the concept into operation. For example, how should we implement EHIM? Where does EHIM fit into the organizational structure and what are the benefits of EHIM?"

The EIM team had its next steps and divided their work. Shirlee and Denise volunteered to prepare an overview of EHIM functions, Bob and Linda would take a stab at developing an organizational structure, and Val and Monte would identify EHIM benefits.

## EHIM Domains

The EHIM model the St. Rita's EIM team adopted (figure 4.3) has 10 domains. Using this model as a foundation, the following sections provide an overview of the functions of each domain.

### Data Life Cycle Management

The foundation of any model for HIM practice must acknowledge that data have a life cycle. A life cycle consists of a series of successive stages and has beginning and end points. Plant and animal life cycles are probably the most familiar to us. They have beginning, developmental, maturation, declining, and ending stages. Businesses have life cycles, too. A business usually goes through different phases that include inception, start-up, growth, maturity, expansion, decline, and exit. Each stage in the life cycle has a function that one must manage appropriately to fulfill its purpose. Life cycles are subsystems within a greater system and interface with the environment in which they occur. Therefore, in addition to specific stages, life cycles have inputs from and outputs to a larger system.

There are many models of the data life cycle. While each portrays a slightly different view of life cycle stages, there are striking similarities among them (Chung 2010). From these models, the St. Rita's EIM team developed a data life cycle model that fit the institution's needs. The resulting model is similar to the Geospatial Data Lifecycle (Federal Geographic Data Committee 2010). In this model, all stages of the life cycle depend on the organization's business requirements. The data life cycle in figure 4.4 includes the following stages: data planning, data inventory and evaluation, data capture, data transformation and processing, data access and distribution, data maintenance, data archival, and data disposal, which we address later in this text. The core around which the life cycle emanates is different than the traditional HIM model. Here, the core or bedrock of the life cycle consists of content. Typical data life cycle functions of an organization include:

- Establishing what data are to be collected and how they are to be captured
- Setting standards for data retention and storage
- Determining processes for data access and distribution
- Establishing standards for data archival and disposal

Figure 4.4. A data life cycle model

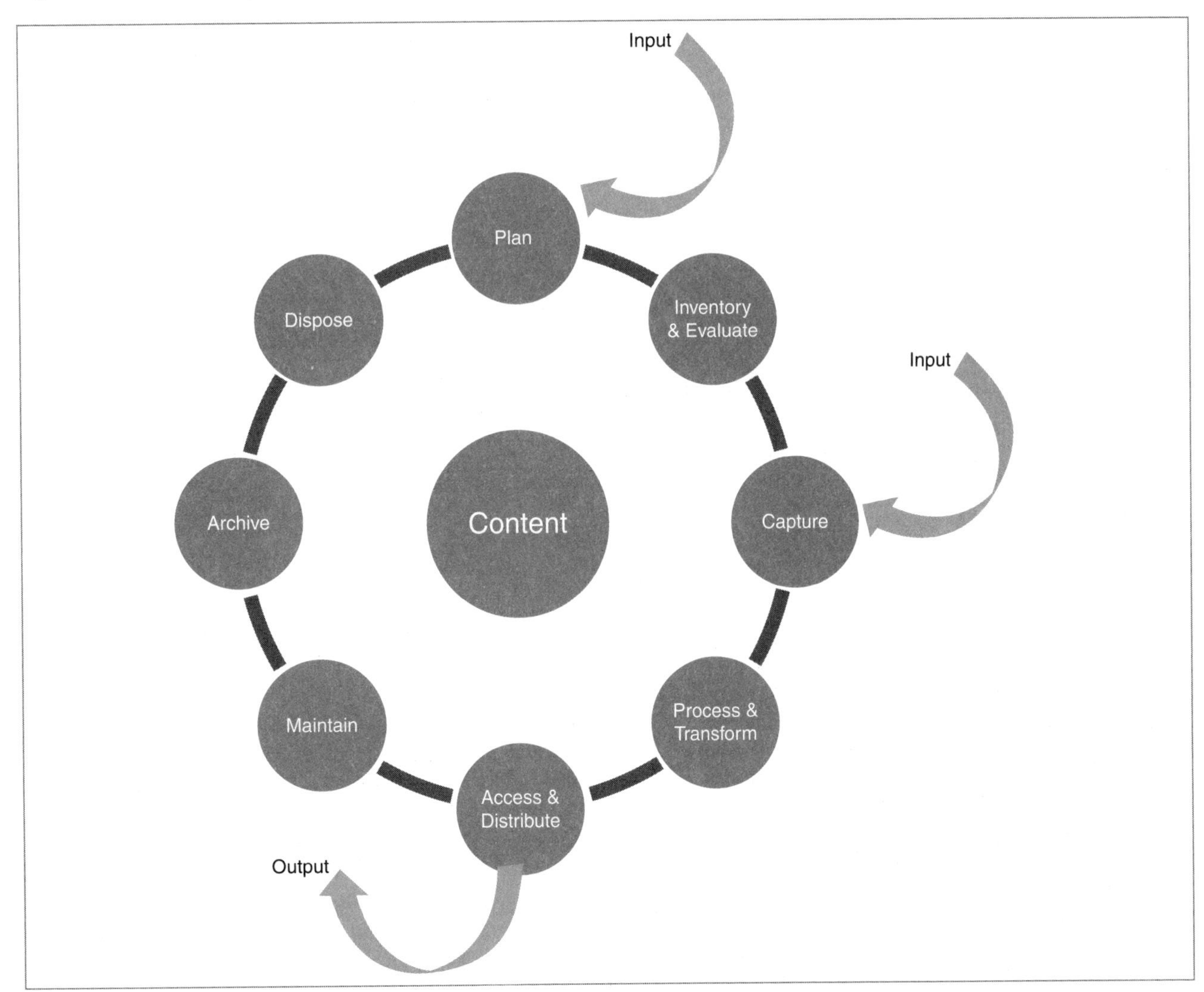


©Merida L. Johns

## Data Architecture Management

**Data architecture**, sometimes called data engineering, or information engineering, can be broadly defined as "an integrated set of specification artifacts (models and diagrams) used to define data requirements, guide integration and control of data assets, and align data investments with business strategy" (DAMA 2010, 63). Similarly, the term data engineering also describes this same concept. For example, the Institute of Electrical and Electronics Engineers (IEEE) defines data engineering as the integration of all disciplines concerned with database design, construction, and use (IEEE Software 1984). The IEEE Technical Committee on Data Engineering further expands the definition of data engineering as "concerned with the role of data in the design, development, management, and utilization of information systems" (IEEE 2014). Whatever terminology one uses to describe the concept, the fundamental principle is that data are essential components in complex systems and, as such, require abstractions and models to describe the data and the relationships among data and the processes they support.

Data architecture is to data what an architect's blueprint is to a building. It is the composite of models and artifacts that provide the underpinning of an organization's information system. Typical functions of data architecture management include:

- Establishing standards, policies, and procedures for the collection, storage, and integration of enterprise data and design of information systems
- Identifying and documenting data requirements that meet the needs and support the organization's processes
- Developing and maintaining enterprise and conceptual data and process models that represent the organization's business rules.

## Metadata Management

**Metadata** are often referred to as "data about data." In today's world, however, metadata go beyond providing data about data. A formal definition of metadata is "structured information that describes, explains, locates, or otherwise makes it easier to retrieve, use, or manage an information resource" (National Information Standards Organization 2004, 1). The purpose of metadata is to enhance the effectiveness of data use. There are different types of metadata. Some metadata describe data for the purposes of discovery, like metadata used in search engines. Other metadata provide information on when users created or changed data, such as metadata used in computer audit trails. And still other metadata identify who has access rights to certain data, like metadata used for access control purposes. In databases, metadata are descriptive and include the data element name, data type, and field length. There are many metadata standards, many of which are industry sector-specific.

Metadata are important because they promote interoperability among different computer systems as well as provide better search and navigation capabilities. Today, metadata are frequently used by organizations for discovery purposes in order to maintain, update, and retain data to meet compliance regulations. Organizations often maintain metadata in large metadata repositories. Usual metadata management functions include:

- Managing data dictionaries
- Establishing enterprise metadata strategy
- Developing policies, goals, and objectives for metadata management and use
- Adopting metadata standards
- Establishing and implementing metadata metrics
- Monitoring procedures to ensure metadata policy implementation

## Master Data Management

**Master data management** refers to managing data that an enterprise maintains about key business entities such as customers, employees, or patients. It also includes managing reference data that the organization or healthcare industry uses to classify other data or identify allowable values for data such as codes for state abbreviations or products. Master data are critical for carrying out an organization's day-to-day business functions. For example, "patient" and "provider" are key entities in a healthcare organization. Patient master data may include data such as a patient's health record number, birth date, gender, address, and last, middle, and first names. Provider master data may include provider certification or licensing number, name, and address. Since master and reference data are used across the organization, consistency is critical. Data quality issues are often attributable to poor management of one or both of these types of data. Inconsistencies or redundancies among either can have profound, negative effects on data quality and make it impossible to share data across computer applications both internal and external to the organization. One of the most familiar types of master data in healthcare is the master patient index. Typical functions associated with master data management include:

- Identifying reference data sources (such as databases and files)
- Maintaining authoritative reference data values lists and associated metadata
- Implementing change management processes for reference data
- Establishing organizational master data sets
- Defining and maintaining match rules for master data
- Identifying duplicate master data and reconciling to provide the "system of record" or "single source of truth"

- Establishing policies and procedures for applying data quality and matching rules, and incorporating data quality checks for master data
- Implementing change management processes for master data

## Content and Record Management

Organizational data are classified as structured data, such as data stored in databases, or unstructured data, such as data contained in text documents. Content management involves processes concerned with unstructured paper-based or electronic data including documents, records, and images. The activities normally associated with content management include the creation, storage, and retrieval of records as well as the cataloguing and the categorizing of information within the records. Content management is becoming an increasingly important function in healthcare organizations. Content management functions include:

- Developing and implementing policies and procedures for the organization and categorization of unstructured data (content) in electronic, paper, image, and audio files for its delivery, use, reuse, and preservation
- Developing and adopting taxonomic systems for the indexing, cataloging, and categorizing of data for purposes of information searching and retrieval
- Developing and maintaining an information architecture and metadata schema that identifies links and relationships among documents and defines the content within a document

## Data Security Management

**Data security** includes protection measures and tools for safeguarding data and information. **Information security** means protecting information and information systems from unauthorized access, use, disclosure, disruption, modification, or destruction in order to guard against improper information modification or destruction, preserve authorized restrictions on access and disclosure to protect personal privacy and propriety information, and ensure timely and reliable access to and use of information (NIST 2008, A-6). **Data security management** consists of policies and procedures that address confidentiality and security concerns of organizational stakeholders (for example, patients, providers, and employees), protecting organizational proprietary interests, and compliance with government and regulatory requirements while accommodating legitimate access needs. The typical functions of data security management include:

- Data security planning and organization
- Developing, implementing, and enforcing data security policies and procedures
- Establishing a data security risk management program
- Developing a business continuity plan
- Monitoring audit trails to identify potential and actual security violations
- Managing employee, contractor, and business partner security and confidentiality agreements
- Implementing employee security awareness training

## Information Intelligence and Big Data

**Business intelligence (BI)** is defined as "a broad category of applications and technologies for gathering, storing, analyzing, and providing access to data to help enterprise users make better business decisions" (Brannon 2010, 2). Typically, information intelligence systems use structured data extracted from source system transactional databases and loaded into a data warehouse. Unstructured data (data in emails, word-processed documents, memos, and blogs), however, can account for upwards of 80 percent of an organization's data (Roberts 2010). Because of its volume and potential importance, any information intelligence system must address incorporating unstructured data into its information intelligence system. By their nature, unstructured data are difficult to define and categorize. Therefore, special technological and other strategies must be used to extract and manage these data so they can be analyzed in meaningful ways. Usual functions associated with enterprise information intelligence include:

- Identifying enterprise intelligence needs
- Assessing current intelligence resources and use
- Determining scope, defining requirements and architecture for enterprise intelligence
- Developing and implementing policies and procedures for enterprise information intelligence
- Identifying, assessing, and resolving data quality issues
- Implementing data warehouses and data marts that store massive amounts of data
- Identifying and implementing appropriate business intelligence tools and interfaces

## Data Quality Management

Enterprise operations, decision making, strategy, and ultimately, business performance all depend upon good data. The purpose of **data quality management** is to ensure data are meeting quality characteristics that ensure organizational success. Data quality management is characterized as "a continuous process for defining the parameters for specifying acceptable levels of data quality to meet business needs, and for ensuring that data quality meets these levels" (DAMA 2010, 291). Typical functions of a data quality program include:

- Identifying data quality requirements and establishing data quality metrics
- Identifying and carrying out data quality projects
- Profiling data and measuring conformance to established quality metrics and business rules
- Identifying data quality problems and assessing their root cause
- Managing data quality issues
- Implementing data quality improvement measures
- Providing training for ensuring data quality

## Terminology and Classification Management

**Terminology and classification management** is an EIM domain unique to healthcare. There are many different healthcare terminologies, vocabularies, classification systems, and data sets. The purpose of the language and classification domain is to manage these in the healthcare organization and provide a central terminology authority for the enterprise. Typical functions assumed by this domain include:

- Ensuring appropriate adoption, maintenance, dissemination, and accessibility of vocabularies, terminologies, classification systems, and code sets for semantic interoperability and data integrity
- Developing algorithmic translations, concept representations, and mapping among terminologies and classifications
- Providing oversight for clinical and diagnostic coding to ensure compliance with established standards

## Data Governance

**Data governance** is the overarching authority that ensures the cohesive operation and integration of all EIM domains. DG includes a formal organizational structure with both authority and responsibility for managing an organization's data assets. The governance structure varies among organizations, but is normally sponsored by an organization executive and led by a high-level DG committee with direction and staff support from an EIM office and council of data stewards. Typical governance functions include:

- Advocating for the data asset
- Establishing data strategy
- Establishing data policies
- Approving data procedures and standards
- Communicating, monitoring, and enforcing data policy and standards
- Ensuring regulatory compliance
- Resolving data issues
- Approving data management projects
- Coordinating data management organization

### *The St. Rita's Healthcare System Case Study*

Joan Morton had tasked the team to identify the functions within each EIM domain and address how these would solve St. Rita's data quality problems. The team met to review Shirlee and Denise's summary of EIM functions.

"Hey, these look great," Monte said. "Your summary gives a good picture of the EIM's scope, but it looks like an immense if not impossible job."

"Yes, it's a big and complex activity. If it were easy, then St. Rita's would not have all the data silos and data quality issues it has today," Val interjected. "Perhaps Linda and Bob can provide some understanding from their research on how we can tackle the big task of EIM," Val stated.

"I can take it from here," offered Linda. "In our research we found that successful EIM must have executive management support and participation. We also realized EIM succeeds just like any other big project: one bite at a time." With that intro, Linda and Bob gave a short presentation on EIM organization.

## EIM Organization and Structure

There is no one prescribed EIM structure across industries or organizations. However, there are some general principles and guidelines organizations can use when they establish EIM. The Data Administration Charter of the University of Pennsylvania, for example, lists the following as critical success factors for enterprise data administration or EIM:

- Having both authority as well as responsibility for enforcing standards
- Securing the active support of senior management
- Being able to measure data quality, security, and ease of access
- Having in place a powerful, flexible data dictionary or encyclopedia
- Engaging data stakeholders, particularly in a decentralized computing environment
- Understanding and appreciating clients' needs and having a determination to meet those needs (University of Pennsylvania 2012)

An EIM organizational structure usually includes an enterprise executive committee, whose purpose is to assume the governance function, providing the overarching authority and responsibility for setting and enforcing data standards, resolving data-related issues, and ensuring the cohesive operation and integration of all EIM functions. The executive committee is a cross-functional committee that typically includes senior and executive managers within the organization. The committee may be supported in its activities by a technical advisory group or tactical teams whose function is to conduct fact finding and to recommend and draft policies and standards for review and approval by the executive committee. This executive-level committee goes by various names.

Because the EIM scope is complex and requires the support of many stakeholders, a network of data stewards and custodians typically oversee and carry out the implementation of EIM policies, procedures, and monitoring. If this is the case, the **data stewards and custodians** report directly to a specific functional unit, responsible for implementing specific EIM functions pertinent to their business unit. Coordination and communication within the network of data stewards takes place through a data steward coordinating committee or similar mechanism.

The EIM program is coordinated by an EIM executive or director and associated EIM office that supports the work of the EIM committee and various data steward and advisory groups. The EIM office also facilitates and coordinates EIM and data stewardship functions. In many instances this office is called the "data governance office" since one can view governance as the overarching domain.

Organizational placement, authority, and reporting relationships among the different EIM committees vary across organizations. For example, in some instances, the EIM executive committee may report directly to the organization's chief executive officer (CEO), and in others it may report to an EIM executive sponsor. Likewise, the EIM office may report to the institution's chief information officer (CIO), or in other cases, report to the CEO or EIM executive sponsor. In other organizations there may be a formal structure with EIM headed by a vice president of information management with direct managerial reports such as managers of DG, data quality capture, data quality maintenance, and data access (Ladley, 2010).

### *The St. Rita's Healthcare System Case Study*

"There are several existing organizations or agencies that have implemented EIM organizational structures, such as the US Department of Education, Federal Student Aid Data Governance Plan, the Data Governance Institute of Governance Models, and the State of California Department of Transportation Data Business

Plan. It would be valuable to look at these in detail as we develop a model for St. Rita's," emphasized Linda to the team.

Linda and Bob concluded their report, stressing that EIM's cross-functional nature requires a collaborative rather than a command and control organizational structure. "It is important that form follow function," said Linda.

"The organizational structure," began Bob, "should support the vision, mission, and objectives of the EIM program. The way the program is defined is organization-specific and therefore, there is no cookie-cutter approach. Some EIM programs may include all of the domains we defined. On the other hand, some organizations may define EIM as encompassing only three or four of the ten domains we identified. It depends on the organizational needs, resources, and, of course, politics."

The team considered Linda and Bob's presentation with Monte posing the first questions: "How do we implement something so complex? Where do we start?"

Bob went over to the white board and wrote down four bullet points:

- Vision
- Mission
- Strategy
- Goals

"Before we start this journey, we need to know where we are going. Developing clarity of vision and mission, and identifying high-level strategy and objectives are the foundation for everything else. These four elements—vision, mission, strategy, and goals—determine the EIM scope for our organization, dictate the organizational structure, and influence the resources we need for a successful EIM program," Bob stressed.

"Isn't that too general?" asked Shirlee. "I think Joan wants us to come up with something more specific."

"Given our research on successful EIM programs, it is premature to make decisions on organizational structure. Bob's right. We need a vision and a mission before we can proceed," Val emphasized. "We can craft sets of vision and mission statements for Joan, showing her how each would influence scope, organizational structure, staffing, and other resources," Val added.

The team all agreed that this approach had merit, as it would provide Joan with a richer set of alternatives and challenge them to think about various ways EIM could be structured at St. Rita's.

"Now," said Val, "Monte and I are ready to review the benefits of EIM and show how EIM can help solve St. Rita's data problems.

## EIM Benefits

St. Rita's has silos of isolated data that support only individual application programs or business units and are frequently managed in different ways depending upon the organizational unit responsible for application development and oversight. For example, not all data elements have a data definition, conform to standard naming conventions, or have appropriate constraints to ensure data quality. Given patient care, operational needs, and data reporting requirements, St Rita's must be able to easily share and integrate these data across functional boundaries. St Rita's must ensure the data are meeting data quality characteristics appropriate for each patient care, business, reporting, or research need, and provide data that can be integrated for information intelligence purposes. EIM supports achieving this objective by:

- Making information management a key organizational initiative
- Increasing organizational awareness of the importance of information management
- Promoting collaboration and cooperation to create a single enterprise view of an organization's information asset
- Establishing formal organizational structure tasked with authority and responsibility for EIM
- Improving data quality by consolidating data sources, establishing consistent business rules for managing data, developing guidelines for data quality, and establishing authority for data ownership
- Increasing efficiency and effectiveness of data used for business planning, operations, and patient care by an integrated, cross program view of enterprise data, providing an information delivery framework that accommodates easy access to data by all users
- Optimizing enterprise information delivery, reducing the amount of time stakeholders spend trying to obtain data

- Safeguarding data from misuse
- Improving organization flexibility and agility by providing an organizational data model, improving processes and procedures, and supporting unstructured data (Jennings 2007)

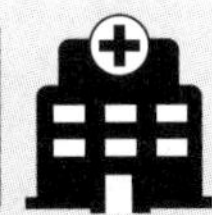

## *The St. Rita's Healthcare System Case Study*

The team knew that Joan Morton would want details of how each EIM domain could help remedy St. Rita's data problems. Therefore, Val and Monte prepared a matrix of selected problem examples matched with EIM domains that would address problem remediation.

Val and Monte took each EIM domain, identifying and matching data problems at St. Rita's to a lack of oversight or implementation of functions in the specified domain. They then listed how implementing an EIM domain could help remedy the problems they cited (table 4.1).

Table 4.1. EIM domains, data problems, and selected actions for St. Rita's case

| EIM Domain | St. Rita Data Problem | Remedy |
|---|---|---|
| **Data Architecture** | System- and application-specific data models that make data integration difficult if not impossible<br><br>Application systems that do not meet operational or reporting needs | Provide data model standards<br><br>Provide enterprise view of data through enterprise conceptual and logical data models<br><br>Implement formalized requirements analysis processes, and documentation |
| **Metadata Management** | Inconsistent data element names and meanings<br><br>Insufficient data quality checks | Implement enterprise data dictionary<br><br>Establish edit check standards<br><br>Establish metrics for data quality<br><br>Institute audit program |
| **Master Data Management** | Duplicate digital records in master data | Implement suite of master data management standards and practices to ensure a "single source of truth" for all organization master data |
| **Content Management** | Inability to access unstructured data in clinical and business documents for BI, research, and other purposes | Implement document management system that includes standards and processes for indexing and cataloging of data for purposes of information searching and retrieval<br><br>Develop an information architecture that identifies links and relationships among documents and defines the content within a document |
| **Data Security Management** | Spotty tracking of disclosures of protected health information among St. Rita's various health delivery entities | Coordinate data security management and link to other EIM functions to ensure compliance with government regulations |
| **Information Intelligence** | Inability to retrieve data in meaningful ways for executives, management, and clinicians for purposes of data analytics | Perform gap analysis between organization needs and current systems for information intelligence<br><br>Develop architecture for effective and efficient information intelligence |

(continued)

Table 4.1. EIM domains, data problems, and selected actions for St. Rita's case (*Continued*)

| EIM Domain | St. Rita Data Problem | Remedy |
|---|---|---|
| **Data Quality Management** | Multiple data quality issues across all systems | Develop and implement data quality standards<br>Develop and apply metrics for data quality<br>Monitor and remedy data quality issues |
| **Terminology and Classification Management** | Lack of harmonization across terminology and classification systems, making data integration and analytics difficult | Develop and implement algorithmic translations, concept representations, and mapping among clinical nomenclatures |
| **Data Governance** | No central source for resolution of data quality or other data issues.<br>No central source for policy for management or monitoring data resource | Implement formal DG framework for centralization of authority and responsibility for managing the organization's data assets that includes resolution of data-related issues |

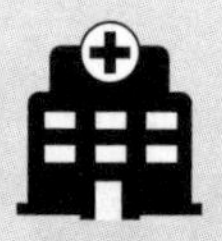

## *The St. Rita's Healthcare System Case Study*

It was 7:00 pm and Joan Morton was just wrapping up her day. "Could I have used the help of an EIM organization today," she thought. At an early morning meeting, the Clinical Informatics Committee grappled with how to capture data in clinical notes in a more meaningful way. The unstructured data in clinical notes was a rich repository of information but practically useless for easy retrieval and reporting requirements. With several national initiatives looming, how could any organization capture all of the unstructured data in an electronic health record to populate structured data in templates, making it easy for reporting purposes? "Today we really could have called on the expertise of data stewards in content and document management to guide our planning on this," Joan reflected.

As she cleared her desk, Joan's thoughts moved to the summary presentation made by the EIM team that morning. The information they compiled was exactly what she needed to develop an EIM concept document to get buy-in from the organization's executive team and start the ball rolling to create an EIM department.

Joan asked the team to spend the following weeks fleshing out each EIM domain in more detail. Wanting to get started, the team scheduled their next meeting for mid-week.

## Part of the Team: Topics of Discussion and Action

1. To help the team expand its information on EIM, conduct an Internet search and retrieve five articles on EIM. Construct a table that lists the EIM domains described in each article. What are some similarities among the articles? What are the differences? What conclusions can you draw about EIM from these articles?
2. If you were at the team meeting, would you agree with Bob's assertion that EIM structure and implementation are dependent on the organization's vision, mission, strategy, and goals for the program? How would you argue your case?
3. The team needs more information on data quality issues in healthcare to help make the case for EIM. Conduct a literature search and retrieve three articles identifying current healthcare data quality issues. Make a list of the data quality issues. Identify the EIM domains that can help remedy the data quality issues you cited and explain your position.
4. Do you agree with the assertion made in the chapter that HIM practice has fundamentally changed? Explain your position.
5. If you were in a discussion with the team about the importance of the EIM domains, which EIM domain would you suggest is the most critical to the success of an EIM program? How would you back up your rationale for your choice?

## Advanced Concepts

Conduct a search in the Internet and locate organization charters that describe the vision, mission, strategy, and goals for an EIM or DG program. In a team, develop what you think might be a good starting point for a vision and mission statement for St. Rita's EIM program. Then, develop two or more strategies that St. Rita's might consider for EIM implementation the team can present to Joan Morton for discussion.

## References


American Medical Record Association. 1984, 1990. *Professional practice standards.* Chicago: American Medical Record Association.

AHIMA. 2011. A new view of HIM: Introducing the core model. http://library.ahima.org/xpedio/groups/public/documents/ahima/bok1_049283.pdf.

Barry, R.E. Managing distinctions: Enterprise information, document, records, knowledge and content management. *Records and Information Management Review,* 18(2). http://www.mybestdocs.com/barry-r-rimr-distinctions.htm.

Berson, A. and L. Dubov. 2011. *Master Data Management and Data Governance,* 2nd ed. New York: McGraw-Hill.

Brannon, N. 2010. Business intelligence and E-discovery. *Intellectual Property & Technology Law Journal,* 22(7): 1–5. http://search.proquest.com/docview/504044279?accountid=10224.

Business Dictionary.com. (2012) http://www.businessdictionary.com/definition/governance.html#ixzz2FAPAVHje.

Chung, Chang. 2010. Data Life Cycle. https://blogs.princeton.edu/onpopdata/2012/03/12/data-life-cycle/.

Thomas, Gwen. Choosing Governance Models. Data Governance Institute. http://www.datagovernance.com/choosing-governance-models/.

DAMA. 2010. *DAMA Guide to Data Management Body of Knowledge.* Bradley Beach: Technics Publications, LLC.

English, L.P. 2009. *Information Quality Applied.* Indianapolis: Wiley.

Federal Geographic Data Committee. 2010. The Office of Management & Budget Circular A-16, Coordination of Geographic Information Related Spatial Data Activities. Stages of the geospatial data lifecycle pursuant to OMB circular. A-16, Sections 8(E)(F), and 8(E)(G). http://www.fgdc.gov/policyandplanning/a-16/index_html#supplemental-guidance.

IEEE Software. Soft News. (July/August 1984), 99–103.

Jennings, M. 2007. Benefits of an EIM initiative. *EIM Insight Magazine* 1(2). http://www.eiminstitute.org/library/eimi-archives/volume-1-issue-2-april-2007-edition/benefits-of-an-eim-initiative.

Jennings, M. 2007. Developing a roadmap for an enterprise information management program. *EIM Insight Magazine* 1(1). http://www.eiminstitute.org/library/eimi-archives/volume-1-issue-1-march-2007-edition/enterprise-information-management-primer.

Johns, M. L. 1991 (August). Information management: A Shifting paradigm for medical record professionals? *Journal of the American Medical Record Association* 62(8): 53–63.

Johns, M.L. 1997. *Information Management for Health Professions.* Albany: Delmar.

Kloss, L. 2013. Leading innovation in enterprise information governance. *Journal of AHIMA* 84(9): 34–37.

Ladley, J. 2010. *Making Enterprise Information Management Work for Business.* Burlington, MA: Elsevier.

Method for an Integrated Knowledge Environment (MIKE 2.0). 2014. What is MIKE 2.0? http://mike2.openmethodology.org/wiki/What_is_MIKE2.0#integrated_with_a_Collaborative_Community.

National Information Standards Organization. 2004. *Understanding Metadata.* Bethesda: NISO Press. http://www.niso.org/publications/press/UnderstandingMetadata.pdf.

National Institute of Standards and Technology. 2008. An introduction resource guide for implementing the Health Insurance Portability and Accountability Act (HIPAA) Security Rule. NIST Special Publication 800-66 Revision 1. http://csrc.nist.gov/publications/nistpubs/800-66-Rev1/SP-800-66-Revision1.pdf.

Roberts, Paige. 2010. "Corralling Unstructured Data for Data Warehouses." *Business Intelligence Journal.* 15, no. 4: 50–55. *Business Source Complete*, EBSCO *host*.

Schneyman, A.H. 1985. Organizing information resources. *Information Management Review*, 1: 35–45.

State of California, Department of Transportation Data Business Plan. http://dot.ca.gov/hq/tsip/datagovernance.php.

Synnott, W.R. and Gruber, W.H. 1981. *Information Resource Management.* New York: Wiley.

Technical Committee on Data Engineering. 2014. http://www.computer.org/portal/web/kde/home.

University of Pennsylvania Information Systems and Computing. 2012. Data Administration Charter. http://www.upenn.edu/computing/da/charter.html.

US Department of Education. 2007 (June). Enterprise Data Management: Data Governance Plan, version 1.0. http://studentaid.ed.gov/sites/default/files/fsawg/static/gw/docs/ciolibrary/ECONOPS_Docs/DataGovernancePlan.pdf.

# Part II

# The Collaborative Domains

# Chapter 5

# Data Governance

One might suspect that data governance (DG) is a straightforward concept and would be easy for an organization to implement. Why would it not be? The two words almost define the concept itself. After all, governing is about setting strategy, policies, and rules and establishing structures to enforce these. In this case, governance is applied to data. But there is more to this term than is apparent; the definition of DG is subjective, and DG is not so easy for organizations to implement.

Over the past decade or so, DG has received a lot of buzz in popular business magazines and blogs and is a favorite topic at meetings and conventions associated with management information systems. More recently, it has been given a lot of hype in healthcare as the industry struggles with the bombardment of digital information and regulatory reporting requirements. Service companies, consultants, and vendors have latched onto the term, but the divergence of thought on DG sometimes makes the concept and its implementation tough to pin down. Fortunately, several professional organizations and academic researchers are treating DG with the respect it deserves and are helping to develop a roadmap for developing sound principles and practices for DG in healthcare. The focus of this chapter is to help clarify the concept of DG, provide approaches for applying DG, and suggest best practices for establishing a DG effort in a healthcare environment. Specifically, this chapter covers topics that can help you:

- Explain DG concepts
- Assess the benefits of DG
- Apply DG frameworks and approaches
- Analyze case studies in applying DG

## The St. Rita's Healthcare System Case Study

Val convened an early morning team meeting to flesh out the specifics of each EIM domain. "Where should we start?" Val asked.

The team pondered Val's question. "We should probably begin with DG, which is the central and most critical domain," Linda offered.

Several team members questioned Linda's statement about DG. "Why do you think DG is the most critical EIM domain?" probed Shirlee.

"DG provides the framework for the standards and the accountability structure for management of the data asset. DG is like glue that holds all the pieces of EIM in place. It allows for the efficient coordination of EIM domains," Linda responded.

"OK, I get it," said Monte. "Let's use the metaphor of a city. A city has many functions like supplying clean water, and providing well-maintained roads, sewers, fire protection, and libraries. But, municipalities can't effectively provide these services unless there are policies, procedures, and standards in place to get things done, and a way of assigning accountability for and monitoring these activities to make sure they are running appropriately."

The team thought through Monte's example and continued their discussion. Some thought data architecture was the foundational domain. Without good architecture nothing would work, they argued. Others felt data quality management was the lynch pin. Without data quality, it didn't matter how well systems functioned from a technical viewpoint. However, the more they discussed the issue, the more they kept circling back to DG being the key organizing domain. Given their discussion, the team agreed that DG was the overarching responsibility. They concurred that while all the other domains were central to quality data, without coordination, they would not achieve the benefits of the functions within these domains. The team decided that DG serves as the central command for all other EIM domains and that they should study it first. Shirlee and Bob volunteered to put together a report on DG and how they might implement it at St. Rita's.

## Data Governance Definitions and Concepts

Views about DG vary and the domain has been defined by various authorities in different ways. Some say DG consists of the management of a broad spectrum of data domains (DAMA 2010). Others view DG as a strategic domain concerned with who should hold decision rights and be held accountable for an organization's decision making about data assets (Kathari and Brown 2010). Definitions vary from solely presenting the "what" aspects of DG to those that include the "how" and "why." The variety of definitions is partly due to the emergence of DG as a new field and to the fact that it is "an industry-led discipline, which can mean that vendors tend to use definitions that focus on the 'what' and 'why' aspects that best match the product or services being promoted" (Berg and Caira 2012, 5). Vendors and others often use the terms DG and information governance interchangeably in popular literature. There is a detailed discussion of the differences between the two in the introduction to this text.

Below are a few examples that illustrate the variety of DG definitions:

- DG is the organization and implementation of policies, procedures, structures, roles, and responsibilities which outline and enforce rules of engagement, decision rights, and accountabilities for the effective management of information assets (Ladley 2010, 115).
- DG is the exercise of authority and control (planning, monitoring, and enforcement) over the management of data assets (DAMA 2010, 37).
- DG is a system of decision rights and accountabilities for information-related processes, executed according to agreed-upon models which describe who can take what actions with what information, when and under what circumstances, and using what methods (Data Governance Institute 2013).
- DG is a quality control discipline for adding new rigor and discipline to the process of managing, using, improving, and protecting organizational information (IBM Data Governance Maturity Model 2007).
- DG is the exercise of authority and control over the management of data assets across an entire enterprise (Reeves and Bowen 2013).
- DG is the formal orchestration of people, processes, and technology to enable an organization to leverage data as an enterprise asset (CDI Institute 2006).
- DG refers to who holds the decision rights and is held accountable for an organization's decision making about its data assets (Kathari and Brown 2010).
- DG is a framework of rights and accountabilities that ensures effective information asset management (Kloss 2013).
- DG specifies the framework for decision rights and accountabilities to encourage desirable behavior in the use of data. To promote desirable behavior, DG develops and implements corporate-wide data polices, guidelines, and standards that are consistent with the organization's mission, strategy, values, norms, and culture (Weber et al. 2009, 4).

While the definitions vary, there are several core concepts. These include:

- Creating enterprise-level authority and accountability for effective data asset management
- Establishing and monitoring data policies, standards, practices, decision rights, and accountabilities for managing, using, improving, and protecting organizational information corporate data
- Executing policies, standards, and practices through formal structures, roles, and responsibilities

Given these concepts, this is a working definition of DG in this text: DG is the enterprise authority that ensures control and accountability for enterprise data through the establishment of decision rights and data policies and standards that are implemented and monitored through a formal structure of assigned roles, responsibilities, and accountabilities.

DG is cross-functional. This means DG policies and procedures, like human and financial policies and procedures, cut across departmental boundaries impacting all organizational departments. Because data flow throughout an organization and do not stop at departmental boundaries, a system must be in place that defines who can take what action with what data, when they can take those actions, under what circumstances, and what methods they can use. This set of actions is normally referred to as **data decision rights and accountabilities**.

To understand how DG compares to the governance of other organizational assets, we can look at how companies govern and leverage human resources. Companies have a system for managing human capital (for example, employees, contractors, and consultants) to increase productivity, comply with regulations, achieve competitive advantage, recruit and maintain a qualified workforce, ensure fair treatment practices, and increase employee satisfaction, among other goals. To accomplish these goals, companies use a framework for establishing standards, policies, procedures, and accountabilities that span the entire organization. Each organizational department and unit must adopt and comply with a common set of human resource policies. In some instances, organizational units may be given special directives tailored to meet their needs. Many times, however, implementation of policy depends on the individual unit. For example, there may be an organizational policy that each new employee receives an orientation to their department on the first day of work. Unit managers may be responsible for the orientation content and how they deliver it.

DG works in a similar way to the human resource analogy. Companies recognize that data are important assets and, like human assets, they want to leverage data to improve the business. DG goals might include increasing the bottom line, productivity, and value, improving decision making, managing cost and complexity, reducing risk and vulnerability, ensuring security and privacy, or complying with regulations. In healthcare, some of the supporting arguments for DG may include:

- Ensuring data integrity to support and improve patient care, business functions, business intelligence, and decision making
- Coordinating and improving access to and protecting sensitive data
- Facilitating data integration and reducing data silos
- Establishing and maintaining a consistent set of business and clinical definitions, clinical terminology, and metadata
- Facilitating seamless exchange of patient data for patient care and health information exchange
- Adhering to compliance and reporting regulations

Like human resource governance, policies, standards, and procedures would be in place at an enterprise level to govern data, but in some cases each department may decide how it implements them. For example, the content of training for data management may be different between employees working in the patient registration department and those working in an HIM department.

## The Case for Data Governance

The case for DG is compelling if we look at the degree to which business processes are dependent on access to good data. The relationship can be framed in the following way: inaccurate data leads to rework, reducing efficiency; incomplete data leads to wasted time in finding missing data, lengthening process cycle time; without timely and quality data, normal business processes break down; late data leads to idle resources, reducing utilization, slowing processes, and increasing costs (Chen 2010).

Looking at the data problems cited in chapter 1, the case for improved data quality and its impact on multiple business and patient care processes at healthcare facilities like St. Rita's could be framed in the following way:

- Duplicate data leads to rework, additional expense, and slows down productivity.
- Discrepancies in data lead to poor executive, operational, and patient care decision making.
- Incomplete data contribute to poor patient care and increase costs.

- Data silos and fragmented data inhibit data integration and sharing, slowing down business processes.
- Conflicting data definitions inhibit business intelligence, performance management, and predictive analyses.
- Incomplete and inaccurate data and data silos have an adverse impact on revenue flow, direct patient care, and the continuum of patient care.

A **business case** is the desired outcome or benefit of implementing or changing a process, activity, or enabling stakeholder interactions. Linking DG to improving business processes helps to make the business case. The impact of DG goes beyond data quality. Ultimately, DG is about providing quality data to support business processes, decisions, and stakeholder interactions. This means the vision, business case, and goals for DG must represent the business opportunity along with the data opportunity (Karel 2012).

One might propose DG as a business case for St. Rita's by stating that it will:

- Improve processes and productivity by reducing rework and increasing efficiency
- Reduce organizational risk by providing better data for patient care and decision making
- Improve revenue flow by integrating and improving timely access and distribution of quality data
- Improve business intelligence, performance management, and predictive analyses for patient care and competitive advantage

The business case and goals for DG provide the foundation for the DG mission, what policies and procedures are developed, and how they are implemented by the organization.

# Data Governance Frameworks and Methodologies

How does a healthcare organization implement DG? DG implementation is contingent on several factors. Among these are the organization's size, culture, strategic goals, business priorities, budget, and the specific objectives of the DG program. One of the most influential factors, however, is the framework or methodology the organization chooses to guide the DG program.

A **framework** is a real or conceptual structure that organizes a system or concept. The Data Governance Institute defines a framework as "a logical structure for classifying, organizing, and communicating complex activities involved in making decisions about and taking action on enterprise data" (DGI 2014).

Usually, someone uses a framework to help outline, guide, or build something. A framework typically describes and shows the synergy and interrelation among the different parts of an approach. Similarly, a methodology organizes a set of principles or rules that describe how to approach something. A professional organization, company, or individuals may develop frameworks. Usually, those developed by a company support their own business service lines, are not available to the public, and are called **proprietary frameworks**. Some may be offered as an **open source framework,** which is typically the product of academic or other research and is offered free for public use. Professional organizations, like the American Health Information Management Association (AHIMA) and Data Management Association (DAMA), usually develop frameworks to educate the public and put forward best practices. The following sections discuss examples of frameworks in each of these categories.

## Method for an Integrated Knowledge Environment (MIKE2.0)

**Method for an Integrated Knowledge Environment (MIKE2.0)** is an open source and comprehensive methodology for EIM. A management and technology consulting company originally developed the methodology, which they based on the experiences of information management professionals around the world in a variety of projects. MIKE2.0 complies with open source concepts; access to the methodology and its use is available to anyone. MIKE2.0 embraces continual enhancement and development that incorporates the concepts of user-generated content. MIKE2.0 information management includes six core information management solutions:

- Business intelligence
- Enterprise data management
- Access, search, and delivery
- Enterprise content management
- Information asset management
- Information management strategy, architecture, and governance (MIKE2.0 Methodology)

The governance domain is divided into six components (as shown in figure 5.1). Each of these is described in the sections following the figure.

Figure 5.1. MIKE 2.0 framework

| | | | | |
|---|---|---|---|---|
| Sponsorship and Scope | Executive Sponsors | Program Scope | Data Stewards | |
| Organization | Governance Council | Governance Team | Resources | Communication Plan |
| Policies | IM Guiding Principles | Best Practices | Industry Standards | |
| Processes | Analysis | Monitoring | Reporting | |
| Investigation and Monitoring | Data Profiling | Metrics | Resolved Data Issues | |
| Technology and Architecture | Compliance with Standards | | | |

Source: Adapted from MIKE2.0 Methodology.

## Sponsorship and Scope

The sponsorship and scope component sets the strategy for the governance program. Typically, this includes establishing the program's mission, charter, strategic goals, and alignment of the program with the strategic objectives, priorities, and business imperatives of the organization. Governance is only effective if it has executive sponsorship. Executive sponsors are individuals holding an executive position in the organization, such as those at a vice-presidential or higher level. Executive sponsors are critical because they can allocate resources, have policy making responsibility and authority, can link DG to specific organization initiatives, and have the necessary influence with management teams to ensure accountability. Executive sponsors may come from business, clinical, or technology areas, and the sponsor would allocate initial resources for the program. Key data or subject areas (business units) to be included in the program scope would be identified by the DG council, and data stewards assigned to manage each key data area. **Data stewards** serve as the bridge between information technology (IT) and business and clinical areas. They are responsible for tasks such as data definition and information quality activities and take responsibility for specific subject data elements as professionals use them across the organization.

## Governance Organization

The governance program requires a formal organizational structure and operating plan to be effective. The organization must establish a high-level **governance council**, sometimes called a data governance board, which is responsible for championing DG initiatives, and developing and overseeing the governance plan. The council should be cross-functional, drawing its members from a variety of functional groups in the organization.

The council should have representation from those in executive and high-level management positions. Ultimately, the council has the final authority in approving governance policies. Data stewards, as part of the DG team, may also be part of the council. In some organizations, there is a separate committee composed of data stewards that drafts initial policies, advises, and reports to the governance council.

Business units or lines of business, who are the generators and users of the data, are considered data owners. Typically, the roles of data owners in the DG organization include:

- Having overall responsibility for the maintenance and quality of the data
- Establishing policies for controlling and granting access to users and other governance determinations

- Determining what data the organization needs to capture (for example, requirements for data, how data is made available, and how data owners will use it)
- Acting as a subject matter expert (SME), as needed
- Approving data standards, definitions for key business rules, and data quality rules in their area of responsibility (MIKE2.0 Methodology)

A governance office or a support team facilitates and coordinates efforts of the council, data stewards, and data owners. It usually is headed by a governance office director and includes a support staff.

Identifying specific responsibilities of each of the above players, as well as developing reporting and other communication channels, and allocating resources is part of establishing the governance organization.

## Governance Policies

Meeting the strategic and tactical objectives of the data governance program requires governance policies. **Policies** are developed by the governance council based on the information management guiding principles adopted by the organization, best practices, industry standards, and the processes to be supported.

Policies can be strategic or tactical. Strategic policies support high-level imperatives of the organization and are guiding principles, whereas tactical policies explain how to put strategic policies into operation. Strategic policies should be developed first, followed by tactical policies. Policies will typically cover topics such as data ownership, data access and security, data retention, data quality and monitoring, and key data element definitions. The following are examples of strategic policies followed by supporting tactical policies.

Example 1

- *Strategic Policy:* DG is a shared organizational responsibility.
- *Tactical Policy:* The data governance council is responsible for defining the roles, responsibilities, and accountabilities for data stewards, data custodians, data owners, and data users.

Example 2

- *Strategic Policy:* Data are a key corporate asset.
- *Tactical Policy:* The DG office is responsible for maintaining a directory of all data assets.

The strategic and tactical policies above are both based on industry best practices. For instance, the policy reflected in example 1 is based on industry best practices that view data governance as a collaborative function and is best exercised by establishing a data governance council that has responsibility, authority, and accountability for defining DG roles. In example 2, best practice is that the organization view data as a corporate asset, and one aspect of protecting the asset is to maintain a directory of all data assets.

Standards support the implementation of organizational policy. Standards may be institutional, industry-specific, or prescribed by accreditation bodies, government agencies, or regulation. Example 3 below demonstrates how organizational standards (rules) are incorporated with organizational policy based on a data classification model (University of Miami 2008).

Example 3

- *Strategic Policy*: Data users are permitted by organization policy to view or query St. Rita's databases for all legitimate health organization purposes in fulfillment of their job responsibilities and are subject to data classification rules and relevant state and federal laws.
- *Tactical Policy*: Data stewards assign each data element and each data view in databases under their authority to one of four categories: confidential, private, public, or sensitive data.
- ***Standard*:** Private, confidential, public, and sensitive data are defined as follows:
  - Confidential data: Data covered by state or federal legislation such as the Health Insurance Portability and Accountability Act, the Family Education Rights and Privacy Act, or is legally covered by contract. Disclosure may have a serious and negative impact on a healthcare facility. Examples of confidential data include all patient protected health information, Social Security numbers, financial, employee, and personal information, and credit card numbers.
  - Private data: Unless otherwise designated, all organizational data are considered private and restricted to the proprietary use by authorized individuals to carry out the organization's business. Disclosure of this data may obstruct operations of the organization. Examples include data about financial transactions, salaries, and employee data.
  - Sensitive data: Sensitive data are for internal use only due to the proprietary nature of the data or for ethical or confidential reasons. Examples include internal reports, meeting minutes, and project reports.
  - Public data: Public data have no access restrictions whatsoever. Examples include data such as physical organization address, organization contact data including phone numbers of organizational departments and divisions, press releases, and websites.

### Governance Processes

Organizations put policies into operation through processes and procedures. These may include analysis, monitoring, and reporting processes and procedures. Governance processes may also include establishing metrics and specific functions that need to be performed, such as establishing a process that monitors the quality of the master patient index (MPI) and provides solutions for improvement.

### Data Investigation and Monitoring

The data investigation and monitoring component focuses on establishing and monitoring data quality metrics and the use of best practices and data standards. A principal function is to conduct data profiling. Data profiling is typically carried out by a cross-functional team of data stewards or custodians who use statistical analysis and algorithms that identify and resolve data quality issues. An example of data profiling is monitoring an MPI to identify duplicate medical record numbers or inconsistency in MPI data.

### Technology and Architecture

The DG team needs to work closely with IT to ensure they are meeting common data standards, and employing and implementing appropriate technology and data architecture so they are meeting the organization's data needs. This may include practices for developing and maintaining data models (chapter 6) or selecting technology and designing architecture for a metadata repository (chapter 7).

## Data Governance Institute Framework

The Data Governance Institute (DGI) framework has several similarities with the MIKE2.0 framework. Both frameworks address the need for high-level sponsorship, definition of program scope, establishment of an organizational structure, and development and implementation of policies, standards, and monitoring procedures. The DGI framework uses terminology and a blueprint that is more closely associated with organizational management and behavior as opposed to the more operations-management-centric MIKE2.0 framework. The DGI framework consists of ten universal components organized into three overarching segments (Data Governance Institute 2014). These include rules and rules of engagement, people and organizational bodies, and processes which are described below, followed by details of the DG life cycle.

### Rules and Rules of Engagement

Examples of **rules** are policies, requirements, standards, accountabilities, controls, and data definitions. **Rules of engagement** are the way that stakeholders (policy makers, data owners, data stewards, and so on) interact with each other. The following are the components of this category.

#### Mission

The **mission statement** is the first rule of engagement. A mission statement is essential so that all stakeholders understand and agree to what they need to accomplish. The mission statement helps unify and motivate stakeholders, keeps goals in the forefront, and holds the organization accountable for achieving the goals. Examples of DG mission statements are in figures 5.2 and 5.3.

Figure 5.2. Sample data governance program mission statement

The mission of the data governance program is to provide leadership in managing data as an enterprise asset, ensuring access to high quality data in meeting the organization's operational and strategic needs. Our mission is accomplished by:

- Coordinating an enterprise-wide governance structure with authority and responsibility for managing the organization's data assets
- Establishing an enterprise-wide data strategy
- Developing and approving data management policies, procedures, and standards
- Communicating, monitoring, and enforcing data policies and standards
- Ensuring organizational and regulatory compliance
- Resolving data issues to maximize the value of data to the organization

Figure 5.3. Wichita State University data governance mission to strategic priorities

**Wichita State University Data Governance Mission to Strategic Priorities**
Several managed data systems exist which the university community can use to inform decision making, planning, and reporting. The mission of the Data Governance Council (DGC) is to provide oversight to these data systems to ensure data integrity, best practices in data management, reporting standards, information consistency, and security access. In addition, the DGC is responsible for identifying data and reporting needs related to strategic planning priorities and the sharing of business knowledge across divisions to ensure data and reporting optimization related to the latest business practices within units. The DGC provides compliance with the Higher Learning Commission (HLC) requirements related to institutional data used for accreditation.

Source: Wichita State University 2014.

### Goals, Governance Metrics and Success Measures, and Funding Strategies

Goals, governance metrics and success measures are a second category in the rules of engagement. Setting goals and fulfilling them is essential to achieving a mission. A mission without goals is a "mission impossible." Goals should be SMART: specific, measureable, attainable, realistic, and time-related. Goals such as "Increase data quality," or "Keep patient information safe" would not be considered SMART goals because there are no metrics or success factors one can measure. To change them into SMART goals one would set measurable standards, such as

- At any given time, the number of duplicate records in the MPI will not exceed .05 percent
- At any given time, 100 percent of all systems have anti-virus tools installed and enabled

The examples above meet SMART goal criteria. Each is specific, measurable, attainable, realistic, and time-related.

All programs require funding to support them. Funding of a DG program depends upon the organization's structure and the DG program's scope, mission, and goals. Strategies for funding can range from budget support for a stand-alone unit, inclusion as a line item in project budgets, to charge-back to business units, to being included in departmental IT budgets.

### Data Rules and Definitions

Data rules and definitions are the third component of the rules of engagement. At its basic level, DG entails policy development, implementation, and enforcement. Typically, a DG program will include the following:

- Policies on data availability, access accountability and ownership that clarify who is accountable for the quality and security of critical data
- Specific roles and responsibilities of data committees, data stewards, and data custodians
- Established data capture and validation standards and reference data rules
- Data access and usage rules
- Security standards; privacy rules; and master data, meta data, data definition, and data model standards

### Decision Rights

Who has the authority to make data-related decisions, when they make them, and how they make them is called **decision rights**. Assigning decision rights is a critical part of the rules of engagement. Organizations must clearly define decision rights to avoid conflict and inconsistencies. For example, decision rights establish who has authority to develop policies about data management, define a data element, determine the length of a data field, determine data modeling notation, or determine what group or persons have access to data.

### Accountabilities

Accountability for policy development and implementation, and continuing processes is an important aspect of the rules of engagement. The organization needs to consider who does what, when, and why. For example, when a security breach occurs, who is responsible for the response, what must they do, and when must they do it? Or, when the organization requires the capture of new data elements, it must be clear who is responsible for data definition, what must they do, and when must it be done.

### Controls

Establishing controls is the final component of the rules of engagement in the DGI framework. **Controls** are measures and functionality established for the purpose of preventing and mitigating risks. Data are at risk at every point of the data life cycle. For example, during data capture, data are at risk for being incorrect or incomplete. Controls put in place by the organization at this stage may include forced field completion, use of pre-defined lists, and automatic edit checks. Controls for the access and distribution stage may include implementing role-based access. Clearly stating who has the responsibility for specifying, designing, implementing, and performing data-related controls is a responsibility of the DG program.

## People and Organizational Bodies

The people and organizational bodies segment of the DGI framework is concerned with identifying who the stakeholders of the DG framework are, who is responsible for DG operations, who the DG decision makers are, and who is responsible for implementing DG policy. Individuals and groups involved in making, enforcing, and implementing rules are data stakeholders, data stewards, and the governance council.

### Data Stakeholders

**Data stakeholders** are those who have an interest or stake in organizational data. This includes individuals and business units who gather, compile, track, use, or are responsible for organizational data. It is almost impossible to think of any category of organization worker or business unit who would not be a data stakeholder. Among obvious internal stakeholders are executive and senior management, line of business units, service units, and information technology groups. External stakeholders include patients, public health and state and federal governmental agencies, other healthcare providers, and vendors.

Understanding stakeholder needs is one of the most important functions of DG. Conducting a formal stakeholder analysis is a useful method for identifying key data stakeholders. The scope of the analysis depends on the mission and scope of the DG program and the specific project undertaken by the DG team. The analysis should evaluate the stakeholders' level of influence such as decision maker, policy maker, auditor, or user; stakeholder role in data creation, transformation, and use; data used and processes supported; and interactions with other stakeholder groups (Sharpe et al. 1999).

The organization should identify a representative of each key stakeholder group as a liaison between the group and the DG program. Frequently, these individuals serve as part of the DG data steward council or on a DG project team.

### Data Stewards

There are several definitions of a data steward, but the central concepts include responsibility and accountability for data. In the context of DG, **data stewardship** is a formalization of accountability. One may view data stewardship as a continuum of stewardship responsibilities across the data life cycle and across the enterprise carried out by a network of data stewards. The way organizations formalize the stewardship function varies. Some organizations elect to have hierarchies of data stewards that have different levels of power and responsibilities. Others organize the function based on DG initiatives while some have designated data stewards as tactical teams throughout the organization.

Data stewards are individuals who are responsible for a number of data management tasks, some of which may include but are not limited to development of data definitions, data issue resolution, data quality monitoring, testing and approval of data security, data compliance, and data modeling. "The data steward's role is to ensure that adequate, agreed-upon quality metrics are maintained on a continuous basis" (Berson and Dubov 2011, 116).

Data stewards are typically designated throughout the enterprise, within business units and IT. The categories of data stewards identified in the DGI framework are:

- Subject matter managers within business areas who have a high level of accountability for the management of the data, but not necessarily the day-to-day hands-on responsibilities.
- Data definition stewards who function in a business, as opposed to a technical role. Major responsibilities include identifying the specific data needed to operate business processes, recording business definitions and metadata, identifying and enforcing quality standards, communicating data issue concerns, and communicating new or changed business requirements.
- Data production stewards who can be either in a business or technical role and are responsible for inserting, updating, and deleting business and technical data in IT systems, validating data that enters and exits business processes, and coding and editing data quality standards such as format and content, and communicating data issue concerns and new or changed business requirements.
- Data usage stewards who are data users who access and use data for its intended purpose, access information about the data (metadata), ensure the quality, completeness, and accuracy of data usage, and communicate data issue concerns, and new or changed business requirements (Steiner 2005).

### Data Governance Office (DGO)

A DG program cannot be coordinated without a dedicated support staff. Most DG efforts are supported by a **data governance office** (DGO). Among the responsibilities of the office are:

- Providing centralized communication and archives for DG initiatives
- Working with stakeholders
- Coordinating DG initiatives
- Facilitating and coordinating data steward committees, task forces, and meetings
- Supporting the data governance council
- Collecting and analyzing DG metrics

Staff support required for the DG program depends upon the size of the organization and scope and structure of the DG program. In many cases, the DGO is headed by a DG officer who may have additional staff to support DG activities.

## Data Governance Processes

DG processes and rules for governing data and coordinating the DG program make up the final component of the DGI framework. Processes and rules contain steps and methods that data stewards follow to govern data and ensure compliance. Processes can be proactive, reactive, or ongoing. The following twelve processes are considered DG best practices and processes and should be incorporated into any DG program.

- Aligning policies, requirements, and controls
- Establishing decision rights
- Establishing accountability
- Performing stewardship
- Managing change
- Defining data
- Resolving data issues
- Specifying data quality requirements
- Building governance into technology
- Providing stakeholder care
- Communications and program reporting
- Measuring and reporting value (Thomas 2014)

## DGI Data Governance Life Cycle

The DGI framework is accompanied by a roadmap to assist in implementing the framework. This is referred to as the DG life cycle. The DGI framework goes beyond the what and why of DG and suggests a seven-step life cycle for how to implement its framework:

1. Develop a value statement
2. Prepare a program roadmap
3. Plan and fund
4. Design the program
5. Deploy the program
6. Govern the data
7. Monitor, measure, and report (Thomas 2014)

### Value Statement Development

The first step is to develop a value statement. The value statement is the business case that describes and substantiates the reasons for a DG program and enumerates the desired outcomes and benefits to be achieved. Executive management support for a DG program will hinge on the belief that the program supports organizational objectives and provides value to the organization. Examples of business case statements are cited earlier in this chapter. The DGI suggests doing an "A-B-C" approach for developing value cases: if we do A, then we can expect B, which should lead to C. Examples using this format for data issues might look like the following:

- If we reduce duplicate records in our MPI, then we will reduce clinical and administrative errors, which should lead to better patient care.

- If we improve the integration of our data, then we will increase our efficiency, which should lead to lower costs and faster efficiency.
- If we establish an organization-wide data dictionary, then we will have better interoperability among different information systems, which should lead to better and faster clinical and administrative decision making.

**Program Roadmap Preparation**

Once the business case is made and executive support is received, the next step is to prepare a **program roadmap**. DG can be an overwhelming endeavor. Therefore, organizations usually start by focusing their program on a specific area or a specific activity. For example, some organizations may focus on developing policies and standards for a specific initiative, such as customer relationship management. Other programs may focus on privacy, compliance, and security. Still others may focus on data quality, business intelligence, or architecture integration. It is best to start the program in small steps that have a chance for success and that bring immediate value to the organization. A DG program based on the value statements enumerated above may initially take the form of focusing on enterprise master data, architecture integration, or development of an enterprise data dictionary.

**Plan and Fund the DG Program**

When direction of the DG program has been agreed upon, planning and funding for program execution takes place. This includes determining what people and organizational bodies will be included or created and how the organization chart will look. What will the authority, responsibility, and accountability lines be? What form will a DG office take? And, how much funding will the program require for the first five years?

**Design, Deploy, and Govern the DG Program**

Designing, deploying, and governing the DG program are dependent upon establishing the rules of engagement, organizational bodies, and developing and implementing the processes described in the DGI framework. The DGI framework suggests that DG programs may have different focuses. The DGI framework suggests the following focus areas:

- Policies, standards, and strategy
- Data quality
- Privacy, compliance, and security
- Architecture and integration
- Data warehouses and business intelligence
- Management support (Thomas 2014)

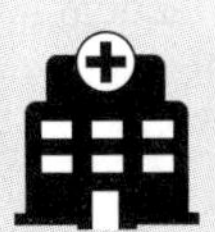

## The St. Rita's Healthcare System Case Study

"My head is swimming," said Linda after reading Shirlee and Bob's report to the team on the MIKE2.0 and DGI frameworks.

"I'm having trouble getting my head around it, too," added Denise.

"Let's bottom line it," suggested team leader Val. "Without all the jargon, what's the end result here?" she asked.

"We anticipated this," Shirlee responded, "so we prepared some bullet points to summarize what we've found so far. The bottom line is this:

- DG varies from organization to organization. There is no one-size-fits-all DG program.
- DG requires executive support and a business case to get that support.
- DG usually focuses on business imperatives, prioritizes its initiatives, and doesn't attempt to do everything at once.
- DG requires a formal organization to support its activities. The organization is usually hierarchical, including a DG council and data stewards.
- DG requires a support staff to facilitate and coordinate DG activities, communication, and support formal DG teams, councils, and committees. Typically this is a DG office."

The team spent the next 30 minutes discussing the significance of the bullet points before Val asked: "Are these the only DG models?"

"Not on your life," Bob responded. "We found at least a half-dozen more." The team groaned, thinking of the details they have yet to review.

"How about a review of a few more models," said Val. "We need to be thorough in our investigation because we'll be making our choices for governance based on this data. We will be living with these decisions for a long time. Shirlee and Bob, can you review and select the methodologies you think are the most representative in the DG field and report back to us at our next meeting? A matrix of each method's components and their similarities might be helpful."

With that directive Shirlee and Bob got down to work.

## Data Management Association Framework

DAMA views DG as a collaborative effort that is most effective as an ongoing program and is the heart of managing enterprise data assets. In the DAMA framework, nine functions are considered essential to managing data (chapter 3).

The DAMA framework supports the principle that DG decisions span the enterprise from decisions made by business management to those made by IT management. Some decisions are primarily made by business management while others are made by IT. For example, the DG model to be used, identification of business needs, data quality requirements, and data issue resolutions are decisions made by business management or stewards. On the other hand, technical decisions are made by IT. Some examples include decisions about database architecture, data integration architecture, and metadata architecture. For example, decisions about a database architecture include, among other considerations, the type of database management system (DBMS) used, how to structure the internal database schema, what file structures will be used in the database, and what indexes will be developed for the database. The technical decisions are based on business management decisions such as outcome of requirements analysis, logical data models, and needs of end users for searching, retrieving, and using data.

In this framework, DG is a shared responsibility supported by two groups: data stewards and data management services. **Data management services** are those normally considered IT roles such as data architects, data analysts, database administrators, data integration specialists, and business intelligence specialists. Both groups work together in carrying out DG initiatives.

DAMA specifies three types of data stewards: executive, coordinating, and business. **Executive data stewards** are senior managers who serve on a data governance council and who are responsible for high-level decision making, including the sign-off on all DG policies. **Coordinating stewards** lead and represent teams of business data stewards. They serve on a data steward coordinating committee, serve as advisors to the data governance council, and work on tactical teams to draft policy, develop standards, resolve data issues, and coordinate DG implementation. **Business stewards** are recognized subject matter experts. They work with data management professionals on an ongoing basis to define and control data and may serve on data steward teams. The following explains the organizational structure of this framework.

- The data governance council has enterprise-wide authority over data management. It is composed of executive data stewards and has responsibility for setting policies, standards, architecture, and resolving data issues.
- The data stewardship program steering committees support the data governance council, draft policies and standards for review and approval by the data governance council, and oversee specific, sponsored initiatives.
- Data stewardship teams are standing, permanent groups that meet regularly and are composed of business data stewards that collaborate on data stewardship activities within a defined subject area. These teams bring together subject matter experts from across the organization to determine data names, definitions, data quality requirements, and business rules and work closely with data architects (DAMA 2010, 42).

In this framework, DG is supported by a DGO and a data management executive, similar to the MIKE2.0 and DGI frameworks. The responsibility of the DGO is to support the data stewardship committees and teams. Like the DGI framework, the DAMA framework emphasizes that the scope of DG depends upon the organization. In some organizations DG may take on a broad scope, others a more focused one aimed at a specific initiative. Below are examples of the variety of scope and related activities that an organization may target for its DG program.

- Data strategy and policy: defining, communicating, and monitoring
- Data standards and architecture: reviewing, approving, and monitoring
- Regulatory compliance: communicating, monitoring, and enforcing

- Issue management: identifying, defining, escalating, and resolving
- Data management projects: sponsoring and overseeing
- Data asset valuation: estimating, approving, and monitoring
- Communication: promoting and building awareness and appreciation (DAMA 2010, 41)

Figure 5.4 provides a blueprint of the organizational structure that a DG program might have using the DAMA framework. This example shows the supporting and reporting relationship of the DGO to the data governance council. It also shows several data stewardship program coordinating committees. The focus of these committees will depend upon the mission and goals of the DG program. For instance, one may focus on regulatory compliance, another on data standards and architecture, and another on issue management. The teams below each of the coordinating committees are likely teams focusing on specific business or subject areas.

Figure 5.4. Example of the DAMA framework DG organizational structure

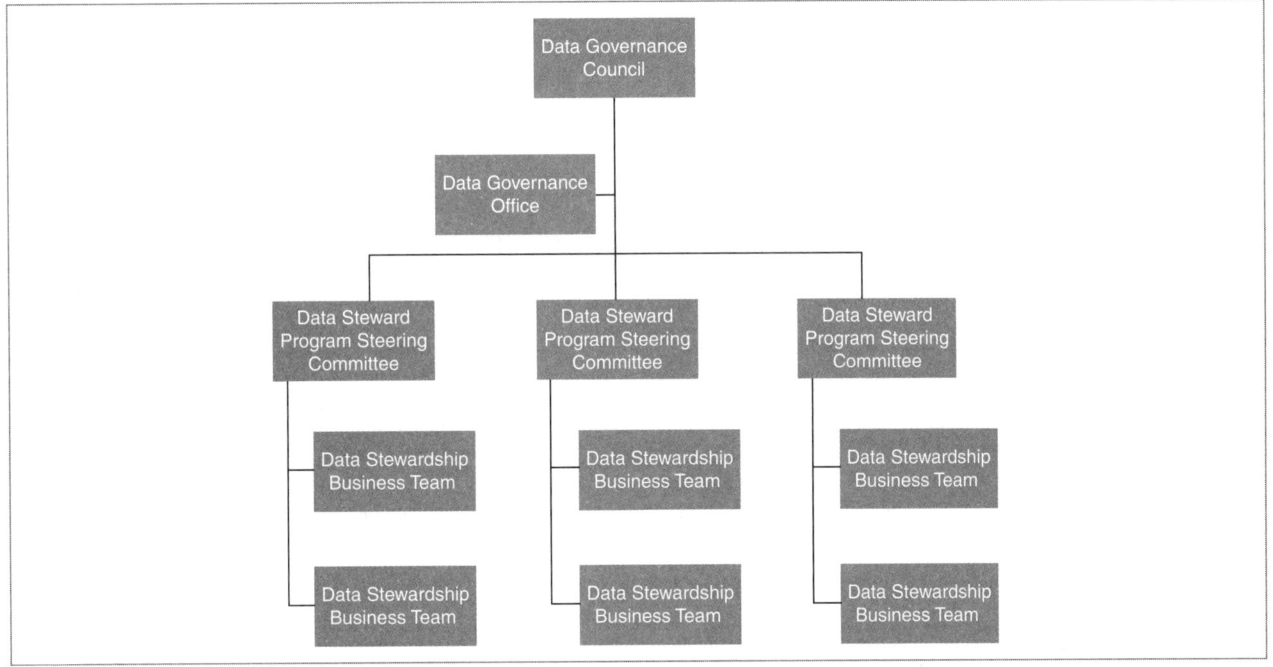




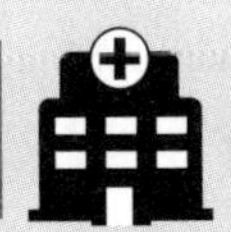

## The St. Rita's Healthcare System Case Study

Bob and Shirlee met for early morning coffee in the hospital cafeteria. "It looks like we've covered a lot of ground," said Shirlee. "When I analyzed the three DG frameworks we've studied, I would say there are more similarities than differences among them. What do you think, Bob?"

Bob stirred an extra packet of sugar in his coffee, processing what Shirlee said. "I agree with your assessment. There are some differences in scope and approach, but essentially the goals are the same."

"Our next step," said Shirlee "is to look at some proprietary and research models."

"Exactly what is the difference between the two?" asked Bob.

"Proprietary models, " Shirlee began, "are typically developed by and implemented within a company or developed under the sponsorship of a company sometimes bringing together a group of thought leaders. In either of these ways, there usually is an implementation track record which mirrors real life."

"Hmmm," pondered Bob. "And what is your opinion about research models? Research models sound a little abstract to me," he added.

"Don't let the word 'research' scare you off. Research models can be extremely useful because they are usually based on data about the real world. The data can consist of case studies, quantitative data, or both. The researcher analyzes the data and develops a model that approximates real world operation. Because of the methods used, research models often times uncover nuances and other information that isn't obvious."

"OK, with that explanation," responded Bob, "I can see the usefulness in exploring both of these models. It will be interesting to see if they are similar to the ones we've already studied." Finishing up their cups of coffee, Bob agreed to check out proprietary frameworks and Shirlee volunteered to look at models developed by researchers in the academic community. They agreed to meet up the next morning and compare their results.

## IBM Data Governance Council Framework and Maturity Model

The IBM Data Governance Council Framework and Maturity model is a proprietary framework consisting of eleven core elements. These are arranged in four categories: outcomes, enablers, core disciplines, and supporting disciplines (IBM 2007, 8-10). Table 5.1 provides a listing and description of each.

Table 5.1. IBM data governance council framework core elements

| Categories | Core Elements |
|---|---|
| Outcomes | 1. Value Creation: Processes that help the organization to maximize the value of its data |
| | 2. Data Risk Management and Compliance: Methods and processes used to identify, qualify, quantify, avoid, and mitigate risks and comply with regulatory rules |
| Enablers | 3. Organizational Structures and Awareness: Identifies responsibilities and cooperation for governing data at different levels of management |
| | 4. Policy: Written articulation of desired organizational behavior |
| | 5. Stewardship: Quality control discipline designed to ensure custodial care of data for asset enhancement, risk mitigation, and organizational control |
| Core Disciplines | 6. Data Quality Management: Measuring, improving, and certifying the quality and integrity of production, test, and archival data |
| | 7. Information Life Cycle Management: Policy-based approach to information collection, use, retention, and deletion |
| | 8. Information Security and Privacy: Policies, practices, and controls used to mitigate risk and protect data assets |
| Supporting Disciplines | 9. Data Architecture: Architectural design of structured and unstructured data systems and applications that enable data availability and distribution to appropriate users |
| | 10. Classification and Metadata: Methods and tools used to create common semantic definitions for business and IT terms, data models, types, and repositories |
| | 11. Auditing Information, Logging and Reporting: Processes for monitoring and measuring the data value, risks, and effects of DG |

Source: IBM Data Governance Council 2007.

The IBM framework uses an associated **maturity model**, consisting of five levels, developed by the Software Engineering Institute (SEI). A maturity model describes successive steps of growth and uses these as a yardstick to measure a program's progression from initiation to full maturity or development. Organizations use a maturity model to help prioritize actions and assess their progress in achieving a fully functional and developed program.

The five levels and the associated measurement criteria of the SEI model include:

- *Maturity Level 1: Initial*: Processes are ad hoc and depend more on the competence of individuals rather than on the use of proven and best practices. Organizations at this level often produce products that frequently exceed budget and overrun schedule.
- *Maturity Level 2: Managed*: Successes are often repeated by the organization, but the processes used may not be repeatable for all projects. There is basic project management that helps track costs and schedules.
- *Maturity Level 3: Defined*: There are a set of standard processes, process descriptions, and procedures the organization uses to establish consistency. These are tailored to suit a particular project or organizational unit.
- *Maturity Level 4: Quantitatively Managed*: The organization sets quantitative quality goals for both process and maintenance. It uses statistical and other quantitative techniques to control selected sub-processes.
- *Maturity Level 5: Optimizing*: The organization firmly establishes quantitative process-improvement objectives and methods and revises them to reflect changing business objectives and for use as criteria for process improvement (IBM 2007, 6–7).

Organizations can assess each of the eleven core elements against the maturity model levels to determine how mature their DG program is. The following example provides an overview of how the data quality management core element might be assessed against the maturity model in a healthcare organization.

- *Level 1*: There is no formal high-level data quality assessment in place. Data quality assessments are performed on an ad hoc basis by individual business and service units.
- *Level 2*: The HIM department may have processes in place for measuring data quality of ICD-10 codes, but these processes are not repeatable by other departments.
- *Level 3*: Processes that track the completeness of the clinical record at the time of discharge are regularly reported by the HIM department to senior administration and the medical staff.
- *Level 4*: There are processes and standards in place for how data are entered and accessed by end users in the MPI data, which is a mission-critical system. These processes and standards are repeatable across the enterprise in all departments, and the quality of the MPI is assessed by the HIM department or other accountable group regularly.
- *Level 5*: This level represents a true organizational DG level. Policies and processes are standardized with regular audits and reporting to ensure continuous improvement.

## Oracle Best Practices in Data Governance Framework

The Oracle best practices in data governance framework is a proprietary model and focuses on the goals and outputs of a DG program. It emphasizes that DG is not about performing specific data management tasks such as change management, data cleansing, data warehousing, or database design. Instead, the goals of DG are focused on governance activities such as:

- Defining, approving, and communicating data strategies, policies, standards, architecture, procedures, and metrics
- Tracking and enforcing conformance to data policies, standards, architecture, and procedures
- Sponsoring, tracking, and overseeing the delivery of data management projects and services
- Resolving data-related issues
- Understanding and promoting the value of data assets (Oracle 2011, 5)

Given these goals, the products of a DG program include data policies, data standards, resolved data issues, data quality and data management projects and services, and valuation of core data assets, similar to the other frameworks discussed earlier.

Similar to the DGI and DAMA frameworks, this model emphasizes that the organization determines the specific functions and deliverables of the program. For example, one organization may focus its DG program only on data quality. Another may focus on data security and compliance that involves aligning data security architecture frameworks and initiatives, assessing risk and defining controls to manage risk, and enforcing regulatory and contractual requirements. A multi-focused DG program's activities are broader in scope than a program with one focus.

Like the IBM model, this framework is associated with a maturity model. Oracle's maturity model has six levels, called milestones, similar to those of the IBM model. The Oracle framework suggests a three-phased approach for navigating the maturity model and includes recommended steps in each phase.

The first phase is an exploratory period in which the program is established on a small scale. A goal of this phase is to build a DG foundation and identify and groom DG leaders. One step in this phase is establishing a DG council that has enterprise-wide authority over data management. Associated steps comprise creating a planning document and selecting a DG framework. Organizations should define the mission and vision of the DG program in this phase along with establishing goals, governance metrics, success measures, and securing funding for the program. DG is a big initiative and this framework suggests starting small, with perhaps one focus, project or target area, that provides immediate benefits.

The second phase is expansion of the program. During this phase DG should expand from a local target area to cross-functional business units. This phase might include developing a federated DG organization (data stewards); establishing enterprise-wide data policies, standards, and metrics; and instituting monitoring and reporting.

The third phase is transformation of the organization through DG. In this phase DG becomes business as usual, and is when an enterprise-wide DG program is truly established.

Oracle suggests six best practices for establishing a successful DG program:

- *Take a holistic approach, but start small. DG is an iterative process.* Try to achieve key benefits as soon as possible.
- *Obtain executive sponsorship.* DG has a significant cultural impact. Organizations need funding to support the program and securing strong executive support is essential. Identifying key decision makers in core functional areas and lines of businesses to back and participate in the program is essential for program success.
- *Define data stewardship early.* Find data stewards that include subject matter experts from all business areas. Define the stewardship role and ensure that data stewards have sufficient time allocation for stewardship work.
- *Build a business case.* The executive sponsor must build a business case based on how DG brings value to business processes. Focus on key data and the business processes they support. Calculate the cost of managing these data through repeated and duplicated manual integration and validation and quantify the business risk of unavailable, incomplete, or incorrect data in business transactions.
- *Establish, collect, and report on metrics to measure progress.* The initial goal is to show the benefits of a DG program through quick wins while establishing an approach for long-term benefits.
- *Link and build in incentives to reward performance and maintain engagement.* DG is a collaborative effort and depends upon the commitment of all business units. Building in incentive-based reward systems that link performance to participation helps with sustained commitment. Best practices suggest both formal and informal recognition (Oracle, 2011, 16–17).

## Khatri and Brown DG Framework

The Khatri and Brown DG framework is a research framework that includes five domains for which governance decisions must be made by an organization. The framework differentiates between governance and management. Governance refers to what decisions the organization makes to ensure effective management and use of data, and who makes and is accountable for these decisions. This is in contrast to management which is defined as implementing decisions. As an example, the governance council establishes a policy that standards for data quality are in place across the enterprise and assigns decision rights to subject matter experts and data quality analysts to be accountable for development of those standards. Management is responsible for developing the processes for ensuring the data quality standards are met.

The five decision domains included in this model are:

- Data principles that clarify the role of data as an asset in the organization and define the desirable behaviors of IT professional and business users
- Data quality that establishes the requirements of intended use of data including establishing standards for data quality, evaluation of data quality, and monitoring and reporting of data quality
- Metadata (addressed in chapter 7) that establishes the semantics or content of data, including standards for data definition and modeling of data, so users can interpret it
- Data access that specifies access requirements of data, risk assessment, data access standards and procedures, monitoring and auditing, security awareness and education, and back-up and recovery programs

- Data life cycle that determines the definition, production, retention, and retirement of data including standards for data inventory; programs for data definition, production, retention, and retirement of data; and impact of compliance and legislation issues on data use, storage, and retirement

Table 5.2 provides a guide in determining governance decisions and assigning decision rights based on the Khatri and Brown DG framework.

Table 5.2. **Guide for establishing governance decisions and decision rights with examples**

| Decision Domains | Domain Decisions | Decision Rights |
|---|---|---|
| **Data Principles**<br>Enterprise-wide principles | What are enterprise-wide principles for governing and managing data as an asset?<br>How are these principles communicated? | Data governance council<br>Data stewards |
| **Data Quality**<br>Requirements for data quality | What are data quality policies and standards?<br>How are data quality standards and policies communicated?<br>How are data quality standards enforced?<br>How is data quality monitored?<br>How and to whom is data quality communicated? | Data governance council<br>Data stewards<br>Subject matter experts<br>Data quality analyst |
| **Metadata**<br>Establishing a concise description of the representation of data | What are metadata standards and policies?<br>What metadata must be maintained?<br>How are metadata maintained?<br>How are metadata used?<br>How are metadata modeled? | Data governance council<br>Data architect<br>Data modeler<br>Data stewards |
| **Data Access**<br>Establishing access requirements and permissions | What are data access standards and policies?<br>How is risk assessment, mediation, and control handled?<br>How is data access monitored and audited? | Data governance council<br>Chief security officer<br>Chief privacy officer<br>Data stewards |
| **Data Life Cycle**<br>Governing data throughout its life cycle including definition, creation, retention, and retirement | What are standards for data definition?<br>How are data inventoried?<br>What are standards for requirements analysis?<br>What are standards for retention? | Data architect<br>Data stewards<br>Data analysts |

Source: Adapted from Khatri and Brown 2010.

## Framework for Corporate Data Quality Management

Corporate data quality management, a research based framework, aligns technical aspects of corporate data management with business-related issues and governance and execution practices (Otto et al. 2007). The framework consists of two components, governance and execution, and includes three practices for each.

Data governance practices include:

- Developing a data quality strategy
- Designing a data quality organization
- Designing a data quality architecture

The execution practices include:

- Communicating and controlling the strategy
- Executing and monitoring the processes
- Operating and maintaining the data quality information system architecture

Table 5.3 summarizes each of these practices.

Table 5.3. Framework for corporate data quality

| | Practice | Summary |
|---|---|---|
| **Governance** | | |
| | Develop strategy | Includes strategic objectives aligned with business goals and scope of the data quality program. Baseline assessment of current data quality and data quality issues leads to development of a business case for the program and identification and planning of data quality initiatives and projects. |
| | Design organization | Define roles and responsibilities to ensure accountability, authority, and supervision of data quality. Establish policies, procedures, standards, and metrics. |
| | Design architecture | Develop a common information object model from which metadata are collected in a business data dictionary. |
| **Execution** | | |
| | Communicate and control the strategy | Develop and implement communication plan and change management. |
| | Execute and monitor processes | Monitor compliance with standards, policies, and procedures. |
| | Operate and maintain architecture | Operate and maintain systems for storage and distribution of data, data quality analysis, data cleansing and transformation, metadata management, and other data management processes. |

Source: Adapted from Otto 2007.

## Contingency Approach to Data Governance

The contingency approach to data governance, a research-based framework, suggests, like the DGI framework, that there is no one model for a DG program. Rather, the approach, priorities, and organizational structure are based on contingencies or a set of organization-specific factors that impact the success of DG (Weber et al. 2009). This model is based on the contingency theory of organizational design that argues that the relationship between some characteristic of an organization and the organization's effectiveness is determined by contingencies.

The seven contingency factors in the model include:

- Performance strategy
- Organization structure
- Competitive strategy
- Diversification breadth
- Process harmonization
- Market regulation
- Decision-making style or culture

The model asserts that there are two dependent variables affected by the contingencies which include the organizational placement of DG management and the coordination of decision making for DG. In other words, the placement of DG and coordination of DG decision making depends upon the seven contingency factors.

The seven contingency factors are moderator variables that affect the relation between the organization-specific DG model and the success of DG. The DG program is only successful when the organization appropriately aligns governance design and contingencies. For organizations that harmonize business process across the enterprise, a centralized organizational DG approach would do better than a decentralized approach. The same would hold for organizations that operate in a heavily regulated marketplace and need to coordinate compliance initiatives. Healthcare fits this last example and has a hierarchical decision making culture, so centralized DG placement and coordination would fit with these contingencies. A centralized approach means that one person or group assumes responsibility and authority and it applies across the enterprise, whereas a decentralized approach is when multiple persons or groups assume responsibility and authority. Decentralized DG is more likely to apply to extremely large companies that have multiple affiliates and vastly different lines of business and operate on a global basis.

The DG contingency approach includes both strategy and organization. From a strategy perspective, the main tasks include developing a business case for an enterprise-wide DG program, developing a DG strategy and objectives, defining a set of data quality initiatives, conducting a baseline data quality assessment, and establishing a review process.

From the organizational perspective and similar to other models in this chapter, the DG contingency model usually uses one committee and a set of four roles:

- Data quality board: Defines the DG framework and controls its implementation. The data quality board is usually a committee and includes the chief steward, business unit and IT leaders, and data stewards as members. Other terminology some use to refer to this committee includes DG council.
- Executive sponsor: Provides program sponsorship, funding, advocacy, and oversight for DG and is usually an executive or senior manager such as a chief executive officer (CEO), chief information officer (CIO), or chief financial officer.
- Chief steward: Responsible for putting the data quality board's decisions into practice, enforces the adoption of standards, and helps establish data quality metrics and targets. The chief steward is usually a senior manager with a data management background and is also called director of data management or corporate steward.
- Business data steward: Responsible for implementing corporate-wide data standards and policies for the specific business area represented. The business data steward is usually a professional from the business or functional area.
- Technical data steward. Responsible for providing standardized data element definitions, formats, profiles, and data flows between systems (Weber et al. 2009, 11).

This model suggests assigning responsibility roles using a RACI chart. The following are descriptions of the specific roles:

- **Responsible (R):** Responsible for implementing a specific DG task or activity
- **Accountable (A):** Holds ultimate accountability for authorizing a decision for a specific DG task or activity
- **Consulted (C):** Must be consulted or provide input and support for a DG activity or decision before it is completed
- **Informed (I):** Must be informed of the completion or output of a decision or activity

The structuring of decisions and activities may be either centralized or decentralized, or hierarchical or collaborative. In the case of a centralized decision-making structure, decisions are placed in one central authority or role such as the data governing board. In a decentralized structure, decision-making authority is placed with business and IT stewards. The hierarchical model takes a top-down decision-making approach where decision making is vested in the top authority with tasks delegated to lower levels. The collaborative approach, on the other hand, uses working groups, task forces, and committees with cross-functional team members to make decisions. In this approach, no decision is vested in one single authority (Weber et al. 2009).

## The St. Rita's Healthcare System Case Study

The next morning, Bob and Shirlee met and compared their findings. "The conclusion I've reached is that all of these frameworks have substantial similarities," said Shirlee. "DG implementation requires high executive support for the program we gain through a strong business case. Assessment of the current status of data quality is important and using a maturity model provides an excellent base line by which the organization can measure itself," she added.

"A big takeaway for me," said Bob, "is that DG is a huge undertaking and that the best tactic is to start small with immediate wins and essentially grow the program over time. All models suggest developing organizational structure to support the DG program. Clarifying roles and responsibilities is essential. The mainstays of the program are policies, standards, and processes."

The two finished summarizing their findings for a final report to the team. "Something's missing," said Shirlee.

"Yes," responded Bob. "We have all these frameworks, but we don't have any real life examples on how all of this is implemented. I still feel that we are in a black hole on how and where to begin," he added. Over the next few minutes they continued to discuss the matter. They decided to explore some more and find examples of case studies that would be of value to the team. Shirlee agreed to do the initial research and later she and Bob would narrow down the cases to present to the team. The case studies that Shirlee and Bob decided to present to the team included both non-healthcare and healthcare organizations.

## Non-healthcare DG Implementation Cases

The following two cases show how industries outside of healthcare have implemented DG (Otto 2011). A research study matched two telecommunications companies, BT and Deutsche Telekom, for evaluation purposes on key criteria including company size, geographic coverage, and organizational structure. Researchers interviewed key individuals responsible for IT, DG, and business units. Finally, the researchers collected additional information through documents that described the respective DG programs. The research study results showed that the two companies implemented DG in different ways.

### Case of BT: Data Quality Focus

At BT, DG started with a focus on data quality with an initial project that, over time, evolved into the organization's information management (IM) program. BT was a telecommunications company headquartered in London, operating in 70 countries with a staff of 96,000. BT had four principle lines of business. These included BT Retail, BT Wholesale, BT Global Services, and Outreach. The program sponsor was a highly placed executive, referred to as the "Group Chief Information Officer." The initial project focused on identifying opportunities to better leverage information systems (IS) investments. The top finding was that data quality was rated as the project's number one priority to leverage IS investments.

A team of two people was assigned to address this finding. Quality of customer names and addresses used by the retail portion of BT was the first data quality project targeted by the team. Customer data was extremely important since it was the basis for billing, delivery, repair, and marketing. One result of this effort led to standards for customer names and addresses. In addition to these standards, the organization licensed new software and implemented new marketing systems to improve data quality. The company recovered the cost of these within three months through postage savings after the cleansing of address data. The success of this project led to additional data quality projects and, subsequently, the company established an IM steering group whose main responsibility was to oversee data quality projects.

Later, BT Wholesale, another line of BT, joined the data quality initiative. The company expanded the IM steering group to the IM forum. The IM forum included the group CIO, CIOs from the different BT lines of business, and a representative from the central information and knowledge management practice. The principal functions of the IM forum encompassed management of all data quality projects, planning and budgeting for data quality projects, identification of opportunities for data quality initiatives, and implementation of IM policies.

As the DG program matured, specific governance roles for business units and the IT department were established by the IM forum. A senior manager from each line of business was appointed by the organization as an information manager responsible for data quality communications, organizational change and improvement efforts, and data cleansing. Business lines, not IT, owned the definitions of data quality and data quality metrics.

To ensure success, BT found that it needed to establish a methodology for data quality. The methodology was composed of five steps and standardized the process across the enterprise:

1. Identify data quality problems/issues and their impact on business processes
2. Diagnose data quality issues through investigative techniques such as data discovery and data profiling
3. Develop a solution and prepare a proposal
4. Design and implement the solution
5. Ensure a sustainable solution

### Case of Deutsche Telekom: Data Quality Focus

The second case involved Deutsche Telekom, another telecommunications company, headquartered in Bonn, Germany. Deutsche Telekom operated in 50 countries with a staff of 260,000. The company had three major lines of business including Broadband Fixed Network, Mobile, and Business Customers. Before 2006, this company did not have any systematic data quality or governance programs in place. When two different business divisions tried to consolidate data, several problems occurred. Among these were data defects such as inconsistency of customer data, lack of enterprise-wide guidelines and processes for maintenance and modification of business objects, and the lack of data definitions.

The exposure of problems such as these spurred the development of an enterprise-wide data quality program. Deutsche Telekom set up five organizational units with responsibility for addressing the issue of data quality management. These units consolidated data quality management activities. The business side established a unit that dealt with business requirement consolidation for data, particularly customer data.

The IT side established a master data management department for launching data quality management and translating business requirements to the IT level. A second department responsible for data cleansing activities was created. The company also formed two additional departments: data governance and data quality measurement. The purpose of these departments was to plan and execute data quality measures. The DG unit was responsible for defining standards for DG, developing guidelines and rules to ensure data quality, specifying data ownership, and designing and implementing enterprise data models and data architecture. The second department addressed short-term projects involving data quality measurement.

### Interpretations of BT and Deutsche Telekom Cases

The researchers developed a conceptual model to examine the two cases above. This model views DG as an organizational design task consisting of three goals: development of organizational goals, design of an organizational structure to support those goals, and process transformation and organizational change. After study of the BT and Deutsche Telekom cases, the researchers came to the following conclusions:

- There is no "off-the-shelf" approach for organizing DG. The organizational design depends on how companies configure the variety of organizational dimensions related to DG.
- The effective design of a DG organization is contingent on external and internal factors. These factors determine the configuration of organizational dimensions related to DG.
- The positioning of the mandate for action and the awareness of DG within the company are two contingency factors for DG organization. They determine the configuration of organizational dimensions related to DG and, thus, the effectiveness of DG.
- In companies with the mandate for action allocated to a business function, the business benefits related to or caused by DG are eventually attributed to DG to a larger extent than those with a mandate for action in IT (Otto 2011, 59–61).

## DG in the Healthcare Sector

Because DG is a relatively new activity in healthcare, there are not many case studies in published literature. While there are articles that provide anecdotal accounts, most of these do not have the research rigor that provides an in-depth analysis. An illustrative case, however, is DG implementation at Medco Health Solutions (Medco 2012). Medco Health Solutions, now called Express Scripts, was awarded the 2012 Data Governance Best Practice Award at the Data Quality and Information Governance Conference (DGIQ 2012).

### Case of Medco Health Solutions

Medco is a pharmacy benefit manager with the nation's largest mail order pharmacy operation. The foundation of the Medco DG program was a longstanding effort in data quality. Data quality was important to Medco for several reasons. First, clinical rules and practices, essential to their products and services, were data-driven. Because of a highly regulated industry, privacy and compliance were additional drivers for data quality. Medco has found that their DG program has gained the company improvements in cost effectiveness, risk reduction, and gains in revenues. In 2011, the total cost avoidance attributable to improved data quality and DG exceeded $20 million.

As Medco expanded from a claims processing service to a company that provided services and managed patient care, its awareness of the critical nature data quality played in its operations heightened. It realized there were significant opportunities related to their data-related processes. Among these were instituting uniform data definitions across the enterprise, establishing enterprise-wide data quality standards and processes, and assuring the company was in compliance with all regulations and contractual agreements. Thus, in 2010 Medco launched its enterprise master data management (MDM) and enterprise DG initiatives. Medco developed its DG and MDM activities in parallel. The IT group was responsible for the MDM program, while the company established the DG program in a strategic business unit. The Chief Medical Officer had overall responsibility for the DG program and the Chief Data Officer (CDO) led it.

The principal DG mission as a company that manages data as a core corporate asset was to ensure a culture of appropriate accountability and responsibilities. Specific goals to reach this mission focused on assuring consistent, enterprise-wide definitions and protection of data against misuse or inappropriate use. Specifically, the DG program deliverables included the following:

- Policies, standard operating procedures, processes, and best practice guidelines
- Stakeholder engagement and business level commitment
- Business guidance to MDM implementation in the form of the business data model and user stories
- Enterprise data definitions, strategy, and content
- Data monitoring and continuous improvement including published improvement metrics
- Data-related issued adjudication, escalation, and resolution
- Detailed communication strategy with multiple communication vehicles both within the program and between the program and wider organizational community (Medco 2012, 4)

Medco's approach to DG was to first gain executive sponsor support. Sponsorship and authorization for the program came from the company's chief operating officer (COO). The company established an ongoing process to ensure that the DG goals and objectives supported all of the program sponsors' expectations. These are documented in sponsor maps or contracts between the DG program and the sponsors and stakeholders.

To initiate the program, Medco identified a small team of representatives from critical functions and data business owners to develop strategy, draft a charter, create a beginning roadmap for implementation, and launch the program. The company also brought in consultants to provide additional expertise and industry perspective.

The DG organization grew from the small core team to a multi-level organizational structure consisting of a DG steering committee, board, council, program office, and data steward organization. Each of these groups included key stakeholders from across the enterprise (figure 5.5). The downward arrows indicate the authority and authorization hierarchy, and the upward arrows show reporting and communication relationships; the data governance program office supports the governance board, council, and data stewards. The alliance among colleagues in corporate privacy and compliance, global information security, and IT functional areas is an important aspect of the model. DG does not take over these areas, but instead, works in collaboration with them, developing and communicating policies and standard operating procedures.

Figure 5.5. Schematic of DG program for Medco Health Solutions

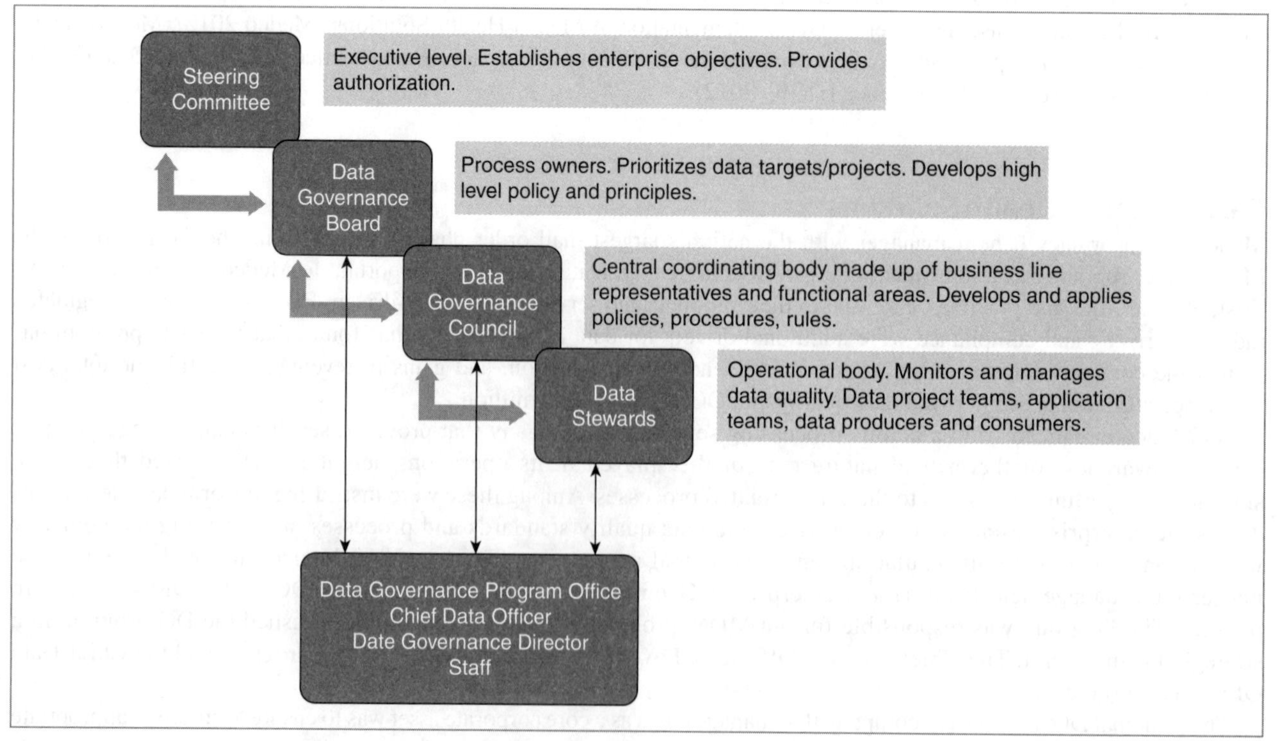

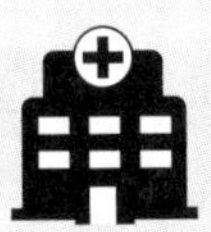

## The St. Rita's Healthcare System Case Study

Val convened the weekly team meeting. Bob and Shirlee's report on the key similarities among the various DG frameworks and summary of key principles was the primary agenda item. Below are the summary and recommendations they presented.

Shirlee and Bob emphasized that a framework is not a strategy. They provided a jigsaw puzzle analogy they found during their research that was useful in clarifying this fact.

"A framework depicts pieces of a jigsaw puzzle, but it doesn't say how to put the puzzle together or show what the puzzle picture ultimately looks like. The strategy for any DG program is unique to the organization. St. Rita's can use a framework to guide strategy, but ultimately the organization is responsible for developing a strategy, an organizational structure, and policies that fit the organizational culture and strategic priorities. We can reference frameworks to guide us, but ultimately St. Rita's is responsible for developing its own DG program. Essentially, every organization is responsible for putting the jigsaw pieces together in a way that creates the right picture for their strategic and business objectives," said Shirlee.

Success of any DG program, they stressed, hinges on how well the program fits within the context of its environment. This includes consideration of organizational culture, current DG maturity, organization size, available resources and funding, the organization's business and strategic priorities, and internal political factors. "In other words, the organization has to place DG into its own context before it can draw a picture and put the puzzle pieces together. All these factors must be examined and taken into consideration in the design of St. Rita's DG program," Bob emphasized.

"The conclusion is that no one size fits all organizations when it comes to a DG program," finished Shirlee. Frameworks are guides, not a cookie-cutter approach. With this caveat in mind, Shirlee and Bob listed the DG pieces that appeared to be key principles for any program success.

"After review of all these frameworks and case studies, we were certainly correct to place DG as the foundation for any EIM program," commented Denise.

"This is a huge and critical first effort," Val emphasized. "But before we can move forward, we need to nail down a definition of DG that works here at St. Rita's."

The team divided into two groups. For 30 minutes the groups studied the definitions presented by Shirlee and Bob and wrote down the key concepts they thought they should include as a definition for St. Rita's. When the groups finished, Val facilitated discussion that brought the key concepts together from both groups. Ultimately, the team thought this definition best represented their thoughts:

> DG is the enterprise authority that ensures control and accountability for enterprise data through the establishment of decision rights and data policies and standards that are implemented and monitored through a formal structure of assigned roles, responsibilities, and accountabilities.

To add structure to their findings, the team decided to develop a table that provides the DG deliverables for each of the nine EIM domains, starting with DG (table 5.4). This would help the team track synergies or overlaps among the areas and serve as an initial planning tool for EIM implementation.

Val then challenged the team to think about how they could put into operation a DG program at St. Rita's. A brainstorming session was scheduled for the team's next meeting to identify key first steps in designing the DG program for St. Rita's.

Table 5.4. DG deliverables by EIM function

| Data Governance | Data Architecture Management | Metadata Management | Master Data Management | Content Management | Data Security and Privacy Management | Business Intelligence Management | Data Quality Management | Terminology and Classification Management |
|---|---|---|---|---|---|---|---|---|
| Identify mission and scope | | | | | | | | |
| Establish goals and success measures | | | | | | | | |
| Put in place DG structure, processes, and communications plan | | | | | | | | |
| Secure funding | | | | | | | | |
| Establish decision rights | | | | | | | | |
| Identify accountabilities | | | | | | | | |

## Part of the Team: Topics for Discussion and Action

The St. Rita's team scheduled a brainstorming session for the next meeting. The objective of the meeting is for the team to identify the next steps they should take in designing a DG program at St. Rita's. In preparation for the team meeting develop the following:

1. A matrix listing each DG framework discussed in this chapter and its key components with regard to the following:
   - Key principles
   - Key DG functions
   - DG organizational bodies and stakeholders
   - Key DG processes
   - Key steps (if any) in establishing a DG program
2. Assess your matrix against the recommendations that Bob and Shirlee identified. Did Bob and Shirlee hit the mark with their recommendations? Do you have other recommendations you would add to their list?

## Advanced Concepts

1. Participate in a brainstorming session with your classmates with the objective of identifying the next steps St. Rita's should take in designing a DG program. Be sure to take into consideration the key principles outlined by Shirlee and Bob in their report to the team.
   - Given your assessment or results of the brainstorming session with your classmates, develop a preliminary proposal of how St. Rita's might proceed in designing their DG program. Include the following in your proposal:
     - The definition of DG for St. Rita's
     - The business case for DG at St. Rita's
     - Key stakeholders
     - Proposed design for organizational governance (committees, stakeholders, and so on) and roles each should play in governance

- Key success factors (what are the principle factors that contribute to DG success?)
- First steps the team should take and why these steps are important
- Road map for implementation

2. To gain a deeper perspective of DG program implementation, read the case studies from the research of Otto, and Berg and Caira cited in this chapter:

   Otto, B. 2011. Organizing data governance: Findings from the telecommunications industry and consequences for large service providers. Communications of the Association for Information Systems (29)1. http://aisel.aisnet.org/cais/vol29/iss1/3/.

   Berg, C. and Caira. T. 2012. Exploring the SME quandary: Data governance in practise in the small to medium-sized enterprise sector. The Electronic Journal of Information Systems Evaluation 15(1): 3-13. www.ejise.com/issue/download.html?idArticle=825.

   List the key the similarities in findings between the case studies. Are there any significantly different conclusions between the two cases? List three or more points of key takeaways you gained from examining these cases. From your analysis, create a matrix of the key findings from these cases and how St. Rita's might apply these to their situation.

## References


Berg, C. and Caira, T. 2012. Exploring the SME quandary: Data governance in practise in the small to medium-sized enterprise sector. *The Electronic Journal of Information Systems Evaluation* 15(1): 3-13. www.ejise.com/issue/download.html?idArticle=825.

Berson, A. and Dubov, L. 2011. *Master Data Management and Data Governance*. New York: McGraw Hill.

CDI Institue. 2006. Corporate data governance best practices: 2006-07 Scorecards for data governance in the global 5000. A CDI Institute MarketPulse In-Depth Report. http://www.tcdii.com/PDF/Data_Governance_white_paper_-_April_2006.pdf.

Chen, W. 2010. Kalido Conversations. Building a Business Case for Data Governance: Enterprise Data Governance Blog Series: No 8. http://blog.kalido.com/building-a-business-case-for-data-governance/#sthash.vwsBCDjR.dpuf.

Data Governance Institute. 2014. http://www.datagovernance.com/the-dgi-framework/.

Data Governance Institute. 2013. Definitions of Data Governance. http://www.datagovernance.com/adg_data_governance_definition/.

DAMA. 2010. *The DAMA Guide to the Data Management Body of Knowledge*. Bradley Beach: Technics Publications LLC.

DGIQ. 2012. Data Governance Best Practice Award Submission. http://www.debtechint.com/dgiq2012/DGBestPracticeAwardWinners.html.

IBM Data Governance Council. 2007 (October). The IBM data governance council maturity model: Building a roadmap for effective data governance. http://www-935.ibm.com/services/us/cio/pdf/leverage_wp_data_gov_council_maturity_model.pdf.

Khatri, V. and Brown, C.V. 2010. Designing data governance. *Communications of the ACM*, 53(1): 148-152. http://dl.acm.org/citation.cfm?id=1629210.

Karel, R. Perspectives: The Informatica Blog. 2012 (June). Data Governance Framework Walkthrough: Vision and Business Case. http://blogs.informatica.com/perspectives/2012/06/18/data-governance-framework-walkthrough-vision-and-business-case/.

Kloss, L. 2013. Leading innovation in enterprise information governance. *Journal of AHIMA* 84(9): 24-37.

Ladley, J. 2010. *Making Enterprise Information Management (EIM) Work for Business: A Guide to Understanding Information as an Asset*. Burlington, MA: Elsevier Inc.

Medco. DebTech International. 2012. 2012 Data Governance Best Practices Award Submission. http://www.debtechint.com/dgiq2012/pdfs/Submission_2012_Medco.pdf.

MIKE2.0 Methodology. www.openmethodology.org.

Oracle. 2011 (May). Enterprise information management: Best practices in data governance. An Oracle white paper on enterprise architecture. http://www.oracle.com/technetwork/articles/entarch/oea-best-practices-data-gov-400760.pdf.

Otto, B. 2011. Organizing data governance: Findings from the telecommunications industry and consequences for large service providers. *Communications of the Association for Information Systems* 29(1). http://aisel.aisnet.org/cais/vol29/iss1/3/.

Otto, B., K. Wende, A. Schmidt, and P. Osl. 2007. Towards a Framework for Corporate Data Quality Management. *Proceedings of the 18th Australasian Conference on Information Systems*, pp. 917–926. Toowoomba: ACIS. http://aisel.aisnet.org/cgi/viewcontent.cgi?article=1101&context=acis2007.

Reeves, M.G. and R. Bowen. 2013. Developing a data governance model in health care. *Healthcare Financial Management* 67(2): 82.

Seiner, R. 2005 (October). Data steward roles and responsibilities. *Real-World Decision Support (RWDS) Journal* 1(29). http://www.ewsolutions.com/resource-center/rwds_folder/rwds-archives/issue.2005-10-06.9442499950/document.2005-10-06.1879501317.

Sharp, Helen, A. Finkelstein, and G. Galal. 1999. Stakeholder identification in the requirements engineering process. *Database and Expert Systems Applications, 1999. Proceedings. Tenth International Workshop on*, 387–391. IEEE.

Thomas, Gwen. 2014. The Data Governance Framework. Data Governance Institute. http://www.datagovernance.com/wp-content/uploads/2014/11/dgi_framework.pdf.

University of Miami. 2008. Data Classification Policy. http://www.miami.edu/index.php/a110_data_classification_policy/.

Virginia Commonwealth University. 2012. Data Governance at VCU. http://test3.ts.vcu.edu/webcms/cie/decisions/datagov.html.

Weber, K., B. Otto, and H. Osterle. 2009 (June). One size does not fit all—A contingency approach to data governance. *Journal of Data and Information Quality (JDIQ)* 1(1).

Wichita State University. 2014. Data governance by-laws for Wichita State University data systems and reporting standards. http://webs.wichita.edu/depttools/depttoolsmemberfiles/opa/DataGovernance/WSU_DataGovernance_ByLaws.pdf.

# Chapter 6

# Data Architecture Management

**Data architecture**, sometimes called data engineering, is the development and maintenance of specifications about data that reside in electronic databases. These may be abstractions or models, called **artifacts**, which describe the data and the relationships among data and processes. Databases are the foundation for electronic health information systems. Data architecture is as fundamental to the design of databases as an architect's blueprint is to a building or a civil engineer's blueprints are to public works efforts such as the construction of roads, bridges, and dams.

Applied in the context of enterprise information management (EIM), data architecture comprises the design and maintenance of the enterprise information architecture. This includes development and implementation of policies, standards, processes, and methodologies for identifying and defining what information an organization collects, and how they store it, standardize it, and integrate it throughout the enterprise. Data architecture activities include the development, use, and maintenance of artifacts such as diagrams of business processes and data flows and data models that support information systems development and maintenance.

A comprehensive definition of data architecture includes the following:

> A single organization-wide data architecture means one set of formal data names, which may have one or more sets of formal abbreviations; one set of comprehensive definitions that limit any connotative meaning, based on the formal data names; multiple data structures based on the data names and data definitions; one set of data integrity rules, with a corresponding set of physical data edits, based on data names, data definitions, and data structures; and all documented in one place that is readily available for anyone to view. Any data architecture that does not contain all of these components is incomplete data architecture. (Brackett 2013)

Data architecture assumes a holistic view of enterprise information requirements. This notion emphasizes supporting the information needs and organizational processes of the entire enterprise. Fundamentally, data architecture is concerned with the design of information systems that provide end users the right tools to collect, access, and manipulate the right data to perform their jobs. Specific functions for the EIM model at a facility, such as St. Rita's, might include:

- Establishing standards, policies, and procedures for design of information systems and integration of enterprise data
- Identifying and documenting data requirements that meet the needs and support the processes of the organization
- Developing and maintaining enterprise and conceptual data and process models that represent the organization's business rules and processes

This chapter elaborates on topics that support EIM functions and will help you to:

- Differentiate among system development life cycles and management
- Apply system development methods

- Use requirements analysis techniques
- Prepare data architecture documentation
- Establish data architecture governance

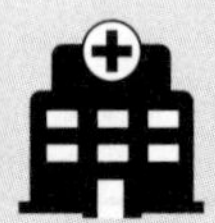

### The St. Rita's Healthcare System Case Study

Linda and Monte took on the review of the data architecture function. Monte had background in systems analysis and Linda had front line participation using databases for decision support. Because of their experiences, they felt they brought a comprehensive perspective to studying the function.

## Life Cycles for Managing Systems Development

For consistency, efficiency, and effectiveness, common organization policies, standards, and procedures must be in place for guiding systems development life cycle activities. A life cycle consists of a series of steps with a beginning and end point (chapter 4). Systems development, the foundation of a data architecture, has two different but related life cycles. These include the project management life cycle and the systems development life cycle.

The **project management life cycle** consists of activities used to manage a project. These include developing the rationale and business case for the project, prioritizing and selecting projects, identifying the project sponsor, developing the project charter, developing communication plans, establishing costs and timeline, selecting the project team members, and ensuring the project remains in scope, on budget, and on time. The project management life cycle is generic and its activities apply to any type of project.

The **systems development life cycle (SDLC)**, on the other hand, consists of the usual stages of development an information system goes through. Typical SDLC tasks include: conducting a requirements analysis, developing process models, defining the logical data model, producing functional specifications, defining technical requirements, and constructing, testing, and implementing the new system. Data architecture tasks, such as data modeling, are usually embedded within the SDLC.

### The St. Rita's Healthcare System Case Study

Linda and Monte were having an early coffee in the hospital cafeteria. "I've found an enormous amount of information on data architecture. It's pretty overwhelming," Monte said, shaking his head.

Linda could tell by the tone of Monte's voice that he was uneasy.

"I could really use your input to sort things out," Monte continued. "I've learned that data architecture activities fit within the systems development life cycle, principally in the requirements analysis, system design, and system construction phases. But data architecture also depends on project management life cycle activities, too. I'm getting stymied on what actually falls within the scope of data architecture. Should data architecture policies, procedures, and standards include only the developmental activities that apply within the SDLC or should the functions for project management life cycle be incorporated as well?"

Linda stirred her coffee as she thought about Monte's question. "It seems to me," she began, "that project management is a methodology. And the methodology can be applied for managing any type of project, not just the data architecture activities within the SDLC. Because of this, I think the project management activities fall outside the scope of what we are attempting to investigate right now," Linda replied.

Frustrated, Monte said, "I'm still going around in circles about this. If data architecture activities aren't managed well or don't follow a prescribed method, then project failure is a real possibility. That's a big reason why we're starting an EIM office, isn't it?

"All right, let's take this approach," Linda suggested. "A project is a temporary effort whose goal is to produce a specific product or implement a process. Once the product is produced, then the project ends. While data architecture functions may be part of a project, they also have a continuing life-span. They don't end with completion of a project."

"Ok, I think I'm getting where you are going with this," Monte said.

"Project management is a supervision function. It's concerned with planning, organizing, coordinating, directing, and controlling a specific undertaking and to make sure that cost, budget, time, and resource parameters are met. We should draw on project management functions when data architecture activities are part of a project. But what we are most concerned with from an EIM perspective is that we have in place policies, standards, and procedures that actually guide the data architecture functions themselves, not the project management effort. Project management may be better positioned as another EIM function or as a separate organizational office," Linda concluded.

"Wow! That perspective really helped out," Monte exclaimed in relief. "And since you mentioned it, in some organizational charts I have seen an office of project management as a separate organizational unit. So for now, I'll focus on what data architecture activities we need to do."

## Systems Development Life Cycle

The SDLC follows a set of stages that include several different tasks. There are various models and descriptions of the SDLC. For example, some models have four phases consisting of planning, analysis, design, and implementation. Others may include six steps such as project feasibility, analysis, design, implementation, testing, and maintenance. Still others like the New York State Office of Technology describe a life cycle made up of the following stages (figure 6.1):

- **System Initiation**: In this stage, the business case and solution the project sponsor presented in the initial project proposal are validated by the project team to ensure they still meet an existing business need. The project team identifies the resources, including staff, budget, and time, they need for the project to progress through the successive SDLC stages. The team establishes a schedule for moving the developmental effort through the SDLC stages.
- **Requirements Analysis**: Once a project has been approved by the appointed authority in the organization, information system analysts work with end users in defining the business requirements that the system will support. This is usually done by identifying current business processes (the "as-is" system), determining what improvements or changes they need to make to the current processes, and identifying the characteristics and functions of the new ("to-be") system. The project team uses specific methodology and automated design tools to carry out this stage, resulting in a set of deliverables or artifacts that may consist of data flow diagrams, data models, use cases, initial screen or form designs, and other similar artifacts. The automated design tools they use are frequently referred to as computer-assisted system engineering (CASE) tools. This stage is the most significant in managing data architecture.
- **System Design**: In this stage, the supported functionalities and processes are translated by the project team into a technical design or architecture. This includes identifying the hardware and system software, creating the physical database, security strategy, performance requirements, and prototyping system components.
- **System Construction**: System construction consists of all the activities required to build and test the system. This includes building and testing the individual system components, integrating and testing the components as a whole, and producing user and technical documentation.
- **System Acceptance**: In this stage, the system is validated (tested) by the project team and end users in a number of ways to determine if it meets all of the functional and technical specifications. This may include system walk-throughs, manual and automated testing, and revision of technical and user documentation.
- **System Implementation**: The last stage includes system deployment into the real world environment. It comprises user education, putting the system into production and transitioning ongoing support and maintenance of the system to the appropriate units of the organization (New York State 2003).

One of the functions of EIM is to prescribe the use of methodologies and establish policies, standards, and procedures for various aspects of the design of information systems. The benefits of adopting a standard methodology include streamlining project execution, increasing accountability, enhancing communication among project staff through use of consistent documentation tools, setting performance requirements, and decreasing the learning curve of employees because they are

Figure 6.1. Systems development life cycle stages

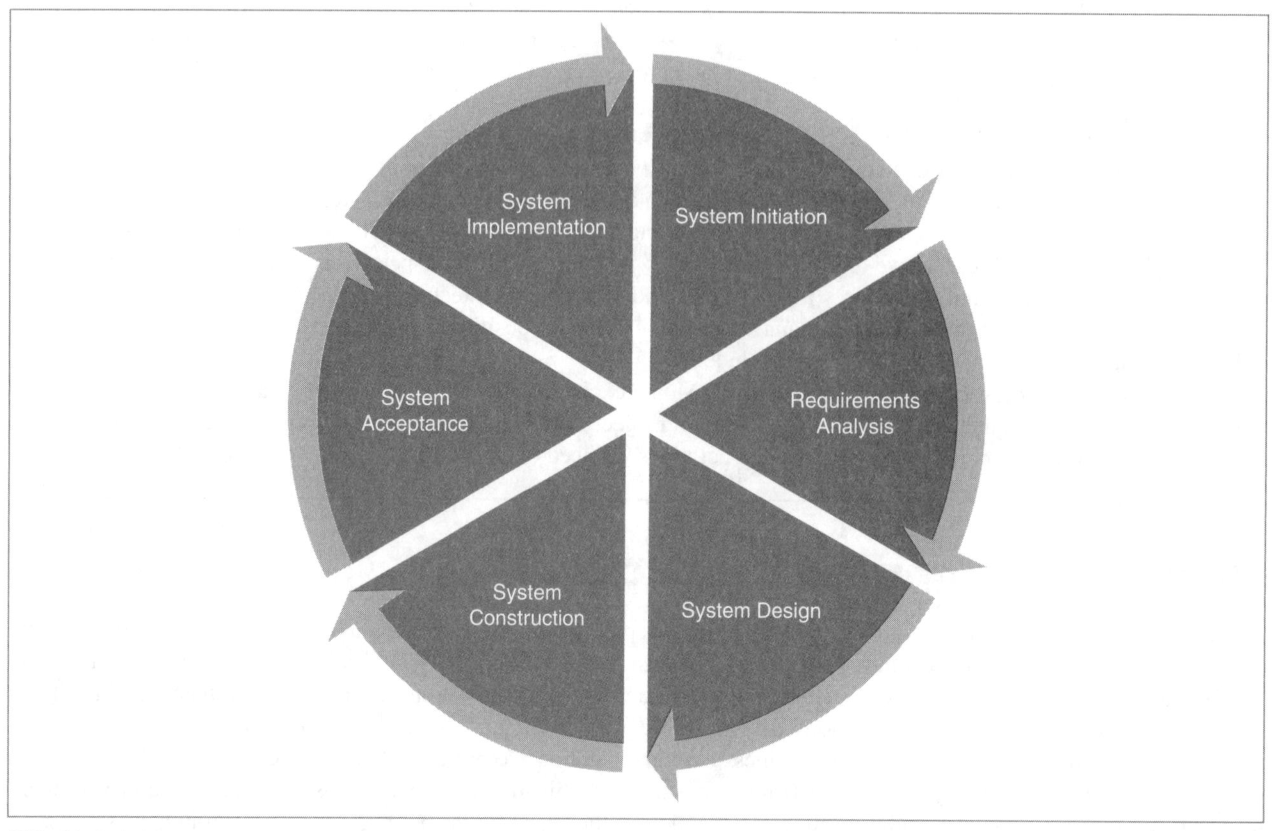


©Merida L. Johns

familiar with a methodology consistently used throughout the organization. Adopting a specific methodology would be an example of a type of data governance (DG) standard specification.

This chapter covers the first two phases of the life cycle, system initiation and requirements analysis, since the outputs of these are consistent with the data architecture definition provided earlier. The accompanying student manual provides the remainder of the life cycle phases as a reference.

# System Initiation

The systems development project or procurement process usually includes a series of steps (figure 6.2) and starts with a requisition document submitted to an information systems planning or oversight committee in the organization. The responsibilities of this committee vary among organizations. Typically, the committee is responsible for developing the information technology (IT) strategic plan and ensuring that all IT initiatives are aligned with the organization's business initiatives. The committee usually has authority for approving all major IT projects, establishing priorities among competing IT projects, assessing the IT resources and budget needs for each project, and monitoring and evaluating the project's progress.

The **requisition**, or official list of requirements, is usually completed by the **project sponsor**. The project sponsor is normally the individual responsible for oversight of the project from the business perspective. The requisition makes the business case for the project and includes an overview of the system purpose; the business issues, opportunities, or problems the project will address; desired functions; anticipated benefits; and departments, stakeholders, or services the project might affect. Cost projections may be also requested by the executive sponsor, as well as categorization of the project as a system enhancement, new development, infrastructure, or hybrid effort.

The requisition typically requires senior executive sign off. For example, if the health information management (HIM) department is the project sponsor, the most senior manager the HIM department reports to would signoff, such as the CIO or CFO. This individual is usually identified as the executive sponsor of the project.

Figure 6.2. Project initiation process

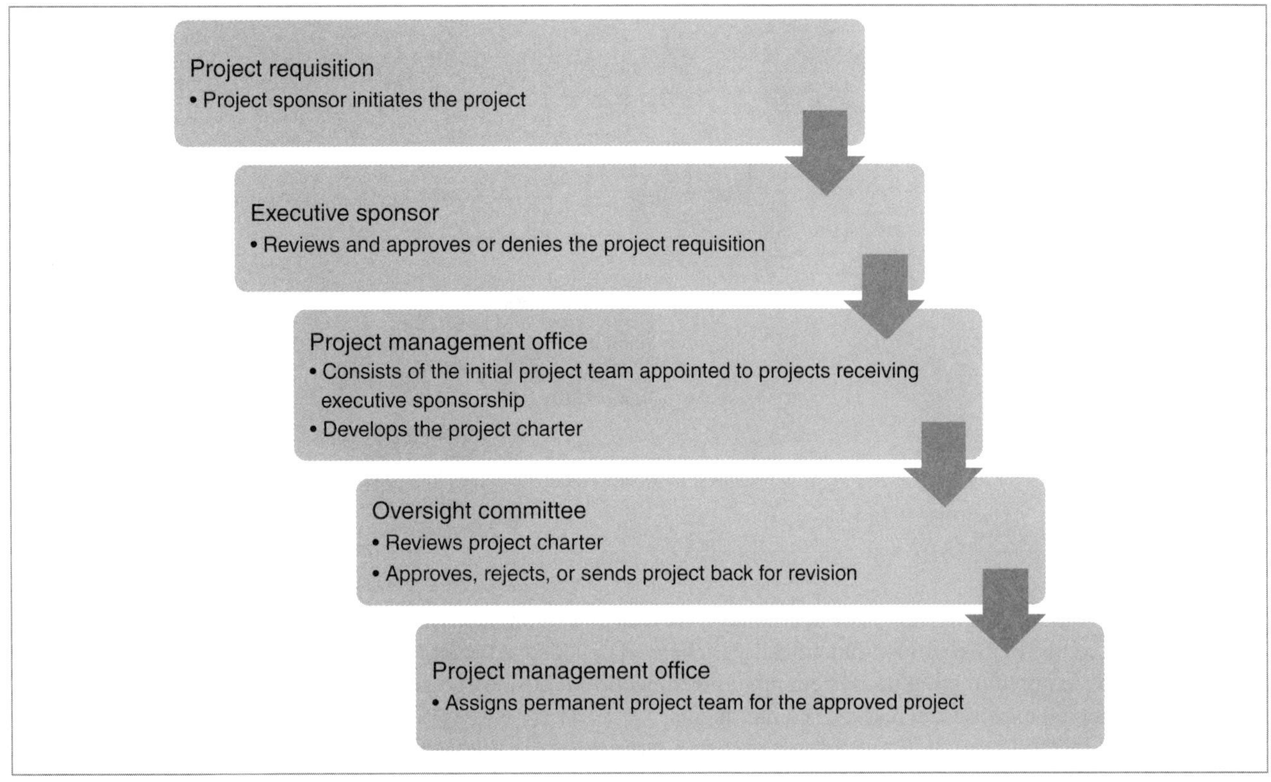




Once the executive sponsor signs off, the project sponsor normally submits the requisition to the organization's project management or similar office for vetting and preparation of a project charter. The **project charter** clarifies the project objectives, and identifies project scope, major milestones, risks, budget, timeline, personnel and other resources required to complete the project.

At this point, an initial project team is usually appointed by the IT department, project management office, or other designated organizational entity. The project team typically consists of the project sponsor, IT business analyst(s) and technical staff, and stakeholders. The project team is responsible for steering the project through the SDLC phases described earlier in figure 6.1.

# SDLC Development Methods

After system initiation, management of the life cycle depends upon the model and the development method the team uses. Several common methods include waterfall, parallel, and rapid application methods such as iterative, spiral, and agile development. These development methods essentially direct how the next stages of requirements analysis and system design are handled. Each of these is described below.

## The Waterfall Method

The stages of the SDLC are often implemented by the project team sequentially from planning through implementation. Because development proceeds serially from one stage to the next, flowing forward like a waterfall, it is often called the **waterfall method**. This is the oldest implementation method of the SDLC (figure 6.3). One key advantage of this approach is that the project team completes all design planning prior to the beginning of programming and software development. This decreases the possibility of scope creep, or the unintended project growth resulting from end users redefining or identifying more functionality for inclusion in the product.

This advantage, however, is also a disadvantage. Because the project team must complete one step before another can begin, there can be a significant time delay between the requirements analysis stage and actual deployment of the system.

Figure 6.3. The waterfall method

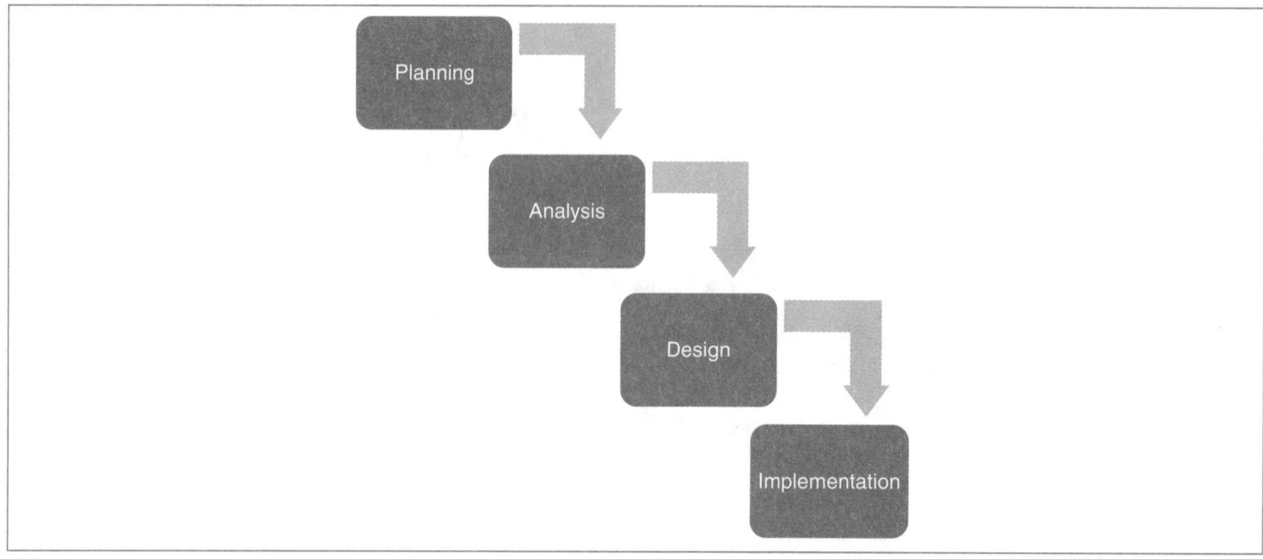


©Merida L. Johns

Between project start and completion, user needs may have changed significantly, and the delivered system might not meet current business needs. Furthermore, if functionality is changed or added at the end of development, a considerable amount of rework will be required to bring the system up to meeting current business conditions. The rework causes deployment delays, and additional expense and resource commitments.

The waterfall method severely limits the end user role throughout the life cycle. It also assumes that all requirements can be specified by the project team in advance. Unfortunately, this is often not the case. Moreover, system validation and testing are conducted by the project team in conjunction with the end users only during the implementation stage, rather than parallel with other stages. This means errors made in previous stages may go undetected until the final product is developed. For example, an error made in specifications during the analysis stage in defining the length of the unique patient identifier may not be caught until development was completed. Caught at the end of the development cycle, such an error may require a significant amount of rework to make the system compliant with business needs. This introduces time delays and cost overruns in system deployment.

Because of these disadvantages, other SDLC variations have emerged. Among these are parallel and spiral models, and rapid application development methods.

## Parallel Method

In a typical **parallel method**, the development cycle begins with planning and analysis, and the project team developing a high level design of the system. They then divide the project into smaller sub-projects that they develop and implement parallel with each other (figure 6.4).

For example, in a patient-scheduling and registration system, a project team creates a high-level design from the data model, process models, and use cases they developed during the analysis stage. The high-level design might include a mockup of end-user screens and navigation functionality that would represent the total system such as registration, scheduling, cancellation, rescheduling, and insurance verification processes. Rather than developing modules sequentially, the team develops all modules in parallel and integrates them during the final implementation stage for the entire project. The parallel method reduces development time. However, it may introduce integration problems if development of each subpart is completely independent and there are not good communication channels among the subpart teams.

## Validation and Verification Model

The **validation and verification model** (V-model) integrates testing design with all the life cycle stages, beginning at the requirements analysis stage and extending through the implementation stage. Working concurrently with the design team, the testing team develops test documents that detail how they will test each part of the system (figure 6.5).

Figure 6.4. The parallel method

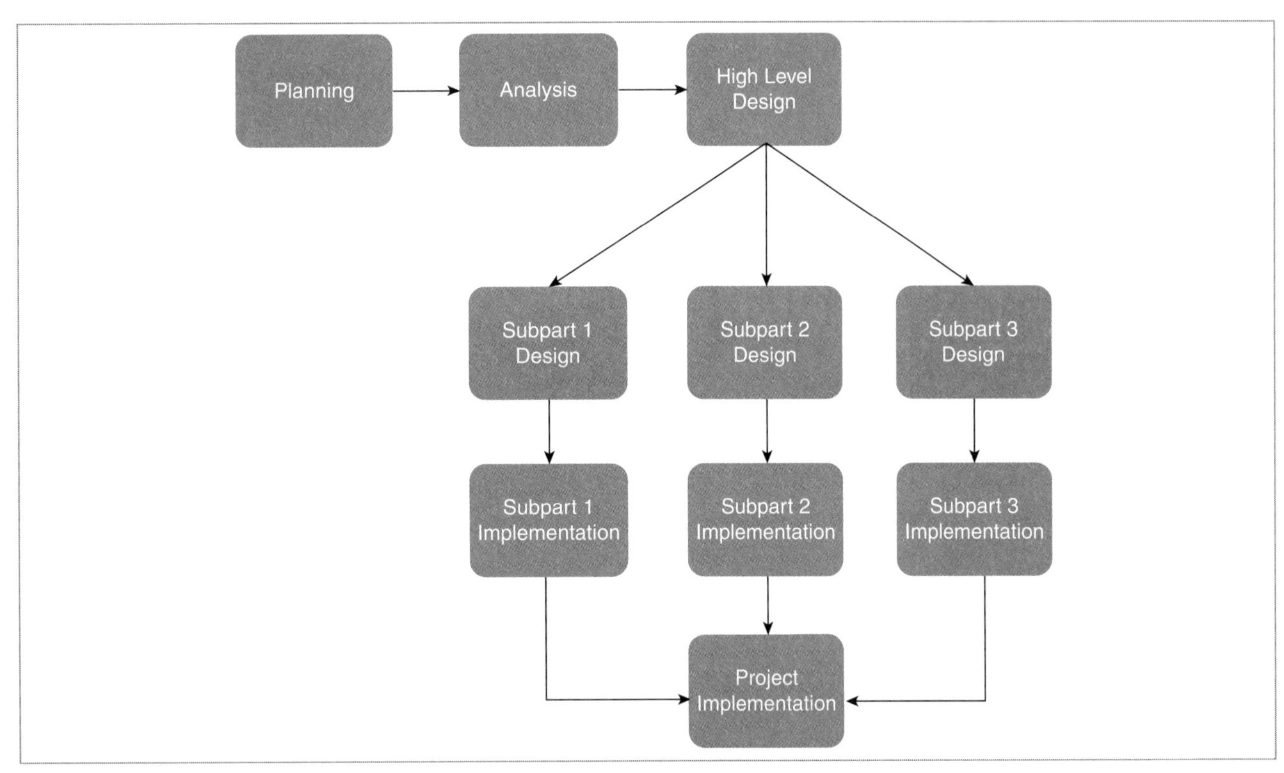




Figure 6.5. The validation and verification model (V-model)

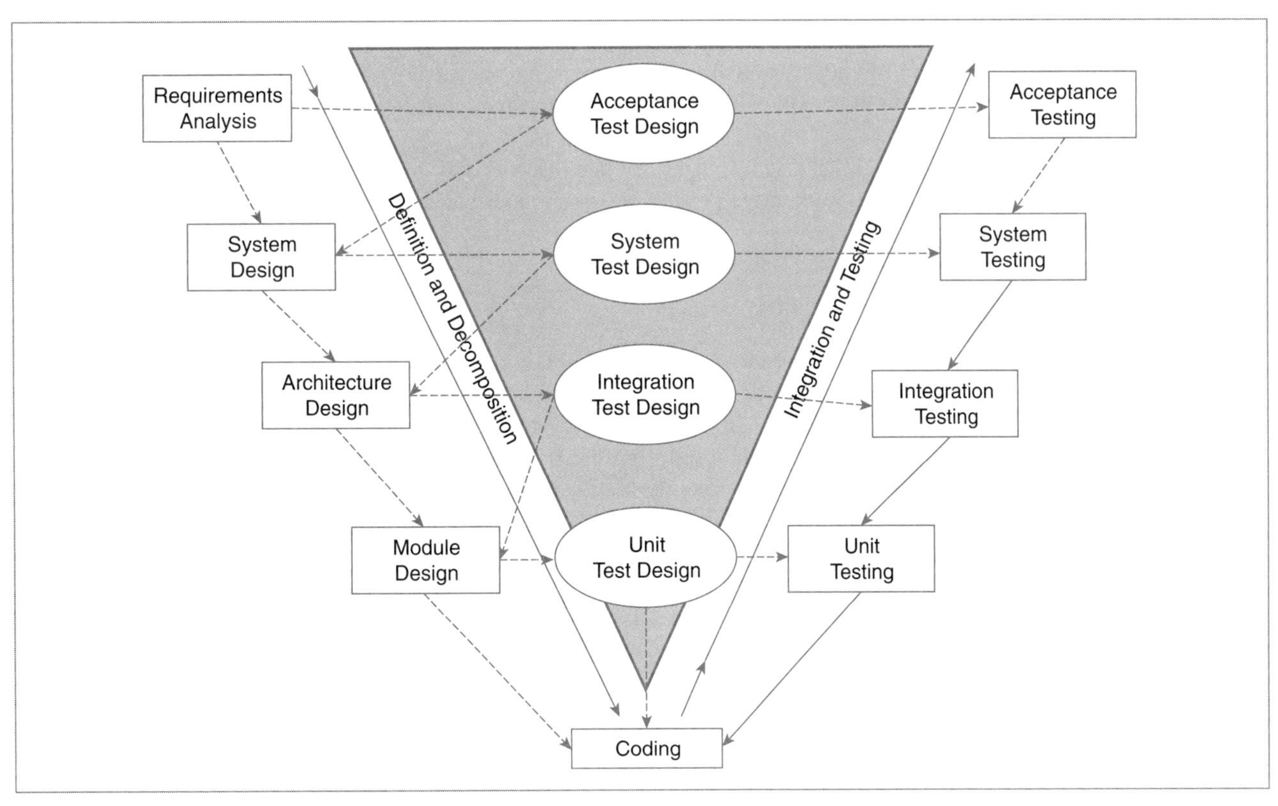

To illustrate, in the patient-scheduling and registration system example above, during the analysis stage, the design team specifies the end-user functionalities of the system, such as the ability to input new client information on the registration form. Concurrently, the testing team develops a testing document (script) that specifies the criteria the team should use to test the system to determine if it performs in the expected way. Likewise, during the construction stage, the test team develops the procedures to test the technical parts of the system, integration among the system parts, and system performance, and designs the test environment. Because the method integrates testing development at each stage of the SDLC, the overall quality of the information system improves (Dennis et al. 2009). The V-model, however, still retains the rigidity of having to follow the sequential steps of the waterfall method (Balaji and Murugaiyan 2012).

## Rapid Application Development Methods

**Rapid application development** (RAD) is a group of developmental methodologies that attempt to address the long development time problem of the waterfall and similar sequential methods. The goal of RAD methods is to go through the analysis, design, construction, and acceptance stages of the SDLC quickly and get essential parts of the system to the end user as soon as possible for their evaluation and feedback. RAD uses a combination of tools and techniques to move through the SDLC stages quickly. Principal among these are various types of iterative development and prototyping techniques and the use of joint application development (JAD) sessions for identifying system functional requirements. JAD is covered later in this chapter.

### Iterative Method

The **iterative method** divides system development into small parts, or versions, each going through all stages of the SDLC. This method combines the flexibility of RAD with the discipline of the waterfall method. This method is referred to as iterative development because a part of the application is built by the development team and tested and then is refined by another iteration of building and testing. The most important functionalities are reflected in the first versions of the product. Subsequent parts go through the same cycle and are essentially extensions of the previous version or part.

Unlike the waterfall or parallel methods, an advantage of iterative development is a timely feedback loop that provides critical information for the development of subsequent parts of the project. The iterative model also accommodates faster deployment of software products, as each version is ready for implementation by the company when completed. Another advantage is the inclusion of end-user involvement throughout the development process. As the development team creates a version of the system, they solicit end user review, and they make refinements to the product based on end user input.

The iterative model is not without its disadvantages. Inflated scope and over-complication of design are main disadvantages. Another drawback is that successive product versions require continual end-user retraining, and updates and revisions for technical staff to implement.

### Prototyping

A **prototype** is a simple version of an intended system. Like the iterative approach, the analysis, design, and implementation stages are completed concurrently. Unlike the iterative approach, where the system delivers functional components to the end user in successive versions, the goal of prototyping is to produce a simplified model of the entire system, gather input from end-user review, and then redesign the prototype based on that input. Many times, project teams use prototypes solely to help identify system requirements and to give end users a feel for what the end system may look like. Other times the team continually refines the prototype until a working system is produced. This is called a working prototype.

A downside of prototypes is that they are usually just a model of a system. The background work, such as data model development, coding, and testing, is not necessarily done. End users may come away with high expectations for the proposed system as seen in the prototype, only to discover later that the actual system does not include the functionality displayed in the prototype.

Systems developed solely through a prototype methodology often lack disciplined and thorough analysis and development and result in poorly designed working systems (Dennis et al. 2009). The focus of this method is on developing the "to-be" system as opposed to studying the "as-is" system. Thus, team members may overlook opportunities for process improvements.

## Spiral Method

The **spiral method** is a type of iterative development that incorporates the best features of the prototyping and waterfall methods. Like prototyping, iterative versions of a complete system are produced by the project team, but there is an emphasis on risk assessment at each iteration. Iteration allows the project team to identify system functionality and to refine software code and implementation. Similar to the waterfall method, this method imposes discipline on the development effort. The spiral method has four steps: 1) Identifying system objectives; 2) Examining alternatives and determining risks of project failure; 3) Establishing requirements and developing the software; and 4) Seeking evaluation from the end user. These four steps are repeated (iterated) for each prototype cycle, called a spiral process, until the project teams delivers a fully functional and working product.

The spiral method is useful when the requirements of the system are not easily specified or are rapidly changing due to environmental business conditions. Another of its strengths is the discipline imposed on the process through iteration with the four steps and emphasis on risk assessment during each prototype cycle. This helps ensure that the project teams is continually identifying the system objectives, that risks, constraints, and alternatives are considered, and end user input is solicited and used. The risk assessment step is considered to be one of the method's principal strengths.

## Agile Development

**Agile development** is a group of practices that, when used together, are intended to shorten and improve the SDLC. The method emphasizes short, simple, and iterative development cycles. There are many variations to the agile approach but the essential concept is to break the project into small component parts and to eliminate constructing artifacts such as data flow diagrams, data models, and other documentation tools in preference to face-to-face collaboration with end users. Each iteration includes the project team identifying requirements to design, test, and validate. End user involvement is a critical component of this method. End users engage in requirements analysis and provide essential feedback during the design, testing, and validation of the project.

Reduced documentation is an element that separates agile development from other iterative approaches. Agile is based on the *Agile Manifesto* and adheres to the following values:

- Individuals and interactions over processes and tools
- Working software over comprehensive documentation
- Customer collaboration over contract negotiation
- Responding to change over following a plan (Agile Alliance 2013)

Agile development has many strengths including close collaboration between the project team and end users and a fast, iterative approach. However, it does have potential drawbacks. The process requires that end users dedicate potentially large periods of time to the project. There is a possibility for project scope creep (continual growth of the project's scope of work) since system requirements can evolve as the iterations progress, as opposed to being identified at the beginning of the project (Waters 2007). Lack of design documentation is also a drawback, particularly from the standpoint of system maintenance and auditing for large, complex systems. This weakness is often called the audit documentation gap. Specific design and development documentation and details are essential for system maintenance, particularly in the case of complex and mission-critical systems. Furthermore, organizations may need detailed system development documentation to meet auditing requirements in industries such as healthcare and finance (Solarte 2012).

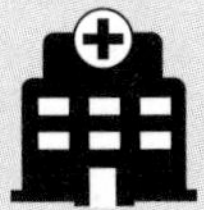

### The St. Rita's Healthcare System Case Study

Linda and Monte felt they had done a comprehensive search of different development methods. Although they had both worked in the IT arena, they were surprised at the number of development methods they found. They put together a comprehensive slide deck and presented their findings on SDLC methods to the rest of the team at their regular team meeting.

"OK, I'm starting to get it," said Bob. "EIM includes several functions. Data architecture management is one of the nine functions we've identified. If St. Rita's had a DG program, policies and standards would be established across the enterprise to better manage our organization's data architecture processes. For instance, one policy may require that we use a specific method such as iterative development or prototyping for systems development efforts. This policy would help ensure we develop projects in a consistent way, right?"

"You got it," responded Val. "We might say that DG is the coordinating function of all other EIM functions."

Shirlee posed a follow-up question for the team: "Do we have a consistent developmental methodology at St. Rita's?"

"Not really," replied Val, "and this has posed innumerable problems for us. Without standards to follow, we've missed important steps for process improvements, and several of our projects have ended up with expensive and time-consuming errors."

"Yes," Monte concurred. "I remember when the field length for vendor numbers was not allocated sufficient space. The project team skipped testing with live data and didn't catch the error until they uploaded the data from the old system to the new database. Vendor numbers were not only truncated in the new system, but the trailing numbers from the previous vendor number were added to the next vendor number. What an incredible mess. We had to stop everything and find where the error originated. This set us back several weeks, not to mention the trouble it caused for procurement."

"So, is an EIM office responsible for the entire SDLC?" asked Linda.

"Well, it *is* called *enterprise information management*," responded Val. "But what's considered in and out of EIM is an organizational decision. In some organizations, EIM may encompass responsibility for the entire spectrum of functions we've identified. With regard to data architecture management, the most significant stage is requirements analysis."

"I recall that one framework we studied suggests that organizations may decide to focus their DG programs on specific areas. For example, some organizations may focus on data quality while others may choose to focus on data architecture, or data privacy, security and compliance," said Monte. "I suppose this approach could apply to EIM as well," he added.

"Correct," Val responded. "So our responsibility is to understand all of the potential functions of EIM, how they mesh with our organization's strategic initiatives, and how they might relate to establishing a DG program. We still have a long way to go."

"Right, added Linda. "The SDLC is only the tip of the iceberg. For each stage in SDLC, there are specific steps to follow. And, many of these have their own embedded methodologies. For example, in the requirements analysis stage, one method of collecting end-user requirements is conducting a joint application development session. There would have to be specific procedures developed to carry out that session and specific documentation requirements to follow, such as developing use cases."

"Linda and Monte, how do you want to proceed in finishing up the data architecture function?" asked Val.

"Our next steps should be to flesh out the activities and identify examples of standards and policies to establish for the stages of the SDLC. Using the SDLC identified by the New York State Technology Office is a good model, because it has more specificity than others," offered Linda. The team agreed. Linda and Monte were to report their findings at the next team meeting. Linda and Monte began their research that afternoon with the next step in the SDLC life cycle.

## Requirements Analysis

**Requirements analysis** is the second step in the SDLC and the most pertinent to data architecture management. Requirements analysis is the set of processes used for identifying what function(s) an information system must perform and how it is to provide them. It is the fundamental building block upon which any information system is based.

Requirements analysis is considered the most difficult step in information systems development, and most defects in delivered projects are not in computer code, but originate in the requirements analysis and design phases of the SDLC (Jones 2008). This is the reason why critical attention should be given by the project team to developing standards, processes, and controls to achieve good requirements analysis.

Requirements can be functional or nonfunctional. **Functional requirements** are observable tasks the system must perform. For instance, in a patient registration system, "must input patient last and first name" or, "must search master patient index" or, "must create a unique master person identifier" are functional requirements. **Non-functional requirements** are standards or characteristics to which the system must comply, rather than tasks it must perform. For example, the system "must be accessible from 0200 hours to 2400 hours seven days a week," or the system "must accommodate 1000 simultaneous users from 0700 to 2300 hours every day" are both considered non-functional requirements.

Information system analysts work with end users to define functional and nonfunctional requirements that a system must support. The analysts usually do this by identifying current business processes (the "as-is" system), determining what improvements or changes the organization should make to the current processes, and identifying the characteristics and functions of the new ("to-be") system. A specific methodology and automated design tools are used to carry out this stage. This results in a set of deliverables or artifacts that may consist of data flow diagrams, data models, use cases, initial screen or form designs, and other similar documents. The automated design tools that help produce these documents are referred to as CASE tools. These are discussed later in this chapter.

## Requirements Gathering Techniques

Several methods for gathering requirements for an information system are available, each with strengths and weaknesses. It is important to study and document the current or "as-is" system, identify necessary improvements, and determine what requirements the new or "to-be" system needs. The goal is not just to automate the current system, but to identify and incorporate improvements that support the requirements for the new or "to-be" system.

### Document Analysis

One method of gathering requirements, called **document analysis**, reviews existing policies, procedures, forms, manuals, databases, data models, and other documentation. This approach provides insights into how current processes are supposed to function and the data the processes need. However, documentation review alone will not necessarily give the full or current picture of the system. Frequently, there is a gap between the "supposed system" and the "actual system." This may be due to outdated, inaccurate, or incomplete documentation, the addition of process workarounds by employees, or changes in processes to keep pace with volume increases, personnel changes, regulations, or other factors that have not been formalized in organizational documents. Thus, review of documentation provides an insight, but doesn't necessarily provide a full picture of the "as-is" system.

### Observation

A technique used to complement document analysis is observation. **Observation** involves systems analysts observing the work environment and learning what processes users perform, how they perform them, and what data they use to carry out the processes. Analysts compare their observations to information in formal documents to identify differences and gaps. The gap analysis provides analysts the opportunity to explore with end users reasons for these differences. When analysts use the review of documentation and observation techniques together, they better understand the current processes in question firsthand.

### Interviewing

**Interviewing** is another method for gathering requirements. Analysts select appropriate subjects who use or are affected by the processes the system supports. These may include managers, end users, and other stakeholders who have an interest in system inputs, processes, or outputs.

Good preparation is key to the success of this technique. First, analysts must select the right participants and the right number of participants to interview. Analysts may draw incorrect findings and conclusions if the participant sample is biased. Second, the analyst must be skilled at developing and asking questions, staying focused on the topic, and probing interviewees for relevant information that only they can provide. For example, asking an operational level employee questions that only a manager could answer potentially confuses interviewees or makes them feel uninformed. Similarly, getting off of the topic wastes time and muddles the interviewee's understanding of the interview goals.

Analysts must carefully develop questions in advance of the interview to elicit the type of information that is important for identifying system requirements. Usually, they use three types of questioning techniques. These include closed-ended questions that require a specific answer such as "yes" or "no," or seek a response to a possible set of alternatives. Open-ended questions allow participants to explain or elaborate, and follow-up questions prod the interviewee into providing more information. There is no one right or wrong questioning technique. Frequently, interviewers use a combination of techniques in an interview process.

Once the analyst develops questions, he or she schedules the interview. The analyst should allocate appropriate time for each interview. Results of the interview must be carefully documented. It is difficult to satisfactorily execute the roles of both interviewer and documenter at the same time. A good practice is for the analyst to be accompanied by a person (scribe) who is responsible for taking precise notes during the interview. After the interview ends, the scribe transcribes the notes into an interview report. The analyst usually provides a copy of the report to the interviewee, who is asked to review it and give additional feedback or provide corrections or clarifications. Once the interviewee gives feedback, the scribe finalizes the report.

The interview method is time consuming because it requires multiple interviews and the task of writing a report with results from each interview. The method has also been criticized as to the completeness and accuracy of the results obtained. Main criticisms of this method include poor interview techniques, poor question creation, the introduction of bias, and not resolving conflicting information among interviewees (Duggan and Thachenkary 2003).

## Joint Application Development

A **joint application development (JAD)** session is a valuable technique project teams use to study the current system and to identify the goals, objectives, and required functions of a proposed system. The JAD technique was developed by IBM in the late 1970s to address the shortcomings and problems of requirements analysis of other methods (Duggan and Thachenkary 2003).

A JAD session is made up of the project manager and a group of organization business experts, system end users, system analysts, and technical development professionals who come together in a workshop format to analyze the strengths and weaknesses of a current system and to propose functionalities improvements or to identify requirements for a new system. Preparation for the JAD session includes identifying project scope, purpose, and objectives; determining workshop participants; and gathering project background information such as current problems or issues participants need to address.

A trained facilitator conducts the JAD session. The role of the facilitator is to guide the group through the process. As a neutral participant, the facilitator does not contribute personal opinions. The workshop should have clearly defined goals, objectives, outcomes, and an agenda. The facilitator and the group should establish ground rules for conduct, participation, and arriving at a consensus. The facilitator keeps the group on track, follows the agenda, and is ultimately responsible for documenting the workshop proceedings and outcomes.

A JAD session can last a few hours or up to several days. The workshop session is frequently held away from the organizational campus so participants are not distracted or interrupted. The JAD meeting room configuration consists of tables usually in a U-shaped configuration so all participants can see and interact with each other. "Face-to-face communication of interfacing users promotes a clearer understanding of needs, more rapid resolution, enhanced system quality, and the all-important user buy-in" (Hollander and Mirlocca 1993, 18). A white board, flip charts, projector screen, or e-board are at the front of the room and are used by trained scribes to document ideas, discussions, and proceedings of the session.

By the JAD workshop conclusion, the participants have identified essential system functions. One strength of the JAD method is that end users, analysts, and developers come together to collaborate in analysis for the proposed project. This allows for the free exchange and input of information among all concerned groups. The premise underlying JAD is that a group of individuals working together at the same time and leveraging their knowledge can perform an analysis faster and better than individuals working independently.

While research shows that JAD improves requirements analysis, shortens development time, and reduces scope creep by up to 50 percent, it has drawbacks consistent with group dynamics and processes. These include such issues as one person dominating group discussions, introspective group members who fail to participate, reluctance to challenge opinions, group think, and group conflict (Dennis et al. 2009). Effective facilitation can mitigate many of these negatives.

More recently, project teams have used other methods such as brainstorming, anonymous idea generation, and nominal group technique in conjunction with JAD (Duggan and Thachenkary 2003). Automated groupware tools that help people virtually collaborate such as electronic meetings software and automated real-time polls and survey applications can also reduce these issues.

After the JAD session, the facilitator develops a report of the proceedings, outcomes, and deliverables and circulates it to all session attendees for signoff. If necessary, the facilitator adds clarifications. Sometimes, the project team may develop a prototype of the system as a deliverable of the JAD session. The requirements specified in the JAD document, including any process flows, data models, or other documentation will be used by the project team to guide the project through the design, construction, acceptance, and implementation stages.

### Requirements Analysis Outputs

Among the outputs of requirements analysis are a group of key artifacts that guide the system's design and construction. Normally, these include data flow and process flow diagrams, use cases, data models, and functional specifications. Some of these are described in the next sections.

# Data Architecture Documentation Techniques and Tools

Several tools, techniques, and documentation strategies are used by the project team in the analysis phase to provide discipline, structure, communication, and integration among analysis tasks. The design diagrams and documents produced from these techniques are commonly referred to as artifacts. Design artifacts are crucial for communication among the development team members and stakeholders. The effectiveness of these tools, techniques, and artifacts, however, depends upon the extent that standards for their use are developed, applied, and monitored by the organization across all projects. An overview of some of these tools and techniques is provided in this section.

## Use Cases

A **use case** is a technique used by analysts for capturing and documenting user requirements. Use cases are developed in conjunction with requirements gathering because they identify and clarify the interactions between an end user and the proposed system in achieving a specific goal. One way to think of a use case is to view it as a story of the steps or actions that are taken between a user and a system in order to achieve an end result.

There are two types of use cases. The first type, an **essential use case (business use case)**, describes the business process and interaction of the end user with the system without specifying any technology details. The second type, a **system use case**, provides the technology and operational details of the system and is used by the technical staff.

There are many documentation formats for use cases. The format type and components of a use case depend upon the standards each organization establishes for requirements gathering and analysis. Some use cases include only visual modeling, while others use textual descriptions, and still others use a hybrid of both.

Common elements and components exist among format types. Each use case should have a specific name identified by a verb or a verb plus a noun. Take the requirement for searching for a patient record, for example. The use case name is "search" (verb) plus "patient" (noun). Or, for registering a patient, the use case name is "register" (verb) plus "patient" (noun). End users are identified with the label "actor." A primary actor is the end user who usually initiates the interaction with the system and triggers the action. A supporting actor is external to the proposed system but provides a service to it. A supporting actor can be a person, another system, or a device, such as a printer.

Most use case formats include a section that describes the main steps necessary to achieve the system goal. Sometimes this is referred to as major steps performed, main success scenario, or successful course. Other components include extensions and variations. An extension is an alternate flow where users cannot take the usual steps. In searching for a patient in the master patient or person index (MPI), an alternate flow includes steps for the user to take if the patient was not already registered in the MPI.

Three examples of essential use case formats that describe requirements for searching for a patient record are reviewed below. The first is a textual version for searching an MPI for a specific patient (figure 6.6) (Cockburn 2001).

Notice that the use case is given a unique number and title. It also lists the primary actor and the goal to be achieved. Authentication is a precondition, which means the system must authenticate the primary actor to perform the task. This usually means actors must have user names and passwords before they perform tasks. Notice this use case provides the steps for a successful scenario and also provides extensions which are alternate flows of what can happen during a scenario.

The second example is another textual use case (figure 6.7). This example identifies major inputs, outputs, and the information the user needs to perform each step. Extensions or alternate flows are identified by "if" statements (Dennis et al. 2009). Notice in this use case, there are no descriptions for minimum or success guarantees, preconditions, or scope.

The third example is a hybrid of text and figures (figure 6.8). In this use case, the actor, a physician, and the system are represented by icons. A sequence diagram is included that provides a high level description of the case steps. This is followed by the sequence table which includes both a successful course of steps and alternatives or extensions of an unsuccessful course. Pre-conditions and post-conditions are also included.

Figure 6.6. Textual use case example #1

**Use Case 121 Search Patient**

**Primary Actor**: Requestor
**Goal**: Requestor wants to find a patient record
**Scope**: Master Patient Index – The overall searching mechanism to find a patient record
**Level**: User

**Stakeholders and Interests**:

Requester: Wants to retrieve a patient record for view or update
**Precondition**: Authentication
**Minimal Guarantees**: Any record existing in master person index can be identified
**Success Guarantees**: Specific patient record is identified
**Trigger**: Requester submits request for a specific patient record

**Main Success Scenario**:

1. Requester clicks on link for find patient record
2. System displays screen form
   - Patient last name
     and/or
   - Patient first name
     and/or
   - Patient date of birth
     and/or
   - Medical record number
3. Requester fills in search criteria and clicks link to submit
4. System returns search results that meet requestor criteria
5. Requester selects record from search results

**Extensions**:

4a. System returns no search results
    4al. System displays form to close search or resubmit another search
    4a2. Requester clicks link to close search
        4a2.1. System closes search
    or
    4a3. Requester clicks link to submit another search
        4a3.1. Resume from 2

Figure 6.7. Textual use case example #2

**Use Case ID: 121**

**Use Case Name: Search Patient**

**Description: This use case describes how a requestor searches for the record of a patient who has been admitted or seen as an outpatient in the facility.**

**Trigger: Requestor requests a search of the master person index**

**Type: External Temporal**

| Major Inputs: | | Major Outputs | |
|---|---|---|---|
| **Description** | **Source** | **Description** | **Destination** |
| Patient Information | Requestor | Patient Record | Requestor |
| | | | |
| | | | |
| | | | |

| Major Steps Performed | Information for Steps |
|---|---|
| 1. Search for Record<br>  1. Requester clicks on link for search patient record<br>  2. System displays screen form for requester to input data<br>  3. Requestor fills in fields<br>  4. Requestor clicks link to submit | Patient Last Name<br>Patient First Name<br>Patient Date of Birth<br>Patient Medical Record No. |
| 2. Search results returned<br>  1. If record is in search results, requestor selects record<br>  2. If no results returned Requestor<br>    1. Closes search by clicking close button<br>    2. Resubmits search by clicking search button<br>  3. If results are returned that don't meet search criteria Requestor<br>    1. Closes search by clicking close button<br>    2. Resubmits another search by clicking search button | |



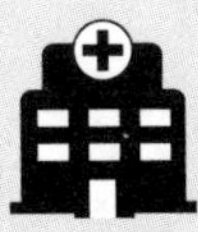

## The St. Rita's Healthcare System Case Study

Linda and Monte briefly met to go over what Monte found out about use cases. "I didn't realize there are so many different use case formats," said Monte when he and Linda met for their briefing. "I identified at least three formats and I know there are a lot more out there. Since design documents are used not only to develop a system but also to make updates or changes, I can understand why standards are essential for communication purposes among current and future analysis and technical teams. How does one developer understand what another one has done without good documentation? It looks like it is the Tower of Babel out there without standards."

"You bet," said Linda. "As I review the examples you've shared, I definitely can see the strong points for use cases in requirements analysis. They tell the story end users and technical professionals both can understand. But standards need to be in place so that everyone is speaking the same language." Linda and Monte agreed they would tackle the data flow diagramming technique next.

Figure 6.8. Use case with sequence diagram and table

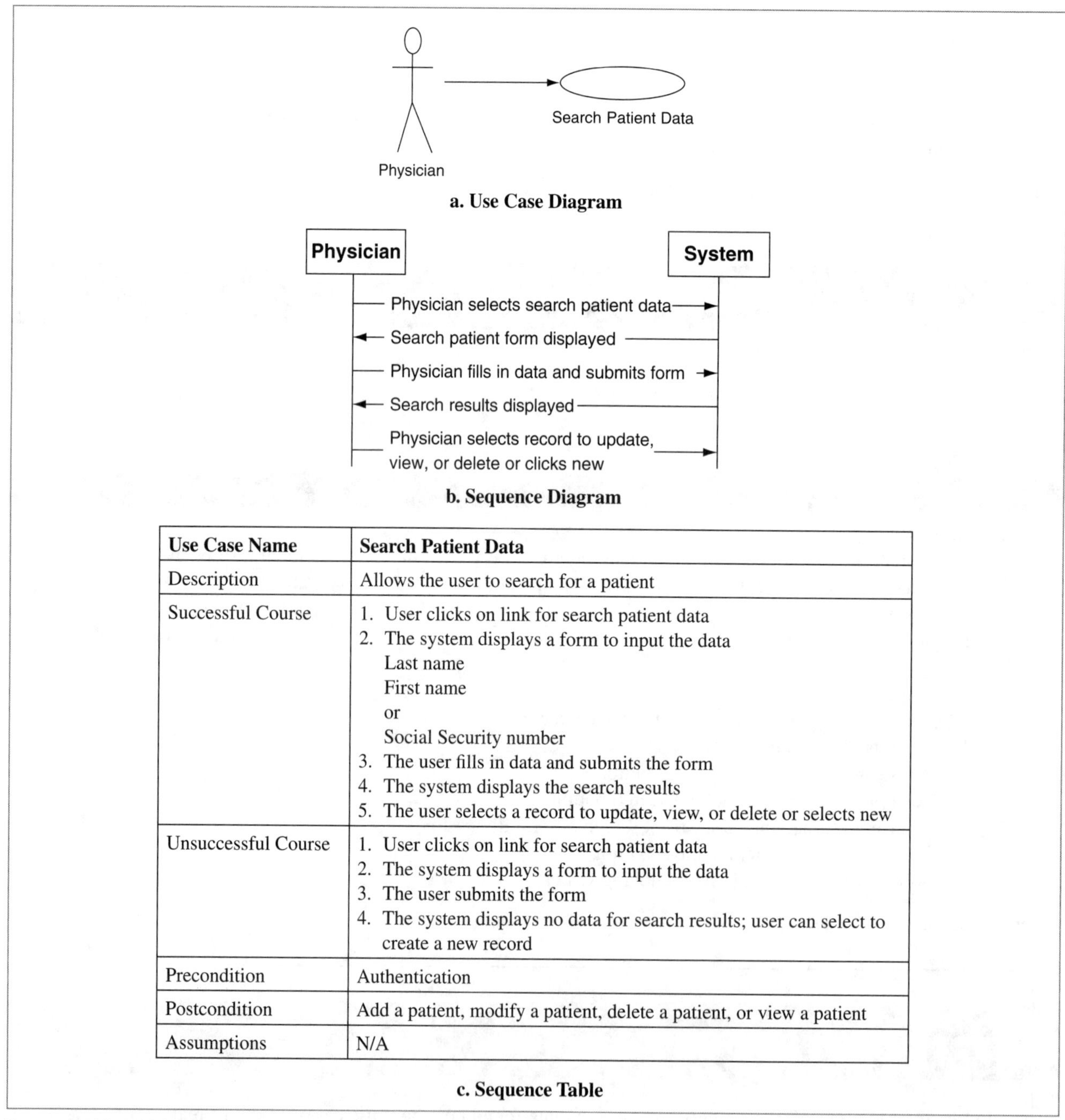


| Use Case Name | Search Patient Data |
|---|---|
| Description | Allows the user to search for a patient |
| Successful Course | 1. User clicks on link for search patient data<br>2. The system displays a form to input the data<br>Last name<br>First name<br>or<br>Social Security number<br>3. The user fills in data and submits the form<br>4. The system displays the search results<br>5. The user selects a record to update, view, or delete or selects new |
| Unsuccessful Course | 1. User clicks on link for search patient data<br>2. The system displays a form to input the data<br>3. The user submits the form<br>4. The system displays no data for search results; user can select to create a new record |
| Precondition | Authentication |
| Postcondition | Add a patient, modify a patient, delete a patient, or view a patient |
| Assumptions | N/A |

**c. Sequence Table**

Source: Smith, M. J. 2012.

## Data Flow Diagrams

A **data flow diagram (DFD)** is a visual process model used by analysts to model the processes, flow, and transformation of data in a system. When analysts model the "as-is" and "to-be" system processes, they can identify differences between the two systems. Finding the differences between the two systems is critical for information for system development, training, and from change management perspectives. Knowing what is different between the current and future systems helps to put in place change processes that achieve a smooth transition and implementation from one system to the other.

DFDs may be developed by analysts from use cases or created directly from the results of requirements gathering. One strength of a DFD is that it shows a system's functionality at a high level which is easy for end users and technical professionals to understand. It is an easy-to-use and fairly intuitive modeling tool. DFDs, however, do not show the organization of data into structures nor do they show decisions about alternative paths.

Like use cases, DFDs can describe either the business or the technical details of a system. DFDs that describe processes from a business view are called **logical DFDs**, and those that describe the technical details are called **physical DFDs**. Logical DFDs are used by analysts in requirements analysis; physical DFDs are used in the design stage of the SDLC.

DFDs are a top-down method of modeling. Diagramming DFDs begins with modeling a system at its highest level and then breaking it down into subsequent parts. Usually, a set of DFDs are necessary to model a system or complex process.

## DFD Components

DFDs consist of four components, each represented by a unique symbol. These components include:

- **External Entity (EE)**: A person, system, company, or agency outside of the organization or any individual or system unit outside of the system under discussion (SuD). An external entity is the source or destination of data. The EE may provide inputs to or receive outputs from the system. The EE defines the system boundaries. Each EE is labeled with a noun. Examples of names are customer, patient, physician, employee, clerk, clinic, and mainframe server.
- **Process**: Any activity or function performed manually or electronically that transforms data for a business reason. Each process must have at least one input and one output. Each process is labeled with a verb and a unique number. Examples of verbs include make appointment, schedule surgery, create order, create record, and process order.
- **Data Flow (DF)**: An input to or output from processes or data stores. DFs represent data in motion. DFs are labeled with a noun that represents the data, such as patient last name and appointment date.
- **Data Store (DS)**: An organized collection of data the organization stores for use, either electronically or manually. DSs represent data at rest.

There are several notation styles organizations use for DFDs. The most common of these are the Gane and Sarson style, and the DeMarco and Yourdon style. These notation styles have very minor differences. However, development tool vendors and others may have unique notation styles. Therefore, standardizing the notation used within an organization is important for communication between the development team on a current project as well as for communication with future developers who make changes to the system. Figure 6.9 provides a comparison of the two prominent styles and their syntax rules.

## Data Flow Diagram Example

DFD modeling of a system usually consists of a set of hierarchical DFD diagrams. The underlying concept of DFD modeling is that analysts will achieve sufficient detail to model the system by sequentially breaking down a process to its most basic parts. This detail serves as the basis for describing the requirements of the system and is used as a foundation for the rest of the systems development process.

Modeling begins with a high level visual representation of the SuD. This is called the context diagram. It consists of the highest-named process or system and includes the EE and the data that flows from and to the process. However, the context diagram does not provide the specificity needed to explain the details of the system. Analysts need to construct additional DFDs to accomplish this. As an example, examine the context diagram for an outpatient registration system in figure 6.10. In this DFD, the process is the outpatient registration system. Each DFD should have a meaningful title and brief summary of its purpose.

In figure 6.10, the external entities include new patient, master person identification system, and electronic patient record system. What this DFD tells us is that data flows from the:

- New patient external entity to the outpatient registration process
- Outpatient registration process to the new patient external entity
- Outpatient registration process to both the master person identification and electronic patient record systems

This high-level view sets the system context, but it does not provide enough detail to identify all the requirements of the system. To handle this, the context diagram is "exploded" to the next level to reveal additional process details. Figure 6.11 shows the next level DFD, called a Level 0 diagram, for the outpatient registration process.

Figure 6.9. Common DFD notation styles and rules

| Component | Rules | Gane and Searson Style | DeMarco and Yourdon Style |
|---|---|---|---|
| External Entity | **Must have:**<br>A noun name<br>Output flow to one or more processes<br>Input flow from one or more processes | Name | Name |
| Process | **Must have:**<br>A verb name<br>A unique number<br>One or more incoming data flows<br>One or more outgoing data flows<br>May connect to any system component | Number<br>Name | Name |
| Data Flow | **Must have:**<br>Name of the data being passed<br>One or more connections to a process<br>**May have:**<br>Connection to a data store or entity | → | → |
| Data Store | **Must have:**<br>A noun name<br>A unique number preceded by "D"<br>One or more input flows<br>One or more output flows | D1 Name | D1 Name |



Figure 6.10. DFD context diagram

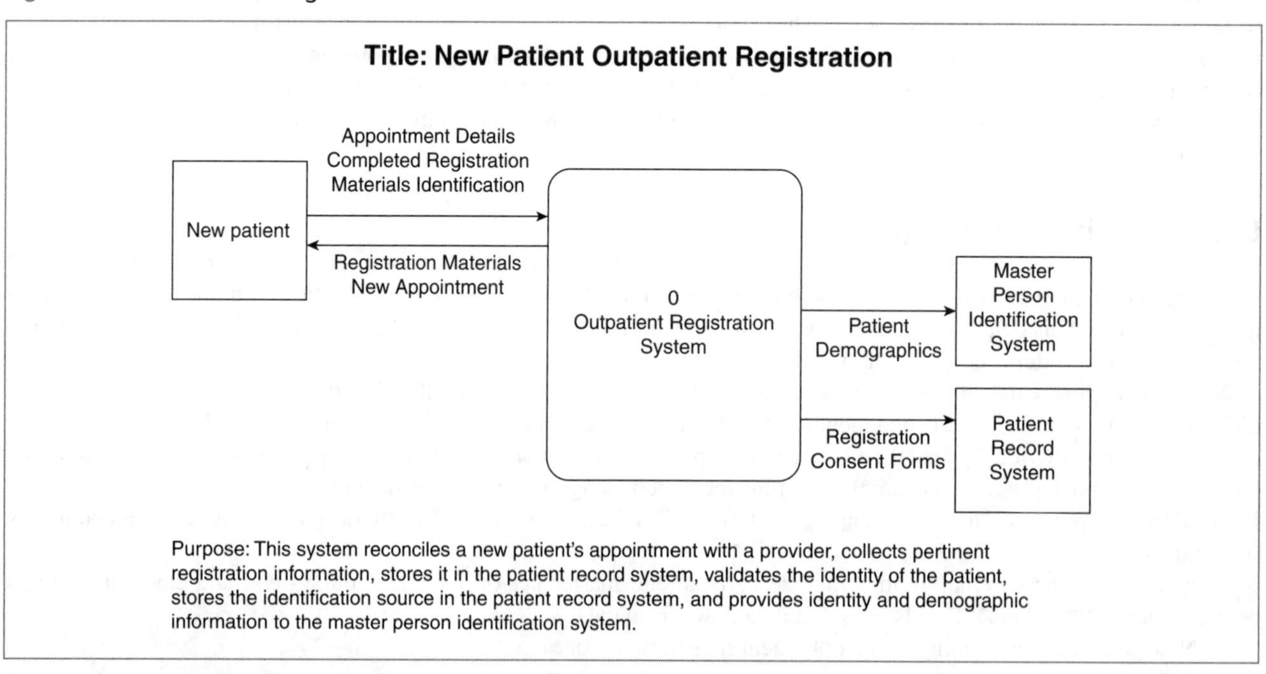




The example in figure 6.11 reveals more of the system details. It identifies four processes:

- Verify the appointment
- Update demographics
- Scan registration form
- Scan consent forms

Figure 6.11. Level 0 DFD diagram

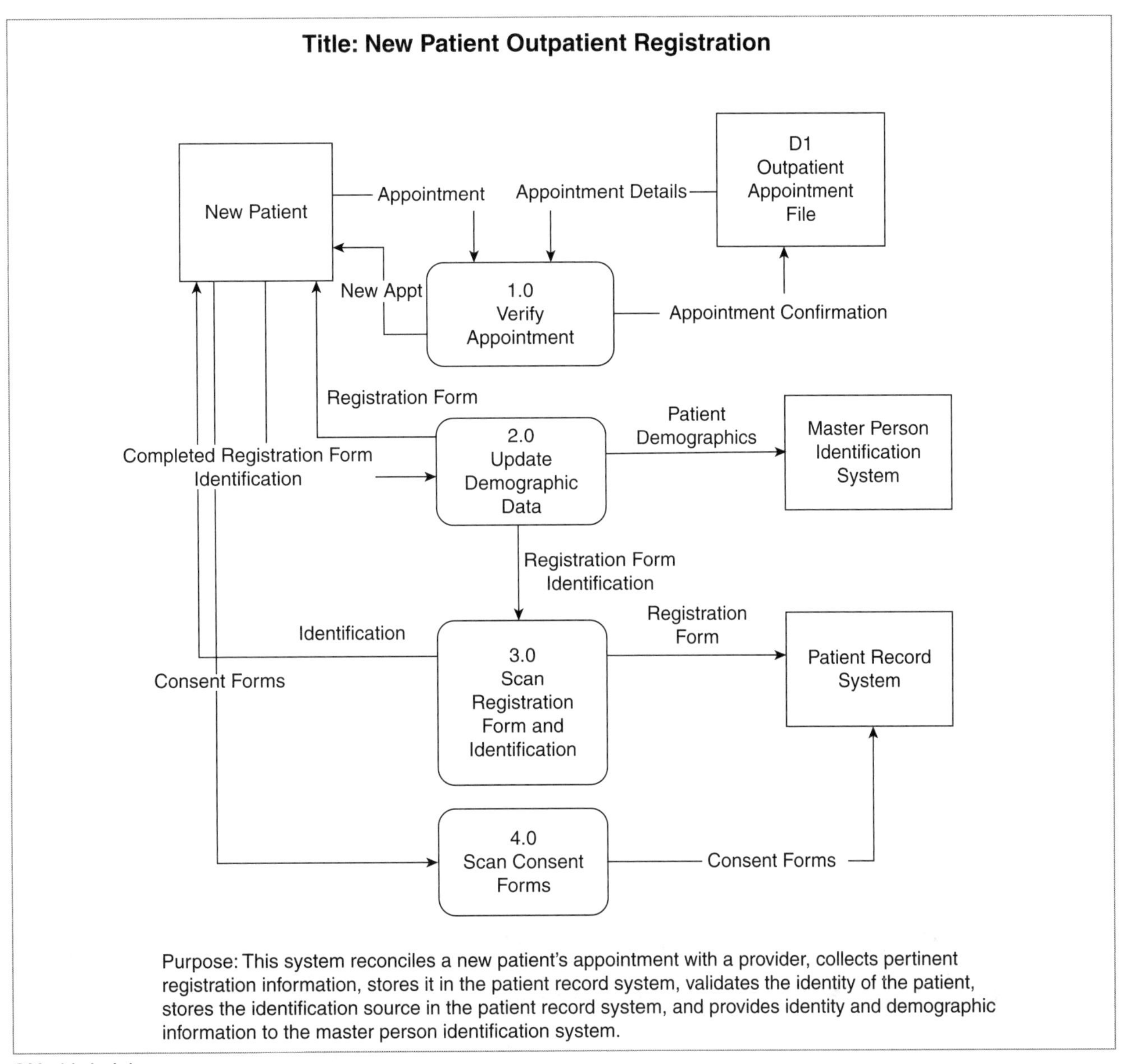




From a syntax perspective, each process is labeled with a number and given a name that consists of a verb and a noun. The data store is labeled with a number and a name. Each data flow is named and shows the direction of the flow to and from each process. Notice that the notation conforms to the DFD syntax rules. Each process has at least one input and one output. Each DS has at least one input or one output, and the EE has at least one output or one input. Observe that the DS "outpatient appointment file" does not appear in the context diagram. This is because data stores that are owned by the SuD are considered within the system, are not EEs, and therefore are not depicted in the context diagram.

Figure 6.12 shows the next DFD level for the "outpatient registration system." This is called a Level 1 diagram. Here, the process 2.0 "update demographic data" is defined in more detail. Note that the numbers on each process at this level are labeled with the prefix "2," such as 2.1, 2.2, and 2.3. This ensures that all the subprocesses in the Level 1 diagram are referenced correctly to originating process in the Level 0 diagram.

If required, analysts can "explode" a Level 1 diagram for more detail. For example, if any of the processes in figure 6.12 required more explanation, a new DFD at Level 2 would be developed by the analysts.

Figure 6.12. Level 1 DVD diagram

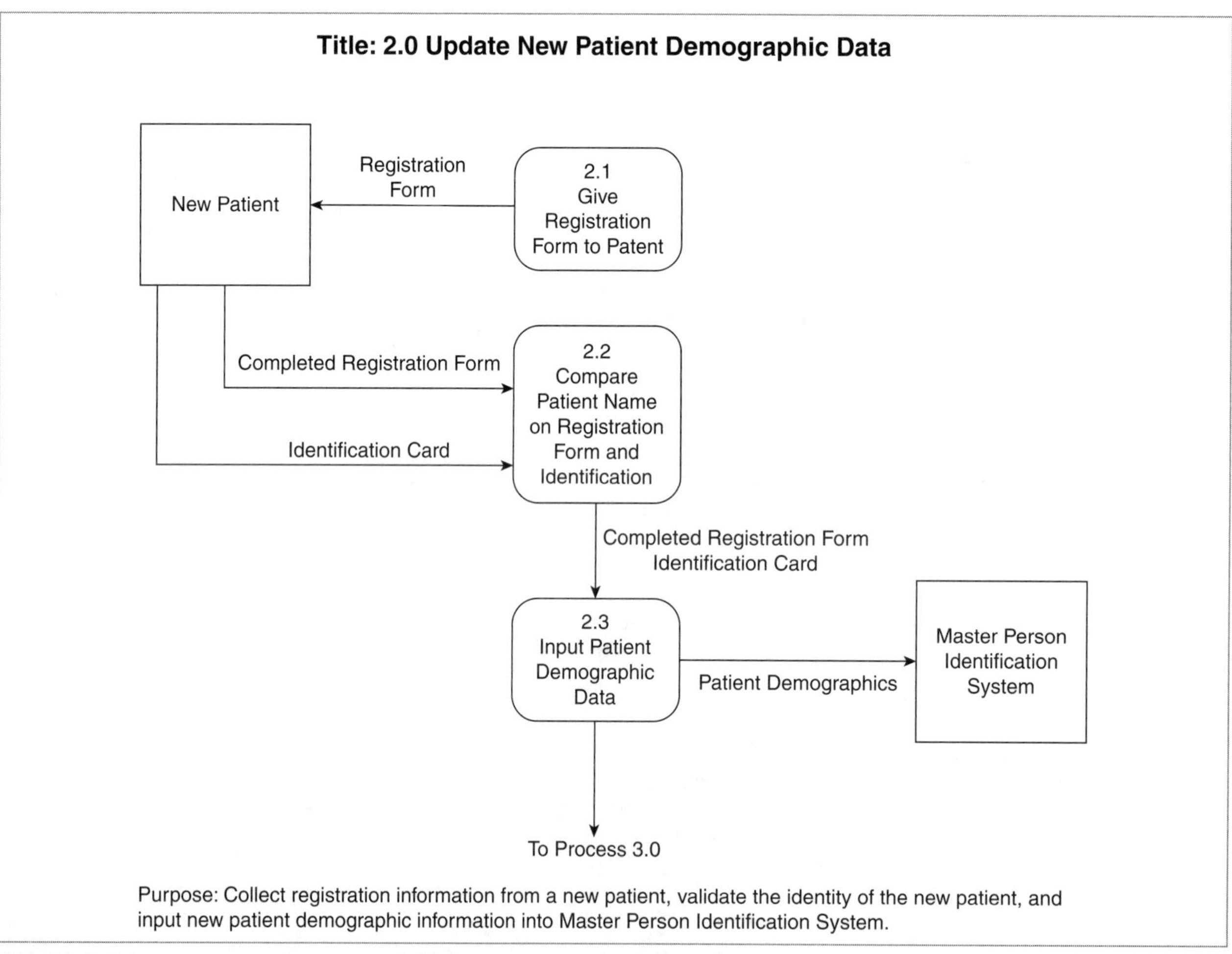


©Merida L. Johns

## The St. Rita's Healthcare System Case Study

"Wow," said Linda. "Now I get how important process modeling is in requirements analysis. I studied this in college, but I never really connected the dots until working on this EIM project. How can we ever correct our data problems at St. Rita's if we don't model our processes?"

"Spot on," responded Monte. "I think a lot of times we've just purchased systems without thoroughly analyzing whether or not they support how we do our work. Then we have to readjust our work flow to accommodate the system. That results in workarounds that many times are inefficient and cost us time, money, and frustration," he added.

"I can think of one system right now," added Linda. "That's the new physician documentation system that's been installed. The residents are complaining that it's taking them between 7 to 10 minutes more per patient to document in the EHR than in the paper system. They're saying that the new EHR doesn't support how they do their work. They have to skip from screen to screen and the flow of data input doesn't match the way they logically interpret or collect data. I think if we were to take a random sample of our systems and assessed if they supported the way we do work we might be unpleasantly surprised by the results."

Linda and Monte continued to discuss the interruptions to work flow that they had observed with several new installations before moving on to identifying next steps.

"I think the next requirements analysis technique to investigate is data modeling. I wonder how process and data modeling differ? I can see how process modeling can help us at St. Rita's, but I'm not sure about data modeling. I've been involved in database development, but frequently on those projects we did not develop data models. I'm interested in finding out some answers to why data modeling is so important," added Monte.

## Data Models

**Data modeling** is another technique that is used in requirements analysis. The DFD represents a visual model of system processes, but it does not model the logical structure of the data or data relationships. Therefore, another type of model is needed to document this information. This model is called a data model. Data modeling is important because it identifies the data about people, places, or things upon which business processes depend, and how these data are related to each other. Importantly, the data model serves as the blueprint for database development.

There are several types of data models, each serving a different purpose. Some of these are described here:

- **Conceptual Data Model**: The highest representation of the entities in a business and the relationship among them. It does not contain attributes of entities. Many times, this model precedes development of the logical data model.
- **Logical Data Model**: A representation of the logical organization of the data, usually for one system or subject area of the business. This model does not reference any technical details such as how the data are stored, indexed, retrieved, or manipulated.
- **Enterprise Data Model**: A logical data model that is a representation of the logical organization of enterprise data showing overlaps between enterprise systems.
- **Physical Data Model**: A representation of the actual structure of the database and how the data are physically stored in the database. This model includes the tables and columns as well as the metadata such as data type and field length. The physical data model is based on the business requirements identified in the logical data model (West 2011).

Part of requirements analysis includes the identification of data that support the SuD. Data models are essential for visually organizing these data and identifying the relationships among them. The data model provides the blueprint for the database which is the foundation for all healthcare information systems. Before examining the construction of data models, it is useful to review the database structures that are used to implement data models.

### Database Structures

Not all database structures are the same. There are several structures that are used in database design and development. Among these are the flat file, hierarchical, network, relational, and object-oriented models. The predominant type used today is the relational model (Harrington 2009). Although, several healthcare information systems use the hierarchical model (Schwarz 2010). Data problems frequently exist due to the architecture of the database. For example, flat file databases produce data redundancy and introduce data integrity problems; hierarchical databases are not an optimal choice for analytics, and multiple relational databases may not integrate well. For these reasons, a brief overview is provided here of these database types and their strengths and weaknesses.

#### Flat File Structure

**Flat files** constituted the first type of database systems. In early processing systems, data were stored in sets of data files that were used by application programs. The files were composed of records that represented a specific person, place, or thing, and each record contained individual pieces of data called fields. For example, a customer file might be composed of records of specific customers, and each record would contain fields associated with the customer such as customer name, customer street address, customer phone number, and so on. Each field in a record was allocated a fixed length to store the data.

Flat files suffer from data redundancy, consistency, insertion, and update problems primarily because there is no way to relate one file to another. Take the example in figure 6.13. A patient's name is included in the patient demographic file, but it is also included in the admission file and the accounts receivable file. The data redundancy in the three files introduces a high probability of data inconsistency among them. When patient data needs to be updated, such as an address when a patient has moved, the data must be separately changed in each file containing that field. Such problems also contribute to the inability to cross-reference files or perform queries across files. Flat file architecture is considered a historical forerunner

Figure 6.13. Flat file database example

| Patient File | MRN | Last Name | First Name | DOB | Street Address | City | State |
|---|---|---|---|---|---|---|---|
| | 0001 | Smith | Dorothy | 08-15-1944 | 112 Oak | Anytown | Anystate |
| | 0002 | Parker | Mary | 06-31-1954 | 344 Pine | Anytown | Anystate |
| | 0003 | Booker | Charles | 03-16-1967 | 567 Oak | Anytown | Anystate |

| Accounts Payable File | Last Name | First Name | DOB | Street Address | City | State | Amount Due |
|---|---|---|---|---|---|---|---|
| | Smythe | Dot | 08-14-1943 | 112 Oak | Anytown | Anystate | $2345.00 |
| | Parker | Marie | 06-30-1954 | 344 Pine | Anytown | Anystate | $3200.00 |
| | Booker | Charles | 03-16-1967 | 567 Oak | Anytown | Anystate | $1500.00 |

| Admission and Discharge File | Last Name | First Name | DOB | Date Admitted | Date Discharged |
|---|---|---|---|---|---|
| | Smithe | Dorothy | 08-15-1944 | 04/16/2013 | 04/20/2013 |
| | Parker | Marie | 06-31-1954 | 04/07/2013 | 04/20/2013 |
| | Booker | Chuck | 03-16-1967 | 04/19/2013 | 04/21/2013 |



of modern architectures and rarely used today, except perhaps in a few legacy systems. However, many departments will use an electronic spreadsheet to store their data. Electronic spreadsheets are like a flat file and suffer from all flat file data issues and should be avoided for the use as a database.

### Hierarchical Structure

The hierarchical structure, usually referred to as a **hierarchical model**, is a tree structure and first appeared as a commercial product in the mid-1960s. It is based on the concept of "parent" and "child" relationships where the parent table, called the root, is placed at the top of the tree and points to child tables that contain related data.

A parent table can be related to many child tables, but a child table can be related to only one parent table (figure 6.14). This is called a many to one relationship. In figure 6.14, the patient file has three children tables: Dorothy Smith, Mary Parker, and Charles Booker. Dorothy Smith has two admission and discharge records and two accounts payable records. To retrieve data, the user must access the parent table first, and then traverse the database down the hierarchy to the appropriate table until the required data are found.

Octo Barnett developed one of the first applications that used the hierarchical model for database development in healthcare in the 1960s at Massachusetts General Hospital (Collen 2012). Barnett and his colleagues designed the Massachusetts General Hospital Utility Multi-Programming System (MUMPS), now called M. MUMPS, to manage complex medical databases.

One strength of this model is its ability to traverse a hierarchy very quickly. This is an important characteristic in the healthcare environment where the operational focus is on an individual entity (for example, a patient). Thus, accessing data about a specific patient is extremely fast. However, random access to data across patients, non-routine, and ad hoc queries can be extremely slow. In figure 6.14, for example, executing a query to view all patients who were administered ampicillin would require traversing every entity occurrence in the hierarchy. This is one reason why modern medical healthcare information systems that use a hierarchical model frequently offload transaction data into a data warehouse that is specifically designed for querying and reporting purposes. VistA, EPIC, and Meditech are among the healthcare systems that use a hierarchical model for their database architectures.

### Network Structure

The **network database model**, first developed in 1967 by the Conference on Data Systems Languages Database Task Group, addressed one of the major problems of the hierarchical database model; namely, faster access of data across

Figure 6.14. Hierarchical model example

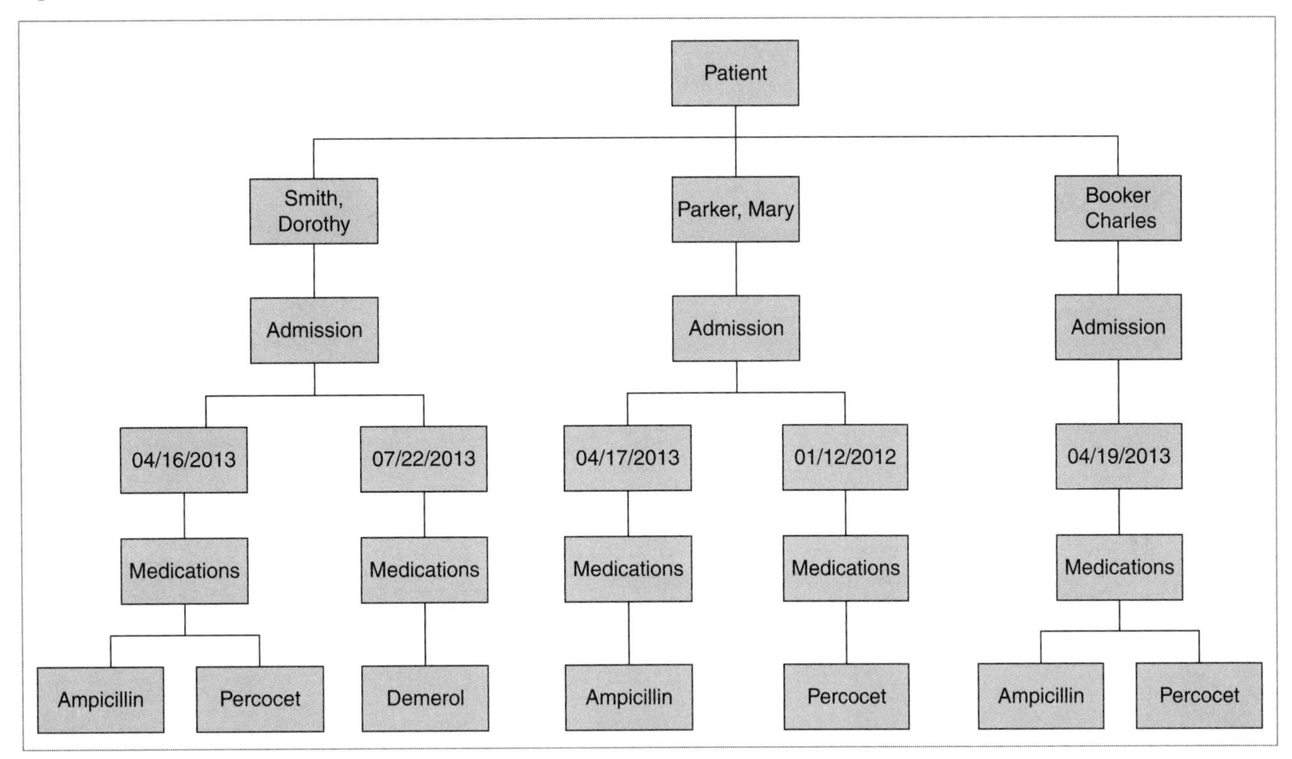


©Merida L. Johns

entities. It accomplished this by allowing more than one parent table to share child tables. The benefit of this model is that users can still access data quickly through the hierarchical tree for transaction purposes that focus on one person, place, or thing, while speeding up data access from any set of tables in the tree. A drawback of this method is that if the logical data model changes, the physical structure of the database is not easily modified. While there are still legacy databases that may use this method, it is extremely unlikely that an organization would develop a new system based on this model.

**Relational Structure**

The **relational database model** is the most prominent architecture used today (Harrington 2009). The relational model was first published in a series of papers by E.F. Codd and is based on the concepts of relational algebra, thus its name (Codd 1970). The relational database made many improvements in data management over the flat file, hierarchical, and network models. The relational database has the following benefits:

- Enables quick access to data
- Permits flexibility in changing database structure
- Accommodates the use of complex queries to retrieve data
- Ensures propagation of data changes throughout the database
- Offers data integrity controls
- Allows efficient modification and development of application programs
- Provides a standard query language (SQL) (Stephens and Plew 2001, 45)

The primary unit of storage is a **table** that holds a group of related data. Each table represents a single entity. An **entity** can be a person, place, thing, or event. For example, there could be a PATIENT table that represents the entity patient, an EMPLOYEE table that represents an employee, an ENCOUNTER table that represents a patient encounter, and so on.

Tables have rows and columns. The column, called an **attribute**, is equivalent to a field in a table. Attributes hold specific values across records in a database. An attribute describes an entity. For example, date of birth, gender, name, or address might describe a PATIENT entity. A row, also called **tuple**, is the equivalent of a record. For example the PATIENT table has one row (record) of data describing Patient A, another row describing Patient B, and so on.

At first glance, the relational model looks like a flat file. However, the relational database allows tables to be related, making it significantly different from the flat file database. Tables are related to each other through common column values called **keys**. The **primary key (PK)** of one table is inserted as a **foreign key (FK)** in a related table. The ability to relate or link tables to each other is what provides this model with the benefits listed earlier. Figure 6.15, describing a simple patient appointment system, illustrates these concepts.

Figure 6.15. Relational database example

Patient Table

| MRN [PK] | Last Name | First Name | Middle Name | DOB | Street Address | City | State | Zip | Gender |
|---|---|---|---|---|---|---|---|---|---|
| 0001 | Smith | Jane | Mae | 4/21/1956 | 123 Oak | Anytown | Anystate | 90900 | F |
| 0002 | Jones | Adam | Mark | 5/16/1976 | 45 Bell | Anytown | Anystate | 90900 | M |
| 0003 | Johnson | Gerald | Richard | 9/15/1946 | 181 Pine | Anytown | Anystate | 90900 | M |

Appointment Table

| Appt. ID | Date | Time | Provider ID | MRN [FK] |
|---|---|---|---|---|
| 5689 | 11/19/2013 | 09:00 AM | Moore | 0001 |
| 5690 | 11/19/2013 | 10:30 AM | Lyons | 0002 |
| 5691 | 11/19/2013 | 9:00 AM | Lyons | 0003 |

©Merida L. Johns

In this example there are two tables: one is the PATIENT table and the other is the APPOINTMENT table. Each table has a list of attributes that describe it; the last name, first name, and so on describe the PATIENT table, and the date, time, and provider describe the APPOINTMENT table. But how do users retrieve data about a patient's appointment?

To retrieve information about what appointments exist for a specific patient, the two tables must be related in some way. To accomplish this, the PK of the parent table is included as an FK in the child table. In this case the parent table is PATIENT and the child table is APPOINTMENT. Notice the PK, or the medical record number (MRN), in the patient table is an attribute in the entity APPOINTMENT and labeled as an FK. This creates a relation between the two tables. When a user executes a query that requires data from both of the related tables, the database management system combines the tables, identifies the columns holding the requested data, and selects the data that meet the requested criteria. When Jane Smith arrives for her appointment, the system allows the receptionist to access both Jane's demographic and appointment information.

Unlike a flat file, there is less data redundancy. For example, the user enters the patient's name once in the PATIENT table and does not have to enter it again in the APPOINTMENT table. Having just one entry eliminates the chance for data errors as shown in figure 6.13. Furthermore, users can more easily make updates and better preserve data integrity. For instance, if a user makes a change to a patient's name, he or she only needs to make the change in one table, unlike the flat file where the user must make changes in multiple tables.

**Object-Oriented Structure**

The **object-oriented (OO) database** was developed by researchers and turned into commercial products by vendors to deal with increasingly complex data types such as graphics, engineering designs, spatial, and audio-visual data that other database types were not designed to handle. The OO database combines the concepts of the hierarchical database and object-oriented programming.

OO databases use the concept of an object. This is somewhat different than the concept of an entity used in relational databases. Recall that an entity can be a person, place, thing, or event. An entity (table) in a relational database identifies attributes about the entity. For example, the entity "PATIENT" may have the attributes of last name, first name, date of birth, gender, and so on. An object can also be a person, place, thing, event, or concept. But unlike an entity in a relational database, an object includes not only attributes but also the instructions for actions that users perform on the object or its attributes. Actions might include, for example, insert new data, update data, or delete data.

The concept of combining the attributes (the data) and the programming code (methods) that can operate on those data in an object is called **encapsulation**. Designing objects in this way keeps the internal workings of the object separate from the rest of the system. Therefore, if the programming code to insert, change, or delete data in an object is changed, it will not affect the function of other parts of the system. This makes OO databases attractive because it modularizes a system. Object design also permits reuse of the object by different parts of the system because all essential actions to be performed on the object are encapsulated in the object itself.

OO databases are organized in a hierarchy and incorporate the concept of inheritance. The highest part of the hierarchy is called a superclass or general class. A superclass could be a person, thing, a place, event, or concept. Subclasses are below the superclasses. For instance, "PERSON" is a superclass and "EMPLOYEE" and "PATIENT" are subclasses. The subclasses inherit the superclass's attributes and methods. Figure 6.16 illustrates these concepts.

In figure 6.16, PATIENT, EMPLOYEE, and PHYSICIAN are subclasses of the object PERSON and inherit the attributes and methods of the person superclass. Inheritance minimizes the amount of duplicate data and duplicate code.

Figure 6.16. Object oriented database example

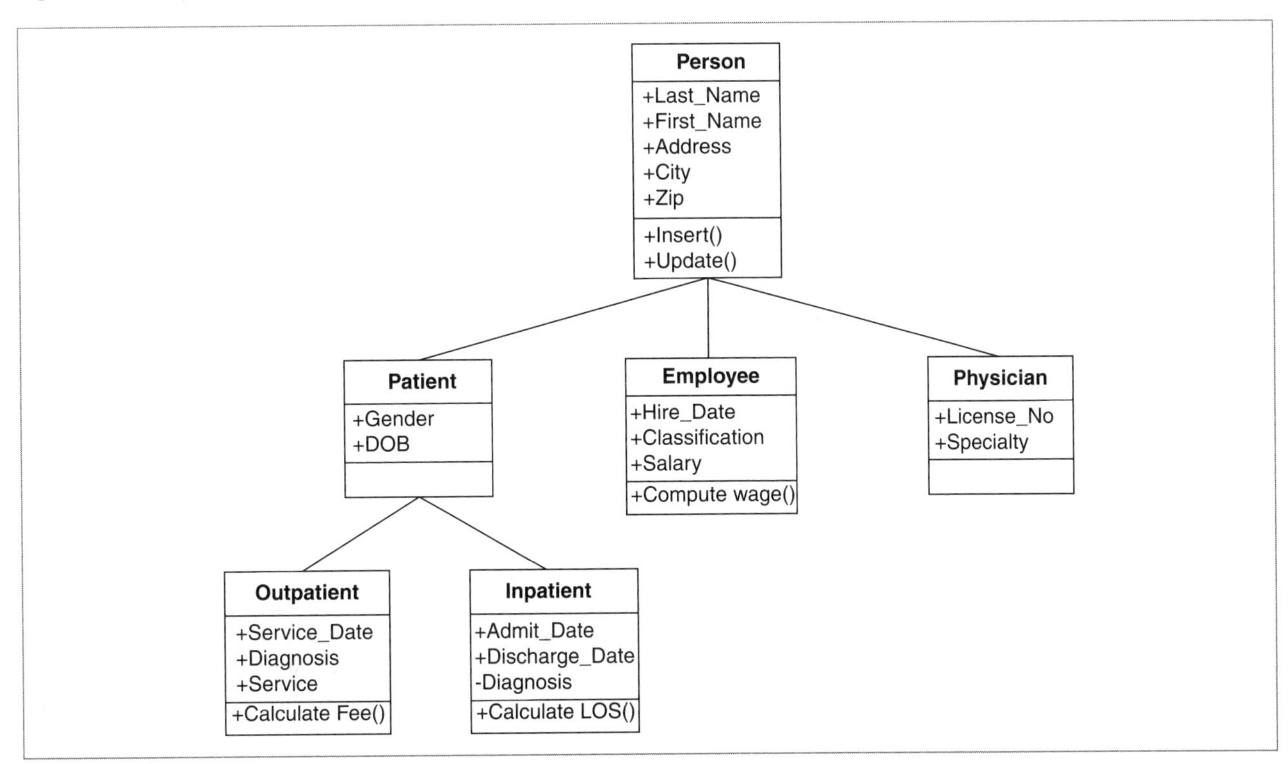

## The St. Rita's Healthcare System Case Study

"Thanks to this research I now understand the differences among the components of database architectures," said Linda. "It looks like healthcare organizations use the hierarchical and relational models the most in supporting EHRs. But, I'm not sure how this relates to overall EIM or DG."

"I can help you out there," replied Monte. "Different database structures support different business needs. For example, businesses that primarily focus on transaction processing and are concerned with record keeping, data gathering, and data generation to support business work flows want a database structure that supports those needs. Healthcare facilities that provide direct patient care are among these types of businesses. Managing a patient admission, a patient medication order, accounts payable, and inventory control are considered transaction processes. On the other hand, businesses that have strong analytical needs and have an extremely high volume of data need a different type of database structure. Then there are other types of businesses that use complex data types such as 3D images and biometric sensor readings that require yet another type of data architecture. So it all boils down to defining the business needs, business data, and business processes in an overall data architecture and getting the right database structure or structures to support these."

"OK, the picture is becoming clearer," said Linda. "But don't some businesses have a variety of needs? Maybe a business's primary functions are transactions, but the company also needs to use its data for analytic functions such as research and development, or to support making business decisions. Can one database structure fit all these needs?" Linda asked.

"Probably not," replied Monte. "And that's where the skills of the technical development team come in to play. The IT professionals make the decision of what structure fits best for what needs. But, before they can make those decisions, they need to know what the business needs are and what the data architecture looks like. They need the blueprint which is the data model."

"OK, I get it!" said Linda. "EIM and DG are concerned with the data architecture. This includes the models we talked about earlier, like the conceptual, logical, and enterprise models. The technical team makes the call as to how to implement these models into a physical database structure and appropriate operating environments. So, EIM's job is to focus on getting the business needs right and developing the data architecture that represents the organization and supports its needs. Understanding the database structures we've researched fills out the overall picture and helps us understand why it's important to get the data architecture right."

"So what's the next step?" asked Monte.

"We need to dive right into the next data architecture artifact, which is the data model," replied Linda.

As they were leaving their meeting room, Monte had an additional thought. "It would be helpful to add a technical person to our EIM team. Collaboration and communication are keys to success in EIM. Certainly, IT is a big stakeholder, and we need all stakeholders aboard. The more IT understands about EIM, the better technical decisions they can make to support it."

## Data Modeling

Data modeling is a critical part of documenting user requirements. The resulting data model focuses on the logical organization of data. It is not concerned with how those data are physically created or stored in a database or manipulated. As Linda and Monte's discussion highlights, the physical implementation of data requirements is a determination made by the IT staff.

The purpose of data modeling is to describe the things about which an organization wishes to collect data and to convey this meaning to two audiences (Hay 1999). The first audience is the end-user group who uses the data models to verify they represent the actual requirements needed in the system. The second audience is the system designers and technical staff who use the data models to execute the business rules represented in the data model to design and construct the actual system (Hay 1999).

One of the most common of data modeling methods, the entity-relationship diagram (ERD) used for modeling relational databases, is described here.

### Components of an Entity Relationship Diagram

Three principal items are modeled in an ERD diagram. These include entities, attributes, and relationships among entities. Although there are different notation styles, the differences among them are aesthetic rather than substantial. The Information Engineering notation, a scientific notation specifically for diagraming an ERD, is used in this section.

In the Information Engineering notation, a rectangle represents an entity. An entity has a unique identifier, the PK. In healthcare, the medical record number is usually the unique identifier for a patient. An employee number is a unique identifier for an employee. For an entity PATIENT, attributes are last name, first name, date of birth, and address. An attribute-name expressed as a noun and listed within the entity rectangle represents an attribute.

Relationships usually assume that a parent-child relationship exists between two entities. The entity from which a relationship originates is called the parent entity, and the entity where the relationship terminates is called the child entity.

Relationships also have two other important properties. These are cardinality and modality. **Cardinality** is how many times a parent instance occurs to a child instance. In cardinality, a parent-child relationship is assumed. In the example above, a patient can have one appointment or many appointments. Cardinality between two entities is expressed as a one to one relationship (1:1), as a one to many relationship (1:M), or as a many to many relationship (M:N). A relationship is represented by a line between two entities with a verb phrase describing the relationship noted on the line. Special notations on the relationship line, explained later in this chapter, express the relationship.

A **modality** of a relationship refers to whether or not an instance of a child entity can exist without a related instance of a parent entity. For example, can you have a procedure without a patient? Can you have an invoice without providing a service? In these examples, the parent instance must exist. Before you can have a procedure, there must be a patient. Before you can have an invoice, there must be a service for which to invoice. The modality in these examples is said to be required. On the other hand, can you have a patient who is not an outpatient? The answer is yes. A patient could be either an inpatient or outpatient. In this example, the modality is said to be null or not required. Modality is modeled in relationships and is illustrated in the series of data models that follow.

Figure 6.17 is a simple example of an ERD showing the relationship between the two entities, PATIENT and APPOINTMENT.

Figure 6.17. Entity-relationship diagram

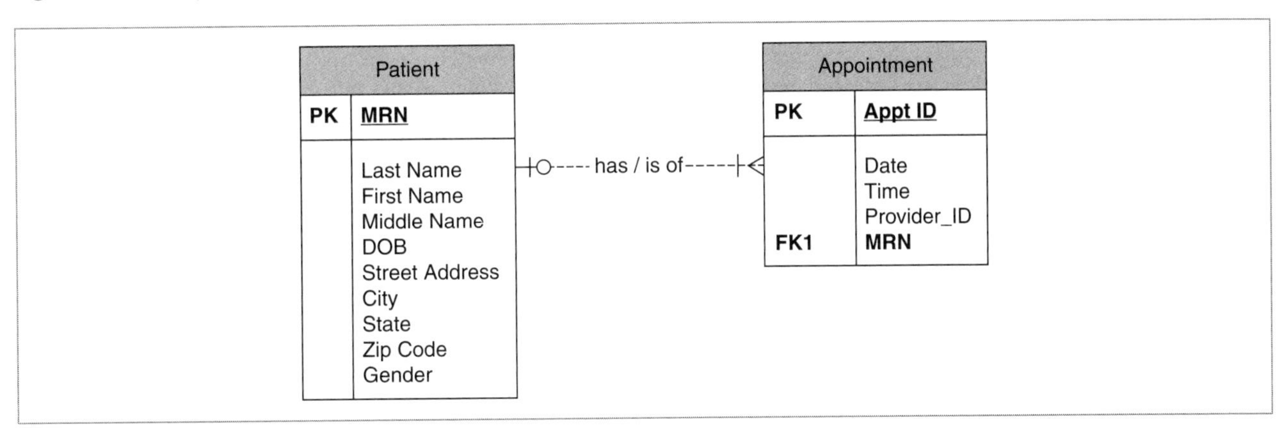




PATIENT and APPOINTMENT are entities about which the hospital wants to store data. Note that both entities are represented by rectangles and have names. Each of the entities has an identifier. For PATIENT the identifier is MRN, and for APPOINTMENT it is appointment number (Appt_ID). Each entity has a list of descriptive attributes included in the entity rectangle.

A line represents the relationship between the two entities. The line has a verb phrase. In this case, the phrase reads that a patient has an appointment and that an appointment "is of" or belongs to a specific patient. This relationship represents a 1:M cardinality, meaning that a patient can have one or many appointments, but a specific appointment can belong to only one patient. The parent entity is the PATIENT and the child entity is the APPOINTMENT. Special notation on the relation line represents this cardinality. The many side is represented by crow's feet and a bar. This reads that a patient can have one or many appointments. The one side is represented by two bars. This means that an appointment can have only one patient associated with it and that an appointment cannot occur without a patient.

## Conceptual, Logical, and Physical Data Modeling

Data models are usually developed by analysts from the abstract to more specific. Here are descriptions of three of these relational data models.

### Conceptual Data Model

The **conceptual data model** is a high-level model consisting only of entities and their relationships. Entity attributes, PKs, and FKs are not represented in the model. The conceptual data model is often used by analysts during the initial requirements definition stage of system development and is the precursor to development of the logical data model. The diagram in figure 6.18 represents a conceptual data model for an outpatient clinic.

Figure 6.18. Conceptual data model example

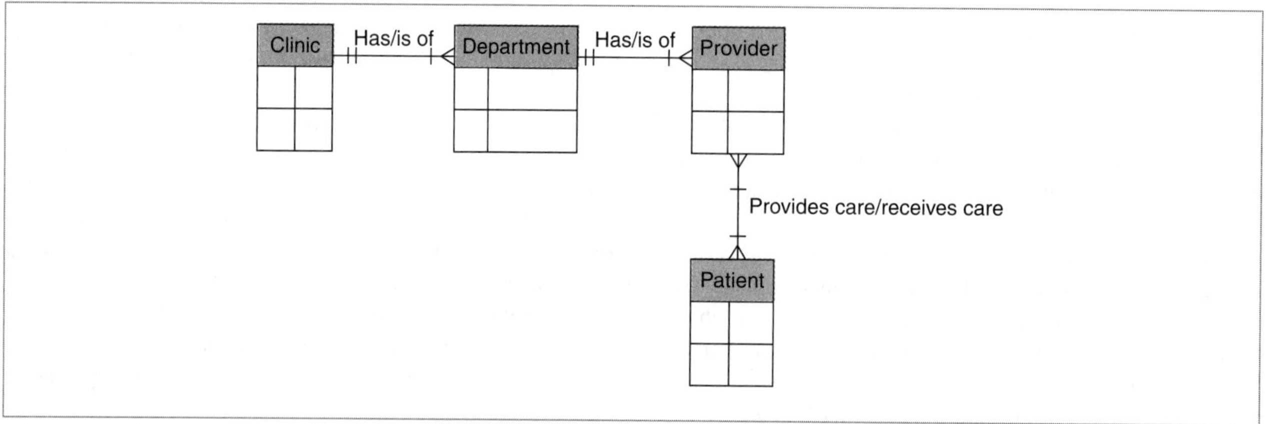


©Merida L. Johns

Here, the entities are CLINIC, DEPARTMENT, PROVIDER, and PATIENT. Verb phrases describe the relationships among the entities. This ERD reads as follows:

- A CLINIC has one or many departments and a department is associated with only one clinic. The clinic is the parent entity and the department is the child entity. The crow's feet notation and bar on the department entity side of the relationship show a 1:M relationship. The double bar on the clinic side of the relationship indicates that a department is only associated with one clinic. The relationship between CLINIC and DEPARTMENT is a 1:M relationship.
- The DEPARTMENT entity has one or many providers and the PROVIDER entity is associated with only one department. Here we see crow's feet associated with the PROVIDER entity and the double bar on the relationship line associated with the DEPARTMENT entity. This represents a 1:M relationship.
- A PROVIDER entity provides care to one or many PATIENT entities and a PATIENT receives care from one or many providers. Notice that crow's feet and a single bar are located on both sides of the relationship line. This represents a M:N relationship.

Conceptual and logical data models are important in maintaining data quality and ensuring that systems are built to support business rules (Stiglich 2006). Unfortunately, this step in analysis requirements is often overlooked, resulting in customer needs not being met due to miscommunication or unfounded assumptions.

One cannot automatically transfer data models from one organization to another. To illustrate this, ask this question: "Can the conceptual data model in figure 6.18 work for every hospital?" The answer is, probably not. To explain why, let us assume that Medical Center A has a department of internal medicine and three clinics in a geographic area. Let us also assume that the internal medicine department provides services at all three clinics. If this is the case, the data model here will not work for this medical center because it limits a department to belonging to only one clinic. If Medical Center A used this data model to develop a database, the flaw would severely disrupt business processes. Appointment clerks would only be able to make appointments for internal medicine patients at one clinic, not all three.

Conceptual and logical data models should be developed for each organization, rather than using a template. This example also emphasizes why healthcare organizations should develop and compare their own data models to those of prospective vendor systems before they make a purchasing decision. Without this comparison, organizations run the risk of selecting a system that is not compatible with their processes or how they conduct business.

### Logical Data Model

A **logical data model** expands the conceptual model by including entity attributes, PKs, and FKs. The logical data model also goes through a process called normalization. **Normalization** is a formal process applied to database design to determine which variables should be grouped in a table to reduce data redundancy. Figure 6.19 shows a logical data model that derives from the conceptual model in figure 6.18. This model includes the entities CLINIC, DEPARTMENT, PROVIDER, and PATIENT. The attributes for each entity, PKs, and FKs are added to this model, making it more descriptive of the data needs than the conceptual model.

Figure 6.19. Logical data model example

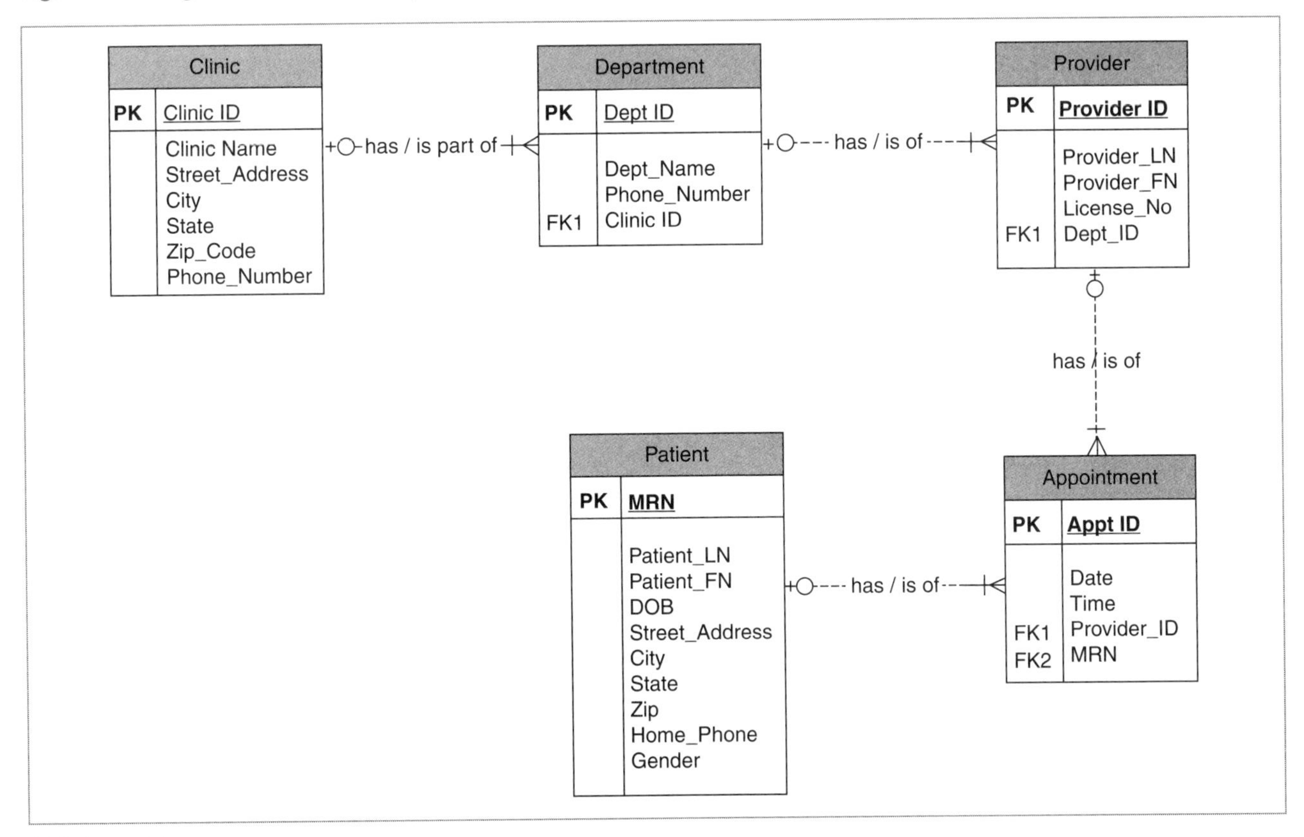




This model includes an additional entity, APPOINTMENT. This is called an associative or intersection entity and is a product of normalizing the database. An associative entity must be created when there is a M:N relationship between two entities. Recall that in the conceptual model in figure 6.18, there is an M:N relationship between provider and patient. Relational databases cannot accommodate M:N relationships. To resolve this situation, analysts create another entity to associate both entities. In this case, APPOINTMENT is the associative entity.

**Physical Data Model**

The conceptual and logical data models describe an organization's data requirements from a business perspective. The **physical data model** provides implementation details for developing the physical database. In the physical data model, entities become tables and attributes become fields.

In the physical model, metadata associated with each field are added by analysts or the technical team. These include descriptions such as field type and length. Figure 6.20 is an example of the physical data model derived from the logical model in figure 6.19. Here we see descriptions of field data type and length and labels for relationships that represent a physical rather than a business view.

Not all metadata necessary for physical implementation of the database appears on the physical model. Analysts add these additional metadata in a data dictionary. The **data dictionary (DD)** functions as the central repository for information about tables, attributes, and relationships which analysts, programmers, and end users can consult to understand the system. Examples of metadata in a DD include default values, validation criteria and messages, and data definitions. The DD is explained in further detail later in this chapter.

Healthcare organizations should establish strict naming conventions to produce consistent, understandable, and unambiguous table and field names. Notice the consistent naming standards in figure 6.20. The analyst named each table with a singular noun and used the table name as the beginning of the label for each field. Standardization helps reduce cryptic names and miscommunication problems among developers. Table 6.1 shows examples of naming standards for tables and fields developed by one organization. Naming conventions vary from organization to organization. Many database systems, such as Oracle, have strict naming conventions users must observe.

Figure 6.20. Physical data model example

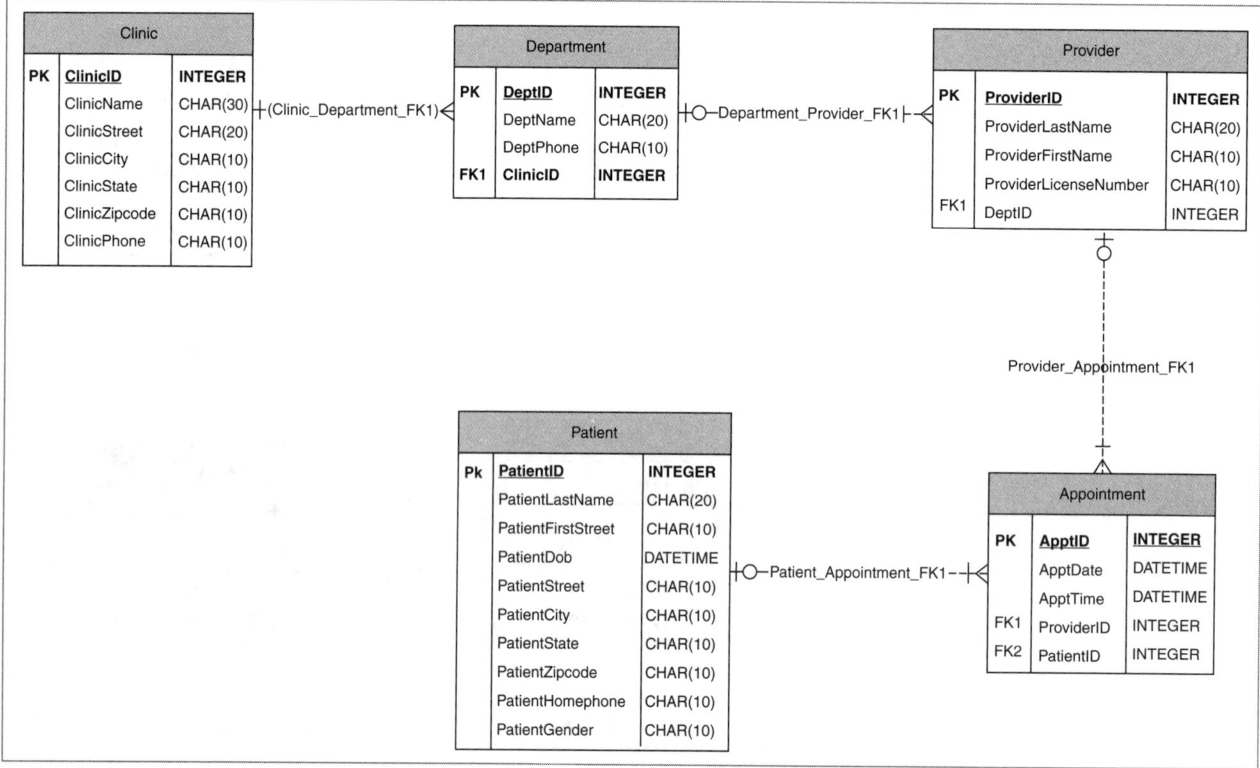




Table 6.1. Example of naming standards for tables and fields

| Naming Convention | Example |
|---|---|
| **General** | |
| Use singular name | "Patient" not "Patients" |
| Limit name to less than 50 characters | |
| Use Pascal Code | "PatientAccount" not Patientaccount" |
| Avoid underscores | "PatientAccount" not "Patient_Account" |
| Avoid abbreviations | "Diagnosis" not "DX" |
| Avoid using spaces | "PatientAccount" not "Patient Account" |
| **Tables** | |
| Use singular name | "Patient" not "Patients" |
| Do not use prefixes | "Patient" not "TBL_Patient" |
| Do not use numbers in table name | "Patient" not "1Patient" |
| **Fields** | |
| For primary key field names include table name | "PatientID" not "ID" |
| Foreign keys should have exact name as they do in the parent table | "PatientID" not "MedicalRecordNumber" |
| Do not prefix names with datatype | "PatientID" not "IntPatientID" |
| Do not include numbers or special characters in field names | |

## CASE Tools

There are a number of **computer aided software engineering (CASE)** tools available that support documentation and communication aspects of the SDLC. These tools help integrate tasks throughout the life cycle stages. Drawing, changing, maintaining, integrating, and tracking analysis artifacts such as DFDs, use cases, and ERDs, is a daunting challenge. Projects contain hundreds and perhaps thousands of such artifacts. Manually maintaining these for large projects and providing easy accessibility to all project stakeholders is impossible. Therefore, CASE tools are used by analysts and developers to support creating, storing, integrating, and accessing this documentation.

The general features of CASE tools fall into the categories of visual aids, prototypes, DD development, analysis, design, and code generation (Post et al. 1999). Tools that support the SDLC analysis phase are called *upper* CASE tools, while those supporting design and implementation are called *lower* CASE tools. Analysts and developers use these tools to produce documentation such as DFDs, data process diagrams, use cases, logical and physical ERDs, screen designs, and develop prototypes. The tools may include utilities that help with code generation for table development, debugging, testing, component integration, and reverse engineering.

There are many benefits of using CASE tools, including:

- Reduced time to complete analysis and development tasks
- Decreased analysis and developmental costs
- Better documentation than manual processes
- Disciplined development approach
- Higher software quality
- Improved communication among developers and other stakeholders
- Shared project and system documentation repository that assists in system maintenance and allows analysts, developers, and end users to share project diagrams and technical specifications (Dennis et al. 2009, 67)

There is a wide spectrum of functionality among CASE tool vendors. At the most basic level, some provide only diagramming functions, while more complex ones provide a full suite of fully integrated functions. Vendors call tools offering integrated functions from analysis through design iCASE tools. Some vendors for large scale products include Rational and Visible Analyst.

## Data Dictionary

Collecting, categorizing, storing, and providing easy access to data about data models including entities, attributes, and relationships is a daunting challenge. The collection of this information can result in thousands of pages of documentation. However, the organization must preserve these data for project coordination and communication purposes among developers and between developers and end users. After development completion, the organization must also preserve the documentation as a continuing reference to its data architecture as well as for legal, regulatory, and other purposes. Just as a company saves information about its financial transactions for reference, auditing, regulatory, or legal purposes, so to must it save information about its data architecture.

To help with collecting, categorizing, maintaining, and storing these data so that they are coordinated and easily accessible, most CASE tools include an automated DD. These data are referred to as metadata or simply "data about data." When ERDs are created using a CASE tool, the developer enters data about entities such as entity name, and entity attributes such as attribute name, data type, field length, and data definition, and the CASE tool stores the data in the DD. The DD also documents relationships among entities and stores the data model. The format and features of DDs vary among CASE tool vendors. Figure 6.21 provides a screen shot of a data entry screen in the software program, Visio®, for inputting data about attributes. At the bottom of the data entry screen for the entity CLINIC, there is a listing of the entity's attributes, names, data types, field length, and definition. Data about each attribute in the data model depicted here is documented by the CASE tool in the same format and in the same way. Chapter 7 provides a more complete discussion of DDs.

Figure 6.22 is an example of a DD that provides data descriptions of the CLINIC entity and primary key Clinic ID in figure 6.20.

Figure 6.21. CASE tool data entry screen example

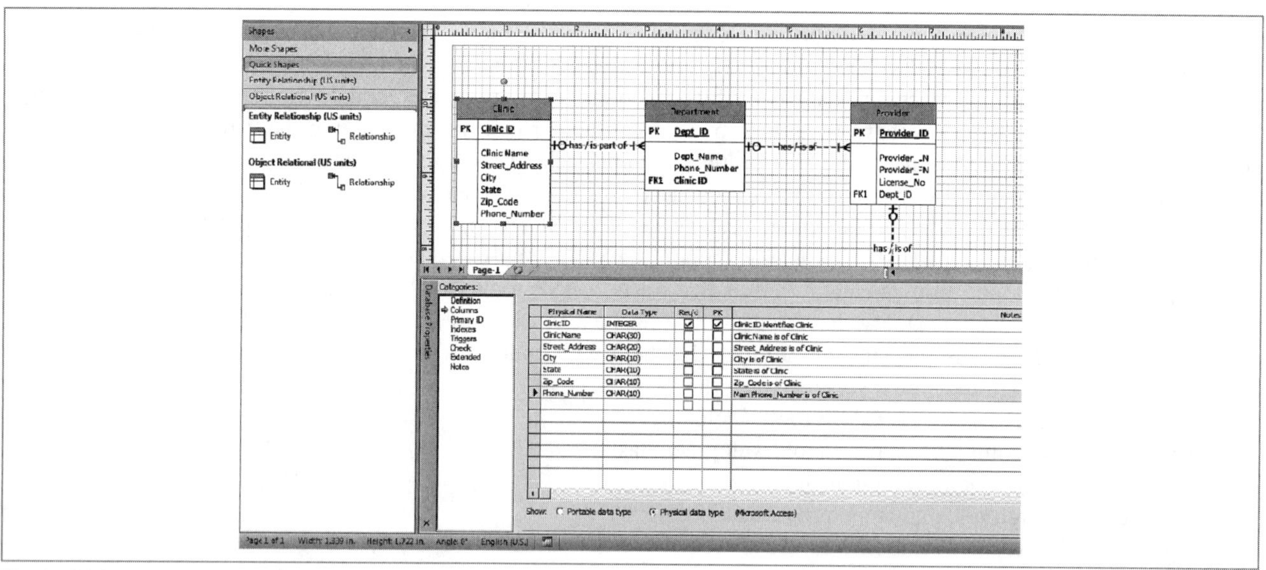


Used with permission from Microsoft.

Figure 6.22. Data dictionary for entity clinic example

**Columns**

| Name | | Type | Size |
|---|---|---|---|
| ClinicID | | Long Integer | 4 |
| AggregateType: | –1 | | |
| AllowZeroLength | False | | |
| AppendOnly | False | | |
| Attributes: | Fixed Size, Auto-Increment | | |
| Collating Order: | General | | |
| ColumnHidden: | False | | |
| ColumnOrder: | Default | | |
| ColumnWidth: | Default | | |
| CurrencyLCID: | 0 | | |
| DataUpdatable: | False | | |
| Description: | ClinicID is unique identified for Clinic | | |
| OrdinalPosition: | 0 | | |
| Required: | True | | |
| ResultType: | 0 | | |
| SourceField: | ClinicID | | |
| SourceTable: | CLINIC | | |
| TextAlign: | General | | |

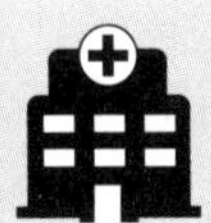

## The St. Rita's Healthcare System Case Study

Linda and Monte presented their findings on data architecture management to the EIM team. Linda provided a review of data gathering techniques for identifying user requirements. Next, Monte gave an overview of analysis design techniques and tools. They spent a significant amount of time on DFDs and conceptual and logical data models since these are primary activities associated with the specification of data architecture. Both Monte and Linda stressed that quality data and efficient information systems development depend upon disciplined and consistent use of tools such as these. Linda suggested that establishing policies and standards for information requirements analysis and documentation might be a DG target at St. Rita's since data problems frequently originate from poor specifications and lack of documentation.

The team members had several questions about the pros and cons among different database architectures. Monte reminded them that database selection was critical but that the fit between the database type and the medical center's needs relies on how well they identify business requirements, and how well artifacts such as DFDs, use cases, and conceptual and logical data models represent these requirements. "The technical staff cannot design and construct good systems out of thin air," Monte stressed. "They have to have well-documented blueprints, in this case, all of the artifacts we've been talking about, to do their jobs."

"Thank you for a thorough review," Val complemented Linda and Monte. "This has helped the team understand the significant role that discipline and consistency play in identifying business requirements and translating these into documents—artifacts as you've called them—that provide the foundation for the entire developmental effort."

"You have great points that data models are the essential blueprints for developing and maintaining EHRs and other systems at St. Rita's," said Denise. "But how do we apply data models to the next steps in the SDLC?" she asked.

Monte replied that the artifacts compiled during requirements analysis serve as the blueprints for system development, construction, and evaluation throughout the remaining steps of the SDLC. "We use these," he said, "to guide the rest of the system design including hardware selection, interface design, navigation design, and data storage design."

"That's a great transition, Denise, and good response, Monte," said Val. "How far should we go in studying the next steps of the SDLC?" she asked the team.

"The rest of the SDLC is important and will interface with some of the other areas of EIM," Bob offered, "If we could develop a summary document on these activities, we could use it to identify areas that we may want to target for DG activities." The team agreed, and Monte and Linda offered to put together a summary document on the other life cycle stages.

Before the meeting adjourned, Monte volunteered that the team would benefit from adding a technical professional to the group. The team concurred that for EIM to be successful at St. Rita's all primary stakeholders should be involved in establishing the program. Each team member prepared a short list of individuals who would make good candidates. Amazingly, at the top of everyone's list was Fred. Fred was a unit manager in the IT department. He was a 20-year veteran of St. Rita's and respected for his IT savvy as well as his quick wit and strategic views. Val said she would talk with Joan Morton and ask if they could add Fred to the team.

Val wrapped up the meeting by asking Monte and Linda to sum up their discussions and prepare a list of recommendations that pinpointed how data architecture should fit as a DG initiative at St. Rita's. The following is the list that Monte and Linda prepared.

# Applying Data Governance

Linda and Monte evaluated how DG activities apply to the data architecture domain. Broadly, these DG functions are to

- Develop, update, and maintain data models
- Develop, evaluate, update, and maintain data model policies and standards
- Define roles, responsibilities, and accountabilities for data architecture management
- Develop, maintain, and evaluate policies and standards for requirements analysis
- Develop and maintain data artifacts and standards
- Develop and implement a quality control program and metrics for data architecture management

They then added these functions to the data architecture management deliverables in the EIM deliverable table (table 6.2).

After reviewing DG plans from other organizations, Linda and Monte decided that a roles and responsibility chart (table 6.3) was essential to specify how deliverables for each EIM function would interface with the DG program. The chart lists the EIM function deliverables and identifies roles and responsibilities for each. They defined the roles as being responsible for, accountable for, consulted, or informed of each deliverable. The intent of the chart is to provide a sample of how they might assign and document DG responsibilities in the future. The EIM team members will use the chart at a later time when they compile their final report to Joan Morten.

Table 6.2. DG deliverables by EIM function

| Data Governance | Data Architecture Management | Metadata Management | Master Data Management | Content Management | Data Security and Privacy Management | Business Intelligence Management | Data Quality Management | Terminology and Classification Management |
|---|---|---|---|---|---|---|---|---|
| Identify mission and scope | Develop and maintain data models | | | | | | | |
| Establish goals and success measures | Develop, maintain, and evaluate data model policies and standards | | | | | | | |
| Put in place DG structure, processes, and communications plan | Define roles, responsibilities, and accountabilities for data architecture management | | | | | | | |
| Secure funding | Develop, maintain, and evaluate policies and standards for requirements analysis | | | | | | | |
| Establish decision rights | Develop and maintain data artifacts and standards | | | | | | | |
| Identify accountabilities | Establish quality control program and metrics for data architecture management | | | | | | | |

Table 6.3. Data governance roles and responsibilities for data architecture management

| Activity | Executive Sponsor | Data Governance Council | Data Governance Office | Council of Data Stewards | Business Data Stewards | Technical Data Stewards |
|---|---|---|---|---|---|---|
| Develop and maintain data models | | | | | | |
| Develop, maintain, and evaluate data model policies and data standards | | | | | | |
| Define role responsibilities and accountabilities for data architecture management | | | | | | |
| Develop, maintain, and evaluate policies and standards for requirements analysis | | | | | | |
| Develop and maintain data artifacts and standards | | | | | | |
| Establish quality control program and metrics for data architecture management | | | | | | |

R=Responsible A=Accountable C=Consult I=Inform

## Part of the Team: Topics for Discussion and Action

1. Monte and Linda added data management architecture functions to the deliverable chart in table 6.2. If you were part of the team reviewing this document, what comments would you make at the team meeting about the completeness of the deliverables list? Would you approve the document as is or suggest additions to it? Explain your reasons for either approving or adding to the document.

## Advanced Concepts

1. Review the advanced case study for this chapter provided in the student manual that accompanies this text.
    1. Develop a set of data architecture artifacts for the case study using either a CASE tool or a diagramming tool such as MicrosoftVisio. These artifacts should include:
        - Data flow diagrams
        - Use cases
        - Conceptual data model
        - Logical data model
        - Physical data model

2. In the student manual for this chapter, read the summary document Linda and Monte prepared describing the activities in the SDLC stages from system design through implementation and answer the following:
   1. How would you categorize the deliverables of each stage?
   2. How would you define these and where would you assign these on the deliverable chart in table 6.2?
   3. Are there opportunities within these stages for DG? If so, what are they and how might they be shown on the DG roles and responsibilities chart in table 6.3?

## References

Agile Alliance. 2013. Agile Manifesto. http://www.agilealliance.org/the-alliance/the-agile-manifesto/.

Agile Alliance. 2013. Twelve Principles of Agile Software. http://www.agilealliance.org/the-alliance/the-agile-manifesto/the-twelve-principles-of-agile-software/.

Balaji, S. and S. Murugaiyan. 2012 (June). Waterfall vs V-Model vs Agile: A comparative study on the SDLC. *International Journal of Information Technology and Business Management.* 2(1): 26–29. www.jitbm.com/Volume2No1/waterfall.pdf.

Brackett, M. 2013 (June). Dataversity. Data Architecture and Data Structures. http://www.dataversity.net/data-architecture-and-data-structures/.

Codd, E.F. 1970. A relational model of data for large shared databands. *Communications of the ACM,* 13(6): 377–387.

Collen, M. 2012. *Medical Computer Databases: The First Six Decades (1950–2010).* London: Springer-Verlag.

Cockburn, A. 2001. *Writing Effective Use Cases.* Boston: Addison-Wesley.

Dennis, A., B.H. Wixom, and R.M. Roth. 2009. *Systems Analysis and Design,* 4th ed. Hoboken: John Wiley & Sons.

Duggan, E.W. and C.S. Thachenkary. 2003. Higher quality requirements: Supporting joint application development with nominal group technique. *Information Technology and Management* 4(4): 391–408.

Harrington, J.L. 2009. *Relational Database Design and Implementation: Clearly Explained,* 3rd ed. Burlington, MA: Morgan Kaufmann.

Hay, D.C. 1999. A Comparison of Data Modeling Techniques. Essential Strategies International. http://www.essentialstrategies.com/publications/modeling/compare.htm.

Hay, D.C. 2003. Data model quality: Where good data begins. *Cutter IT Journal* 16(1).

Hollander, N. and N. Mirlocca. 1993. Facilitated workshops: Empowering users to develop quality systems faster. *Industrial Engineering* 25(10): 18.

Jones, C. 2008. Measuring defect potentials and defect removal efficiency. *Journal of the Quality Assurance Institute* 22(4): 5–11. http://www.qaiglobal.com/Design/Newsletter/attachments/nov_09/oct_2008.pdf.

New York State. Office for Technology. 2003. *The New York State Project Management Guidebook,* Release 2.

Post, G.V., A. Kagan, and R.T. Keim. 1999. A structural equation evaluation of CASE tools attributes. *Journal of Management Information Systems* 15(4): 215–234.

Smith, M. J. 2012. Fundamentals of Electronic Information Systems. Chapter 14 in *Health Information Management Technology: An Applied Approach,* 4th ed. Chicago:AHIMA.

Solarte, K. 2012. Is agile documentation an oxymoron? Understanding the role of documentation in an agile development environment. IBM developerWorks. http://www.ibm.com/developerworks/rational/agile/agile-documentation-oxymoron/agile-documentation-oxymoron-pdf.pdf.

Stephens, R. K. and R. R. Plew. 2001. Database Design. Sams Publishing.

Stiglich, P. 2006. Necessity of conceptual data modeling for information quality. InfoAdvisors. http://208.106.190.209/ArticlesVideos/ConceptualDataModelingforInformationQuality.aspx.

Waters, K. 2007. Disadvantages of Agile Development. All About Agile. http://www.allaboutagile.com/disadvantages-of-agile-development/.

West, M. 2011. Some Types and Uses of Data Models. Chapter 3 in *Developing High Quality Data Models*. Burlington, MA: Morgan Kaufmann.

# Chapter 7

# Metadata Management

Metadata is frequently defined as data about data. This definition, however, fails to provide a comprehensive description of what metadata are or how they are important as a business asset. A better description, provided by the National Information Standards Organization, explains metadata in the following way: **metadata** is structured information that describes, explains, locates, or otherwise makes it easier to retrieve, use, or manage an information resource (NISO 2004, 1).

Metadata have existed for centuries. In the paper environment, metadata are recognized as titles and headings in reports, indexes, catalogues, and directories. One of the most common metadata examples is the library card catalog. The card catalog identified what books were stored in the library and where. Each card in the catalog file provided information on a specific book such as title, book author, publication date, publisher, and subject tags. Library staff and members used these metadata to find and locate books on specific topics, and collect statistical data such as the number and types of books in a library's holdings, the number and percentage of books in subject areas, and retrieval and loan rates by book titles, category, author, and so on. In the healthcare field, an analogy for metadata is a master patient index (MPI). The metadata in the MPI such as "name," "birthdate," "gender," and "address," identify a patient and track specific data such as admission and discharge dates, change of address, and so on.

Today, metadata are everywhere and all industries use them universally. The digital data explosion created with it an explosion of metadata. Metadata describe people's purchasing patterns, Internet searching preferences, and can track physical location and movement. Companies' metadata provide detailed information about individual data elements and records, such as where and in what format they store the data, the date and time, and by whom each was created or modified. They also allow companies to define, categorize, and group data for a variety of analytic purposes. Without metadata it would be virtually impossible to efficiently locate and retrieve information in the massive jungle of a company's data stores. Also importantly, metadata are the key for facilitating data sharing, authenticating content, and determining data retention and destruction.

Metadata are usually categorized as either technical or business metadata. **Technical metadata** are used by technical information systems professionals for the design, development, implementation, and maintenance of an electronic information system. Technical metadata in a database environment include data such as table name, field name, field type, and field length.

**Business metadata**, on the other hand, are data that are useful to the people who conduct the organization's day-to-day business. Business metadata provide the context that makes data understandable and meaningful to end users. In healthcare, examples of business metadata are the headings "chief complaint," "history of present illness," and "past history," commonly found in a patient's history report. These headings, or metadata, provide the context for end users to interpret and understand the data. Taxonomies, also called classifications, and codes are other examples of business metadata. The codes in The International Classification of Diseases (ICD) are a type of metadata that is familiar in healthcare. These metadata are abstractions of the digital resource and provide the context for other data.

Technical metadata are essential for the operation of application software and databases. For example, if a database table had no field names, it would be difficult to extract meaningful data. Without metadata, even simple data entry tasks such as entering a patient's name, date of birth, or gender would be impossible. The metadata, working behind the scenes and transparent to the end user, locate the right database and correct table and fields for the end user to enter, store, and retrieve data. When a registration clerk looks up the name of a patient in the MPI, the system uses metadata to search and locate the data the clerk requested.

In an era of data-driven decision making, business metadata are crucial. For example, the response to the simple question "how many patient encounters have occurred during the past 30 days at all of St. Rita's clinics?" depends upon how the terms patient, encounter, and clinic are defined. Who is considered a patient? What is considered an encounter? Is a telephone request for a prescription refill classified as an encounter? How is a clinic defined? Does "clinic" exclusively mean a formal hospital department or does it include blood-pressure check or flu shot clinics? Numerous cases like this demonstrate the need for defining and making good business metadata available to the end user.

Metadata are vital to creating, maintaining, and exchanging data associated with electronic health records (EHRs), ensuring data integrity and authenticity, as well as leveraging the increasing volume of patient and administrative-related information for decision making and evaluation purposes. Because of these factors, a comprehensive approach to metadata and their management is essential in any enterprise information management (EIM) program.

This chapter lays out the importance of technical and business metadata management as part of a total EIM program and covers topics that will help you to:

- Distinguish among the types of metadata, their use and benefits
- Summarize the role of metadata in the data life cycle
- Explain metadata capture and delivery
- Evaluate metadata management
- Assess data governance for metadata

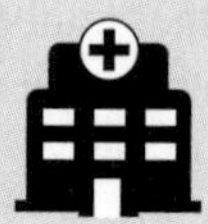

## The St. Rita's Healthcare System Case Study

Denise and Bob met mid-afternoon to plan out how they would approach gathering information about the metadata EIM domain. Both had done some preliminary Internet searching on the topic.

"Metadata looks like it could be a very complicated function," Denise began. "I'm familiar with technical metadata and its maintenance in CASE tool data dictionaries, but the topic of business metadata is pretty new to me."

"I'm on the same page as you, Denise," Bob replied. "From the research I did, business metadata and its management is a relatively new topic not only in healthcare, but in other industries as well. It seems that interest in metadata developed as a result of data warehousing and data integration efforts. This is because getting the technical aspects and meaning of the data correct is essential in any data migration effort. If an account number is defined as nine characters in one table and seven characters in another table, or if the term revenue in one database is calculated differently than in another database, this presents problems in data integration and consistency, and in loading data into a data warehouse."

"I found the same thing," said Denise. "And I also discovered that there are a number of metadata standards for several disciplines or domains. These standards are basically a set of metadata elements, called schema, that are grouped together for a specific purpose. For example, there are metadata standards for archiving social science data, audio-visual content, ecology, education, and geographic data, just to name a few. Apparently, however, there are no equivalent metadata standards in healthcare."

Denise and Bob wrote down a list of topics to include in their presentation to the rest of the EIM team. They divided the work and each agreed to develop a narrative and slides for their portions and to meet again at the end of the week to produce final documents for the next team meeting.

# Metadata Purpose and Types

A principal purpose for the use of metadata in the electronic world is to organize digital resources and identify them. Identifying digital resources supports a second important purpose, which is the retrieval and dissemination of these resources for a variety of uses. More recently, the purposes of using metadata expanded with the need to meet compliance and regulatory mandates with respect to preservation of digital resources, tracking their authenticity, and ensuring their privacy and security (Smallwood 2013).

Depending upon the authority, metadata are categorized in different ways. For example, The Data Management Association (DAMA) categorizes metadata into four major types: business, technical and operational, process, and data stewardship (DAMA 2010, 262). Another authority, The Sedona Conference, a think tank that confronts challenging legal issues, also categorizes metadata into four types: application, file system, document, and embedded metadata (The Sedona Conference 2010). The National Information Standards Organization categorizes metadata into three main types: descriptive, structural, and administrative metadata (NISO 2004). Others provide two general classifications: technical metadata and business metadata (Inmon et al. 2008). Though metadata may be categorized in these various ways, this text uses Inmon's technical and business metadata as key terms because these are generally familiar across industries and the boundaries are clearer than other classifications.

Both technical and business metadata are important for efficient and effective information systems and the communications they support. Technical metadata directly support the development, operation, and maintenance of the technical operations of an information system. Principally, this is in association with software applications and databases. Business metadata provide the context and meaning to data so end users know what the data mean and use data in business operations. Each of these types is explored here.

## Technical Metadata

Most individuals who have worked with a database or word processing application are familiar with technical metadata. In a word processing application, whenever a user creates, opens, or saves a document, the application saves metadata documenting these events at the same time. This may include metadata such as file size, the name of the computer and network server, names of previous document authors, document revisions, and document versions. Some of these metadata are visible to the end user, while others are not. Figure 7.1 provides a sample of these metadata from a Microsoft Word document. The technical metadata here provide a description of the document including the document's size in bytes, number of pages, word count, title, date created, date modified, and author.

In a database application such as Microsoft Access, examples of technical metadata include table name, column name, column type, column length, column description, default value, validation rule, and required field. Figure 7.2 is a screen shot of a table named PHYSICIAN and the metadata for the field Physician Last Name.

Technical metadata include information about where the database physically or electronically stores data. For instance, for a specific data attribute such as "employee last name," the storage location such as the names of the database and table where the attribute is stored, may be represented by metadata like "staff_db, employee_tbl." Other technical data include file attributes such as file size, file creation and last modified dates, file owner, group owner, primary and foreign key (PK and FK) attributes, and access permissions and whether the file is a directory or a link. Figure 7.3 provides another example of a catalog of technical metadata that describe a clinic appointment.

Technical metadata also provide information about data capture such as the date and time an entry is made, how the entry is made, and who made the entry; data changes such as date and time of updates, how the updates were made, and who made the update; and data accesses such as date and time of accesses, who made the accesses, and how accesses were made. These type of data, often referred to as **embedded metadata**, are most often associated with automated records of these kinds of operations (audit trails) and are stored with the data themselves. If data move from a source system to another system (sometimes called a target system), then the system can attach metadata that identify where the data originated. In this way, metadata helps track data movement from one system to another.

In a database environment, technical metadata are typically stored in system tables in the database management system, but separate from the data themselves. Organizations usually have many databases, sometimes hundreds or thousands, that are not integrated with each other. This creates silos of data where coordination of metadata is difficult, if not impossible. Therefore, to help with coordination and maintaining consistency in metadata, some organizations create a metadata repository (discussed later in this chapter) that physically stores and catalogs metadata from different systems and databases (Inmon et al. 2008).

Figure 7.1. Microsoft Word document metadata example

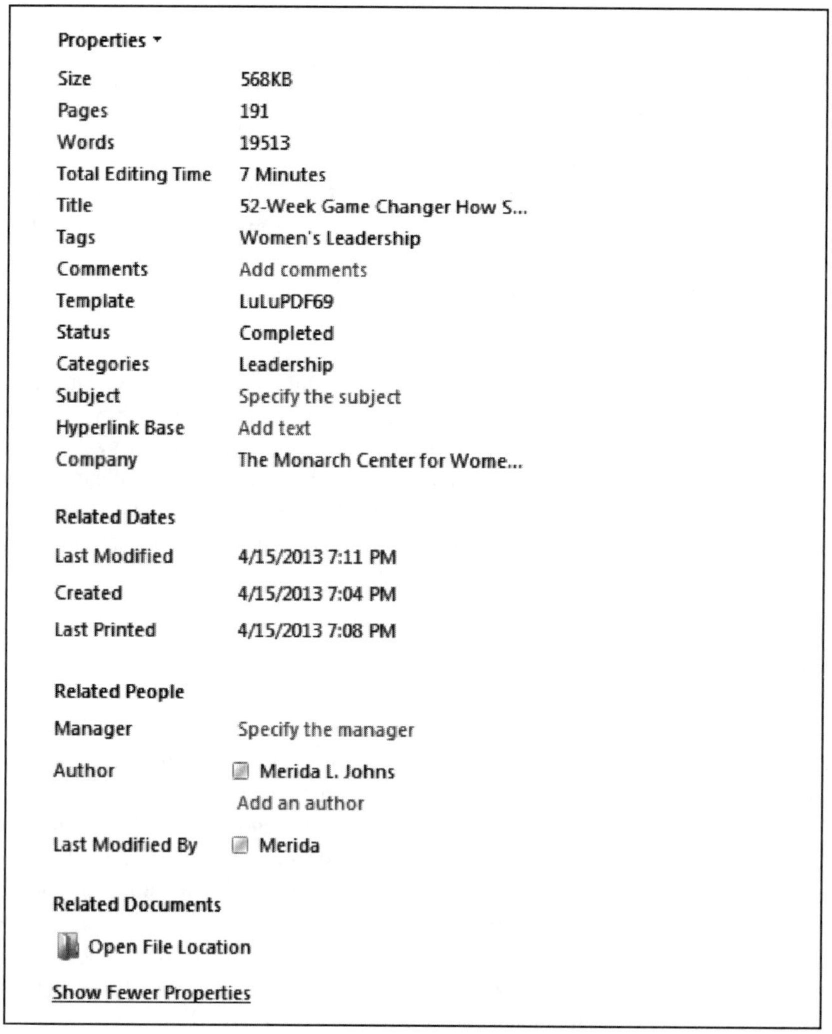

Properties ▾

| | |
|---|---|
| Size | 568KB |
| Pages | 191 |
| Words | 19513 |
| Total Editing Time | 7 Minutes |
| Title | 52-Week Game Changer How S... |
| Tags | Women's Leadership |
| Comments | Add comments |
| Template | LuLuPDF69 |
| Status | Completed |
| Categories | Leadership |
| Subject | Specify the subject |
| Hyperlink Base | Add text |
| Company | The Monarch Center for Wome... |

Related Dates

| | |
|---|---|
| Last Modified | 4/15/2013 7:11 PM |
| Created | 4/15/2013 7:04 PM |
| Last Printed | 4/15/2013 7:08 PM |

Related People

| | |
|---|---|
| Manager | Specify the manager |
| Author | Merida L. Johns<br>Add an author |
| Last Modified By | Merida |

Related Documents

Open File Location

Show Fewer Properties

Used with permission from Microsoft.

## Business Metadata

Business metadata provide the context for data so that data are useful to the end user. For example, think of the number 101. What might come to mind? If you live in California, the number might mean the historic and beautiful Highway 101 that traverses the coastline of the state. If you are a college student, it could mean the first course in a subject area, such as Math 101. Or, if you are a nurse, it could mean a high temperature or a low blood pressure. The number "101" without any context does not give the end user enough information to understand its intended meaning. But, if headings or tags (metadata) such as "Fahrenheit temperature" or "diastolic blood pressure" are added to the number "101," the data becomes meaningful.

In a health information management (HIM) environment, a disease index is an example of metadata. This index contains the following metadata tags: International Classification of Diseases (ICD) code, health record number, admission date, discharge date, patient gender, date of birth, and attending physician. Other examples of business metadata include field definitions, permissible values for fields, source system identification, keywords, system of record for data elements, names of reports, headings in reports, and business rules (addressed later in this chapter).

Essentially, business metadata are everywhere within the healthcare organization. They are on reports, headings on computer screens, documents, proposals, bank statements, and on just about every document or report that an organization creates or maintains (Inmon et al. 2008). Frequently, metadata are also contained in computer code. For example, a typical

Figure 7.2. Microsoft Access database metadata example

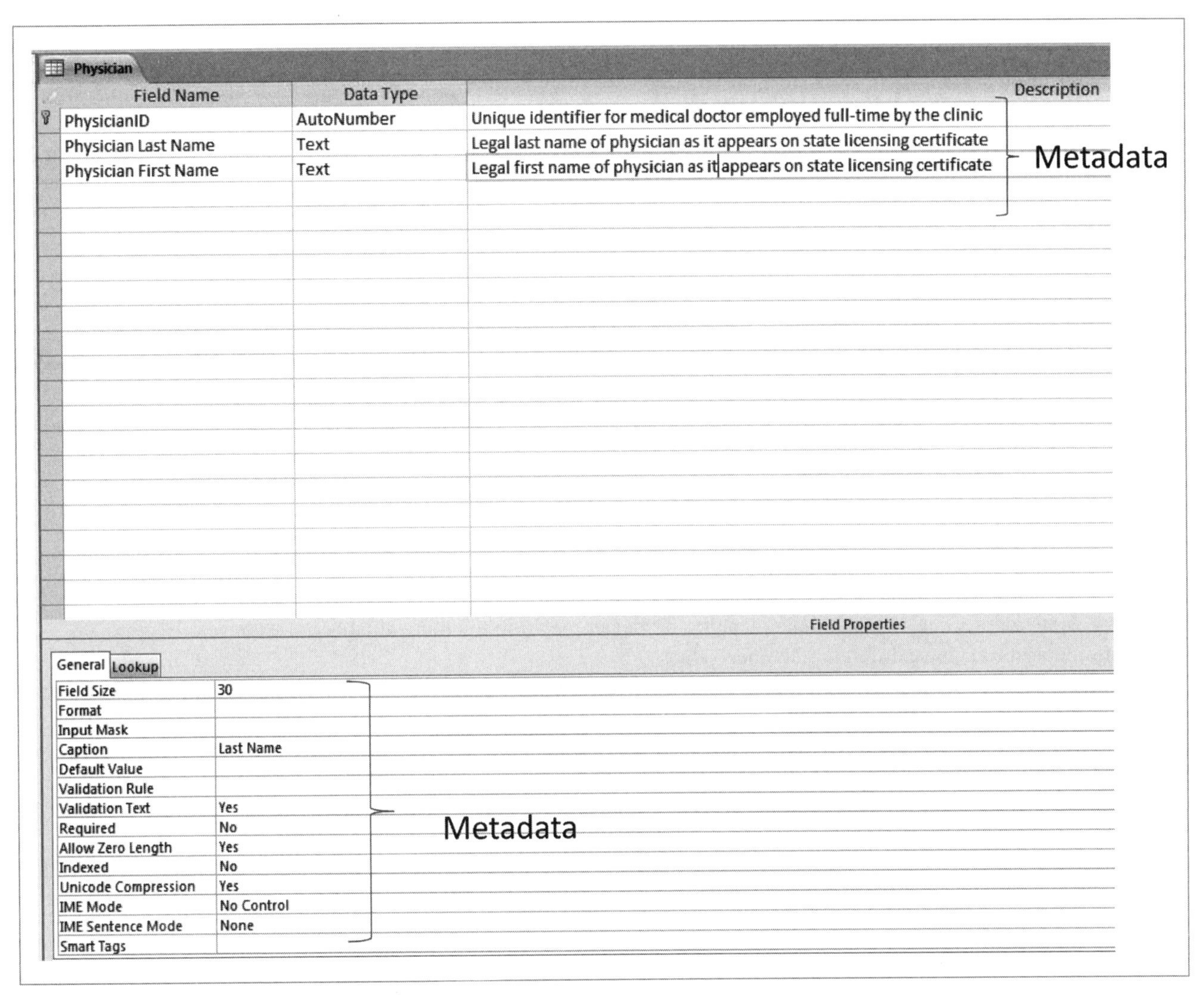


Used with permission from Microsoft.

Figure 7.3. Technical metadata example

| Table Name | Column Name | Column Null | Column Datatype and Length | Primary Key | Foreign Key |
|---|---|---|---|---|---|
| CL_APPT | Patient ID | NO | NUMBER(13) | YES | NO |
| | APPTDATE | NO | DATE | NO | NO |
| | APPTTIME | NO | TIME | NO | NO |
| | PROVIDER | NO | NUMBER(6) | NO | YES |
| | SERVICE_TYPE | NO | NUMBER(8) | NO | YES |
| | CLINIC | NO | NUMBER(5) | NO | YES |

"if-then" statement in computer code often reflects a business rule, such as "if the patient is less than 15 years old, then the patient is categorized as an adolescent patient."

## Benefits of Metadata Management

A good analogy for metadata management is the comparison between the current big data era and the transportation revolution. In the early days of transportation when there were few cars, controls like traffic lights and stop signs were unnecessary. But when roads filled with a critical mass of cars, traffic control and management became essential. The same was true for flight transportation. In the early years there was no airway traffic control center, but as the number and use of planes increased, controls were essential to manage air traffic (Varonis 2013). The same situation is proving true for data.

In the beginning of electronic data processing, when the data load was much less, simple technical metadata were all that organizations required to identify and track data. Business metadata frequently resided in the brains of managers, supervisors, and employees. But as the world's data storage capacity grows, old ways of cataloging and informally documenting metadata do not work (Hilbert and Lopez 2011). Take, for the example, the following healthcare metadata issues which are documented in a 2013 report by the Office of the National Coordinator (ONC 2013):

- Inconsistent data element classification throughout the organization. For example, departments may categorize provision of clinical services differently; one may classify the provision as a "visit" while others may classify it as an "encounter."
- Inconsistent data element data types among databases. For example, in one database alpha characters (for example, M, F, or U) classify gender while in another it is classified by a numeric character (for example, 1, 2, or 3).
- Inaccurate reports due to lack of data mapping. For example, different clinical laboratories have different names for different tests and have different reference values.
- Inability to retrieve data due to format inconsistencies. For example, free text fields that allow for variable input across patients.
- Inability to track patient clinical trends due to lack of labels. For example, blood pressure measurements analysis provided different results due to failure to label blood pressures as resting, sitting, or standing.
- Inaccurate reports due to incomplete or redundant data. For example, essential data elements are not documented in the patient record or are documented in two different places.
- Inaccurate reporting due to inconsistencies in coding. For example, using non-standardized codes for reporting diagnosis or treatment.

Organizations can mitigate many of these data issues by properly using metadata and metadata repositories. Metadata and its management aids organizations in repurposing data and avoiding the expensive process of recollecting it. This means that when an organization establishes definitions for data and makes them available across the organization, end users can use the data in multiple ways. Another benefit is that metadata facilitate decision making by providing fast and efficient retrieval of data that are consistent and accurate. In these cases, the metadata allow end users to easily locate and retrieve information from the organization's data stores. Metadata also serve as the backbone of electronic records by providing consistent record identification, and preserving their authenticity by documenting their provenance, creation, modification, and use. And equally as important, metadata play a vital role for conducting data conversion and migration projects (Franks and Knude 2006). Metadata benefits include:

- Increasing the value of strategic information for data warehousing, customer relation management (CRM), and similar activities by providing context for data and aiding executives and managers in making better decisions
- Reducing training costs and lowering the impact of staff turnover because organizational knowledge is retained by documenting data context, history, and origin
- Decreasing data-oriented research time because business analysts can find the information they need in a timely manner
- Improving communication by bridging the gap between business users and IT professionals, leveraging work done by other teams, and increasing confidence in IT system data
- Increasing system development speed because organizational data are fully defined by the organization, both from technical and business views
- Identifying and reducing redundant data and processes, thereby reducing rework and redundant and potentially out-of-date or incorrect data use (DAMA 2006, 259–260)

Various stakeholders including administrators, technical professionals, and knowledge workers receive benefits from metadata management (National Forum on Educational Statistics 2009). Figure 7.4 shows how each stakeholder benefits in different ways and the breadth and versatility of metadata management paybacks.

Figure 7.4. Some benefits of metadata

| Benefits for Policy Makers, Managers, Knowledge Workers |
|---|
| • Improves data analysis and use by providing interpretation guidance<br>• Improves accessibility and presentation of data<br>• Identifies why individual data elements are collected (for example, compliance, legal reasons)<br>• Reduces the likelihood of incorrect or inconsistent reporting<br>• Reduces collection demands by identifying redundant data<br>• Improves data comparability and continuity over time<br>• Improves data auditing |
| **Benefits for Technical Staff** |
| • Provides a clear list of technical attributes<br>• Improves understanding of the business processes requiring data collection and use<br>• Identifies sensitive and confidential data<br>• Simplifies and expedites data access and retrieval<br>• Reduces user inquiries to technical staff through improved system navigation and data accessibility<br>• Simplifies the exchange of data between systems |

Source: National Forum on Education Statistics 2009.

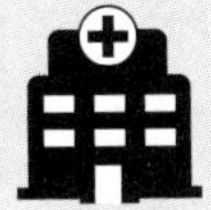

## *The St. Rita's Healthcare System Case Study*

Denise's research looked at the various ways metadata are identified. She and Bob agreed that metadata exist everywhere in an organization but wondered how an organization went about identifying them. "If metadata are everywhere," said Bob, "it seems like it could be a daunting task to begin to identify what digital resources have metadata and how to categorize them."

"Another thought crossed my mind," Denise added. "I'm questioning whether or not we have metadata silos at St. Rita's, similar to other data silos, where metadata are not only duplicated but also have different definitions applied to the metadata themselves."

"Yikes, I never thought of the metadata issue from that perspective," Bob responded.

"Well, I don't think St. Rita's should reinvent the wheel in developing methods for identifying metadata. We should look for and use proven techniques to identify and capture metadata," Denise advised.

# Identifying Metadata

Organizations can identify metadata in several ways. One approach is to review existing organizational sources for metadata, such as documents, reports, and database catalogs (Inmon et al. 2008). Another is to apply techniques similar to those used in requirements analysis. In this approach, following data through its life cycle is the basis for identifying both technical and business metadata requirements (DAMA 2010). A third alternative is to use an existing categorization (schema) or expand upon one by adding other metadata elements (Franks and Knude 2006). These three approaches are described below.

## Existing Sources of Metadata

There are many existing sources, in digital and other formats, within an organization that analysts use to identify metadata. One good source is reports. The date, author, title, headings, column titles, aggregate data, and formulas for derived data are all types of metadata. For example, the spreadsheet in figure 7.5 is a download of a partial report available on the Centers for Medicare and Medicaid Services (CMS) website. Note there are no headings in this spreadsheet, so the data are of no value because one cannot interpret them.

In Figure 7.6, however, there are headings at the top of each column. These headings are metadata. They describe the data in each column. However, headings may not provide enough specificity to identify the meaning of the data. For instance, what does "Hospital Cost" in the title mean? What does "Report Record Number" signify? What is "Provider Control Type Code" and what does the numeral in that column represent? These are basic questions and the answers should be documented in an organization's data dictionary (DD).

Documents are also rich sources of metadata. Take, for example, the document in figure 7.7. Among the metadata on this document are facility, date of destruction, destroyed records, method of destruction, name of party responsible for

Figure 7.5. **Example report with no headings**

| | | | | | | | | | | |
|---|---|---|---|---|---|---|---|---|---|---|
| 517462 | 2 | 340036 | | 1 | 10/1/2012 | 12/31/2012 | 6/14/2013 | N | N | B |
| 517709 | 2 | 420043 | | 1 | 10/1/2012 | 12/31/2012 | 6/18/2013 | N | N | B |
| 517800 | 2 | 500015 | | 1 | 10/1/2012 | 12/31/2012 | 6/19/2013 | N | N | B |
| 518289 | 4 | 220098 | | 1 | 10/1/2012 | 12/31/2012 | 6/24/2013 | N | N | B |
| 518387 | 4 | 220017 | | 1 | 10/1/2012 | 12/31/2012 | 6/24/2013 | N | N | B |
| 518388 | 4 | 220020 | | 1 | 10/1/2012 | 12/31/2012 | 6/24/2013 | N | N | B |
| 518389 | 4 | 220036 | | 1 | 10/1/2012 | 12/31/2012 | 6/24/2013 | N | N | B |
| 518390 | 4 | 220067 | | 1 | 10/1/2012 | 12/31/2012 | 6/24/2013 | N | N | B |
| 518391 | 4 | 220073 | | 1 | 10/1/2012 | 12/31/2012 | 6/24/2013 | N | N | B |
| 518392 | 4 | 220080 | | 1 | 10/1/2012 | 12/31/2012 | 6/24/2013 | N | N | B |
| 518393 | 4 | 220111 | | 1 | 10/1/2012 | 12/31/2012 | 6/24/2013 | N | N | B |
| 518394 | 4 | 220126 | | 1 | 10/1/2012 | 12/31/2012 | 6/24/2013 | N | N | B |
| 518395 | 4 | 220174 | | 1 | 10/1/2012 | 12/31/2012 | 6/24/2013 | N | N | B |
| 518508 | 4 | 364048 | | 1 | 10/15/2012 | 12/31/2012 | 6/25/2013 | N | N | B |
| 518765 | 4 | 364049 | | 1 | 10/23/2012 | 12/31/2012 | 6/27/2013 | N | N | B |
| 518766 | 5 | 364050 | | 2 | 11/20/2012 | 12/31/2012 | 6/27/2013 | N | N | B |
| 518847 | 9 | 131313 | | 1 | 10/1/2012 | 12/31/2012 | 6/28/2013 | N | N | B |
| 519423 | 9 | 111310 | | 1 | 11/1/2012 | 12/31/2012 | 7/23/2013 | N | N | B |
| 519579 | 2 | 420027 | | 1 | 10/1/2012 | 12/31/2012 | 7/23/2013 | N | N | B |
| 520078 | 1 | 42004 | | 1 | 10/1/2012 | 12/31/2012 | 8/5/2013 | N | N | B |
| 520079 | 1 | 42008 | | 1 | 12/1/2012 | 12/31/2012 | 8/5/2013 | N | N | B |
| 521521 | 11 | 241362 | | 1 | 10/1/2012 | 3/31/2013 | 9/10/2013 | N | Y | B |
| 521840 | 5 | 673025 | | 1 | 1/1/2013 | 4/7/2013 | 9/17/2013 | N | N | B |
| 522024 | 2 | 40051 | | 1 | 10/1/2012 | 3/31/2013 | 9/23/2013 | N | N | B |

Source: CMS 2014.

destruction, witness to destruction, and department manager. Looking closer at this document, there are opportunities to refine the metadata. For example, what does "description" mean? Since the document does not include a formal title, such as "Certificate of Destruction of Patient Records," or "Certificate of Destruction of Employee Records," the description could be a patient record number, an employee number, or a financial report title. Another improvement would be to provide a definition for "inclusive dates covered." If referring to patient records, does this mean admission dates or discharge dates? If referring to an employee record, does this mean hire date or discharge date?

Organizations also apply metadata to business rules. A **business rule** is a statement that defines or constrains how someone conducts a particular aspect of a business (Business Rules Group 2013). Business rules can apply to data as well as to organizational guidance. From the data perspective, business rules are defined as individual pieces of logic an organization uses to carry out its operational and managerial activities (Chisholm 2004, xix). More specifically, defined in the context of

Figure 7.6. Example report with headings

| Hospital Cost Report | | | | |
|---|---|---|---|---|
| **Report Record Number** | **Provider Control Type Code** | **Provider Number** | **NPI Number** | **Report Status Code** |
| 517462 | 2 | 340036 | | 1 |
| 517709 | 2 | 420043 | | 1 |
| 517800 | 2 | 500015 | | 1 |
| 518289 | 4 | 220098 | | 1 |
| 518387 | 4 | 220017 | | 1 |
| 518388 | 4 | 220020 | | 1 |
| 518389 | 4 | 220036 | | 1 |
| 518390 | 4 | 220067 | | 1 |
| 518391 | 4 | 220073 | | 1 |
| 518392 | 4 | 220080 | | 1 |
| 518393 | 4 | 220111 | | 1 |
| 518394 | 4 | 220126 | | 1 |
| 518395 | 4 | 220174 | | 1 |
| 518508 | 4 | 364048 | | 1 |
| 518765 | 4 | 364049 | | 1 |
| 518766 | 5 | 364050 | | 2 |
| 518847 | 9 | 131313 | | 1 |
| 519423 | 9 | 111310 | | 1 |
| 519579 | 2 | 420027 | | 1 |
| 520078 | 1 | 42004 | | 1 |
| 520079 | 1 | 42008 | | 1 |
| 521521 | 11 | 241362 | | 1 |
| 521840 | 5 | 673025 | | 1 |
| 522024 | 2 | 40051 | | 1 |

Source: CMS 2014.

Figure 7.7. Example document with headings

**Facility Name**

The information described below was destroyed in the normal course of business pursuant to a proper retention schedule and destruction policies and procedures.

Date of destruction:________________________________________

Description of records or record series disposed of: ___________

____________________________________________________________
____________________________________________________________

Inclusive dates covered:_______________________________________

Method of destruction:

( ) Burning ( ) Shredding ( ) Pulping
( ) Demagnetizing ( ) Overwriting ( ) Pulverizing
( ) Other:___________________________________________________

Records destroyed by:_________________________________________

Witness signature:____________________________________________

Department manager:____________________________________________

*Note: This sample form is provided for discussion purposes only. It is not intended for use without advice of legal counsel.*

Source: AHIMA 2002.

metadata, business rules are constraints on data and what users can and cannot do with them (Hay 2002). A data business rule falls into one of the following four categories:

- **Definitions of business terms**: Rules that define business terms. Terms are traditionally documented in glossaries, data dictionaries, or as entities in a conceptual model.
- **Facts relating terms to each other**: For example, relating the terms patient and appointment with each other in a business rule that allows a patient to make an appointment. Facts can be represented in natural language, data relationships, attributes, or in a visual model, such as a data model.
- **Derivation**: An attribute that is derived through a mathematical calculation or inference from other attributes or system variables. For example, average length of stay is the sum of the length of stay of all inpatients for a given period divided by the number of days in the period.
- **Constraint**: A condition that determines what values an attribute or relationship can or must have. For example, a patient must have a unique identifier consisting of seven digits (Business Rule Group 2000).

Business rules such as these are represented in data models and other business requirement artifacts such as data flow diagrams and data dictionaries. Policy and procedure manuals, user documentation, memos, guidance documentation, emails, government regulations and compliance documentation, and legal documentation also contain business rules (Inmon, et al. 2008, 186).

Other good sources for identifying metadata include system directories and system catalogs associated with database management systems. Many times, the database management vendor provides an interface for reading and extracting metadata. Figure 7.8 displays the metadata extraction for two fields in a physician database table in Microsoft Access. Notice, however, that even though the metadata are identified there is still a need to further define these. For example, what does the code for "aggregate type" or "other descriptors" mean? Computer-assisted system architecture (CASE) tools, which analysts use to develop data models, use cases, and other requirements analysis artifacts, are also a good source of metadata.

Metadata can also be found in the business intelligence environment when data from many sources are brought together through an integration process, are placed in a data warehouse, and are used for statistical analysis and decision making. Mappings from data in the source systems for extracting, transforming, and loading (ETL) data into data warehouses produce metadata. To illustrate, if a hospital wanted to determine physician activity over a period of time, the hospital may need to consolidate data from multiple databases, such as the physician, billing, and electronic health record (HER) databases.

During the consolidation process, the system collects metadata that identify the database where each data item came from, the date and time it was loaded by system to the data warehouse, and what changes were made during the process to the data while they were being transferred. Data changes may include transformations such as making the data value for gender consistent among all three sets of data. For example, changing "male" and "01" from the source systems to "M" in the target or data warehouse system.

## Data Life Cycle and Metadata

Similar to the information systems life cycle, data have a life cycle (as described in chapter 4). The data life cycle can be used by analysts as a basis for identifying metadata. Various models of the data life cycle exist, but essentially, they all consist of the phases data go through from their conceptualization to their final disposition. For example, the nonprofit organization for higher education information technology, Educause, has a seven-stage model that includes creation, collection and description, data storage, archiving and preservation, data access, discovery and analysis, data reuse, and transformation (Owen and Fary 2013). The American Health Information Management Association (AHIMA) describes the health information life cycle in four stages: creation, utilization, maintenance, and destruction (AHIMA 2011). The Canadian Health Information Management Association uses a six-stage model for information management planning:

- Capture and collection
- Preservation
- Access, use, and dissemination
- Maintenance and protection
- Disposition
- Evaluation (Abrams and Gibson 2013)

This text uses the data life cycle in figure 3.4 as a composite of the various data life cycle representations. Data life cycle stages can be used as a foundation for deriving questions about the type of metadata that the organization should collect

Figure 7.8. Example of extraction of metadata from a database table

**Columns**

| Name | | Type | Size |
|---|---|---|---|
| PhysicianID | | Long Integer | 4 |
| AggregateType: | -1 | | |
| AllowZeroLength: | False | | |
| AppendOnly: | False | | |
| Attributes: | Fixed Size, Auto-Increment | | |
| CollatingOrder: | General | | |
| ColumnHidden: | False | | |
| ColumnOrder: | 1 | | |
| ColumnWidth: | Default | | |
| CurrencyLCID: | 0 | | |
| DataUpdatable: | False | | |
| GUID: | {guid {271ECED9-E9AA-44CB-BED4-893EFE33AD88}} | | |
| OrdinalPosition: | 0 | | |
| Required: | False | | |
| ResultType: | 0 | | |
| SourceField: | PhysicianID | | |
| SourceTable: | Physician | | |
| TextAlign: | General | | |
| Physician Last Name | | Text | 30 |
| AggregateType: | -1 | | |
| AllowZeroLength: | True | | |
| AppendOnly: | False | | |
| Attributes: | Variable Length | | |
| CollatingOrder: | General | | |
| ColumnHidden: | False | | |
| ColumnOrder: | Default | | |
| ColumnWidth: | 2295 | | |



about each stage. For example, for the data capture stage, the series of questions might include: Where did the data come from? When was the data collected? How was the data collected? Who owns the data? How are the data defined or derived? Why are the data collected (for example, required by mandates)?

Another perspective of the data life cycle focuses on the information in clinical documents in paper, electronic, or hybrid form, rather than on data (Payne and Graham 2006). The concepts in this model provide another dimension for looking at how one can identify and categorize metadata. This model is composed of three axes: stage, role, and action. Stage refers to the life cycle of the document from the cognitive or conceptualization phase (for example, when the author mentally formulates the content of the document) to collection, draft, final development, and finally, use. Role refers to the function of the individual who is collecting or using the document. For example, this could be a physician, resident, or other healthcare provider. The third axis refers to the type of action taken on the document such as dictating, printing, and editing.

These models provide the basis for figure 7.9, a diagram of the influencers of metadata, and are a guide for identifying metadata at St. Rita's. Here, a diagram shows the potential metadata for a data element, object, or set of data sits at the intersection between the data, the user role, the life cycle stage, and the actions on the data.

This model provides a reference for asking questions that metadata address. For example, assume the data are the set of data elements needed for making an appointment. Suppose the role is an end user, such as the receptionist. Also assume the metadata support the action of capturing the data. The following are questions about the data in this life cycle stage, and how metadata might address them:

- Where do the data come from?
  - Metadata: Source ID
- By whom were the data collected?
  - Metadata: User ID
- When did the receptionist collect the data?
  - Metadata: Date and time stamp

Figure 7.9. Influencers of metadata identification

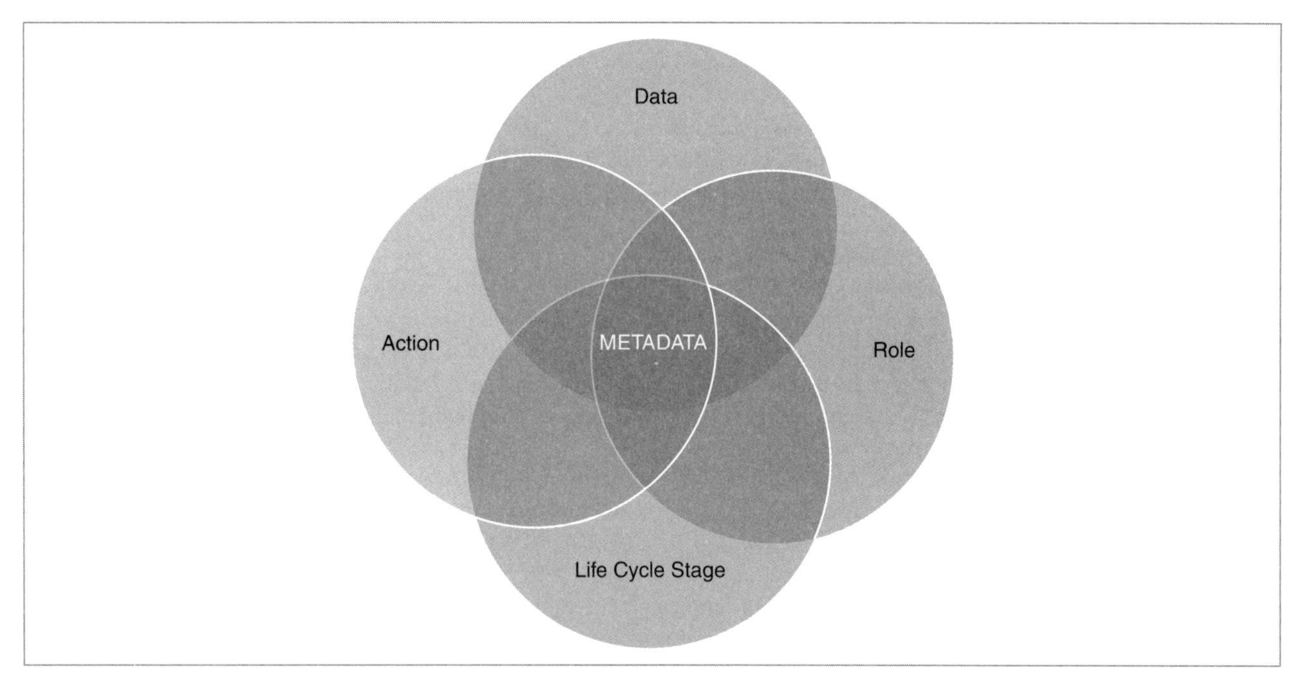


©Merida L. Johns

- What is the definition of the data?
  - Metadata: Data definition
- Why is the receptionist collecting the data?
  - Metadata: Process ID
  - Metadata: Data definition
- What is the format of the data?
  - Metadata: Data type and field length

## Metadata Schemas

Metadata elements that are grouped together to represent a particular emphasis or domain are called **metadata schemas**. There are metadata schemas for the publishing, geospatial, and social science data, for digital libraries, e-commerce applications, education, government, and images, among many others. A primary purpose of a metadata schema is to promote common understanding of the meaning of data. The meaning of data is often referred to as semantics. Other purposes of metadata schema are to ensure proper data use and interpretation, and to facilitate data exchange. Many schemas have been formalized by professional associations and standards organizations and are recognized as official standards. Metadata schemas consist of all of the following:

- A collection of metadata elements gathered to support a function, or a series of functions such as resource discovery, administration, and use
- A collection of metadata elements forming a structured container to which data values are added
- A collection of data elements with their attributes formalized in a specification (for example, a DD) (Greenberg 2005)

A metadata schema is usually associated with some type of framework or structure. The framework specifies what the data are, how they are arranged, and how they are supposed to be exchanged. A good way to conceptualize this framework is to view it as having the following five key components:

1. Schema—The categories for classification of the data
2. Vocabulary—Specific words or values entered into the schema categories
3. Conceptual model—The underlying model that describes how the data and concepts inherent in a resource are related to one another
4. Content standard—Practical standards that describe how users should enter specific information (for example, vocabularies) within metadata schema categories (for example, cataloging cultural objects)
5. Encoding—The way the metadata are presented (for example, XML format) (JISC 2014)

The following schemas represent two different industry sectors and demonstrate how any business segment can apply or adapt a framework for schema development.

## Dublin Core Schema

The Dublin Core is a good example to illustrate a metadata schema. One of the most widely used metadata standards, organizations frequently use **the Dublin Core** to describe any type of online digital resource library (for example, documents, books, art, and images). The Dublin Core is a set of 15 generic elements (table 7.1) for describing any resource type (Dublin Core 2012).

The resource can be electronic, conceptual, or real-world.

Each term in the Dublin Core has a specific label. In table 7.1, the label is the same as the term name. In the comments column, there are references to several standards and vocabularies. For example, for the date element, the recommended best practice is to use an encoding scheme, such as the W3CDTF profile of ISO 8601 to document the date. In this case, the encoding appears as YYYY-MM-DD. For the subject element, the recommended best practice is to use a controlled vocabulary, for example the Library of Congress Subject Headings (LCSH) for identifying the subject of a book.

Not all of the terms in the Dublin Core have to be used to describe a resource, only those that are applicable to the resource. Terms are also repeatable. For example, if there are two creators, both can be included in the metadata for the resource. The Dublin Core uses XML for encoding and data exchange. An example of the metadata for a resource, in this case a fictional book on healthcare metadata, appears in figure 7.10. This metadata describes the specific elements of the book such as its title, creator, publisher, and language. The description does not use all the Dublin Core terms, only the applicable ones. Notice the format for date conforms to the W3CDTF profile of ISO 8601 for complete date: YYYY-MM-DD.

Table 7.1. **Dublin Core Schema and recommended best practices**

| Term Label | Definition | Comments |
|---|---|---|
| Title Label: Title | A name given to the resource | Typically, a title will be the name by which the resource is formally known. |
| Creator Label: Creator | The entity primarily responsible for making the resource | Examples of a creator include a person, an organization, or a service. |
| Subject Label: Subject | The topic of the resource | Typically, keywords, key phrases, or classification codes represent the subject. Recommended best practice is to use a controlled vocabulary. |
| Description Label: Description | An account of the resource | Description may include, but is not limited to an abstract, a table of contents, a graphical representation, or a free-text account of the resource. |
| Publisher Label: Publisher | An entity responsible for making the resource available | Examples of a publisher include a person, an organization, or a service. Typically, the name of a publisher indicates the entity. |
| Contributor Label: Contributor | An entity responsible for making contributions to the resource | Examples of a contributor include a person, an organization, or a service. Typically, the name of a contributor indicates the entity. |
| Date Label: Date | A point or period of time associated with an event in the life cycle of the resource | Date may express temporal information at any level of granularity. Recommended best practice is to use an encoding scheme, such as the W3CDTF profile of ISO 8601. |
| Format Label: Format | The file format, physical medium, or dimensions of the resource | Examples of dimensions include size and duration. Recommended best practice is to use a controlled vocabulary such as the list of Multipurpose Internet Media Types [MIME]. |
| Identifier Label: Identifier | An unambiguous reference to the resource within a given context | Recommended best practice is to identify the resource by means of a string conforming to a formal identification system. |

(continued)

Table 7.1. Dublin Core Schema and recommended best practices (*Continued*)

| Term Label | Definition | Comments |
|---|---|---|
| Source Label: Source | A related resource from which the described resource is derived | The described resource may derive from the related resource in whole or in part. Recommended best practice is to identify the related resource by means of a string conforming to a formal identification system. |
| Language Label: Language | A language of the resource | Recommended best practice is to use a controlled vocabulary such as RFC 4646. |
| Relation Label: Relation | A related resource | Recommended best practice is to identify the related resource by means of a string conforming to a formal identification system. |
| Coverage Label: Coverage | The spatial or temporal topic of the resource, the spatial applicability of the resource, or the jurisdiction under which the resource is relevant | Spatial topic and spatial applicability may be a named place or a location specified by its geographic coordinates. Temporal topic may be a named period, date, or date range. A jurisdiction may be a named administrative entity or a geographic place to which the resource applies. Recommended best practice is to use a controlled vocabulary such as the Thesaurus of Geographic Names (TGN). Where appropriate, named places or time periods can be used in preference to numeric identifiers such as sets of coordinates or date ranges. |
| Rights Label: Rights | Information about rights held in and over the resource | Typically, rights information includes a statement about various property rights associated with the resource, including intellectual property rights. |
| Type Label: Type | The nature or genre of the resource | Recommended best practice is to use a controlled vocabulary such as the DCMI Type Vocabulary (DCMITYPE). To describe the file format, physical medium, or dimensions of the resource, use the format element. |

Source: Dublin Core 2012.

Figure 7.10. Example of XML encoding using Dublin Core elements

```
<dc:title>XYZ Title</dc:title>
<dc:creator>John Doe</dc:creator>
<dc:subject>Metadata in Health Care</dc:subject>
<dc:description>Guide to developing metadata for healthcare</dc:description>
<dc:publisher>ABC Publisher</dc:publisher>
<dc:date>2014-01-16</dc:date>
<dc:type>text</dc:type>
<dc:identifier>ISBN 333-3333-33333</dc:identifier>
<dc:language>en</dc:language>
```



## Continuity of Care Record (CCR)

The **continuity of care record** (CCR) is both a content and a structure standard commonly referred to as ASTM E2369 – 12 by its developer, ASTM International. The US-based international standards development organization produces standards for various industries, including healthcare. The notation E2369 is a unique identifier assigned by ASTM. The "E" stands for miscellaneous subjects, "2369" is the assigned sequential number, and "12" is the year of original adoption or in the case of revision, the year of the last revision.

The purpose of the CCR is to provide a snapshot in time of a patient's pertinent clinical, demographic, and administrative data and to enable electronic exchange of this data among healthcare providers. The CCR is a collection of data from many clinical documents that are compiled and parsed into a uniform and easily interpreted format (NIST 2011). The CCR has three core components: the CCR header, the CCR body, and the CCR footer:

- The header defines the document's context including its unique identifier, language, the version of the CCR standard used, date and time, the patient about whom the data addresses, who generated the CCR, to whom the CCR is directed (recipient), and the CCR's purpose (for example, transfer, referral, or request).
- The body contains the patient-specific clinical data such as problems, medications, procedures, alerts, and so on.
- The footer defines all of the individuals, organizations, or devices associated with data in the CCR.

Each of the core components has sections that provide the actual data about a patient. Figure 7.11 enumerates these. Some sections are required while others are optional. The sections can be used in any combination. Within sections are specific

Figure 7.11. **Continuity of care record sections and objects**

| CCR Section | CCR Data Object | Required or Optional |
|---|---|---|
| Header | Unique Identifier | Required |
| | Language | Required |
| | Version | Required |
| | Creation Date/Time | Required |
| | Patient | Required |
| | From | Required |
| | To | Optional |
| | Purpose | Optional |
| Body | Payers | Required |
| | Advance Directives | Required if known |
| | Support | Optional |
| | Functional Status | Optional |
| | Problems | Optional |
| | Family History | Optional |
| | Social History | Optional |
| | Alerts | Optional |
| | Medications | Optional |
| | Medical Equipment | Optional |
| | Immunizations | Optional |
| | Vital Signs | Optional |
| | Results | Optional |
| | Procedures | Optional |
| | Encounters | Optional |
| | Plan of Care | Optional |
| | Healthcare Providers | Optional |
| Footer | Actors | Required |
| | References | Optional |
| | Comments | Optional |
| | Signatures | Optional |

Source: Health Level Seven International 2007.

data elements, some of which the CCR requires and others optional. Unlike the Dublin Core, the CCR is not extensible. This means it does not allow end-user customization.

Together, the core components describe the most important aspects of a patient's health condition. From a structure perspective, the standard specifies XML coding when the CCR is created in a structured electronic format. The CCR supports the use of coding and standard vocabulary systems such as Systematized Nomenclature of Medicine Clinical Terms (SNOMED CT), Logical Observation Identifiers Names and Codes (LOINC), RxNorm, and Current Procedural Terminology (CPT). However, it does not mandate them, and it is up to the end user to use this functionality (Ferranti, et al. 2006).

**CCR Syntax and Encoding**

The CCR uses XML as its encoding scheme. This permits data exchange among information systems that use XML. Figure 7.12 displays a segment of XML code from a CCR file. In this XML segment, the healthcare provider prescribed the medication Digoxin.

A sample output file of the CCR is shown in the formatted document appearing in Figure 7.13.

Figure 7.12. Example of XML code segment from CCR

```
Digoxin 0.125mg, 1 PO qDay, #90, 5 refills.

<Medications>
  <Medication>
    <Description>
      <Text>Digoxin 0.125mg, 1 PO qDay, #90, 5 refills</Text>
    </Description>
    <Product>
      <ProductName>Digoxin</ProductName>
      <Strength>
          <Value>0.125</Value>
          <Units>mg</Units>
      </Strength>
    </Product>
    <Quantity>
      <Value>90</Value>
    </Quantity>
    <Directions>
      <Direction>
          <Dose>
            <Value>1</Value>
          </Dose>
          <Route>
            <Text>po</Text>
          </Route>
          <Frequency>
            <Value>qd</Value>
          </Frequency>
      </Direction>
    </Directions>
  <Refills>
      <Refill>
          <Number>5</Number>
      </Refill>
    </Refills>
</Medication>
```

Source: Kebbe 2005.

Figure 7.13. Formatted output of continuity of care record

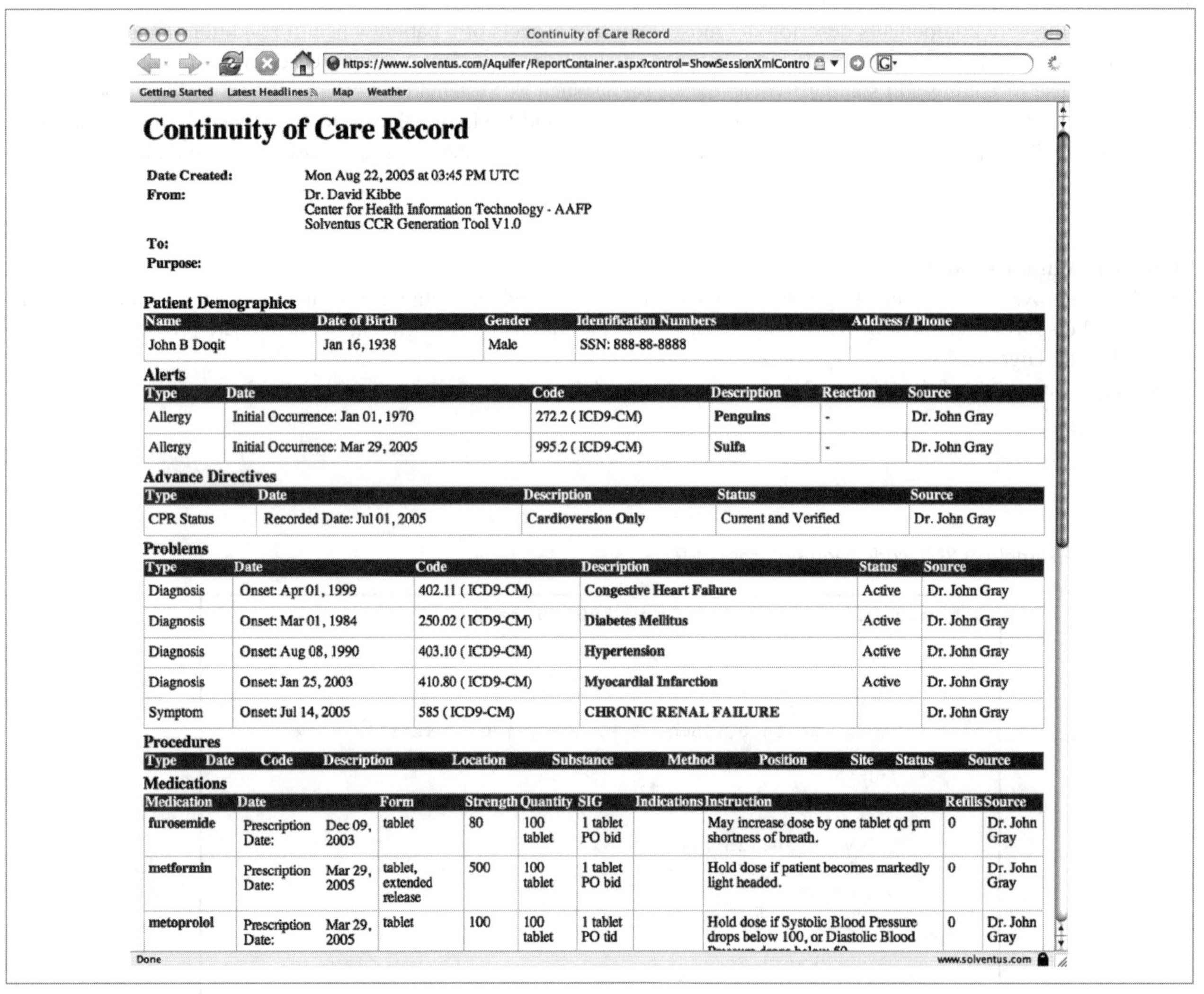

Continuity of Care Record

https://www.solventus.com/Aquifer/ReportContainer.aspx?control=ShowSessionXmlContro

Getting Started Latest Headlines Map Weather

# Continuity of Care Record

**Date Created:** Mon Aug 22, 2005 at 03:45 PM UTC
**From:** Dr. David Kibbe
Center for Health Information Technology - AAFP
Solventus CCR Generation Tool V1.0

**To:**
**Purpose:**

**Patient Demographics**

| Name | Date of Birth | Gender | Identification Numbers | Address / Phone |
|---|---|---|---|---|
| John B Doqit | Jan 16, 1938 | Male | SSN: 888-88-8888 | |

**Alerts**

| Type | Date | Code | Description | Reaction | Source |
|---|---|---|---|---|---|
| Allergy | Initial Occurrence: Jan 01, 1970 | 272.2 ( ICD9-CM) | **Penguins** | - | Dr. John Gray |
| Allergy | Initial Occurrence: Mar 29, 2005 | 995.2 ( ICD9-CM) | **Sulfa** | - | Dr. John Gray |

**Advance Directives**

| Type | Date | Description | Status | Source |
|---|---|---|---|---|
| CPR Status | Recorded Date: Jul 01, 2005 | **Cardioversion Only** | Current and Verified | Dr. John Gray |

**Problems**

| Type | Date | Code | Description | Status | Source |
|---|---|---|---|---|---|
| Diagnosis | Onset: Apr 01, 1999 | 402.11 ( ICD9-CM) | **Congestive Heart Failure** | Active | Dr. John Gray |
| Diagnosis | Onset: Mar 01, 1984 | 250.02 ( ICD9-CM) | **Diabetes Mellitus** | Active | Dr. John Gray |
| Diagnosis | Onset: Aug 08, 1990 | 403.10 ( ICD9-CM) | **Hypertension** | Active | Dr. John Gray |
| Diagnosis | Onset: Jan 25, 2003 | 410.80 ( ICD9-CM) | **Myocardial Infarction** | Active | Dr. John Gray |
| Symptom | Onset: Jul 14, 2005 | 585 ( ICD9-CM) | **CHRONIC RENAL FAILURE** | | Dr. John Gray |

**Procedures**

| Type | Date | Code | Description | Location | Substance | Method | Position | Site | Status | Source |
|---|---|---|---|---|---|---|---|---|---|---|

**Medications**

| Medication | Date | | Form | Strength | Quantity | SIG | Indications | Instruction | Refills | Source |
|---|---|---|---|---|---|---|---|---|---|---|
| **furosemide** | Prescription Date: | Dec 09, 2003 | tablet | 80 | 100 tablet | 1 tablet PO bid | | May increase dose by one tablet qd prn shortness of breath. | 0 | Dr. John Gray |
| **metformin** | Prescription Date: | Mar 29, 2005 | tablet, extended release | 500 | 100 tablet | 1 tablet PO bid | | Hold dose if patient becomes markedly light headed. | 0 | Dr. John Gray |
| **metoprolol** | Prescription Date: | Mar 29, 2005 | tablet | 100 | 100 tablet | 1 tablet PO tid | | Hold dose if Systolic Blood Pressure drops below 100, or Diastolic Blood | 0 | Dr. John Gray |

Done www.solventus.com

Source: Kebbe 2005.

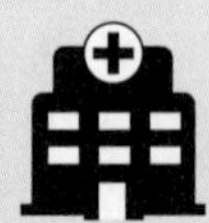

## The St. Rita's Healthcare System Case Study

Denise and Bob got together for an early afternoon meeting to consolidate their information and pull together a concrete and concise presentation for the EIM team meeting that was scheduled in two days.

"I think we have a good foundation of material about metadata for the team, but we need to pull it all together in a meaningful way. We need a way of practically putting this information into operation or it won't mean much to the team," said Bob.

"I've got an approach in mind for that," responded Denise. "During my research, I came across a number of examples about the importance of having a metadata plan that includes development of a metadata repository. Companies have all of this metadata, but the questions are: what do they do with it, how do they organize it, and how do they manage it?"

"You've hit the nail on the head. That's exactly the point," Bob answered. "I think posing and answering those three questions is a great organizing scheme. How should we get started putting the pieces together?" Denise and Bob took the rest of the afternoon to pour over the materials that Denise identified and searched for more data to confirm what information they already had.

# Managing Metadata

Managing metadata requires coordination of people, processes, architecture, and technology. To meet the challenge of organizing, documenting, searching, and retrieving the vast digital resources, organizations are developing a **managed metadata environment** (MME) that includes a metadata repository supported by a data governance (DG) structure, standards, and processes. A **repository** is a data structure where data are stored for subsequent use by multiple, disparate systems. Like any good management strategy, the goals and benefits to be achieved must be identified by the organization before dedicating any other resources to the effort. Once the organization clarifies these, alternatives for implementation are identified and the optimal solution selected by the organization. An important part of any management effort is to put in place organizational structures for governance and management. This process is described in this section with a focus on metadata repositories as an option for metadata management.

## Metadata Planning

Developing a metadata plan is similar to any planning development initiative. The metadata planning process should address the following general questions:

- What is the goal?
- What is the justification?
- What are the benefits?
- Where are we now (situational analysis)?
- What are the alternative options for achieving the outcome?
- What is the best option (evaluation and selection)?
- How will the organization implement the option?

Metadata programs differ across organizations. Organizations vary on the goals to achieve and the assets to manage through a metadata management program. For instance, one organization's goal may be to ensure interoperability across systems, another may want to demonstrate compliance with standards for records management, and still another's goal may target improving information retrieval and sharing. Consequently, the scope and depth of metadata projects differ.

One strategy may be "narrow and deep," focusing on a specific subset of metadata to manage. An example is focusing on metadata for specific organization master data, such as patient or provider master data. Another approach is a "broad and shallow" strategy focusing on management of some metadata for all operational areas. An example of this might include a focus on email metadata throughout the entire organization. And still another plan may be opting for a "broad and deep" strategy, focusing on the management of all metadata throughout the organization. Regardless of the approach selected, metadata management is an enormous undertaking. Like other large initiatives, such as EHR implementation, developing a **migration path**, is essential. A migration path is a series of coordinated and planned steps required to move a plan from one situation level to another.

Metadata management does not occur in a vacuum. It requires executive management support and the inclusion of stakeholders to develop and manage the process. A first step is development of a metadata **management charter**; the charter is usually developed by executive management and lays out the program's vision, justification, and expected result. Then management names a program manager and designates a start date. In conjunction with a charter, executive management usually appoints a task force, or council, and lays out its responsibilities in a written document. Ideally, this group is part of the organization's DG structure and includes business data stewards, IT staff, data owners, and others, as appropriate.

One of the initial metadata program activities is scope document development. Similar to a scope document for an information systems development effort, the task force needs to perform a requirements analysis that answers these questions:

- What is the current state of metadata management (define the "as-is" system)?
- What is its desired future state (define the "to-be" system)?
- What are the functional end-user needs?
- What are the technical needs?
- What are the alternative options?
- What is the best option given needs and resources?

Once the team answers these questions, they identify the program scope. Next, the task force determines critical success factors, risk factors, assumptions, and required resources, and develops a program plan (Smith 2007). Table 7.2 provides an outline of a requirements document for a metadata program (National Center for Education Statistics 2009).

Table 7.2. **Outline for metadata program needs assessment**

| | |
|---|---|
| Introduction | Background, objectives, and scope |
| System Contents | Types of metadata, schema, standards, volume |
| System Functions | Capture, storage, and retrieval functions such as<br>• Locating metadata definitions and attributes<br>• Entering metadata into the system (automatic and manual)<br>• Searching by key words<br>• Updating and maintaining metadata items<br>• Tracking metadata modification history<br>• Mapping metadata items to individual data elements<br>• Identifying data element stewards and owners<br>• Mapping data items to their physical storage<br>• Assessing data quality<br>• Regulating system access |
| Access and Capacity | Interface requirements, transmission volume, number of users, security, and access requirements |
| Technical Functions | Relevant technical standards and specifications<br>Performance requirements<br>Ease of use by end users (interface)<br>Maintains version control for the data dictionary and business rules<br>Automated loading and updating capabilities |

Source: National Center for Education Statistics 2009.

Purdue University Data Services and Administration developed an excellent example of a metadata program document and associated implementation plan (Purdue University Data Services and Administration 2014). The document includes the following:

- The definition of metadata
- The goal for metadata management
- The business case/justification for building and maintaining a metadata repository
- The criteria for a successful metadata repository
- The scope of the metadata repository
- The intended audience for the document
- The categories that make up the repository
- The centralized metadata repository implementation and maintenance

## Using and Developing Metadata Schema

Having good metadata relies on the use or development of a metadata schema. In a digital environment, a schema is as important to a metadata repository as a data model is to a database. The schema is essentially the blueprint of not only a registry of what metadata is stored but also explains how the metadata relate to each other. The use of schema is particularly critical in healthcare because of the vast amounts of unstructured stored data, whose value the organization cannot leverage because of data retrieval challenges. Metadata schema are the keystone to opening the knowledge that lays dormant in the vast amounts of unstructured data. From a legal perspective, metadata schema are essential for identifying and locating information to respond to legal litigation, compliance, and regulatory mandates.

The first step in the use of a schema is to identify what metadata to collect and how to structure it. Once this is determined, an organization can decide if it can use or adapt an existing schema or if it needs to develop its own. There are several benefits from using an existing schema that is regarded as a standard. First, the organization can use a well-modeled and supported schema. The organization gains the immediate benefit of prior work and knowledge, and has access to support in the form of manuals, documentation, and usually forum groups and training. Using pre-developed schema and conforming to accepted standards reduces development time and potentially lowers development costs and human resources allocated to the effort. It also increases the level of data exchange, as the Dublin Core example demonstrates. Unfortunately, both vendors and providers have identified standardizing metadata tags as a challenge in healthcare (AHIMA 2013).

If there is no readily available schema the organization can use or extend, then metadata management becomes more complex because the organization must create a new schema. The key elements in developing a metadata schema include establishing the metadata element set including the element meaning (semantics), expression (syntax), and optionality; determining the business rules for how to use elements; and establishing a controlled list of acceptable values (Hodgson 2008). The Dublin Core example (table 7.1) is a good illustration of all three of these elements. This example includes an established element set and defined meanings. Required syntax and values are specified, for example, for date format and the use of controlled vocabularies for media types. No element is required in the Dublin Core and how the elements are to be used are specified in comments provided with the schema. Two examples of strategies for developing a new metadata schema are described below.

The first example focuses on a particular type of digital resource, in this case web pages across the enterprise. To begin the process, the schema was developed by the analyst by dividing the metadata into four categories: descriptive, administrative, rights, and technical metadata (Kelway 2008). Descriptive metadata are the record content and include elements such as title or subject. Administrative metadata include a unique identifier, date created, date modified, security classification, and relationship to other metadata. Rights metadata may identify the author, copyright, or any other types of rights associated with the digital resource. Technical metadata includes information about the file type, format, or size. Once the schema is developed and metadata identified, then syntax rules, optionality, values, and parameters for encoding the metadata must be specified by the schema developer.

Another metadata schema development example is the Australian Government Recordkeeping Metadata Standard (Australian National Archives 2008). This framework has five categories, called entity types, including record, agent, business, mandate, and relationship. Of particular interest is the relationship entity which defines any relevant association between two or more entities. This convention is important because it allows users to combine entities and their metadata, providing a more complete description of a record. The schema includes 26 properties that describe each of the entities. Some examples include identifier, name, date range, security level, and description.

## Metadata Repository Options and Management

How organizations store and manage metadata has a direct effect on how they govern it. Different approaches require different governance strategies. To understand why this is so, approaches, technical strategies, and management issues are discussed below.

### Metadata Repository Approaches

One approach for storing metadata is to embed it directly into a source file. An image file, like a JPEG, is an example of a digital resource with embedded metadata. The properties of a JPEG file reveal all types of metadata such as the file creation date, the file size, the image dimensions, and so on. The benefit of embedded metadata is that it transfers with the digital resource, thus making metadata access straightforward. However, embedded metadata pose challenges with search and retrieval, as well as identifying relationships among digital resources. Therefore, organizations often choose to store these types of metadata in a repository.

A manifest (or, other files) associated with a specific source file can also contain metadata. An e-book is an example of a digital resource that links metadata from manifest files. Metadata for an e-book are in the manifest associated with the specific e-book such as the book cover image file and the text files for the book. This approach allows for reusability of the metadata.

A metadata repository is the third way to store metadata. A repository stores metadata in a location separate from source files. It points the metadata back to the appropriate source file. A benefit of a repository approach is that it makes searching and retrieval more efficient, allows for bulk metadata updates, and potentially reduces redundancies.

A **metadata repository** consists of the physical database tables used to gather, store, and disseminate metadata (Marco 2004). Sometimes the term "data dictionary (DD)" is also used to refer to a metadata repository. However, the DD is traditionally associated with maintaining metadata for a specific database, or databases, and thus contains only a subset of an organization's metadata. The concept of a metadata repository goes beyond a traditional DD. The metadata repository houses the entire range of metadata, both business and technical, and its architecture resembles a data warehouse architecture, but one designed specifically to handle metadata (Inmon et al. 2008).

There are four common approaches to the technical architecture of a metadata repository. These include a centralized, federated, distributed, or hybrid model. Each model has its strengths and drawbacks. A **centralized metadata architecture** consists of a single repository that holds all the organization's metadata. A centralized system works well if a single metadata model meets all data and user needs. It has several advantages such as high availability, quick data retrieval, and centralized governance, management, and operation (DAMA 2010). An example of the use of this approach is an organization that wants to extract all of its email metadata from source files into one repository. Figure 7.14 is a schematic of a centralized system.

Figure 7.14. Centralized metadata repository architecture

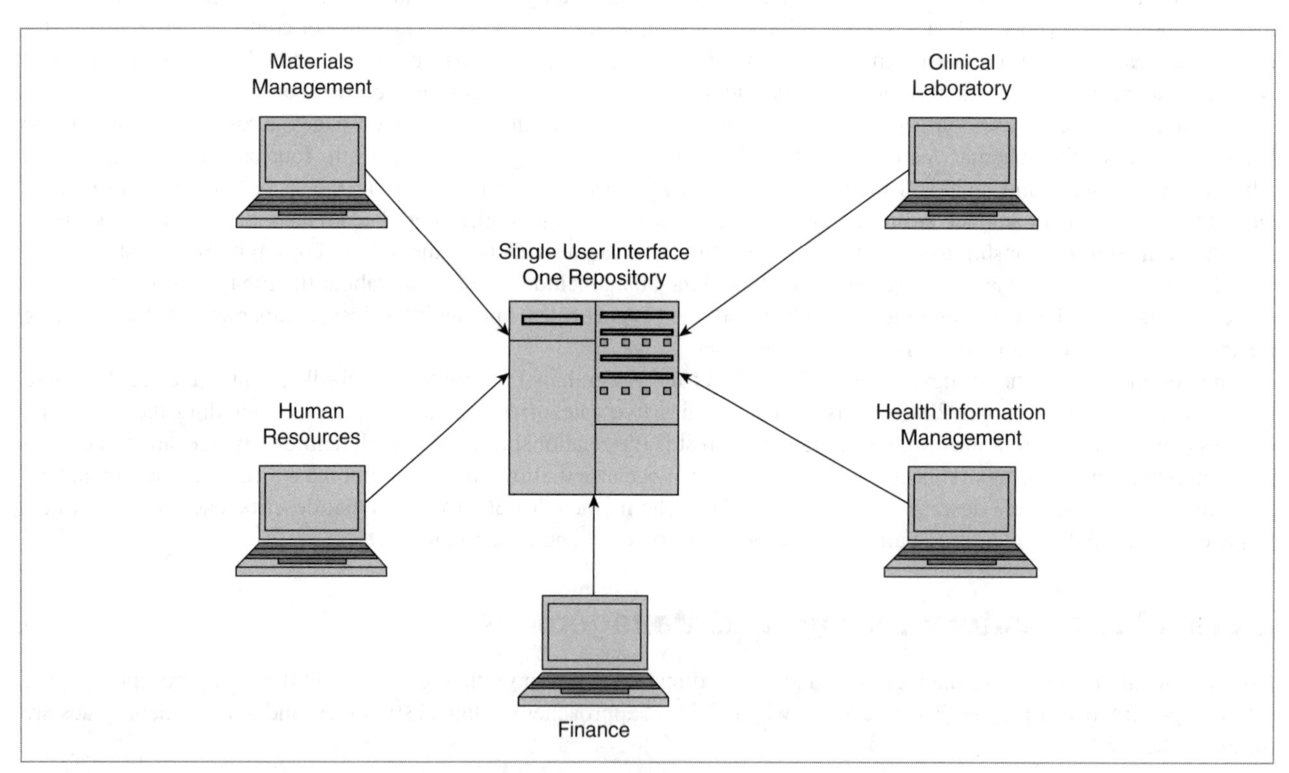




In a **federated metadata architecture**, each data system maintains its own metadata repository but conforms to a centralized technical framework and governance structure (NCES 2009). In other words, the metadata are held with the source systems, but users can extract metadata that affect more than one system on demand for communication with other systems through the use of an integration engine and a single user interface. The benefits of this type of structure are that organizations can design metadata to fit the specific needs of a business area but can also easily share them with other systems. Because data stewards distribute and manage metadata at a business unit level, strong governance processes are necessary to ensure synchronization among the separate systems (figure 7.15).

In a **distributed metadata architecture**, each stand-alone data system has a corresponding stand-alone metadata system, but unlike the federated architecture, there is no communication among systems or centralized governance. Because of this, the systems may contain duplicate metadata, differing definitions for the same type of metadata, a general lack of

Figure 7.15. Federated metadata repository architecture

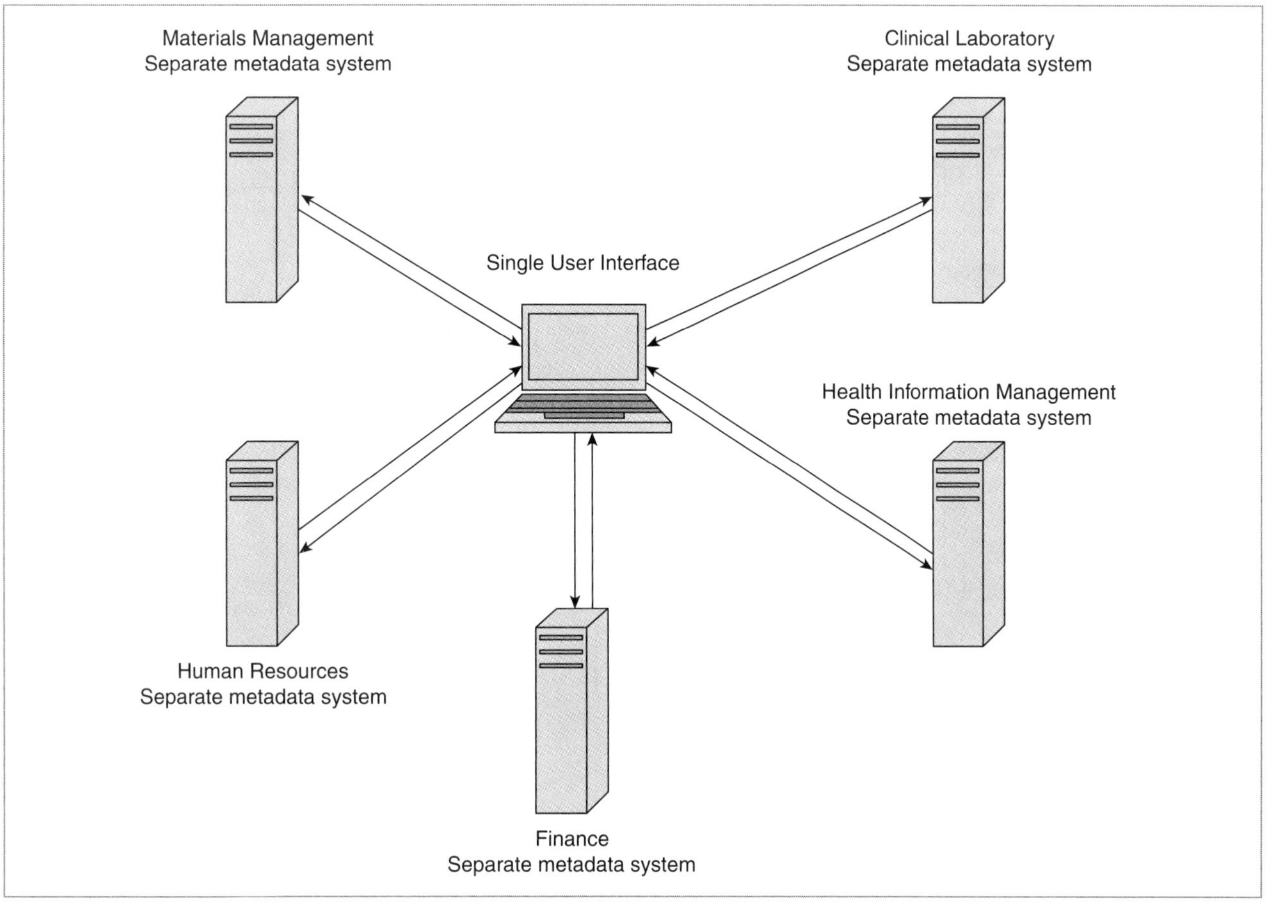

©Merida L. Johns

cohesion among systems, and an inability to share data results. This creates metadata silos, the very problem a metadata program aims to remedy (figure 7.16).

Finally, a **hybrid metadata architecture** is a combined architecture of a single repository and a federated system. In this implementation, each data system maintains its own metadata system while the central repository accommodates critical standardized metadata extracted by the system or that are manually created by data stewards from source files (DAMA 2010).

No matter which architecture an organization chooses, specialized software must be developed or purchased to operate a repository. By purchasing a software package, an organization does not have to develop the data model for the repository or the necessary technical or end user functionality. However, as with all **commercial off-the-shelf software** (COTS) products, there are trade-offs to consider. Does the data model of the COTS match the organization's needs? Can the organization customize the data model? Does the functionality of the COTS meet end-user needs? Does the COTS meet the required performance and technical functionality?

## Respository Management

A primary purpose of the metadata repository is to maintain high quality metadata for searching, retrieval, and analysis of information and to facilitate data exchange. To meet these goals, organizations need to put evaluation processes in place to monitor metadata quality and the appropriateness of the mechanisms to support it such as metadata capture, storage, and dissemination. An organization normally assigns these activities to a governance team and data stewards.

A number of technical control activities must be implemented by a technical team to manage the metadata repository. These are similar to any other software or hardware asset management. DAMA identified 15 control activities:

- Backup, recovery, archive, and purging
- Configuration modifications
- Job scheduling or monitoring

Figure 7.16. **Distributed metadata repository architecture**

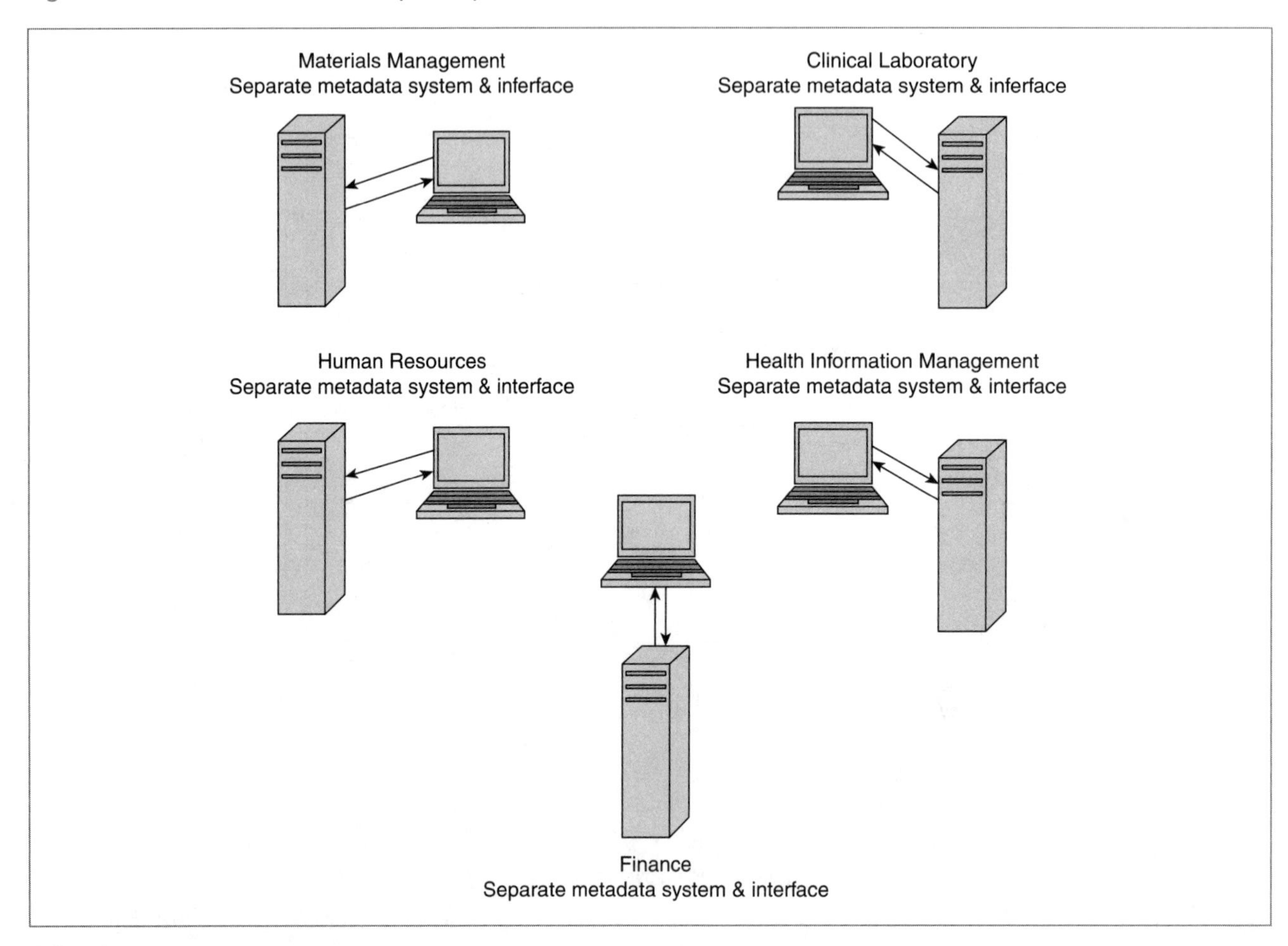


©Merida L. Johns

- Load statistical analysis
- Management metrics generation and analysis
- Performance tuning
- Quality assurance and control
- Query statistics analysis
- Query or report generation
- Repository administration
- Security management
- Source mapping or movement
- Control activities training
- User interface management
- Versioning
- User and data steward education and training (DAMA 2010)

## Metadata Quality

Metadata are useful only if they are high quality. Quality always starts at the beginning of the data life cycle and continues through all of its phases. The metadata life cycle has the following phases: creation, collection and description, data storage, achieving and preservation, data access, discovery and analysis, and data reuse and transformation. At each stage, organizations need to have processes in place to ensure high quality metadata. For example, in the creation phase, a well-modeled schema is used by the organization that governs semantics and syntax, and there are processes in place to regularly assess its appropriateness. In the collection phase, applicable interfaces and electronic collection mechanisms facilitate metadata collection and updating. Oversight for metadata quality is usually a DG function. Data quality metrics and processes are examined in detail in chapter 11.

## Applying Data Governance

Metadata management is a domain that is intricately related to DG activities. In fact, it is a core foundation of DG activities. This is because a two-part relationship exists between metadata and DG. The first is that stored metadata are a valuable resource for DG monitoring and auditing activities, such as identifying data creators and users, the data source, and so on. The second part of the relationship is that to achieve the purposes of metadata, organizations must have practices in place to govern metadata. Denise and Bob identified several DG functions for metadata management in their research. Some sources cited specific management tasks (Smith 2012). Others focused on the management of metadata from the perspective of various stakeholders (Seiner 2012). Denise and Bob were able to condense these valuable insights into the following responsibilities for metadata management:

- Establishing structure, process, and accountabilities for metadata approval, creation, collection, use, storage, distribution, integration, and security
- Developing and maintaining metadata policies, standards, and procedures
- Ensuring metadata meets functional requirements and organizational needs
- Confirming the selection and appropriate use of applicable metadata schema through policy and procedures
- Identifying data domains requiring metadata such as patient data, vendor data, human resources data, financial data, research data, materials data, and so on
- Defining metadata domains such as data definition metadata, data production metadata, data usage metadata, privacy-security metadata, compliance metadata, technical metadata, and so on
- Guaranteeing the appropriate use of metadata through policy, procedures, and training
- Establishing metadata creation and documentation
- Ensuring appropriate metadata integration
- Developing and implementing controls for metadata quality

In reviewing the list, Denise and Bob consolidated these into the EIM functional deliverables matrix that appears in table 7.3.

Table 7.3. DG deliverables by EIM function

| Data Governance | Data Architecture Management | Metadata Management | Master Data Management | Content Management | Data Security and Privacy Management | Business Intelligence Management | Data Quality Management | Terminology and Classification Management |
|---|---|---|---|---|---|---|---|---|
| Identify mission and scope | Develop and maintain data models | Develop policies, procedures, and standards | | | | | | |
| Establish goals and success measures | Develop, maintain, and evaluate data model policies and standards | Ensure metadata meets functional requirements | | | | | | |
| Put in place DG structure, processes, and communications plan | Define roles, responsibilities, and accountabilities for data architecture management | Develop and maintain appropriate metadata schema | | | | | | |

(continued)

Table 7.3. DG Deliverables by EIM Function (*Continued*)

| Data Governance | Data Architecture Management | Metadata Management | Master Data Management | Content Management | Data Security and Privacy Management | Business Intelligence Management | Data Quality Management | Terminology and Classification Management |
|---|---|---|---|---|---|---|---|---|
| Secure funding | Develop, maintain, and evaluate policies and standards for requirements analysis | Ensure metadata capture, maintenance, distribution, and integration | | | | | | |
| Establish decision rights | Develop and maintain data artifacts and standards | Ensure metadata security | | | | | | |
| Identify accountabilities | Establish quality control program and metrics for data architecture management | Develop and implement quality controls for metadata | | | | | | |

## The St. Rita's Healthcare System Case Study

Denise and Bob met late in the afternoon to finish consolidating their information and prepare a brief summary of metadata management for presentation to the EIM team. After the presentation, the team engaged in a lively discussion about metadata concepts and the state of metadata management at St. Rita's. They all agreed that they would describe the current state as "Ground Zero." St. Rita's was using standards for clinical data exchange, but there was no serious metadata program within the organization. There may be bits and pieces for areas such as clinical research data and some master data, but having no schema for healthcare makes metadata management even more challenging. The team concurred that metadata management will be a cornerstone of the future of HIM. But, getting a handle on metadata was daunting and something they could not accomplish without good planning and a DG process to establish policies, procedures, standards, and accountabilities for metadata. The team placed specific steps of establishing a managed metadata environment on their "to do" list, which they would address once they launched an EIM and DG effort.

## Part of the Team: Topics for Discussion and Action

1. The EIM team concurred that metadata management relied on strong DG. Denise and Bob outlined the activities associated with metadata DG and added these to the list of activities by functional area (table 7.3). The team left the actual steps for setting up metadata DG for another time. To help the team complete this task, prepare a table that lists the steps they need to take to establish DG for metadata at St. Rita's. Include with each step the rationale, why it is important, and who the likely players in the DG structure would be (for example, data steward, data custodian, and so on).

## Advanced Concepts

1. According to AHIMA, "there is perhaps no more important use of metadata than in the management of the information life cycle—especially as it relates to information created and maintained in EHRs" (AHIMA 2013). However, as of 2014 there were no metadata standards for this type of schema. Given this, what is the current research in this area and how might you approach metadata management for data St. Rita's creates and maintains in the EHR?

## References


Abrams, K. and C. Gibson, eds. 2013. *Fundamentals of Health Information Management*, 2nd ed. Ottawam, ON: Canadian Healthcare Association.

AHIMA. 2011. Retention and Destruction of Health Information. http://library.ahima.org/xpedio/groups/public/documents/ahima/bok1_049252.hcsp?dDocName=bok1_049252.

Australian National Archives. 2008. Australian Government Metadata Record Keeping Standard Version 2.0. http://www.naa.gov.au/Images/AGRkMS_Final%20Edit_16%2007%2008_Revised_tcm16-47131.pdf.

Business Rules Group. 2013. What is a Business Rule? http://www.businessrulesgroup.org/defnbrg.shtml.

Chisholm, M. 2004. *How to Build a Business Rules Engine: Extending Application Functionality Through Metadata Engineering.* San Francisco: Morgan Kaufmann Publishers.

DAMA. 2010. *DAMA Guide to the Data Management Body of Knowledge.* Bradley Beach: Technics Publications.

Dublin Core. 2012. Dublin Core Metadata Element Set Version 1.1. http://www.dublincore.org/documents/dces/.

Ferranti, J.M., R.C. Musser, K. Kawamoto, and W.E. Hammond. The clinical document architecture and the continuity of care record: A clinical analysis. *Journal of the American Medical Informatics Association* 13(3): 245-252.

Franks, P. and N. Knude. 2006. Why metadata matters. *The Information Management Journal* 40(5): 55-61. http://www.arma.org/bookstore/files/Franks-Kunde1.pdf.

Greenberg, J. 2005. Understanding Metadata and Metadata Schemes. *Cataloging & Classification Quarterly.* 40(3-4): 17-36.

Haugen, M., B. Herrin, S. Slivochka, L. McNeil Tolley, D. Warner and L. Washington. 2013. Rules for handling and maintaining metadata in the EHR. *Journal of AHIMA* 84(5): 50-54.

Hay, D.C. 2002. A Repository Model - Business Rules - Part 1. *The Data Administration Newsletter.* http://www.tdan.com/view-articles/4978/.

Health Level Seven International. 2007. HL7 Implementation Guide: CDA Release 2 - Continuity of Care Document (CCD).

Hilbert, M. and P. Lopez. 2011. The world's technological capacity to store, compute, and communicate information. *Science* 332(6025): 60-65.

Hodgson, C. 2008. Building a metadata schema: Where to start. *NISO.* http://www.niso.org/apps/group_public/download.php/5271/N800R1_Where_to_start_advice_on_creating_a_metadata_schema.pdf.

Inmon, W.H., B. O'Neil, and L. Fryman. 2008. *Business Metadata: Capturing Enterprise Knowledge.* Burlington, MA: Morgan Kaufmann Publishers.

JISC Digital Media. 2014. Putting Things in Order: A Dictionary of Meta Schemas and Related Standards. http://www.jiscdigitalmedia.ac.uk/guide/putting-things-in-order-links-to-metadata-schemas-and-related-standards.

Kelway, J. 2008. Building a Metadata Schema. User Pathways. http://userpathways.com/2008/06/building-a-metadata-schema/.

Kibbe, D. 2005. An Overview of the ASTM Continuity of Care Record (CCR). http://www.nchica.org/Past/06/presentations/Kibbe.pdf.

Marco, D. 2004. Managed Meta Data Environment (MME): A Complete Walkthrough. The Data Administration Newsletter. April 2004. http://www.tdan.com/view-articles/5185.

NIST. 2011. CCR Suitability Analysis. http://healthcare.nist.gov/resources/docs/CCRSuitabilityAnalysisVer2.pdf.

National Forum on Education Statistics. 2009. *Forum Guide to Metadata: The Meaning behind Education Data.* Washington, DC: National Center for Education Statistics. http://nces.ed.gov/pubs2009/2009805.pdf.

NISO. 2004. *Understanding Metadata.* Bethesda: NISO Press. http://www.niso.org/publications/press/UnderstandingMetadata.pdf.

Office of the National Coordinator for Health Information Technology. 2013 (July). Capturing High Quality Electronic Health Records Data to Support Performance Improvement: A Learning Guide. http://www.healthit.gov/sites/default/files/onc-beacon-lg3-ehr-data-quality-and-perform-impvt.pdf.

Owen, K. and M. Fary. 2013. Establishing a data management plan consulting group on campus. *Educause Review Online.* http://www.educause.edu/ero/article/establishing-data-management-plan-consulting-group-campus.

Payne, T.H. and G. Graham. 2006. Managing the Life Cycle of Electronic Clinical Documents. *Journal of the American Medical Informatics Association* 13(4): 438–445.

Purdue University. 2014. Data Services and Administration: Metadata. http://www.itap.purdue.edu/ea/data/standards/metadata.cfm.

The Sedona Conference. The Sedona Conference Glossary: E-Discovery & Digital Information Management, 3rd ed. September 2010. https://thesedonaconference.org/publications.

Seiner, R.S. 2012 (Feb. 16). Real World Data Governance Webinar 2: The Role of Metadata in Data Governance. http://www.dataversity.net/slides-the-role-of-meta-data-in-data-governance/.

Smallwood, R.F. 2013. *Managing Electronic Records Methods, Best Practices, and Technologies.* Hoboken: John Wiley & Sons, Inc.

Smith, A.M. 2007. Turning data in knowledge: Creating and implementing a meta data strategy. *Proceedings of the MIT Information Quality Industry Symposium,* Vol. 1 (Session 2D). Cambridge, MA: MIT IQ. http://mitiq.mit.edu/IQIS/Documents/CDOIQS_200777/Papers/01_23_2D.pdf.

Smith, A.M. 2012. Metadata in Data Governance. The Data Administration Newsletter. http://www.tdan.com/view-articles/16101.

Varonis. 2013. Preparing your organization for the metadata era. https://varonis-assets.s3.amazonaws.com/pdfs/howtoprepare-metadata-era.pdf.

# Chapter 8

## Master Data Management

Frequently called the "single version," the "record of truth," or the "golden record," **master data** are an organization's high value, consistent, and uniform data about an organization's key entities shared across the enterprise in supporting the mission-critical processes of an organization. An organization infrequently changes and typically retains master data for long periods of time, if not indefinitely (Sourabh 2013).

The most notable master data in healthcare are probably related to the patient. Master patient data that identify and describe a patient are the backbone of any healthcare enterprise information system. These data are normally stored electronically in the master patient index (MPI). While master patient data are usually the most prominent type of master data, other categories of master data are also significant. For example, there are master data relating to providers, employees, vendors, and insurers. In addition, another category of master data, called reference data, is essential for healthcare operations. As its name implies, **reference data** are used by the organization to classify or categorize other data and are frequently represented by codes or acronyms. Codes or acronyms used for gender, country, or postal districts are familiar to many of us. Typical examples in healthcare include supply codes, service codes, and diagnostic codes such as International Classification of Diseases (ICD), Systematized Nomenclature of Medicine (SNOMED), and Logical Observation Identifiers Names and Codes (LOINC) codes.

Master data are important because they are the key to identifying, locating, and retrieving data about essential entities a company uses in its mission-critical processes. For example, think about the impact on a company's main processes if a company associate could not find information describing a customer (name, address, or phone number), or if the information was inaccurate or matched with the wrong customer. This adversely affects billing, shipping, and marketing, among other functions. In addition, the company may not be able to prepare invoices, the invoices may go out late, or the wrong person may receive them. Purchases, shipments, and marketing collateral would also be similarly affected.

In the healthcare environment, consider the adverse impact if a healthcare professional could not locate information identifying a patient, the information is inaccurate, or the system has matched information with the wrong patient. The most significant impact is poor, or potentially disastrous, quality of patient care. Other major implications include inaccurate reporting for compliance, regulatory, and business decision-making purposes, and a negative impact on essentially the entire continuum of enterprise internal operations. The damaging effect, however, does not stop at the organization's walls. Like a water ripple, it affects a broad range of areas, as data are exchanged by the organization with regional healthcare networks, insurance companies, and public health and other government agencies. Furthermore, from a compliance and legal standpoint, organizations must have good master data. Because organizations need to produce a variety of records and reports whose validity is based on "goodness" or quality of master data and must also track and document all changes to master data to meet legal, compliance, and regulatory mandates, master data management (MDM) is a key to corporate compliance and meeting regulatory mandates.

This chapter describes the role of master data, how it is managed, and its central importance for ensuring quality, efficiency, and effective enterprise information systems. It covers topics that will help you to:

- Apply master and reference data concepts in the healthcare environment
- Assess administrative and technical management of master data
- Explain data profiling, cleansing, and identity management
- Design master data governance (DG) activities

## The St. Rita's Healthcare System Case Study

The first agenda item for the enterprise information management (EIM) team's regular weekly meeting was to review the project timeline and complete their interim project report to Joan Morton. The team's assessment was that the project was right on track, but they could not afford any schedule slippage.

Joan Morton needed the team's comprehensive recommendations well in advance of St. Rita's yearly strategic planning retreat. This was a key meeting, and if EIM was to go from dream to reality, Joan would have to present a formal proposal at this meeting. Joan's expectation was that the team's report would provide her with a fair assessment of EIM concepts, components, benefits, risks, and if EIM provided the solution to the data problems at St. Rita's.

The team assigned Monte and Shirlee to investigate the next EIM domain, master data management, for the upcoming week, and they were excited to get started.

"Master data management is a key issue for St. Rita's," said Shirlee. "We've had enormous problems with our MPI, particularly since we've acquired other healthcare facilities and practices. These problems adversely impact just about every operation in the organization and I, for one, want to see them resolved."

"I know about those issues," replied Monte. "I've worked on interfaces among our systems, and I can't agree more with you, Shirlee. Identity management should be one of St. Rita's key efforts. Without it, information coordination and management is a moot point."

The team took care of other business items and then adjourned, looking forward to reviewing Monte and Shirlee's findings at the next meeting.

# Master and Reference Data Concepts

Master and reference data are the backbone that supports an organization's operations. Unavailability or error in these can cause significant disruption to a company. Because of this, the governance and management of these is just as mission-critical as the data themselves. Before applying effective management and governance, it is important to understand the fundamentals about the things that need monitoring and controlling. The following sections provide an overview of the basic concepts of master and reference data management.

## Master Data

As its name implies, master data are the main or principal data about an organization's key entities. Recall the discussion about data modeling in chapter 6 that defined an entity as a person, place, thing, or event. In framing a view of master data, it is helpful to think about master data as the data about an organization's **master entities**. In other words, master entities are the key entities upon which almost all other entities are related to or dependent upon. Key entities are widely distributed across information applications, and represent a high volume of records.

It is important to note that master data are not transaction data. **Transaction data** are data generated and captured by operational systems in business transactions. Examples include data related to sales (what was bought and for how much), deliveries (what was delivered and where), and so on. Master data are applied to transactions throughout the organization and are used by the organization to categorize, aggregate, and evaluate transaction data (Deloitte 2005). While master data are company-specific and depend upon a company's key operations, most companies recognize customer, product, account, organization, and location as master data (Berson and Dubov 2011, 7).

Before an organization can manage master data, it must identify master entities. In carving out the master entities among the hundreds or thousands of an organization's entities, the following three questions are useful to consider:

1. Is this entity a building block of critical business transactions?
2. Are the data related to the entity created and managed in multiple systems?
3. If those data are incorrect, inaccurate, incomplete, or mismanaged, do they have the potential to harm the organization (Lawson 2011)?

Examining these criteria against a healthcare organization's data model shows that the entity "patient" is a building block of critical business transactions and that a significant number of applications and processes depend on the entity "patient": laboratory, dietary, operating room, appointment, materials management, release of information, clinical coding, financial systems, and so on. Any data quality issues associated with this entity are potentially harmful. The same is true for the entity "provider." A provider is a key building block for critical transactions, and is associated with clinical and administrative applications across the enterprise, such as laboratory, pharmacy, radiology, operating room, scheduling, and financial systems. Any data quality issues would potentially be harmful.

Because so many processes and applications depend upon key entities, it is important that there is a common understanding across the organization of what master data define these entities and that there is one authoritative and trustworthy source of truth for them. For instance, all clinical systems and administrative systems such as billing, risk management, and health information management (HIM) use a patient's name (identity). It is essential that each of these systems has access to the same correct patient identity data. One system shouldn't be using Joe Paul Doe, while another system is using Joseph Paul Doe. Or in the case of patient address, the billing and cancer registry systems should be using the same correct patient address information.

The determination of master data for key entities depends upon the organization. But as examples, master data for a patient are likely to include a unique identifier, such as a health record number, and the patient's legal name, date of birth, gender, address, phone number, e-mail address, dates of admission and discharge, and health plan code. Master data for a provider are likely to include a unique identifier, provider legal name, state license number, national provider identifier, and so on.

Master data are classified into four customary categories: party, financial, product, and location categories (DAMA 2010, 178–180). **Party data** refers to individuals or organizations. For example, this includes employees, patients, providers, companies, and vendors. In healthcare, the MPI systems manage master data relating to patients. Customer relationship management (CRM) systems leverage master identity data to help organizations stay in contact with their customers, or in the case of healthcare, with their patients. On the other hand, a CRM-like system called a provider relationship management system (PRM) can manage provider master data to help organizations leverage referrals and relationships with physicians and other providers.

**Financial master data** include data about business units, cost centers, and accounts, among others. Organizations use these master data in functions such as accounts payable, payroll, and materials management. For example, master data about a cost center may include cost center name, cost center code, description, responsible person, and department.

**Product master data** describe an organization's products and include data about components that make up a product, product versions, pricing, and discount terms. For example, master data about products may include the product and service identification codes, description, price, and manufacturer identification.

**Location master data** include data such as the location of the organization's customers, suppliers, and others such as postal code, latitude and longitude, geopolitical boundaries, and sales territory. In healthcare, location master data are critical from the standpoint of public health and associated surveillance of disease and health hazards.

In the health arena, a major focus has been patient master data management because almost all healthcare organization operations are either directly or indirectly involved with patients. However, organizations must make equal efforts to manage other types of party master data and location master data, too (Fernandes 2013). From the standpoint of party master data, parties in healthcare include providers, insurers, and other organizations. The category of provider itself goes beyond physicians and includes any credentialed healthcare provider. It also includes pharmacies, home health agencies, dentists, and physical therapy clinics. Maintaining up-to-date and accessible master data about all of these entities is critical to a healthcare organization's operations as well as meeting legal, compliance, and regulatory obligations.

## Reference Data

Reference data are used by industries to classify or categorize other data (DAMA 2010, 174). The organization's business rules or other standards usually prescribe what values are permitted for specific types of data. Organizations define reference data values either externally or internally. Some examples of externally defined reference data are state abbreviations, whose values are prescribed by the United States Postal Service, or diagnostic codes such as ICD and SNOMED. Examples of internal reference values include department codes, employee codes, clinical laboratory abbreviations, or product codes.

Reference data play a large role in ensuring data quality if organizations enforce their use and use them consistently. A good illustration of this is using reference data to define gender for administrative purposes in an electronic health record (EHR). The reference data might be "F" for female, "M" for male, and "UN" for undifferentiated. Having a reference set is not sufficient without consistent and uniform use. For instance, if employees type in either "male" or "M" for gender value, then the data for gender among records are incomparable for decision support and other purposes. To enforce consistent use of reference data and codes, developers create reference tables (sometimes called look-up tables) and link them to other tables in a relational database. Drop-down lists and constraints put on fields, such as field type, ensure correct reference values use.

From a documentation perspective, reference data should provide not only the code and its description, but also the meaning of a code and other descriptive information. Figure 8.1 provides an example of what the gender description values might look like. This set of values is often referred to in the organization as the reference data set.

Figure 8.1. **Sample administrative gender reference data set**

Administrative Gender:
The gender of a person used for administrative purposes (as opposed to clinical gender), such as hospital bed assignment

Business Name: Patient Gender

| Code | Description | Display name |
|---|---|---|
| F | Female | Female |
| M | Male | Male |
| UN | The gender of a person could not be uniquely defined as male or female, such as hermaphrodite. | Undifferentiated |



Frequently, multiple reference data sets represent the same thing. Different applications may use different reference sets to represent the same concepts or things. In healthcare, for instance, various applications use different classification systems such as ICD-10-CM, SNOMED, Current Procedural Terminology (CPT), and LOINC to identify disease processes and procedures. This situation requires a master cross-referencing data set so the organization can translate a code from one code set to another. Cross-referencing, sometimes also called cross-mapping, is essential for data exchange for patient care purposes, access to longitudinal data, reimbursement, epidemiology, public health data reporting, and reporting to regulators and state data organizations (McBride et al. 2006).

# Master and Reference Data Management

**Master data management** (MDM) includes the processes and controls applied to an organization's core data entities that ensure consistency in their definition, format, and use across an enterprise. In a digital environment, MDM is an independent process that manages the master data through a set of guidelines and supporting technical architectures, ensuring a common and consistent view of key entities across an organization (Smith and McKeen 2008, 65).

Similar to other management processes, MDM needs to start with a focus on how it improves business processes or solves business or operational problems. An organization should establish the following before embarking on MDM (Shankar 2008):

- What business problems will MDM address? What business processes are ineffective, and among those, which are most aligned with the organization's strategic objectives and are the top priorities to address? Answering this question helps identify the master data the organization needs to manage and align the MDM program with the organization's strategic initiatives.

- What is the business use? Identifying who will use the master data and how they will use it helps to determine the most appropriate architectural implementation to support end user needs. For example, in order to make the right patient data available for clinical and business functions, the MDM system needs to make sure the various transaction systems have access to a "golden record" or single source of truth. Patient master data are the foundation for analysis and reporting functions so this information must also be available to analytic or business intelligence systems that include large stores of data, such as data warehouses and data marts, which accumulate data from a variety of application databases across the enterprise.
- What are the business requirements for master DG? Requirements include determining the necessary integrity levels, ensuring the integrity over time, determining who should have access to the master data, who can update or change the data, and how they can reconcile data discrepancies.

As these questions illustrate, the management of master and reference data covers administrative and architectural perspectives. Both are essential for a comprehensive master and reference management program. The following sections describe some of the prominent master data management concerns and functions.

## Identifying Master Data

Master and reference data management begins with the organization recognizing the need for MDM. The organization must define the business case, return on investment, and the benefits of MDM. Because MDM helps produce consistent, non-ambiguous, non-duplicated data and better quality data, frequently cited benefits include:

- Improved customer service (patient care)
- Better visibility into key performance indicators
- Better regulatory and compliance posture
- Improved decision making (Berson and Dubov 2011, 21)

After establishing the business case, the road to MDM begins with knowing what the organization needs to manage and why. This means identifying and prioritizing the key entities and the business processes affected by the program. A conceptual data model (chapter 7) can be used to identify master entities. Usually, organizations prioritize entities based on which have the greatest organizational impact or which are believed to have the most significant problems. In healthcare, master data about the entity "patient" can have one of the biggest impacts and some of the most significant problems (AHIMA 2009).

Once the organization identifies the master entities, it must define the master data associated with the entities. For example, if the entity is "patient," then the organization must answer the question "what are the master data associated with 'patient?'" Defining the master data requires developing metadata such as attribute name, data type, allowed values, constraints, default values, dependencies, and who owns the definition and is responsible for maintenance of the data.

In a good investigation, one question usually leads to others. Since corruption of data can happen anywhere in the data life cycle, organizations need to answer questions such as "where does this master data reside?" or "what applications use the master data?" or "where does the master data originate?" to track, monitor, and ensure data quality. Frequently, organizations may not have maintained a good inventory of information systems and applications. Answering each of these questions forces inventory development and provides insights into the life cycle of the master data itself. Organizations are frequently surprised at the number of data silos where master data reside that they did not know about.

Once the organization identifies sources, it lists the most trusted ones. Usually, these are the sources with the most volume of master data records associated with a specific entity (for example, patient, provider, or customer). In some instances, the master data will have their own unique **system of record** (SOR). An SOR is usually a specialized application system and the authoritative source for data about an entity. For example, the human resources management system (HRMS) is the SOR for employee master data, the CRM system is the SOR for customer data, or the SOR for financial and product information is the enterprise resource planning (ERP) system. (DAMA 2010, 182). In healthcare, the SOR for patient master data is the MPI.

Because business strategy and objectives change over time, creating new services or products, master data may change as well. Therefore, identifying and updating an organization's master data must be an ongoing effort and usually falls within the scope of master data governance.

## Profiling and Cleansing Master Data

To establish the single source of truth, master data in the SOR are first profiled by the organization. In the case where there is no SOR, the most trusted sources of master data are profiled, cleaned, and matched to arrive at the single source of truth.

**Data profiling** applies data and statistical analysis techniques to determine the content, structure, and quality of data held in data stores, such as databases and repositories (Olson 2003, 122). Data profiling cannot eliminate all data problems, but it can identify where the problems exist and help rectify some structural problems, such as format inconsistencies. Data profiling is a key activity for any data quality initiative, and it is also used to harmonize data that are migrated to different databases or to a data warehouse. Once an organization profiles data, it must address problems related to content, structure, or quality through data cleansing processes discussed later in this chapter and in chapter 12. Data profiling must be a multidisciplinary team effort. This includes having data stewards, business analysts, end users, and technical professionals working together. No one group can accomplish profiling and cleansing on its own.

Profiling teams execute profiling using both metadata and data. They use metadata as criteria to assess the data. IT professionals write special computer code, called extraction routines, to extract data from data stores and files and prepare them for profiling. The team uses an automated profiling tool, called a profile engine, to help make initial assessments about the content and structure of the data. Usually, the profiling tool looks for missing and incomplete values and compares the master data to a set of business data rules and metadata to determine accuracy. There are five steps that data should go through during profiling:

1. Invalid value analysis for each column: Inspect items, such as range of values and null fields
2. Structure analysis: Assess how columns and tables relate with each other and include such items as evaluation of primary and foreign keys and redundant columns
3. Simple data rule analysis: Assess data rules that hold true over a column, such as "birth date cannot be greater than current date"
4. Complex data rule analysis: Assess data rules that hold true over multiple columns such as "if diagnosis is uterine fibroids, gender must be female"
5. Value rule analysis: Analyze frequencies, sums, averages, and other statistics to identify data irregularities (Olson 2003, 131)

To illustrate value rule analysis, if the value for "gender" is supposed to be represented by a code such as "M," "F," or "UN" and the automated profiling tool evaluates the master data against this criterion and finds that the frequency of the value of "UN" is extremely high, this may indicate data entry or other errors. This is because it is unlikely that a healthcare organization would have a high number of patients categorized as "UN." Or, if all date fields are supposed to be populated in a specific format such as DD-MM-YYYY, the profile engine conducts pattern matching and evaluates the master data against that format. The profiling engine also produces frequency distribution reports and determines how many records have missing values and in what fields they are missing.

Basic statistics can also be applied to assess the quality of master data. Values can be assessed for data that are numeric, or for values that one can calculate such as date values, minimum and maximum values, and the mean, median, and mode of values. Take date of birth, for instance, which one can calculate in terms of years from the present date. If the average date of birth across all records does not match what an organization would normally anticipate from the demographics it serves, then the profiling team needs to inspect that master data more closely. Or, if a report lists a minimum value for date of birth as a minus value, this warrants closer inspection of the master data. A sample frequency distribution from data profiling of a patient residence data is shown in figure 8.2. If these data are associated with a hospital in Colorado, they would warrant review by the profiling team since one would expect that most of the organization's patients would reside in Colorado and not California.

The profiling techniques above structurally evaluate data, but other methods assess the accuracy of the master data (Loshin 2012). To illustrate, look at the following text entries:

- "181 Bellflower Rd"; "181 Bell Flower RD"; "181 Bellflower Road"
- "03-21-98"; "03-21-1998"; "03-2l-1998"
- "MI"; "myocardial infarction"; "myocardial infraction"

Each of these represents a series of data in specific fields. The first is an address field, the second is a date field, and the third is a diagnosis field. While the format of each entry is different, the meaning is the same. When differences exist, then a query execution must include every possible variation of the value in order to retrieve and report a complete set of data. For example, if the organization wanted to retrieve all of the records of all of the individuals it had treated with a diagnosis

Figure 8.2. Data profiling frequency distribution on state data

Table: Patient
Field: State_of_residence
Field type: Character
Field length: 2

| Value | Count | Percentage |
|---|---|---|
| CA | 4500 | 40.9 |
| CO | 3500 | 31.8 |
| UT | 1000 | 9.0 |
| WY | 1000 | 9.0 |
| NV | 500 | 4.5 |
| NM | 500 | 4.5 |



of myocardial infarction on March 21, 1998, then the query statement would need to include all the date and diagnosis variations to retrieve a complete records listing. It is highly unlikely the query statement would account for all variations. This illustrates the problem of low quality data, also called "dirty" data, and emphasizes the need for maintaining complete and accurate master data.

Once an organization profiles data, it establishes completeness and accuracy thresholds for master data, and separates the master data records into one of two groups: records meeting the threshold or "clean" records, and records not meeting the threshold or "bad" records. The bad records must go through subsequent processes to rectify the data problems. The first process is frequently referred to as cleansing the data and is usually performed by a data steward or technical team member using an automated process. **Data cleansing** attempts to correct inconsistency issues related to format, illegal characters, and empty fields (Oracle 2010). Frequently, data cleansing requires manual intervention. For example, a character string of "Detroit M1" would pass a data value rule that the "city and state" attribute must be a character string not to exceed 30 characters. However, visual inspection of the data reveals that the data are incorrect. The state abbreviation for Michigan is MI not M1.

## Data Matching

Another master data quality question is "are there possibilities of mismatched data?" Mismatched data is also referred to as **identity error**. In healthcare, one of the most problematic areas for identity error exists in patient master data. This problem increases with attempts to match patients with their healthcare data across a variety of settings and institutions (ONC 2014). Identity error in master data is when one or more of the following things occur (Altendorf 2007):

- **Duplicate records** exist for the same entity in the same database. For example, a patient, customer, or provider is assigned two or more unique identifiers.
- An **overlay** occurs for an entity. For example, a patient, customer, vendor, or provider is assigned another entity's unique identifier.
- An **overlap** occurs. For instance, a given entity, such as a patient, provider, or vendor has more than one unique identifier in different databases or different applications.

Identity error is a significant problem across industries. In healthcare, estimates are that between 8 to 14 percent of medical records include inaccurate information that can be traced to identity error (HIMSS 2012). Such inaccuracies impact patient safety, quality of care, and healthcare costs. The techniques for data profiling and cleansing are not sufficient to deal with these types of identity errors in master data. To remedy these errors, an algorithmic-based set of solutions for cross-enterprise and inter-enterprise identity management, frequently called record matching, are used by organizations (ONC 2012). Record matching solutions are explained in the following sections.

## Deterministic Matching

**Deterministic matching** is sometimes referred to as exact match logic (ONC 2012). This is the simplest technique for matching records where comparisons are made by automated record matching systems on selected data elements (AHIMA 2009). In the case of matching master data records for a patient entity, the selected data might include patient name, birth date, gender, social security number (SSN), and zip code. Deterministic matching takes two records and examines both to determine if there is an exact match in the subset data between the two. A problem with deterministic matching is that it often misses matches due to data variations, such as input errors and use of nicknames versus legal names (for example, Pat instead of Patricia). Another problem is that the approach does not take into account attribute frequency in large datasets. For example, a match on the very common last name of "Jones" does not mean as much as a match on the unique last name of "Boetani." Depending upon the attributes in the subset and their frequency, it is possible to have two individuals who have the same name (Jones), the same date of birth and gender, and who live in the same zip code (ONC 2012).

## Matching with Standardization Rules

Matching with **standardization rules** eliminates some of the problems with exact matching. Standardization, or normalization, is an enhancement process for structured data (Oracle 2010). This method leverages the structure already associated with a specific attribute, such as an attribute's data type, length, and definition. It uses equivalencies in performing the match. For example, take the attributes of first name, last name, street address, and state where first name = Bob, last name = Smith, street address = 181 Boulder Street, and state = California. Standardization rules and configurable locale-specific dictionary files that classify "Robert" as the standard name for Bob and CA as the standard name for California, transform the attributes into Robert Smith, 181 Boulder Street, CA (Oracle 2010).

## Probabilistic Matching

The purpose of **probabilistic matching** is to limit false positive and false negative record matches. A **false positive** matches two records to one identity when the records actually belong to two individuals. A **false negative** record match fails to match records of the same individual, leaving a duplicate in the database. An example of a false positive is linking two closely related people with very similar names and dates of birth who live near each other (for example, relatives who share the same name and hometown) or two individuals living in a dense urban area with the same common name, date of birth, and address. The failure to catch such errors results in overlaid health records, and subsequent negative health outcomes, serious privacy breaches, and legal ramifications (AHIMA 2009).

Probabilistic matching is based on the probability of error occurrence. It recognizes that a field-by-field comparison is subject to error in either matching or mismatching records. The approach takes into account both the probability of a mismatch between data values in two records that represent the same entity (for example, failing to identify records associated with the same individual), and the probability of a coincidental match between two records representing distinct entities (for example, matching records associated with different individuals).

Probabilistic matching also takes into consideration incomplete or empty values and usually uses weights or scores to indicate how closely two attribute field values match where one attribute is given a higher weight than another. For instance, a match on phone number gets a higher score than gender because a specific phone number would appear less frequently in a database than gender.

There are various types of probabilistic matching (figure 8.3). The following is a simple example of probabilistic matching concepts. Consider there are two records for a patient, "Declan Smith," and two records for "John Smith." Using a frequency analysis, the first name "John" shows up more often than "Declan" in the data source. From a probability perspective, a match on Declan, a less frequent value, holds more significance than a match on "John." Therefore, in the case of Declan Smith, the field value for first name would be higher than the field value for first name of John Smith. Frequency-based matching usually improves the accuracy of matching by 4 to 10 percent (Berson and Dubov 2011).

Probabilistic matching also uses phonetics, a technique that identifies words with different spellings but the same pronunciation, such as Smith and Smithe. There are several different types of phonetic encoders. Among the more prominent and reliable ones are Soundex, the New York State Identification and Intelligence System (NYSIIS), RefinedSoundex, Metaphone, and DoubleMetaphone (Oracle 2010).

Probabilistic algorithms may also include artificial intelligence and neural network programs that simulate human problem solving. As the program processes more data, it tunes the field weights as required based upon the learning achieved during processing of the entire data set of records (AHIMA 2009).

Figure 8.3. List of entity matching frameworks

| Bayesian Network |
| --- |
| Mapping-based Object Mapping (MOMA) |
| Stanford Entity Resolution Framework |
| Active Atlas |
| Multiply Adaptive Record Linkage with Induction (MARLIN) |
| Multiple Classifier System |
| TAILOR |
| Operator Trees |
| Freely Extensible Biomedical Record Linkage (FEBRL) |
| Self-Tuning Entity Matching (STEM) |
| Context Based Framework |

Source: Kopcke and Rham 2010.

Due to the variety of master data attributes and data sources, there is no one "best" matching algorithm. Some match approaches work better than others depending upon the domain of records being matched. Consensus appears to be that it is often necessary to combine several methods to improve matching quality (Kopcke and Rahm 2010).

In healthcare, it has been observed that organizations are configuring matching algorithms differently and inconsistently, not implementing them correctly, or implementing them too stringently or too loosely for adequate matching purposes. Because many of the records linking applications are proprietary, there is a lack of scientific study on the reliability of these applications, and there are no standards set for performance expectations (HIMSS 2009).

## Steps in Record Matching

The steps for record matching apply to any type of entity such as employee, vendor, provider, part, organization, and so on. The following is an overview of the usual steps an organization takes.

### Identify Attributes for Matching

The attributes used for matching records fall into three broad categories: identity, discriminating, and record qualification attributes (Berson and Dubov 2011). **Identity attributes** identify people, parts, products, organizations, and so on. For a patient, identity attributes would include, among others, the patient's full name, key identifiers such as SSN, driver's license number, patient number, phone number, address, and e-mail address.

**Discriminating attributes**, on the other hand, are used to disqualify two or more similar records, rather than match them. These should be static attributes that do not normally change, such as date of birth, date of death, or gender. A good illustration of their use is in the case where a father and son have the same name, address, phone number, and gender. The date of birth would discriminate between the two persons. Discriminating attributes are usually used in conjunction with identity attributes.

**Record qualification attributes** help pinpoint what identification rules should apply to a record. For example, the country attribute would identify how to evaluate the structure of the attribute address, since addresses are defined differently from country to country: the record matching application would evaluate the postal code for the United States differently than the postal code for Canada. Or the phonetic algorithm used for name matching may be different for individuals living in the United States than in France. For instance, there is a specific phonetic encoder version for French.

### Identify the Framework for Matching

After an organization identifies the attributes for matching, it must select the framework to match attributes and records. There are many types of matching frameworks. Some are proprietary and vendor-specific, whose algorithms are not described in public literature (Kopcke and Rahm 2010). Because these algorithms are not in the public domain and their specific operation is not known, they are referred to as "black box" solutions (HIMSS 2009). Others, like those listed in figure 8.3, are research prototypes and fully described in the literature.

### Define Thresholds

Whether an organization chooses a deterministic or a probabilistic method, or a hybrid of both, for record matching, it needs to identify a **probability level** or, likelihood, for record matches. The probability level is usually a number that serves as the **threshold**, also known as the range or baseline, in determining which records match and which do not. Specific algorithms are used to determine the probability of a match between a record pair and the probability of a non-match between the pair.

An algorithm may calculate the probability of a match and a non-match for each attribute of a pair of records being examined. Using the calculated probabilities, a weight is defined using a mathematical calculation to measure the contribution of each field to the probability of making an accurate decision as to whether the records match or not. The threshold value between accepting a match or non-match is calculated by the accepted probability of false matches and the probability of false non-matches. Upper and lower thresholds should be defined by the organization (Berson and Dubov 2009). The composite weights classify the records into one of three groups: confident match (above the upper threshold value), confident mismatch (below the lower threshold value), and possible match (between the upper and lower threshold levels). Those records in the possible match category are then referred for manual review.

## Data Validation and Remediation

Regardless of the matching algorithm the organization uses, human intervention is required for matches where a definitive decision cannot be made by an automated method. In these cases, the system tags suspect records for review, and manual record match validation methods are used for validation and addressing match issues. Ideally, data stewards knowledgeable in validation procedures and the master data in question perform these reviews. Generally, there are four tasks data stewards must perform manually (ONC 2012):

- Determine if duplicate records exist. This occurs when two records from the same source do not meet the validation threshold criteria after automated review to be duplicates of the same entity. In this case, manual review determines if duplicates exist.
- Determine if record linkage exists. This occurs when two records from different sources do not meet the threshold criteria for record linkage after automated review. In this case, manual review determines if the records identify the same entity.
- Determine if overlay exists. This occurs when one entity is assigned another entity's unique identifier. In this case, manual review must determine which attributes are correct.
- Determine if duplicate identifiers exist. This occurs when two records from the same source do not meet the threshold criteria for a duplicate, but share the same unique identifier. In this case, manual review must determine if they are the same or not.

## Ongoing Surveillance

Data profiling, cleansing, and matching are not one-time efforts. Organizations add master entities to databases or update them each day: new, former, and current patients are treated; new providers are added, and current or former provider data are updated; new products are purchased, and new accounts are created. All of these activities create or update master data and provide the opportunity for error. Therefore, data profiling, cleansing, and record matching must become ongoing information management processes. Key performance indicators (KPIs) that the organization uses to focus on regularly evaluating patient identity (for example, MPI) can be applied to any organization master data (see table 8.1).

Table 8.1. Master patient index key performance indicators

| Key Performance Indicator | Description |
|---|---|
| MPI database size | The total number of records stored in the database. Includes unique individuals, duplicates, un-reconciled records, and so on. |
| MPI person population | The number of unduplicated individuals contained in an MPI or database. |
| MPI database growth | The gross number of new, unduplicated records stored in a given time interval (for example, weekly or monthly) regardless of category. |

(continued)

Table 8.1. Master patient index key performance indicators (*Continued*)

| Key Performance Indicator | Description |
|---|---|
| MPI additions | The number of new patients added to the MPI for the very first time for a given time frame. |
| MPI matches | The total number of potential pair candidates presented by the MPI algorithm for a period of time. |
| Total MPI non-matches | Total number of true matches missed by the algorithm and identified during normal operation processes that require additional validation of records. |
| MPI database duplicates | The numeric count of records that are potential duplicates within the database. |
| False positive matched pairs | The number of candidate pairs generated by the algorithm that are found, after manual validation, not to be matched pairs. |
| True matched pairs | The number of pairs generated by the algorithm as well as external business processes that are found, after manual validation, to be confirmed as matched pairs. |
| False negative non-match pairs | The number of incorrect MPI non-match decisions made in a given period of time. |
| Indeterminate matched pairs | After manual review, the number of algorithm candidate pairs whose identities could not be validated as being the same individual. |
| MPI matching validation | Analysis of the total MPI matches. |
| Database error growth | The number of erroneous records added to the database over a given period of time. |
| Total registrations performed | The total number of registration activities (for example, registration or scheduling) performed in a given period of time. |
| Database activity rate | Ratio of the total number of MPI algorithm matching evaluations performed in a given timeframe to the overall size of the MPI database. |
| Database duplicate rate | Percentage of paired records in the database that are potential duplicates or multiples. |
| Duplicate creation rate | Ratio of newly created duplicate records to the opportunity to create a duplicate through encounters with patients. |
| True match rate | Ratio of the number of true match pairs as determined after manual validation to the total number of MPI matching evaluations presented by the algorithm plus those identified by other business processes. |
| False positive match rate | Percentage of incorrectly matched candidate pairs over a given period of time. |
| False negative (non-match) rate | Percentage of incorrect MPI non-match decisions made in a given period of time. |
| Indeterminate match rate | Percentage of records that were found to be indeterminate matches after validation of the total number of evaluations performed by the algorithm. |
| Matching accuracy rate | Overall accuracy rate of the demographic matching process over a given period of time. |

Source: HIMSS 2012.

## The St. Rita's Healthcare System Case Study

Shirlee and Monte met to assess their progress on master data management. "What strikes me is that MDM is closely aligned with metadata management as well as data engineering," Shirlee stated. "I guess I never connected the relationships between these functions before, but the big picture for me is that one function can affect many other functions in the EIM world."

"I totally agree," said Monte. "Who would have thought the data model could play a role in identifying master data? Having a good data model is truly the foundation for information management. I also suspect the things we learned about data profiling, cleansing, and matching for master data also apply to the functions of data quality and business intelligence. Everything is intertwined. If one function is out of balance or not performing, it impacts all of the EIM functions."

"An observation I've made is that we've been looking at back-end clean-up processes. Doesn't it make sense to have policies and procedures in place to make sure that we're doing data capture and other tasks right in the first place?" asked Shirlee.

"My thinking, exactly," Monte responded. "That's why doing a good job with requirements analysis and constructing good use cases is so important. I also see how DG applies to master data management. In our summary to the EIM team, we need to make a strong case for DG functions in the management of master data."

Shirlee and Monte decided to pool their resources and both research technical solutions for MDM.

## Technical Management

To avoid master and reference data silos there must be an effective data integration plan supported by architecture controls for shared access, replication, and flow of data. Lack of such controls impairs data quality. Organizations can use several architectural approaches to manage master and reference data and keep it synchronized with operational and analytical systems. The choice of technical architecture depends on many factors, including the organization's long-term vision for MDM, the roadmap toward achieving the vision, and financial considerations, such as risk, cost savings, and return on investment.

Worldwide MDM software revenue is forecasted to reach $3.2 billion by 2015 (Gartner 2012). All industries have recognized the need for MDM as a foundation for managing information assets, whether it is for supporting operational or analytical systems, or both. Technological solutions have evolved from systems that manage single domain master data (for example, customer or patient) to those that purport to support multi-domain MDM. As in all technology implementations, arriving at the best choice between "best-of-breed" solutions that support single master data domains and "best-of-fit" options that support multiple domains is a tension point. The goal should be to adopt a solution that meets the business needs of the organization now and into the future.

To understand the dilemma for organizations in selecting an architecture and associated technology solutions, consider the functional capabilities that an MDM system must perform:

- Creating and managing core data stores
- Managing processes that implement DG and data quality
- Managing metadata
- Extracting, transforming, and loading data from source systems to target systems
- Performing backup and recovery
- Performing entity analysis (for example, customer, patient, provider)
- Providing security and availability (visibility)
- Synchronizing and persisting data changes
- Managing transaction
- Matching entity and unique identifiers generation
- Resolving entities and relationships (Berson and Dubov 2011, 84–85)

Fundamentally, an MDM system may need to support two kinds of usage. First, as an SOR, it is an authoritative central source that originates and validates a new patient, provider, or vendor. It provides data for transaction processing systems (referred to as downstream application systems) and to other source systems (referred to as upstream systems). Second, as a reference copy, the master data are copied through automated processes for certain downstream processes (Wadehra 2007). As a copy of the system source and not a system of origination, reference copies may not always be current. Frequently, changes to the SOR are batched together and then applied to the system of reference on a periodic basis. For example, the MPI may be the SOR for the entity patient, but a copy of this master data may be provided through automated processes to a data warehouse on a daily basis (Dreibelbis et al. 2008).

There are four common architecture options for an MDM system. However, there can be many more implementations depending upon the organization's MDM goals, business needs, current technology environment, and systems it supports. The common hub implementations include consolidation, registry, coexistence, and transaction, all of which are discussed below (Dreibelbis et al. 2008).

## Consolidated Hub Implementation

Organizations may have many authoritative sources of record for their master data. For example, the ERP system may serve as the SOR for financial data, the employee's record management (ERM) system may serve as the system of record for employees, and the MPI may serve as the system of record for patients. This makes for a very complex data integration environment. **Consolidated implementation** has each database provide its authoritative reference and master data into a single, managed MDM data store that serves as a hub for all reference and master data for all other systems, both transaction and analytic. The MDM hub is a read-only system; only the systems that feed the hub can make master data changes. An advantage of this design is the standardization of interfaces to the MDM hub from the source systems (DAMA 2010). A primary benefit is that automated processes transform, cleanse, match, and integrate the data to provide a complete golden record for one or more master data domains (Dreibelbis et al. 2008). A drawback of this design is that it does not always contain the most current data. Depending upon the frequency of updates to the hub, it may not meet the needs of downstream transaction systems. Another downside is that entity master data must be present in the systems that feed the MDM hub. If business needs change, requiring a change in master data, then the system that feeds the MDM hub as well as the interfaces and the hub need to be changed by a technical team (Dreibelbis et al. 2008).

## Registry Hub Implementation

The **registry data hub** is an implementation that points to the location of the master data attributes in source systems using a metadata repository. It usually only stores key identifiers and functions as a reference and links to the location of authoritative master data sources. This type of design provides a real-time reference by assembling and integrating a read-only view of master data to application systems. To accomplish this, the system responds to a query by looking up the identifying information in the hub and then using that identity and cross-reference information to retrieve the requested data from other sources.

The registry implementation is a good choice if an organization's MDM strategy is to preserve and enhance their existing source systems. This is one of the least expensive MDM system solutions. However, the hub has to support complex business rules defining how to assemble a single record from two or more records with overlapping attributes that may contain conflicting values. Query performance can be a big concern for organizations when multiple systems must be accessed to retrieve the requested data (Berson and Dubov 2011). A potential governance issue is that the quality of the master data depends upon how well source systems manage it.

## Coexistence Implementation

**Coexistence implementation** is a storage solution where some master data is stored along with the ability to reference other data in the source systems. It is not considered a system of record because it is not the single place where master data are authored and updated (Dreibelbis et al. 2008). It contains metadata with pointers to locations of master records and attributes. However, some master entity attributes are stored redundantly. This can present synchronization problems.

## Transaction Hub Implementation

In the **transaction hub implementation**, master data are physically stored in the MDM hub and are used as the authoritative SOR. As its name suggests, it supports services that apply data access and update transactions to the master data in the MDM hub. This makes it fundamentally different from the consolidated method, which is a system of reference, not a system of record. As updates are made to the master data, it is cleansed, matched, and augmented to maintain the quality of the master data. After updates are validated, the system makes these available to appropriate applications and users. Changes can happen in real time or can be aggregated and batched (Dreibelbis et al. 2008).

An advantage of this system is that it is a comprehensive solution, especially for organizations whose strategy is to phase out legacy systems. However, the system has potential drawbacks. One is the complexity of extracting master data from existing source systems, transforming it, and then loading it into the transaction hub with real-time synchronization and reconciliation. In addition, it must be flexible enough so that if new systems or data sources are added, the entire MDM hub does not require a significant or complete overhaul (Berson and Dubov 2011).

## Applying Data Governance

Implementing master and reference data management is a deliberate course of action. It does not happen overnight. The complexities from administrative and technical perspectives mandate thoughtful planning with a strategic MDM vision and a roadmap of incremental steps to arrive at quality master data.

Implementation of MDM requires both administrative and technical solutions. DG is pivotal to MDM. MDM cannot succeed without development and implementation of policies, procedures, and standards with an administrative structure that is responsible and accountable for oversight of these. The following are the key DG functions for MDM that Shirlee and Monte prepared for further discussion with the EIM team:

- Identify stakeholders and establish decision rights and accountabilities
- Identify master and reference data requirements
- Develop and maintain a master data model
- Identify sources and users of master and reference data
- Ensure maintenance of consistent master and reference data, metadata, and definitions
- Develop policies, procedures, standards, and metrics for ensuring master and reference data quality and security
- Establish validation and verification levels for master and reference data consistency, correctness, and completeness
- Audit master and reference data quality, ensuring that organizational needs are met
- Ensure that master and reference data and processes meet regulatory and compliance requirements
- Ensure that lineage of changes to master data are documented and preserved

In reviewing the list, Shirlee and Monte consolidated these into the matrix of deliverables by EIM domain area that appears in table 8.2.

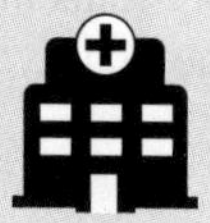

### The St. Rita's Healthcare System Case Study

"From what you've presented, MDM looks like a high priority area for any organization that wants to take DG seriously," said Fred after Shirlee and Monte's presentation.

"It's amazing seeing the complexity of identity management and I know you said you only hit the tip of the iceberg on this subject in your presentation. We've started working on MPI issues here at St. Rita's, but this is the first time I truly understand the general concepts behind the deterministic and probabilistic algorithms," added Denise.

"I think you are spot on in your observations that profiling and cleansing master data are back-end processes," interjected Linda. "If we did better front-end work at the point of data capture and with a better inventory of the sources and uses of this data, there wouldn't be so many data quality problems. This is an area that we need to dig deeper into so we can identify ways of avoiding problems early in the data life cycle."

Val did a round robin asking each member of the team to list their key takeaways from the presentation. When tallied, one the team unanimously agreed upon was that MDM was likely to be one of the top considerations in the launch of the EIM program at St. Rita's. They also agreed that honing the functions of MDM DG would be useful and added that task for completion at a later time.

Table 8.2. DG deliverables by EIM function

| Data Governance | Data Architecture Management | Metadata Management | Master Data Management | Content Management | Data Security and Privacy Management | Business Intelligence Management | Data Quality Management | Terminology and Classification Management |
|---|---|---|---|---|---|---|---|---|
| Identify mission and scope | Develop and maintain data models | Develop policies, procedures, and standards | Identify master and reference data requirements | | | | | |
| Establish goals and success measures | Develop, maintain, and evaluate data model policies and standards | Ensure metadata meets functional requirements | Develop policies, procedures, and standards for management of master data | | | | | |
| Put in place DG structure, processes, and communications plan | Define roles, responsibilities, and accountabilities for data architecture management | Develop and maintain appropriate metadata schema | Establish master data definitions, validation, and verification levels for master data quality | | | | | |
| Secure funding | Develop, maintain, and evaluate policies and standards for requirements analysis | Ensure metadata capture, maintenance, distribution, and integration | Ensure master and reference data meet regulatory requirements, including lineage history and security | | | | | |
| Establish decision rights | Develop and maintain data artifacts and standards | Ensure metadata security | Establish audit procedures and standards for master data | | | | | |
| Identify accountabilities | Establish quality control program and metrics for data architecture management | Develop and implement quality controls for metadata | Identify stakeholders and establish decision rights and accountabilities | | | | | |

## Part of the Team: Topics for Discussion and Action

1. The EIM team concurred that MDM relied on strong DG. Shirlee and Monte had outlined the activities associated with MDM DG and added these to the list of activities by functional area (table 8.2). The team left the actual steps for setting up MDM DG for another time. In helping the team complete this task, prepare a table that lists the steps needed to establish DG for MDM at St. Rita's. With each step, include the rationale, why it is important, and who the likely players in the DG structure would be (for example, a data steward or data custodian).

## Advanced Concepts

1. Read the Department of Health and Human Service's (HHS) Office of Inspector General's Report on *Improvements to Ensure Provider Enumeration and Medicare Enrollment Data are Accurate, Complete, and Consistent* available at the HHS website. Discuss the methodology used and assess the

recommendations made for ensuring better data quality in these databases. What can you learn from this case that you could apply to healthcare organizations generally in use of external databases or in evaluation of their own master data?

2. Read the HIMSS white paper on *Patient Identity Integrity* available at the HIMSS website. Compare the comments regarding the barriers to identity management with other research in the field. Given your assessment, what would be your position on a national unique identifier? Provide a rationale on the issue.
3. Correcting identity error with backend processes requires enormous resources in the form of technology, people, and money. What front-end policies should an organization put in place to ensure better data quality for master patient data, and how should it implement and monitor the policies? What role should DG play in front-end processes? Be specific in your response as to responsibilities and accountabilities.

## References

AHIMA. 2009. Managing the integrity of patient identity in health information exchange. *Journal of AHIMA* 80(7): 62–69. http://library.ahima.org/xpedio/groups/public/documents/ahima/bok1_044000.hcsp?dDocName=bok1_044000.

Altendorf, R. 2007. Establishment of a quality program for the master patient index. *AHIMA's 79th National Convention and Exhibit Proceedings.* Philadelphia: AHIMA.

Berson, A. and L. Dubov. 2011. *Master Data Management and Data Governance.* New York: McGraw-Hill.

DAMA. 2010. *DAMA Guide to the Data Management Body of Knowledge.* Bradley Beach: Technics Publications, LLC.

Deloitte. 2005. Getting Started with Master Data Management: A White Paper by Deloitte Consulting, LLP and Hyperion Solutions. http://www.oracle.com/us/solutions/ent-performance-bi/hyperion-drm-tws-068304.pdf.

Dreibelbis, A., I. Milman, P. van Run, E. Hechler, M. Oberhofer, and D. Wolfson. 2008. *Enterprise Master Data Management: An SOA Approach to Managing Core Information.* Indianapolis: IBM Press. http://my.safaribooksonline.com/book/databases/9780137149674.

Fernandes, L. 2013. Mastering Data in Healthcare: Beyond Patients. The Big Data & Analytics Hub. http://www.ibmbigdatahub.com/blog/mastering-data-healthcare-beyond-patients.

Gartner. 2012 (Jan. 3). Press Release: Gartner says master data management software revenue to grow by 21 percent in 2012. http://www.gartner.com/newsroom/id/1886314.

HIMSS. 2009. Patient Identity Integrity: A White Paper by the HIMSS Patient Identity Integrity Workgroup. http://www.himss.org/files/HIMSSorg/content/files/PrivacySecurity/PIIWhitePaper.pdf.

HIMSS. 2012. Patient Identity Integrity Toolkit: Patient Identity Integrity Performance Indicators. http://www.himss.org/files/HIMSSorg/content/files/PII03_Key_Performance_Indicators_Final.pdf.

HIMSS. 2012 (September). Recommendations to Congress. http://www.himss.org/files/HIMSSorg/policy/d/2012_Ask1_PatientDataMatchingStrategy.pdf.

Kopcke, H. and E. Rahm. 2010. Frameworks for entity matching: A comparison. *Data & Knowledge Engineering* 69(2): 197–210. http://www.sciencedirect.com/science/article/pii/S0169023X09001451.

Lawson, L. 2011. Unified Communications Remain a Difficult Sell. IT Business Edge. http://www.itbusinessedge.com/cm/blogs/lawson/defining-master-data-for-your-organization/?cs=40158.

Loshin, D. 2012. The Practitioner's Guide to Data Profiling. A SAS White Paper. http://resources.idgenterprise.com/original/AST-0087746_PractitionersGuideToData.pdf.

McBride, S., R. Gilder, R. Davis, and S. Fenton. 2006. Data mapping. *Journal of AHIMA* 77(2): 44–48.

Office of the National Coordinator (ONC). 2012. Master Data Management Within HIE Infrastructures: A Focus on Master Patient Indexing Approaches. http://www.healthit.gov/sites/default/files/master_data_management_final.pdf.

Office of the National Coordinator (ONC). 2014. Patient Identification and Matching Final Report. http://www.healthit.gov/sites/default/files/patient_identification_matching_final_report.pdf.

Olson, J.E. 2003. *Data Quality: The Accuracy Dimension.* San Francisco: Morgan Kaufmann.

Oracle. 2010. Identity Resolution and Data Quality Algorithms for Master Person Index. An Oracle White Paper. http://www.himss.eu/sites/default/files/identity-resolution-algorithm-wp-171743.pdf.

Shankar, R. 2008. Getting Off on The Right Foot: Avoiding Common Master Data Management False Starts. The Data Administration Newsletter. July 1, 2008. http://www.tdan.com/view-articles/7932.

Smith, H.A., and J.D. McKeen. 2008. Developments in Practice XXX: Master Data Management: Salvation Or Snake Oil? *Communications of the Association for Information Systems* 23(1): 63-72. http://aisel.aisnet.org/cais/vol23/iss1/4/.

Sourabh, M. 2013. Master Data Management Through a Crystal Ball. *Business Intelligence Journal.* 18(3).

Wadehra, A. 2007. The ABCs of Master Data Management: Architecture, Business Case, and Customer. *Business Intelligence Journal* 12(1): 33-40.

# Chapter 9

# Enterprise Content and Record Management

Documents, documents everywhere! In many people's minds, the implementation of the electronic health record (EHR) would eliminate paperwork and increase work efficiency. The 1997, the Institute of Medicine (IOM) report on the computer-based patient record stated that it "replaces the paper medical record as the primary record of care, meeting all clinical, legal, and administrative requirements" (Dick et al. 1997, 11). However, in the digital world, decreasing or eliminating paper does not necessarily translate into a decrease in documents. In fact, it may actually increase them. Think about all the digital documents created in the course of a business day, including emails, letters, memos, spreadsheets, reports, policies, digital images, blogs, presentations, scanned paper documents, wikis, and manuals, to name a few. The introduction of all of these has actually increased the number of documents healthcare professionals must manage.

There is a truism that has been circulating since the 1990s that "at least 80 percent of business-relevant information originates in unstructured form, primarily text" (Grimes 2008). In the clinical realm, approximately 1.2 billion clinical documents are produced in the United States each year, and 60 percent of those documents are used as the primary source of information for reimbursement and proof of service (Health Story Project 2014). Whatever the percentage, it is apparent that more than ever before, organizations have a larger volume of unstructured content to manage, a significant percentage of which resides in both paper and electronic documents.

Because of their unstructured nature, it is difficult to tap into the store of information that documents hold or subject the data within them to traditional analytic, search, and verification techniques. Getting control over what is frequently called "content chaos" has potentially substantial benefits to organizations, in general, and to healthcare, in particular. Among these are improved consistency and timeliness of content, cost savings, value-added customer (patient) services, better internal and external collaboration, and improved ability to meet regulatory and compliance mandates (vom Brocke et al. 2010).

The field of **enterprise content management** (ECM) is relatively new. The expression was first introduced in 2001 by the Association for Information and Image Management (vom Brocke et al. 2010). ECM is the management of an organization's unstructured data. It includes methods for the capture, storage, retrieval, archival, and delivery of unstructured data to meet an organization's business goals. As an evolving discipline, there has been little related research to ground the field, and case studies on how organizations can put it in practice are limited. ECM may well be more of an integrative concept that brings together data governance (DG), data stewardship, practices such as document and record management, and work in such fields as thesaurus, taxonomy, and ontology development.

The term **enterprise content and record management** (ECRM) expands on ECM by combining electronic records management and ECM concepts (AHIMA 2008). Specifically, ECRM differentiates between content, which is generally considered the intellectual substance of a document, and a record which is considered information that is created or used in a business transaction or to fulfill legal obligations. Because both content and records management concepts are integral to the management of healthcare data, both are covered in this chapter and referred collectively to as ECRM. Rather than providing a definitive approach to ECRM, this chapter delves into the potential advantages of and looks at the differences between practices in the integrated domains of document, record, and content management, and how the collaboration of these can play a role in taming content chaos. Specifically, this chapter examines topics that can help you to:

- Interpret the nature of content, document, and record management
- Develop the business case for enterprise content and record management (ECRM)
- Apply the functions and technologies for electronic document management
- Apply the functions and technologies for content management
- Assess the implementation issues in content and record management

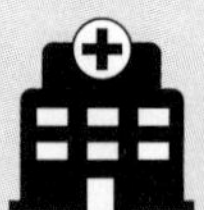

### The St. Rita's Healthcare System Case Study

The EIM team members were enjoying their monthly lunch outing and talking casually about the actions they took at their weekly meeting that morning. "I think it was brilliant to ask David to join the team. We should have thought about that earlier, especially when we were investigating metadata management. He would have been enormously helpful," Shirlee said.

"You're absolutely right, Shirlee. That is why at our next meeting we are going to identify the knowledge gaps on the team and where we could benefit in bringing in additional expertise," added Monte. "The right skill mix on the team is essential for our and St. Rita's success."

David worked in the IT division at St. Rita's as a project manager, but his previous background was in archives and records administration. His special interest was historical archives before getting a master's in information science. The team knew he'd be a terrific addition, particularly in contributing to the next domain, ECRM.

"It looks as if there could be overlap between ECRM and metadata management," Denise observed. "I think there will be a lot of thinking around metadata with all of the unstructured data we have. One of my pet peeves is that in many electronic document installations, there is diligence in identifying a document but not enough thoroughness given to describing the data within a document." Denise's background in health information management (HIM) gave her an excellent perspective of the issues related to document, record, and content management. Paired with David's background, the two were an excellent sub-team to investigate ECRM.

## Concepts of Enterprise Content and Record Management

Often, people use the terms records, documents, and content interchangeably. However, there are distinct differences among them. The distinctions between these are important when it comes to developing organizational policy and meeting legal and other mandates. This section explores these differences and how they impact organizational policy and meeting compliance and legal mandates.

### Records

The International Organization for Standardization (ISO) standard 15489-1:2001 defines a **record** as "information created, received, and maintained as evidence and information by an organization or person, in pursuance of legal obligations or in the transaction of business" (Gunnlaugsdottir 2002, 232). A record, defined by the ISO standard, has three characteristics that include content, structure, and context.

**Content** is the data or information within the record that composes its intellectual substance. For example, the description of a patient's medical history, past illnesses, and current problems constitutes the intellectual substance of a patient history report. **Structure**, on the other hand, refers to the format of the record and its relationship to the record's content. For example, headings in a patient's history, such as present illness, past illness, and so on, are related to and provide structure to the content in the record. The third characteristic is context. **Context** means the circumstances about the record's creation, receipt, and use (for example, how it was created, when it was created, and by whom it was created), and provides links to other records (Gunnlaugsdottir 2002). If a record documents regularly conducted business activities, it is legally considered a business record. As a business record, records must not be changed and must be maintained by the organization in an unalterable form.

There are various definitions of a record depending upon jurisdiction, purpose, content, and legislation. The following provide examples of these definitions:

- The American Health Information Management Association (AHIMA) defines a record as "information created or received in the transaction of business and maintained as evidence in pursuance of legal obligations" (AHIMA 2008, 99A).
- ARMA International defines a record as "recorded information, regardless of medium or characteristics, made or received by an organization in pursuance of legal obligations or in the transaction of business" (ARMA 2012).
- In the Health Insurance Portability and Accountability Act of 1996 (HIPAA), a record is "any item, collection, or grouping of information that contains protected health information and is maintained, collected, used, or disseminated by or for a health plan or health provider" (45 CFR 160, 162, 164).
- The Illinois State Records Act defines a state government record as "all books, papers, digitized electronic material, maps, photographs, databases, or other official documentary materials, regardless of physical form or characteristics, made, produced, executed or received by any agency in the state in pursuance of state law or in connection with the transaction of public business and preserved or appropriate for preservation by that agency or its successor as evidence of the organization, function, policies, decisions, procedures, operations, or other activities of the state or of the state government, or because of the informational data contained therein" (State of Illinois 2003).

One characteristic that all of these definitions have in common is that they all define a record as the documentation of business transactions or documentation to meet a specific mandate, such as state laws or regulation.

Identifying what documentation an organization creates and keeps that constitutes business records for legal compliance is often difficult. Not every note, piece of paper, or reference material is a business record. The following five questions are helpful in determining if something is a record:

- Was it made, sent, or received in the course of business?
- Does it document a decision?
- Does it document advice given?
- Does it document a process of arriving at a decision?
- Is it required by legislation (Queensland State Archives 2008)?

## Documents

The ISO defines a **document** as "recorded information or object which can be treated as a unit" (Gunnlaugsdottir 2002, 232). Documents include filled or unfilled forms, transcribed reports, inventory lists, or notes. One distinction between a document and a record is that unlike a record, a document is not considered to be associated with the criteria for a business transaction or a legal requirement.

Documents do not have the same constraints as records. Documents can be updated and do not have to be maintained by the organization for legal compliance. Take, for example, a Gantt chart used for project timeline planning, such as moving offices from one building to another. The Gantt chart changes several times during a project's life cycle. It requires processes for versioning, sharing, and updating. And, the maintenance of the Gantt chart versions depends on internal organizational policy rather than regulatory or legal mandates. Another illustration is development of a human resources policy where the policy has gone through several draft iterations. The various iterations are considered documents because they are not yet approved or final. But once the policy is approved and organization decisions are made based on it, it becomes a record (Maio 2013). The management needs for this document, and others like it, are different than for an organization's records.

Documents can become records if they are used in a business transaction or created to document a transaction. For example, a blank form used in a business transaction, such as an invoice, becomes a record when the organization uses it to bill a customer. The criteria used by organizations to classify a document as a record vary and depend upon a combination of organization policy, legal, compliance, accreditation, and other requirements, as well as assessment of benefits and risks.

## Content

Content, defined in relation to ECRM, consists of the data or information, including text, video, sound, and images contained in documents and records, that fulfill the intended purpose of the documents or records. Content is the intellectual substance of a document, including structured and unstructured data (AHIMA 2008). For example, the content of a patient's discharge summary is the information about the patient's illness, response to treatment, condition on discharge, and follow-up instructions. The content of a complete blood count (CBC) test report are the values of the test results.

**The St. Rita's Healthcare System Case Study**

Denise and David met for a half hour to review the information they gathered on definitions related to ECRM. "Determining definitions was a good first step to take. It clarifies the differences between records, content, and documents. But, how do these differences impact the management of these?" Denise wondered.

"A big impact is how these artifacts are treated with regard to privacy, security, and retention," replied David. "For example, the privacy and security levels are drastically different between a survey form to determine customer satisfaction than for financial and clinical records that contain protected health information. The organization might want to retain the survey document for a very limited amount of time, but financial and clinical records have longer retention periods."

"OK, I get it," said Denise. "Another angle is that records must remain unaltered. In the case of an operative report, the final report must not be altered by anyone. In the survey example you just gave, someone could change the 'customer survey' document from month to month or year to year and there would likely be no legal statute for its preservation."

"That's a good synopsis," David responded. "And recall that one characteristic of a record is that it can be linked to other records. For example, an operative report is a record. Because it has a relationship to other events, it is linked to other records such as the post-operative record and pathology report for a particular patient."

"Now that we have our definitions down, we should move on to what constitutes document, record, and content management," Denise suggested.

# Document, Record, and Content Management

The Data Management Association (DAMA) defines document management as the storage, inventory and control of electronic and paper documents where any file or record is a document and does not make a distinction between record and document management (DAMA 2010, 239). Others, however, say there is a difference between the two, basing the rationale on the nature of the artifacts themselves (Smith 2007). Recall that organizations make or receive records to meet legal obligations or support business transaction. Records are final artifacts, which organizations must preserve in an unalterable state. Documents, however, have a different definition and do not have the same legal constraints as records. This textbook takes the position that there is a difference between the two and thus the management policies for each are also different.

Source, or original, documents and records come in a variety of media. For example, some are in paper, such as consents, authorizations, contracts, and administrative and clinical records. Others may be images such as photographs or pictures taken as an adjunct to patient care, such as documenting the extent of symptoms or a disease process. And still others may be in a digital format, such as word-processed documents, digital speech files, e-mails, and so on. The type and variety of documents and records requiring management determines the type of electronic system an organization should choose.

In selecting document or record management systems, the organization must first be clear on how it wants to manage documents and records. To do this, a complete assessment and planning process using a methodology like the systems development life cycle (SDLC) should be conducted. This identifies the necessary requirements and functionalities that must support an electronic document or record management system and includes design specifications and implementation plans. One implementation model that organizations can use to guide the process is the global standard for records management: ISO/TR 15489-2:2001, which includes eight steps (Weise 2010). Table 9.1 shows an adaptation of these for an electronic document or records management system.

Table 9.1. **Methodology for implementation of a document or records management electronic system**

| Step | Description |
|---|---|
| Preliminary investigation | High-level assessment of administrative, business, and legal requirements for managing documents and records. Identify the scope of the project. |
| Analyze business activity | Assess organization structures, functions, processes, and activities consistent with the project scope. |
| Identify records requirements | Identify the organization's records and documents needs, such as legislation, regulations, standards, accountability, and stakeholders and business operation needs within the project scope. |
| Assess existing systems | Inventory current systems that capture, update, and store documents and records (both paper and electronic). Assess current status in meeting regulatory, legal, and business needs through strategies such as gap analysis. |
| Identify strategies to meet needs | This may include development and implementation of policies, standards, guidelines, procedures, and practices. Identify data stewards and custodians, document and record classification requirements, and security and confidentiality needs. |
| Design document or records management system | Identify functionalities required for an electronic document or records management system. Identify integration needs with existing electronic systems. Includes development, design, integration, and testing and implementation planning. |
| Implement electronic system | Roll out the project according to the implementation plan. Includes project training and monitoring. |

Source: Adapted from Weise 2010.

## The Continuum of Document, Record, and Content Management

With the continual and rapid advance in technologies and associated acronyms, the definitions of and the differences between electronic document, record, and content management systems in the marketplace can be confusing. For example, the following abbreviations and definitions are frequently used to describe these types of systems, some with varying definitions for the same acronym:

- Document imaging: A system consisting of software and hardware that converts source documents to digital format (ARMA 2012)
- Document management system (DMS): A system that allows capture and simultaneous access to documentation and chart completion and provides a central repository of information (AHIMA 2012, 5)
- DMS: A computer system and software to store, manage, and track electronic documents and electronic images of paper-based information captured through a document scanner (AIIM 2004)
- Electronic document management (EDM): A storage solution based on digital scanning technology in which source documents are scanned to create digital images that are stored electronically on optical disks (Amatayakul 2013, 633)
- Electronic document management system (EDMS): A system consisting of software, hardware, policies, and processes to automate the preparation, organization, tracking, and distribution of electronic documents, including version control and check-in and check-out capabilities (ARMA 2012)
- Electronic records management system (ERMS): A system consisting of software, hardware, policies, and processes to automate the preparation, organization, tracking, and distribution of records regardless of media, including retention, scheduling, and disposition (ARMA 2012)
- Electronic records management (ERM): Systems that capture data from print files and other report-formatted digital documents, such as e-mail, e-fax, instant messages, web pages, digital dictation, and speech recognition, and stores them for subsequent viewing
- Enterprise content management (ECM): The tools and technologies used to capture, manage, store, preserve, and deliver content and documents related to organizational processes (AIIM 2014)

Given the variety of acronyms and definitions, it is no wonder there is confusion. Viewing these systems as a continuum from the simpler ones with less functionality (document imaging systems), to the more complex (ECM), can help sort this out. The following are the characteristics and continuum of functionalities in describing these systems, explaining their differences:

- EDMS: A software system that controls and organizes documents throughout an organization, whether they have been declared records or not. Typically, an EDMS includes the following functions:
  - Document and content creation
  - Document and content capture
  - Document and content editing and revision
  - Image processing
  - Document workflow or business process management (BPM)
  - Document repositories
  - Computer-output laser disk or enterprise report management (COLD/ERM) and other output systems
  - Information retrieval functionality
- ERMS: A software system that allows an organization to assign a specific lifecycle to individual pieces of organizational information. No one may edit or revise documents, records, or content once they are in an ERMS. Typical functions of an ERMS include:
  - Receiving records
  - Using records
  - Managing and maintaining electronic records
  - Managing paper-based and other analog records
  - Managing disposition of records
- ECM: The evolutionary successor to an EDMS, the ECM system has tools and methods to capture, manage, store, preserve, and deliver all forms of content (not just documents and records) across an enterprise. In addition to the tools found in an EDMS and an ERMS, an ECM system has:
  - Collaboration tools
  - Digital asset management tools
  - Web content management tools (OSU Libraries 2014)

The following is another example of the continuum that helps put in order the functions that these systems provide, going from simpler to more complex:

- Document scanning and imaging systems: Computer systems that capture, store, and reprint images of documents. Documents are typically scanned in sequential order, and a separator sheet may be inserted to indicate where each document begins or ends.
- EDM systems: These systems add enhancements to better manage, control, locate, and retrieve documents and other information in digital form. A bar code or other identification technology identifies documents within a record and potentially even parts of a document. There are functionalities included to edit a document and to include electronic signatures.
- ERM systems: These systems may be a component of an EDM or a separate system. They enable output from other information systems to be captured and stored in the same repository as scanned documents such as digital dictation files, word processing files, print files, emails, and so on.
- ECM systems: These systems move beyond ERM systems by providing functions to capture, manage, store, preserve, and deliver both analog and digital documents and are able to index and intelligently search the content within these documents. ECM systems can extend to include collaboration and communication tools to use and share the system's content (Amatayakul 2013).

Figure 9.1 provides a representation of the continuum of these technologies based on the two descriptions provided above.

Because of the lack of marketplace clarity surrounding system titles, it is best for organizations to identify the functionalities they need for electronic documents and records storage than to rely on a specific acronym. Table 9.2 provides an example of a decision chart that provides a partial list of functionalities of electronic document and records management systems. Examples of a robust set of functional requirements for electronic record and imaging systems include the Department of Defense Standard 5015.02 (DoD 2007) and The Ohio Electronics Record Committee Guidelines for Imaging Public Documents (Ohio ERC 2010).

Implementing an electronic document or records management system without integrating it with other organization information systems only creates another data silo. Organizations should identify integration points between an EDM,

Figure 9.1. Continuum of document management technologies

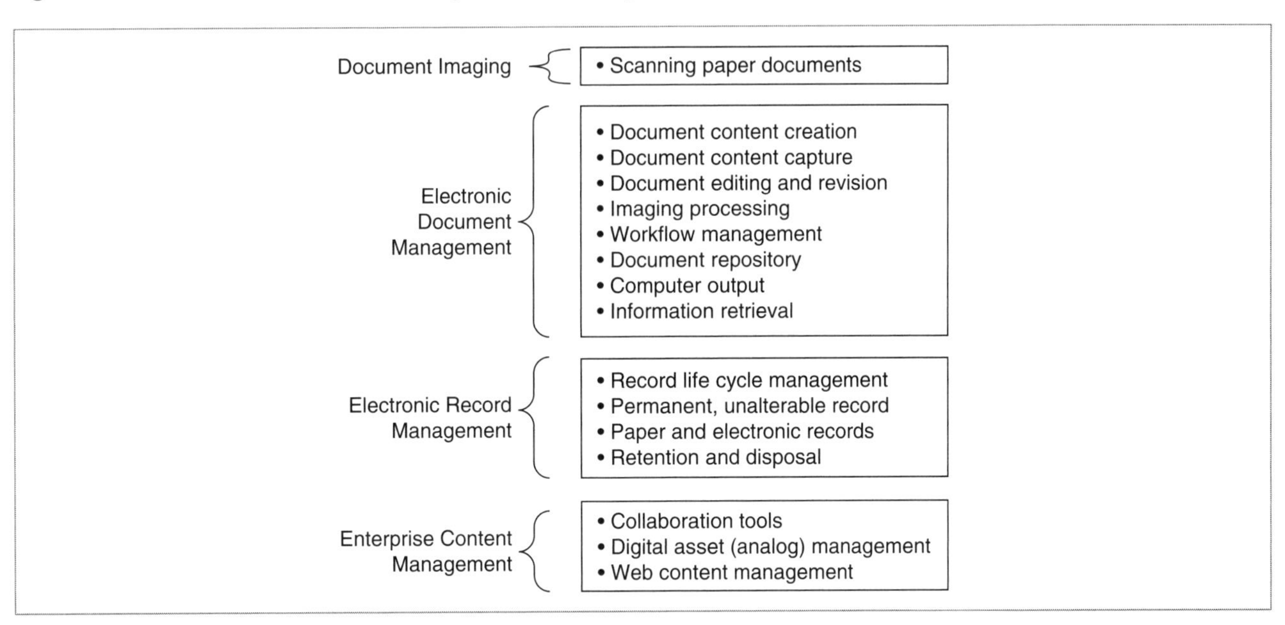


©Merida L. Johns

Table 9.2. Example of functionalities for electronic document and record systems

| Functionality | Description | Required | |
|---|---|---|---|
| | | Yes | No |
| Document imaging | Converts source document into digital format | | |
| Images front and back | Converts both front and back of paper source document into digital format | | |
| Imports documents | Imports electronic documents in their native format (for example, word-processed documents, spreadsheets, audio files) | | |
| Converts documents | Transforms electronic documents to permanent raster-image format | | |
| Full-text indexing | Indexing every word in a document | | |
| Keyword indexing | Indexing by keywords throughout the document | | |
| Document indexing | Indexing by document type | | |
| Document group indexing | Indexing by document group | | |
| Document editing | Ability to edit a document | | |
| Electronic signature | Ability to sign documents electronically | | |
| Check out or check in | Ability to check out and check in a document for editing purposes | | |
| Document lock | Locks document during update so only one person can update it at a time | | |
| Multiple access | Permits access to a document or record by multiple users at the same time | | |
| Version control | Identifies and retains a unique copy of every version of a document uploaded to the DMS | | |
| Roll back | Ability to roll back to earlier versions of a document | | |
| Annotation | Ability to add or remove information about a document without permanently changing the original image, for example, highlighting, stamps, redactions | | |

(continued)

Table 9.2. Example of functionalities for electronic document and record systems (*Continued*)

| Functionality | Description | Required | |
|---|---|---|---|
| | | Yes | No |
| Access rights | Ability to permit or deny access to documents or records | | |
| Feature rights | Ability to assign individuals rights to create, edit, or delete documents or records | | |
| Organize documents or records | Ability to rearrange documents or records to accommodate a specific order | | |
| Bar codes | Ability to use bar codes for automatically separating and indexing documents or records | | |
| Search techniques | Multiple types of search techniques available such as wild cards, Boolean operators, fuzzy logic, and so on | | |
| Distribution | Allows multiple distribution types such as printing, faxing, and e-mailing | | |
| Workflow management | Allows rules-based workflow such as alerts or routing of document to specific individual | | |
| Audit trail | Generates audit trail and reports of system activity | | |
| Integration | Ability to integrate with organization information systems | | |
| Retention | Provides for the retention of documents or records to meet organization, legal, accreditation, or other requirements | | |



ERM, or ECM system during the planning and requirement phases. A good place to start is by identifying the people and processes that create, retrieve, use, store, dispose, and archive these documents and records. A second step is to identify the current information systems that support the processes identified and the linkages among these systems. This analysis helps identify who should have access and other rights to the records and documents and what information systems must interface with the EDMS, ERMS, or ECMS.

# Content Management Tools

**Content management** is defined as "the organization, categorization, and structure of data or resources so that they can be stored, published, and reused in multiple ways" (DAMA 2010, 248). For the most part, content management has become synonymous with the management of unstructured data in documents and records. ECM is the evolutionary successor to EDMS and ERMS noted earlier (OSU Libraries 2014). Such systems deliver all forms of content, including text, video, image, and audio documents or records, and add three additional functionalities: collaboration tools, digital asset management tools, and web content management tools. Key drivers for content management include increased accessibility to content for business operations, meeting regulatory and legal requirements, reduced risk and costs, and increased worker productivity.

## Collaboration Content Management

**Collaboration tools** enable people to create, share, and use common content. A frequent use of collaboration tools is for project and program management. Microsoft SharePoint® and Lotus Quickr® are two examples of such tools. Collaboration tools create virtual workplaces that allow people to create, share, and edit common document types such as word processing, spreadsheet, and presentation documents. Beyond document sharing, these tools also allow social collaboration where teams and employees create blogs and wikis, find expertise, and engage in discussion boards. These tools add an enormous amount of content every day, increasing content chaos. Without management, much of the knowledge associated with this content is lost to the organization. Furthermore, some of the content within these systems may constitute a legal record or be relevant for regulatory compliance (Murray 2009). Therefore, content management is important for business operational purposes and potential regulatory and compliance purposes, and requires that organizations put in place appropriate availability, access, integrity, security, privacy, and retention safeguards.

## Digital Asset Management

**Digital asset management** (DAM) is defined as "the practice and domain of organizing digital files containing both the core content and associated metadata of multi-media, or rich-media items, for example, images, video, audio, graphics, web pages, and photographs" (AIIM 2014b). Not all organizations have the same requirements for DAMs. For instance, a library, museum, hospital, and advertising agency each have different requirements. Therefore, as with all other information system planning, requirements analysis is a key factor in determining the functionalities needed from DAM. Similar to other data and information assets, organizations must consider the development of the metadata model and methods for cataloging the digital assets, providing security safeguards, and developing retention and disposition policies and procedures.

There are a variety of DAM tools in the marketplace. Three categories of vendors offering DAM products, depending on the functions they provide, are Enterprise DAM, Mid-Market DAM, and Light-Weight DAM. Enterprise DAM tools are designed to integrate with larger ECM or enterprise architectures (Regli 2009). They are designed for organizations where DAM is a core business function. On the other extreme are the Light-Weight DAM that provide asset capture, preview, download, and simple transformations.

## Web Content Management

**Web content management** (WCM) is "the process of controlling the content of a website through the use of specific management tools based on a core repository" (MacComascaigh et al. 2009). In addition to tools for creating content (templates), these systems usually include functionality for editing and versioning content, tracking media check out and check in, and cataloguing and indexing content.

# Content Management Classification Alternatives

One of the primary purposes of content management is to make content easy to find. Therefore, it is important for organizations to create methods to manage unstructured content with the same rigor as they apply to managing structured content in databases (Kumar 2010). Taxonomies, thesauri, ontologies, metadata, and indexes are classification alternatives that help to identify content and bring structure to unstructured content.

There is debate whether or not the term "taxonomy" should be used as a narrow or broad descriptor. In the narrow sense, a taxonomy is a hierarchical classification system. In its broader use, the term taxonomy is any means of organizing knowledge and includes thesauri, ontologies, controlled vocabularies, semantic networks, and so on (Hedden 2010). For the purposes of the review that follows, each of these has been divided into separate headings.

## Taxonomies

"**Taxonomy** is the science or technique of classification" (DAMA 2010, 248). In the context of content management, the purposes of a taxonomy are to classify objects, identify them, and help search and retrieve them. There are several approaches to taxonomy development. The simplest is a **flat taxonomy**, which is a controlled set of categories where each object in the set has the same weight. For example, a list of states is a flat taxonomy.

Another type of taxonomy is where multiple characteristics are assigned to one object. This is called a **facet taxonomy** (DAMA 2010). A good illustration of this approach is the use of metadata where each attribute (metadata) is attached to an object. As an example, a book has a set of metadata such as an author, title, copyright date, international standard book number (ISBN), and so on. The object, in this case "book," is the center facet with facets, or other nodes, attached to it.

This taxonomy's value is that it allows searching for an object through multiple facets. For example, a reader can locate a specific book through an author, ISBN, or title search.

Another model is the **hierarchical model** that is based on a tiered order of concepts and their relationships. The hierarchical character presupposes inheritance qualities from the "parent class" to the "child subclass." The child inherits the parent's set of characteristics, but also becomes more specialized.

A well-known hierarchical taxonomy is the classification of plants and animals. To illustrate, figure 9.2 shows an animal taxonomy that classifies a tiger and a house cat. Here, we see the house cat in the animal kingdom category. The animal kingdom has certain characteristics, such as being multicellular and digesting food in an interior chamber. All of those characteristics are passed on to the next level in the hierarchy. Each level in the taxonomy becomes more specialized, but inherits the characteristics from the level above it (Stakhov 2012).

Figure 9.2. Taxonomic example of the animal kingdom

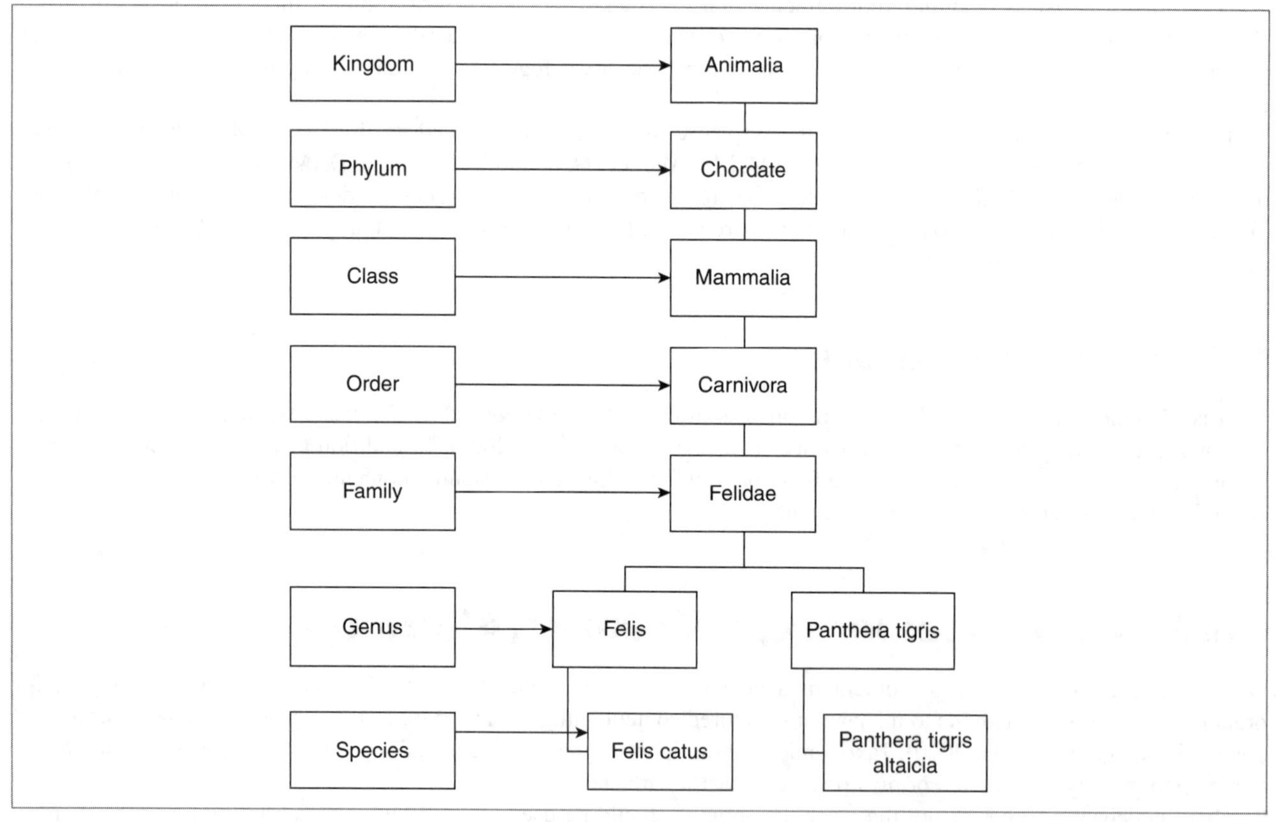




Besides its tiered structure, hierarchical taxonomies also show other relationships. Cats and tigers are related, having the same characteristics through the family taxonomic level. Differentiation then comes at the lower levels of the taxonomic hierarchy. Organizations can use this type of taxonomy approach to categorize and differentiate documents and records. For instance, there could be a document class whose characteristics include a document identifier, document title, and date created. This document class might then have two subclasses: one called internal document subclass, and the other called external document subclass. Both of these subclasses inherit the characteristics of the document class, but have specialized characteristics themselves.

Automatic categorization creates taxonomies through conceptual analysis, using mathematical analysis and comparisons (Felahi 2013). In this approach, an analytics engine mathematically analyzes example documents to calculate concepts organizations can use to develop categories and to categorize documents. This approach allows the system to link the content similar to a network configuration. Such automatic categorization methods have been applied to content in healthcare, for example, in the classification and retrieval of content in medical images (Uwimana and Ruiz 2008).

## Thesauri

Many people are familiar with and have used a thesaurus to help them identify alternative terms for a word. This is called a **dictionary thesaurus**. That type of thesaurus provides all potential alternative terms for a word. The thesaurus makes no distinctions between terms, nor is there an indication of the preferred term, or of how broad or narrow an alternative term is. Users have to make these decisions in choosing an alternate term based upon the context in which they are going to use the term.

In information management, however, a thesaurus is a little different. An **information management thesaurus** is a controlled list of terms linked together by semantic, hierarchical (parent-child), associative (related), or equivalence (synonymous) relationships. Thesauri act as guides to allocating classification terms to individual records (AIIM 2014c). In other words, thesauri categorize concepts and then map associated words to the concept. The thesaurus maps the words to each other indicating broader, narrower, associated, or equivalent terms that represent a concept. Usually, the thesaurus also indicates the preferred term for a concept. In search and retrieval, use of a broader term retrieves more general results. A search with a narrower term retrieves more specific results. Use of a related term provides similar results.

An example of an information management thesaurus is Medical Subject Headings (MeSH), developed by the National Library of Medicine (NLM). **MeSH** is a controlled vocabulary thesaurus. It consists of sets of terms naming descriptors in a hierarchical structure that permits searching at various levels of specificity. MeSH is used to index articles for the MEDLINE/PubMED® database and for the NLM-produced database which includes the cataloging of books, documents, and audiovisuals (U.S. National Library of Medicine 2014). MeSH has a three-level structure: descriptor, concept, and term. The descriptor, which one can also think of as a main heading, is the broadest level in MeSH, and may contain several concepts. Figure 9.3 provides an example of a descriptor in the MeSH thesaurus. The descriptor record is cardiomegaly. Note there are two concepts associated with cardiomegaly, namely cardiomegaly and cardiac hypertrophy. However, cardiomegaly is the preferred concept and the preferred term. Synonymous terms for cardiomegaly are enlarged heart and heart enlargement. A narrower concept related to cardiomegaly is cardiac hypertrophy. Note the preferred term is listed for this narrower concept, and a synonymous term. For indexing and searching purposes within MeSH, all terms are equivalent.

Figure 9.3. MeSH thesaurus example

```
Cardiomegaly [Descriptor]
  Cardiomegaly [Concept, Preferred]
    Cardiomegaly [Term, Preferred]
    Enlarged Heart [Term]
    Heart Enlargement [Term]
  Cardiac Hypertrophy [Concept, Narrower]
    Cardiac Hypertrophy [Term, Preferred]
    Heart Hypertrophy [Term]
```

Source: U.S. National Library of Medicine 2014.

Descriptor records in MeSH can also have qualifiers or subheadings. Take, for example, figure 9.4. Note the main heading is "Health Information Management." The tree number identifies the location of the term in the term tree. The scope note provides a description of "health information management." The allowable qualifiers are subheadings, or how a specific aspect of "health information management" can be described. In this case, the qualifier CL stands for classification; EC represents economics, ED education, and ES ethics.

Standards for the construction of thesauri have been developed such as ISO 2788 and ISO 5964.

Figure 9.4. Result from search for health information management in MeSH browser

| MeSH Heading | Health Information Management |
|---|---|
| Tree Number | L01.399.500 |
| Scope Note | Management of the acquisition, organization, retrieval, and dissemination of health information. |
| Allowable Qualifiers | CL EC ED ES HI IS LJ MA MT OG SN ST TD |
| History Note | 2013 |
| Date of Entry | 20120703 |
| Unique ID | D063025 |



### Ontologies

An **ontology** can be considered a type of taxonomy with more complex relationships between terms than a thesaurus (Hedden 2010). An ontology's focus is in a particular domain or subject. A purpose of an ontology is to share and reuse knowledge. The following are essential points of an ontology:

- An ontology defines (specifies) the concepts, relationships, and other distinctions that are relevant for modeling a domain.
- The specification takes the form of the definitions of representational vocabulary (classes, relations, and so forth), which provide meanings for the vocabulary and formal constraints on its coherent use (Gruber 2008).

An ontology describes terms more richly than a thesaurus. Where a thesaurus describes a term with a scope note, an ontology describes a term by specific attributes in a more structured format, such as noting properties, features, characteristics, or parameters of the term (Hedden 2010). In addition, an ontology also describes relationships between classes or inter-term relationships. For example, a thesaurus might identify formic acid as a term related to vinegar, but an ontology, in contrast, provides a much more precise relationship by indicating that formic acid is an active ingredient of vinegar (Erskine 2009, 9).

With more and more emphasis on exchange of healthcare data, using ontologies can help in the naming, meaning, equivalency, and relationships between core business entities, such as patient, provider, and supplier, within organizations and across healthcare systems. Ontology constructs such as "same as" or "equivalent property" help establish common semantics when the same business entity is called a different name in different processes or by different organizations (Amoussou 2011). Some representative ontologies in healthcare include SNOMED CT and LOINC.

## Metadata

Within the context of document content management, metadata are used to classify documents (refer to chapter 8). As noted, one can conceive metadata as a faceted taxonomy. However, metadata do not provide the richness of association among classes or objects that an ontology provides. Frequently, organizations must maintain cross-reference schemes, and continuously update them manually, to harmonize metadata (or even taxonomies and thesauri) that reside in data silos across an enterprise.

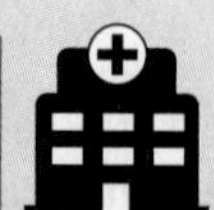

**The St. Rita's Healthcare System Case Study**

Denise and David took some time to assess what they gathered so far on content management. Their appraisal was that content management was indeed the next "battleground" for organizations if they wanted to tame content chaos.

"I didn't realize the proliferation of digital documents, especially with all the collaboration technologies available," said Denise. "There are whole new ways of looking at content that no one has explored or are unfamiliar to most people. Just the area of taxonomies and ontologies can get your head spinning. The content management aspects of this are mind boggling. Where does an organization begin?"

"This is tough territory," David acknowledged. "Not only is there an explosion of content, but it has happened so quickly that the application of technologies and processes to control it just haven't kept up. I agree with you that answering the question 'Where to begin?' is key."

Denise and David agreed that they needed to provide some kind of framework around the whole issue of content management so they could present a potential roadmap for planning and implementing ECM to the EIM team. They decided that using a content life cycle framework should be the foundation for the framework.

# Content Life Cycle Management

The content management life cycle framework views content management as a set of activities and content identification methods that defines documents and records, ensures the assignment of proper ownership, enables the appropriate use, security, retention, and disposition of content, and promotes efficient search, location, and retrieval strategies (see figure 9.5).

In this model, any intellectual substance of a document or record produced in any type of media represents content. The model identifies the ownership, use, security, retention, and disposition of each document and record. However, for records, specific controls are implemented by the organization to meet legal and compliance requirements. Among these are audit, data, and access controls. Data controls ensure required data remain in an unalterable form. Documents can at some point become records. Because organizations use both documents and records to support business operations, the model applies search, location, and retrieval solutions to both.

Figure 9.5. Content management framework

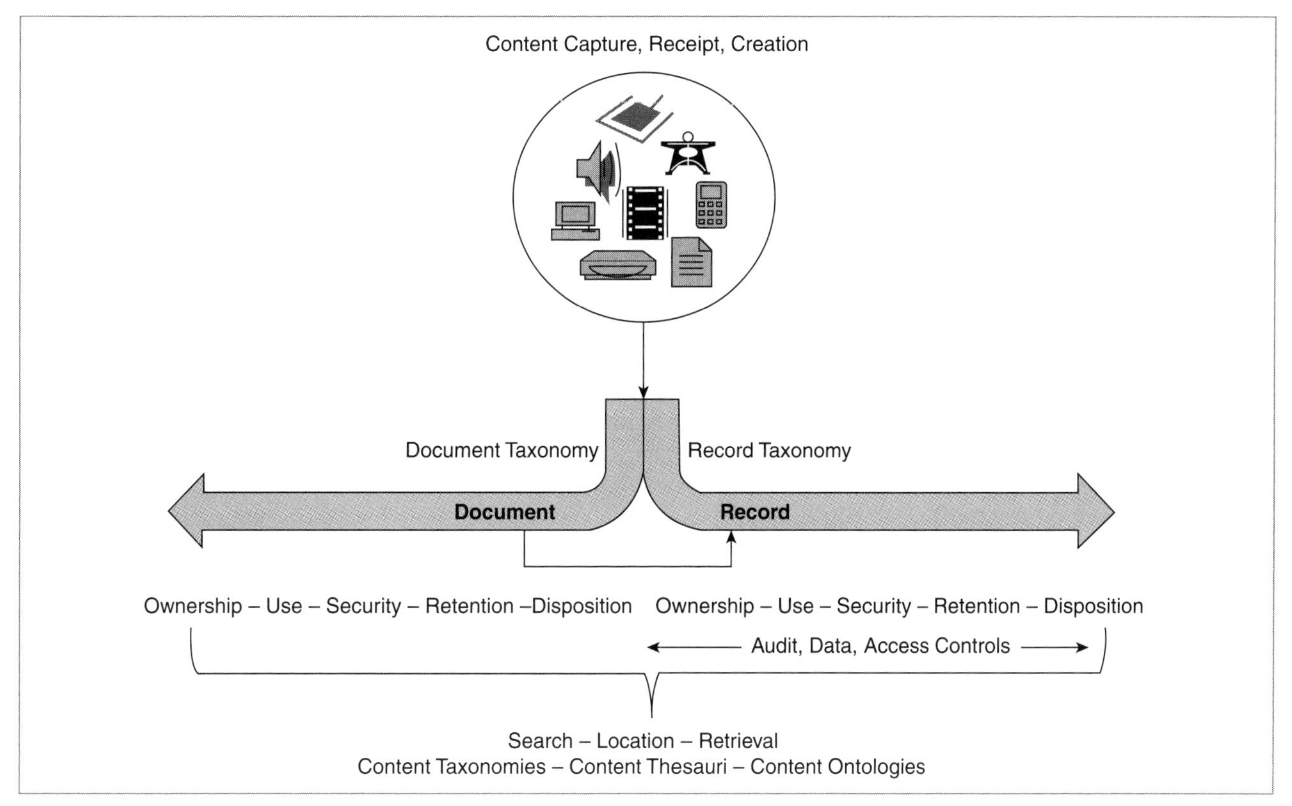

The following is a list of activities, based on the content management life cycle framework, for how an organization might execute the model and begin to plan and organize a content life cycle management program. The list of activities is not necessarily in priority level, except for the first-listed activity (AHIMA 2008).

- **Identify stakeholder and business needs.** Good content management begins with understanding the needs of the organization. The organization should base its determination of what content to create, capture, and maintain on what content it requires to support business processes and end user needs.
- **Identify the creation, receipt, and capture of content**. Who creates, receives, or captures it, when do they create it, and by what means? This is important for business process reasons as well as for meeting legal or other mandated requirements.
- **Identify the uses of content (business processes and functions).** To determine content value (how much is the content worth) and to meet regulatory and legal requirements, businesses must know what content they use to support their business functions and how they use it.
- **Identify the users of content.** Knowing who uses content is as important as knowing how they use it. Businesses should also identify users and the classifications of documents and records they use.
- **Develop a description of what constitutes a document and a record.** Organizations must develop criteria for determining what constitutes a document or record not only for legal and regulatory purposes, but also to develop policies and practices for handling these. Criteria for determining under what circumstances a document may become a record are also necessary, as noted earlier. Associated criteria should include:
  - Identifying document and record ownership and stewardship
  - Assigning access rights to documents and records
  - Developing data and audit controls
  - Assigning security levels to documents and records
  - Developing retention, archival, and disposal policies for documents and records
- **Identify organization documents and records.** Organizations should create processes so criteria for determining documents and records are applied to intellectual content.
- **Select content management technologies with functionalities to meet business needs.** The use of content management technology is essential with the growth of digital media in all business sectors. Technology selection, however, should be based on the needs of the organization for content use, storage, retention, and disposition. An organization may use different types of technology depending on the content and its use. For example, document scanning systems may be adequate for lower value content whereas more sophisticated technologies such as an ERMS may be required for high level and mission critical content.
- **Categorize documents and records.** A document or record's intellectual substance identification is the foundation of content management and classifications like taxonomies or ontologies should be applied. When established, if taxonomies are not available, the organization should develop these to meet its needs and in accordance with established standards for classification development.
- **Develop policies and practices that ensure quality content.** Organizations should develop policies, procedures, and standards to ensure the quality of content from inception through final disposition.

## Applying Data Governance

Developing an enterprise content management program is a deliberate course of action. More than ever before, healthcare organizations have a larger volume of diversified content to manage, a significant percentage of which resides in both paper and electronic documents, and the content of which is largely unstructured. The unstructured content presents several challenges. Among these is the difficulty in locating and retrieving specific documents and records; even more challenging is the content itself. It is essential to support and improve patient care and other business process purposes, and meet legal and regulatory requirements methods for categorizing documents, records, and the content therein. Managing enterprise content is impossible without strong governance that establishes policies, standards, procedures, and auditing processes that manage content throughout its life cycle. The following are key DG functions that Denise and David identified for content management and for further discussion by the EIM team (table 9.3):

- Develop a strategy and roadmap for ECM
- Create policies and procedures for content management
- Establish policies and procedures that meet business, legal, and regulatory requirements
- Apply taxonomies, thesauri, and ontologies for content identification, location, and retrieval
- Implement stewardship processes that ensure content capture, maintenance, quality, and security over the content lifespan
- Institute standards and audit procedures for content management
- Coordinate content management with other DG functions (metadata management)

Table 9.3. DG deliverables by EIM function

| Data Governance | Data Architecture Management | Metadata Management | Master Data Management | Content Management | Data Security and Privacy Management | Business Intelligence Management | Data Quality Management | Terminology and Classification Management |
|---|---|---|---|---|---|---|---|---|
| Identify mission and scope | Develop and maintain data models | Develop policies, procedures, and standards | Identify master and reference data requirements | Develop roadmap for content management | | | | |
| Establish goals and success measures | Develop, maintain, and evaluate data model policies and standards | Ensure metadata meets functional requirements | Develop policies, procedures, and standards for management of master data | Develop policies and procedures for content management | | | | |
| Put in place DG structure, processes, and communications plan | Define roles, responsibilities, and accountabilities for data architecture management | Develop and maintain appropriate metadata schema | Establish master data definitions, validation, and verification levels for master data quality | Apply taxonomies, thesauri, ontologies, and other content management classifications | | | | |
| Secure funding | Develop, maintain, and evaluate policies and standards for requirements analysis | Ensure metadata capture, maintenance, distribution, and integration | Ensure master and reference data meet regulatory requirements, including lineage history and security | Develop policies and procedures that ensure legal and regulatory mandates are met | | | | |
| Establish decision rights | Develop and maintain data artifacts and standards | Ensure metadata security | Establish audit procedures and standards for master data | Establish standards and audit procedures | | | | |
| Identify accountabilities | Establish quality control program and metrics for data architecture management | Develop and implement quality controls for metadata | Identify stakeholders and establish decision rights and accountabilities | Implement stewardship processes over the content management life cycle | | | | |

## The St. Rita's Healthcare System Case Study

The EIM team convened for its weekly meeting. Denise and David presented a high-level overview of content management and its relationship to the other EIM domains studied thus far.

"I've always had trouble understanding taxonomies. So, thanks Denise and David, for making this clearer. But even so, this seems like such an impossible task. Where do we start?" asked Shirlee.

"I think we start by assessing priorities. We can't possibly do everything at once. But what we can do is develop a roadmap that sequences us through the what, why, when, and how," responded Val. "What do we want to achieve? Why do we want to achieve it? When do we want to achieve it? Once we have those questions nailed down we can look at how we can achieve content management."

"Do you really think it is reasonable to launch taxonomy and ontology projects? I keep thinking those are activities for the big research and academic institutions, not for what I'd call the community healthcare systems like St. Rita's," stated Monte. "These are topics I normally see at informatics symposia."

"What David and I have learned," responded Denise, "is that we don't have to reinvent the wheel. There are taxonomies and ontologies out there and one of their purposes is reuse. So if there's a document or other taxonomy available, we can take a look at it and see how well it fits our needs."

"Remember, ECM is evolving. New vendor products are coming out all the time. More research is being conducted and we can be the beneficiary of that new knowledge," Val interjected.

"I think we bite off as much as we can chew. Start small, test the waters, and make some wins. What we need is a roadmap," offered Linda.

The EIM team picked up on that theme and concurred, as they had previously, that a step-by-step roadmap made sense. They all agreed that EIM was a marathon and not a sprint and assigned the roadmap development to the list of activities to be taken up after their final report to Joan Morton.

## Part of the Team: Discussion and Action

1. The EIM team agreed on the value of a roadmap to help them chart how they might develop content management at St. Rita's. Taking the information provided by Denise and David, develop a preliminary roadmap for St. Rita's. Identify "sign posts" of synergies with other EIM domains covered up to this point and where coordination among these will be needed by the organization.

## Advanced Concepts

1. Development of taxonomies and ontologies will be the wave of the future in HIM. Investigate the ontology development tool Protégé, and compare its functionality with one other tool of your choice. What are the similarities and differences? Would you choose one over the other and why?
2. Conduct a literature review of ontologies in healthcare and medicine. Prepare an annotated bibliography of these. Given your review, what is your assessment of the status of content management ontologies in healthcare? What are the opportunities?
3. Document categorization is an important foundational aspect of content management. Develop a simple document taxonomy for St. Rita's. Investigate whether you could reuse other taxonomies for this purpose and include as appropriate.

## References

45 CFR 160, 162, 164: HIPAA Administrative Simplification. 2013 (Mar. 26). http://www.hhs.gov/ocr/privacy/hipaa/administrative/combined/hipaa-simplification-201303.pdf.

AHIMA. 2008. Enterprise content and record management for healthcare. *Journal of AHIMA* 79(10):91–98. http://library.ahima.org/xpedio/groups/public/documents/ahima/bok1_040405.hcsp?dDocName=bok1_040405.

AHIMA. 2012. Document Management and Imaging Toolkit. Chicago: AHIMA Press.

AIIM. 2004. What is Document Management (DMS)? http://www.aiim.org/What-is-Document-Management.

AIIM. 2014. What is ECM? http://www.aiim.org/What-is-ECM-Enterprise-Content-Management.

AIIM. 2014b. AIIM International Glossary. Index D. http://www.aiim.org/community/wiki/view/Index-D.

AIIM. 2014c. AIIM International Glossary. Index T. http://www.aiim.org/community/wiki/view/Index-T.

Amatayakul, M. 2013. *Electronic Health Records: A Practical Guide for Professionals and Organizations*, 5th ed. Chicago: AHIMA Press.

Amoussou, J. 2011 (August 27). "Why Do We Need Ontologies in Healthcare Applications." *The Adventures in Computing* blog. http://efasoft.blogspot.com/2011/08/why-do-we-need-ontologies-in-healthcare.html.

ARMA International. 2012 Glossary of Records and Information Management Terms, 3rd ed. Overland Park, KS: ARMA International.

Department of Defense. 2007. Electronic Records Management Software Applications Design Criteria Standard. http://www.dtic.mil/whs/directives/corres/pdf/501502std.pdf.

Dick, R., E. Steen, D. Detmer, eds. 1997. *The Computer-Based Patient Record: An Essential Technology,* revised ed. Washington, D.C.: National Academy Press.

Erskine, R. 2009. Demystifying Taxonomies: Understanding Taxonomies and Their Use in Content Management. EMC Perspective. http://www.emc.com/collateral/emc-perspective/h4736-demystifying-taxonomies-ep.pdf.

Felahi, J. 2013. Content-categorization in the enterprise. *KM World, 22*(3): S8. http://www.contentanalyst.com/images/images/ECM_ContentAnalyst_Final.pdf.

Grimes, S. 2008 (August 1). Unstructured Data and the 80 Percent Rule. *The Breakthrough Analysis* blog. http://breakthroughanalysis.com/2008/08/01/unstructured-data-and-the-80-percent-rule/.

Gruber, T. "Ontology." In *Encyclopedia of Database Systems*, edited by L. Liu and M. T. Ozsu. Springer-Verlag, 2008. http://tomgruber.org/writing/ontology-definition-2007.htm.

Gunnlaugsdottir, J. 2002. An international standard on records management: An opportunity for librarians. *Libri* 52(4): 231–240. http://www.librijournal.org/pdf/2002-4pp231-240.pdf.

Health Story Project. 2014. About The Health Story Project. http://www.healthstory.com/about/about.htm.

Hedden, H. 2010. *The Accidental Taxonomist*. Medford, NJ: Information Today, Inc. http://www.hedden-information.com/Accidental-Taxonomist-Introduction.htm.

Illinois State Records Act 5 ILCS 160. (Jan 3, 2003). http://www.ilga.gov/legislation/ilcs/ilcs3.asp?ActID=86&ChapterID=2.

Kumar, P. 2010. *Documentum Content Management Foundations: EMC Proven Professional Certification Exam E20-120 Study Guide*. Birmingham: Packt Publishing.

MacComascaigh, M., T. Bell., and M.R. Gilbert. Magic Quadrant for Web Content Management. Gartner RAS Core Research Note G00168694. http://www.day.com/dam/day/downloads/GartnerWCMMagicQuadrant2009.pdf.

Maio, A. 2013. Records Management in Microsoft SharePoint. *Credit Control* 34(3): 46-48. *Business Source Complete*, EBSCO*host*.

Murray, A.C. 2009. Content Management: Collaboration and Social Networks Change the Game. Information Week. http://www.informationweek.com/software/social/content-management-collaboration-and-social-networks-change-the-game/d/d-id/1084425.

Ohio Electronic Records Committee. 2010. Guidelines for Digital Imaging of Public Records. http://ohsweb.ohiohistory.org/ohioerc/wp-content/uploads/2014/09/DIguidelines1.pdf.

OSU Libraries. 2014. OSU Records Management: EDMS/ERMS/ECM Explained. http://library.osu.edu/projects-initiatives/osu-records-management/electronic-records/edms-erms-ecm-explained.

Queensland State Archives, Public Records Brief, "A Recordkeeping Update for Queensland Public Authorities," revised version issued November 2008. http://www.archives.qld.gov.au/Recordkeeping/GRKDownloads/Documents/identifying_pub_record_e_environ_200503.pdf.

Regli, T. 2009. The state of digital asset management: An executive summary of CMS Watch's Digital Asset Management Report. *Journal of Digital Asset Management* 5(1): 21–26.

Smith, K. 2007. *Public Sector Records Management: A Practical Guide*. Aldershot, England: Ashgate Publishing Ltd.

Stakhov, E. 2012. Drawing a Blueprint for a Scalable Taxonomy. *Information Management Journal*, *46*(3): 33–38.

U.S. National Library of Medicine. 2014. Medical Terminologies at NLM. http://www.nlm.nih.gov/medical-terms.html.

Uwimana, E. and M.E. Ruiz. 2008. Integrating an automatic classification method into medical image retrieval process. *AMIA Annual Symposium Proceedings*, pp. 747–751. Washington, D.C.: AMIA. http://www.ncbi.nlm.nih.gov/pmc/articles/PMC2655992/.

Vom Brocke, J., A. Simons, and A. Cleven. 2011. Towards a business process-oriented approach to enterprise content management: The ECM-blueprinting framework. *Information Systems E-Business Management* 9(4): 475–496.

Weise, C. 2010. Implementing electronic records management: A lot more than software. *Infonomics* 24(1): 18.

# Chapter 10

# Data Security Management

As health information moves from paper to digital formats, implementation of digital **data security** measures become increasingly important. Data security is a collection of protection measures and practices that safeguard data, computers, and associated resources from undesired occurrences and exposures. Organizations and their customers profit from good security practices. Effective security programs reduce and mitigate security breaches to sensitive and confidential information. Data protection programs help organizations achieve their business goals by protecting essential operations data from loss and by ensuring regulatory and legal compliance, which increases customer trust. And, data security programs are a good value proposition, providing an excellent return on investment in terms of improved information flows (Ponemon Institute 2009).

This chapter examines the basic elements of a data security program. It explains why each element is important for ensuring the integrity, availability, and protection of patient and organizational data. Specifically, this chapter covers topics to help you:

- Apply the principles of confidentiality, privacy, and security
- Explain the principle components and functions of a data protection program
- Assess types of security threats and data protcction challenges
- Analyze the legal and regulatory issues in data protection
- Practice the principles and functions of data security governance

## The St. Rita's Healthcare System Case Study

Val convened the regular meeting of the enterprise information management (EIM) team. The agenda had one item: identify the information necessary for incorporating data security into EIM and a data governance (DG) program. Val began by asking each team member to write down three to five items, each on a sticky note. Then the team consolidated and categorized the items on flip chart sheets. At the end of the process, the team had identified five overarching questions:

- What is the rationale and the need for data security programs?
- What are the security challenges and vulnerabilities?
- What are the regulatory and legal requirements for data protections and security?
- What are the elements of a data security program and how do we implement it?
- How is data security integrated into EIM and DG?

"Before we go any further," began Denise, "it would be a good idea to get our chief security officer, Wayne, and our chief privacy officer, Shelia, to join our team meetings. Has anyone been keeping Wayne and Shelia in the loop about our activities?" she asked.

"Yes, both have been receiving our weekly minutes and interim reports, but you are right; now is the time to get them more integrated into the team," replied Val. "I think we have very strong privacy and security programs, but we need both Wayne and Shelia on board to integrate their work into an overall DG and EIM program.

The team agreed with Denise's and Val's assessments. Val sent Wayne and Shelia the questions the team identified and invited them both to the next meeting to lead the discussion in answering them. At the next meeting Wayne and Shelia began by giving the team statistics on health information uses, as well as the current data on data security breaches.

# Key Terms in Healthcare Data Security

There are four key terms that are integral to how data security is implemented in healthcare. These terms are included in the privacy and security regulations of the **Health Information Portability and Accountability Act** (HIPAA). HIPAA requires certain healthcare organizations, such as hospitals, clinics, physician practices, and others to comply with the regulations set forth in the Act for protection of health information. While the specifics of HIPAA are discussed later in this chapter and in appendix B, it is important to understand the meaning of the following key terms because they are referred to throughout this chapter.

- **Protected health information** (PHI) means individually identifiable health information transmitted by electronic media, maintained in electronic media, or transmitted or maintained in any other form or medium. There are a number of exclusions. These include individually identifiable health information in education records covered by the Family Educational Rights and Privacy Act (FERPA), in employment records held by a covered entity in its role as employer, and individually identifiable information regarding a person who has been deceased for more than 50 years (45 CFR 160, 162, 164).
- **Individually identifiable health information** is a subset of health information, including demographic information collected from an individual, and: (1) created or received by a healthcare provider, health plan, employer, or healthcare clearinghouse; and (2) relates to the past, present, or future physical or mental health or condition of an individual; the provision of healthcare to an individual; or the past, present, or future payment for the provision of healthcare to an individual; and (i) that identifies the individual; or (ii) with respect to which there is a reasonable basis to believe the information can be used to identify the individual (45 CFR 160, 162, 164).
- **Covered entity** (CE) is a health plan, a health care clearinghouse, or a health care provider who transmits any health information in electronic form in connection with a transaction covered by the privacy and security rules (45 CFR 160, 162, 164).
- **Person:** a natural person, trust or estate, partnership, corporation, professional association or corporation, or other entity, public or private (45 CFR 160, 162, 164).
- **Business associate** (BA) is, with respect to a CE, a person who on the behalf of a CE creates, receives, maintains, or transmits protected health information (PHI) for a function or activity regulated by HIPAA, including claims processing or administration, data analysis, processing or administration, utilization review, quality assurance, patient safety activities, billing, benefit management, practice management, and repricing, or provides legal, actuarial, accounting, consulting, data aggregation, management, administrative, accreditation, or financial services. Some examples include an e-prescribing gateway, or other person that provides data transmission services with respect to PHI; a subcontractor that creates, receives, maintains, or transmits PHI on behalf of the BA; a person that offers a personal health record to one or more individuals on behalf of a CE; a subcontractor that creates, receives, maintains, or transmits PHI on behalf of the CE (45 CFR 160, 162, 164).

# Access and Use of Patient Data

Accounts of the number of individuals who have access to PHI vary widely. While it may be difficult to determine the exact number of individuals who have the opportunity to see the sensitive data maintained in a patient's health record, an Institute of Medicine (IOM) study identified 36 categories of individual users and 32 institutional users (Dick et al. 1997). Many of these people are the healthcare professionals who deliver direct patient care, such as nurses, physicians, and therapists. These individuals are referred to as **primary users**.

Many other users, called **secondary users**, also collect information kept in the patient's health record. Secondary users include researchers, pharmaceutical companies, health and life insurance companies, credit card agencies, banking companies, and the civil and criminal justice systems (U.S. Congress 1993). Indeed, some secondary users and other private companies are enticed by a commercial incentive to gather and sell aggregate healthcare data without the patient's knowledge. Even vendors of healthcare information systems have been known to collect patient data through contractual arrangements with healthcare providers (U.S. Congress 1993).

In the past decade, new entrants into the health information sharing market have emerged. These new users are typically companies that have significant business interests in the collection of individually identifiable health information. Primarily, they provide products and services to the healthcare industry. Examples of such companies are medical and surgical suppliers, pharmaceutical companies, reference laboratories, and businesses that offer information technology services.

Until the passage of HIPAA in 1996, no uniform national standard was in place to protect the confidentiality and security of patient information. HIPAA contained provisions leading to the development of data security standards on a national level. The standards that grew out of this legislation were published February 20, 2003 in the Federal Register, and are based on sound data security practices, and require compliance by certain healthcare and healthcare-related entities regardless of size. HIPAA privacy and security standards strengthened when the Health Information Technology for Economic and Clinical Health (HITECH) Act was enacted on February 17, 2009.

However, not all organizations are covered by HIPAA regulations. For example, HIPAA regulations do not apply to prescription database companies. Prescription database companies buy individual prescription information from prescription benefit managers (PBMs), mine the data, and compile it into reports. These reports cover an individual's prescriptions over a five-year period and include information like the drug name, dosage, dates filled, and prescribing physician. These reports are sold to insurers and are then used to determine risks, set premiums, and in the past, have been used to deny insurance coverage to individuals (Privacy Rights Clearinghouse 2012).

The **Medical Information Bureau** (MIB) is also unaffected by HIPAA. The MIB is a private company composed of about 750 member insurance companies. The MIB maintains a central database of individual medical claims and other information contributed by its member companies. However, when state health exchanges began operating in 2014 under the Affordable Care Act (ACA), insurers could not require individuals to provide them access to their health records when applying for health insurance and thus cannot deny health insurance based on information in the MIB. However, they may access individual information for such things as life, disability, or long-term-care policies (Privacy Rights Clearinghouse 2012[2]).

# Data Security Breaches

Every organization is subject to data security breaches by people from both inside and outside the organization. A **data breach** is an incident in which an unauthorized individual(s) has potentially viewed, stolen, or used sensitive, protected, or confidential data. Data breaches may involve PHI, personally identifiable information, trade secrets, or intellectual property (Rouse 2010). A breach extends to not only personal information, but company information as well. This is a broader definition than the definition of "breach" in the HIPAA rules for PHI.

HIPAA defines a breach as the acquisition, access, use, or disclosure of PHI in a manner not permitted by HIPAA, which compromises the security or privacy of the PHI (HHS 2013). There are three exceptions to the definition of "breach" and these are discussed in appendix B. Other than these exceptions, a breach is presumed to have occurred when PHI has been handled in an unpermitted manner unless the CE or BA demonstrates that there is a low probability the PHI has been compromised based on a risk assessment that meets specific criteria.

Security breaches appear to be increasing in severity and frequency across all industries (Ponemon Institute 2013). As required by the HITECH Act, the Secretary of Health and Human Services (HHS) must post a list of breaches of unsecured PHI affecting 500 or more individuals. Data assessed from August 2009, when breach reporting began, to January 2013 found that a total of 538 breaches of PHI affecting over 21.4 million patient records had been reported to HHS (Redspin 2013). Further analysis of these data show there was a 21.5 percent increase in the number of large breaches in 2012 from 2011, but there was a 77 percent decrease in the number of patient records involved. The analysis also revealed that 67 percent of all breaches were the result of theft or loss (Redspin 2013).

Since 2009, 57 percent of all patient records, or over 12 million records, involved in breaches were due to incidents involving BAs (Redspin 2013). In March 2013, the HIPAA Omnibus Rule took effect and included a number of additional provisions for data security and privacy. One of these provisions requires BAs are held to the same standard as CEs for PHI security. With the new rule, BAs must comply with HIPAA Security Rules just like CEs. They are also directly and civilly liable for PHI breaches.

Security breaches may also occur through hardware or software failures when someone unintentionally releases or loses information. Studies show, however, that breaches occur more often when an employee of the organization either performs an unauthorized access of information or deliberately alters or destroys information. Breaches caused by company insiders have been documented over a long period of time. For example, statistics from the Federal Bureau of Investigation (FBI) show that 70 percent of all security problems begin inside the organization (Balwin 1999). One study reported that hospital employees make up the largest known group of individuals involved in medical identity theft and fraud (Johnson 2009). More recently, a report found the most common cause of PHI breaches is due to theft or loss of unencrypted portable computing devices such as laptops or digital media such as flash drives (Redspin 2014). Another study of healthcare data breaches reported that 65 percent of respondents identified negligent insiders as their biggest concern (Filkins 2013).

A search of the Privacy Rights Clearinghouse database on healthcare data breaches made public found that since 2005 there were 4,076 breaches by employees that compromised over 621 million records (Privacy Rights Clearinghouse 2005). A survey study that included 80 healthcare organizations found that employees are the cause of most breaches. The primary causes of breaches are lost or stolen computing devices attributed to employee carelessness, followed by employee mistakes, and third-party errors (Ponemon 2012).

Among the potential costs of a security breach are disruption of services, inconvenience, loss of critical data, market reputation loss, fines, and indirect and direct financial costs. A recent survey of healthcare organizations found that the financial costs for a data breach ranged between less than $10,000 to more than $1 million over a two-year period. The average economic impact of data breaches by the reporting healthcare organizations was $2.4 million over a two-year period (Ponemon 2012). In addition to economic impact to the organization, there are potential adverse economic impacts to patients or employees whose records are compromised. This is in the form of financial identity theft and medical identify theft.

With the implementation of HIPAA privacy and security regulations, the Office of Civil Rights (OCR), the HIPAA enforcement agency, holds healthcare organizations accountable for security breaches and fines them when these occur. For example, in July 2013, the OCR fined one organization $1.7 million for security weaknesses in an online application database that left the electronic PHI (ePHI) of 612,402 beneficiaries accessible to unauthorized individuals over the Internet. Specifically, the OCR found that:

> The organization, WellPoint, did not implement appropriate administrative and technical safeguards as required under the HIPAA Security Rule. The investigation indicated WellPoint did not: adequately implement policies and procedures for authorizing access to the online application database, perform an appropriate technical evaluation in response to a software upgrade to its information systems, or have technical safeguards in place to verify the person or entity seeking access to ePHI maintained in its application database. As a result, the investigation indicated that WellPoint impermissibly disclosed the ePHI of 612,402 individuals by allowing access to the ePHI of such individuals maintained in the application database. (OCR 2013)

Security breaches can cause computer downtime resulting in a disruption of service. For example, in October 2013, a hospice reported that two months earlier it believed a hacker broke into its computer system. As a precaution, the hospice shut down its computer system immediately (Blumberg 2013). In another case of suspected hacker intrusion, the Montana Department of Public Health shut down its servers until they resolved the security problem (iHealthBeat 2014).

Good data security requires planning and the implementation of realistic policies and procedures that address both internal and external threats. A security program is about mitigating or reducing risks such as the ones noted above. Managing security risk requires organizations to identify and assign value to their data assets, identify risks and threats to each asset, estimate the likelihood of threat occurrence, determine costs from potential loss of each asset, and develop countermeasures and mitigation processes.

# Security Concepts

People frequently misuse the terms privacy, confidentiality, and security. In the healthcare context, **privacy** is usually understood to mean the right of individuals to limit access to information about their person. This is also called **informational**

**privacy** (Gostin et al. 1995). **Confidentiality**, on the other hand, refers to the expectation that information an individual shares with a healthcare provider during the course of care is only used for its intended purpose. Thus, disclosure of information beyond its intended purpose without the patient's knowledge and consent is a violation of confidentiality.

**Data security** is defined in a variety of ways. In general, it is the protection measures and tools for safeguarding information and information systems. The HIPAA rules define security as all of the administrative, physical, and technical safeguards in an information system (45 CFR 164.304). As defined by the U.S. Code on Information Security, information security means protecting information and information systems from unauthorized access, use, disclosure, disruption, modification, or destruction in order to provide:

- integrity, which means guarding against improper information modification or destruction, and includes ensuring information non-repudiation and authenticity;
- confidentiality, which means preserving authorized restrictions on access and disclosure, including means for protecting personal privacy and proprietary information; and
- availability, which means ensuring timely and reliable access to and use of information (NIST 2008).

Regardless of the nuances among definitions, information security includes a variety of protection measures that safeguard data, computer programs, and resources from undesired occurrences and exposures. These measures include:

- *Administrative practices,* such as prohibiting employees from sharing their passwords
- *Physical safeguards***,** such as ensuring doors to areas that house major computer systems are locked to keep out unauthorized persons
- *Technical measures* (or those controlled by the computer software), such as ensuring that only certain passwords allow an individual access to patient data

Thus, any healthcare data security program is concerned with implementing security measures that safeguard both the data and the systems that collect, maintain, and store the data.

Data security embodies three basic concepts: protecting data privacy, ensuring data integrity, and ensuring data availability. Implementation of these concepts varies among organizations. There is no one-size-fits-all blueprint. However, the goals the concepts imply remain the same. This means every security program must:

- Protect informational privacy by ensuring unauthorized persons cannot access data
- Build in safeguards to ensure data are only altered or disposed of by authorized means
- Implement mechanisms to ensure computer systems operate effectively and provide information when and where it is needed

## Protecting Data Privacy

Within the context of data security, protecting **data privacy** means defending or safeguarding access to information. In other words, only those individuals who need to know information should be authorized to access it.

Protecting informational privacy usually refers to patient-related data. However, healthcare organizations should protect the privacy of other information as well. For example, the organization should consider certain information about healthcare providers, employees, and the organization itself confidential. Information leaked to unauthorized individuals about providers, employees, or the organization can have as devastating an effect as information leaked about patients.

## Ensuring Data Integrity

**Data integrity** means that data should be complete, accurate, consistent, and up-to-date. With respect to data security, organizations must put protections in place so that no one may alter or dispose of data in a manner inconsistent with acceptable business and legal rules. Ensuring the integrity of healthcare data is important because providers use data in making decisions about patient care. For example, recording an incorrect drug dosage could lead to the healthcare caregiver administering the wrong amount of medication to a patient, which could result in significant injury or even loss of life. Thus, one important aspect of any security program is to put in place measures that protect data integrity.

The issue of data integrity is serious. Studies on paper medical records revealed that data integrity was a major issue of concern (IOM 1991). Research has shown a link between medical errors and poor data (Verhulst 2006). As digital data increases with electronic health record (EHR) implementation, data integrity issues are a continuing worry. Reports more recently document data quality issues in EHRs. Errors in selecting the wrong patient due to juxtaposition of an identification number, inattention to alerts due to alert overload, and input selection errors due to poor data entry design are among the many error types (Farley, et al 2013). A security program is as much about ensuring data quality and accuracy as it is about maintaining informational privacy.

## Ensuring Data Availability

Ensuring **data availability** means making sure the organization can depend on the system to perform exactly as expected, without error, and to provide information when and where it is needed. One problem with data availability occurs when organizations store data in both paper and digital format. This necessitates looking in paper files as well as digital databases or document management systems to ensure that all necessary information is retrieved for a specific request made by an individual. If links between the paper and digital records do not exist or are not correct, it is very likely that important information will be overlooked or not found by an individual.

Errors also happen when the computer system operation is unreliable. For example, if the system experiences unscheduled downtime, it is unable to process or provide access to information. In one case, a $1 billion EHR system went down for nearly a day at several hospital and clinic locations of a large healthcare system. This left nurses and doctors without access to critical patient data such as medications and patient histories (Charette 2013). Another EHR system reportedly had a history of one or more crashes per week that resulted in the creation of duplicate patient records (Brewin 2009). And in yet another EHR system crash, critical patient information was unavailable for three days (Kirsch 2013). A recent study described acceptable non-scheduled computer downtime as less than one hour per year and estimated that every hour a system is down in a physician practice it costs the practice more than $488 per physician per hour of down time (Anderson 2011). For reasons of good patient care, efficient business operations and costs, a good security program helps ensures data are available seven days a week, 24 hours a day.

# Security Threats

Before implementing a security program, it is important to understand the potential threats to data security. Any number of things can happen to cause the loss of informational privacy or to impair data integrity or availability. The most common threats are discussed in this section.

## Threats Caused by People

Threats to data security from people are classified into five categories. These include:

- *Threats from insiders who make unintentional mistakes:* Such threats could be employees who accidentally make a typographical error, inadvertently delete files on a computer disk, or unknowingly give out confidential information. Unintentional error is one of the major causes of security breaches.
- *Threats from insiders who abuse their access privileges to information:* Such threats include employees who knowingly disclose information about a patient to individuals who do not have proper authorization. They also could be employees with access to computer files who purposefully snoop for information they do not need to perform their job.
- *Threats from insiders who access information or computer systems for spite or profit:* Generally, such employees seek information for the purpose of committing fraud or theft. For example, an employee may use a computer system to skim money from the organization. Another may change files or data in time and attendance records, inventory systems, or long-distance telephone systems causing disruptions in business operations.
- *Threats from intruders who attempt to access information or steal physical resources:* Individuals may physically come onto the organization's property to access information or steal equipment such as laptop computers or printers. They also may hang around the organization's buildings hoping to access information from unprotected computer terminals or to read or take paper documents, computer disks, or other information.
- *Threats from vengeful employees or outsiders who mount attacks on the organization's information systems:* Disgruntled employees might destroy computer hardware or software, delete or change data, or enter data incorrectly into the computer system. Outsiders might mount attacks that harm the organization's information resources. For example, malicious hackers could plant viruses in the computer system or break into telecommunications systems to degrade or disrupt system availability (Johns 2010).

Three of the threats listed above involve the organization's employees. Historically, studies have revealed that disgruntled employees are responsible for nearly 90 percent of computer crimes that result in financial loss to the organization (CSI/FBI 1997). Inside jobs occur as often as external attacks (CSI/FBI 2005). More recently, workers using employer devices on employer time for personal social media and Internet use raise red flags about the potential for increased security threats. What some security studies show is that the Internet and social media introduce security challenges that companies never had to address before (Cisco 2013).

## Threats Caused by Environmental, Hardware, or Software Factors

Natural disasters such as earthquakes, tornadoes, floods, and hurricanes also threaten data security. These can demolish physical facilities and electrical utilities. According to the Federal Emergency Management Agency (FEMA), there has been a yearly average of 33 declared disasters in the United States over the past two decades. There were 62 declared major disasters, five emergency declarations, and 28 fire management assistant declarations in 2013 (FEMA 2014). To recover data from the devastation that natural disasters cause, affected organizations must have good backup and recovery procedures in place. The devastating 2011 tornado outbreak in Joplin, MO demonstrates the importance of good backup systems during natural disasters. In that case, winds scattered paper health records over a 75-mile area. Fortunately, just three weeks earlier, all paper records had been backed up through the regional health system (Russell 2011).

Another cause of security breaches are computer, utility, software, and hardware failures. These include hardware breakdowns such as disc crashes that destroy or alter data, and software problems such as errors in computer code.

Electrical outages and power surges also cause problems. When an electrical outage occurs, for example, information is unavailable to the end user. In addition, data might become corrupted or even lost. Power surges also can destroy or corrupt information. Thus, organizations must have the appropriate equipment to protect information systems from power surges and backup equipment to keep them running during an outage.

Yet another type of threat is a hardware or software malfunction. Adding new software or hardware to the system can introduce security breaches. One well-publicized case occurred when a health maintenance organization (HMO) was upgrading the software on its website. During the upgrade, hundreds of e-mails containing sensitive medical information and the names and home phone numbers of patients were sent to the wrong people by mistake. A programming error that no one caught prior to the upgrade caused the security breach (Wells 2000). Thus, organizations must follow good configuration management procedures to ensure that software and hardware malfunctions do not seriously affect data security.

### The St. Rita's Healthcare System Case Study

At the conclusion of the team meeting, everyone thanked Wayne and Shelia for their presentation and took time for discussion.

"I didn't realize the extent of security breaches," said Bob. "This was an eye opener for me. Now I understand why national legislation like HIPAA was ground breaking in protecting patient information."

"The big take away for me," added Shirlee, "is that security encompasses more than physically protecting computer equipment or keeping hackers out of a system. A big part of security is making sure that information is available when and where it is needed. The security triad really gives a big picture of what security is truly about."

"And talk about being surprised, I couldn't believe how insider purposeful actions and mistakes are probably an organization's biggest security threat," Monte added.

The team agreed the big picture Shelia and Wayne presented made a convincing rationale for data security management and the need for it to be a core component of EIM and data governance. After a brief break, Shelia and Wayne continued a discussion about the regulatory side of data security, specifically the HIPAA Security and Privacy Rules. A brief summary of their presentation follows at the end of this chapter.

After the guests left and the team regrouped, Val facilitated a discussion about including Wayne and Shelia as permanent members of the team. Shirlee reminded the team how much their work benefited when they asked Fred to join the group and how he helped them work through data architecture, metadata, and master data management. Everyone was on board with broadening the diversity of the team.

"Privacy and security are integral to EIM and DG and we really need this expertise and perspective," emphasized Linda.

Val took responsibility for contacting Joan Morton and asking for the formal appointment of Wayne and Shelia to the team. The next assignment was to review the HIPAA security regulations and prepare questions for Wayne and Shelia at the next team meeting.

# The Health Insurance Portability and Accountability Act

No discussion about healthcare data security is complete without addressing HIPAA. Passed in 1996, this law ushered in a new era of protections for health information. The act, also called **Public Law 104-191,** includes provisions for insurance reform as well as administrative simplification (see table 10.1). The administrative simplification provisions require the establishment of national standards to protect the privacy and security of PHI. The HHS was responsible for developing the standards resulting in the Security and Privacy Rules. The Security Rule applies to ePHI and requires organizations to implement certain administrative, physical, and technical safeguards to protect ePHI. The Privacy Rule, on the other hand, applies to all PHI in any form and requires organizations to put safeguards in place that ensure the privacy of PHI. It also provides circumstances when healthcare professionals can use or disclose PHI and gives individuals certain rights over their PHI, including the right to examine and obtain a copy of their health records. The compliance date for the Privacy Rule was April 14, 2003, and the compliance date for the Security Rule was April 21, 2005. Enforcement for HIPAA rests with the HHS OCR. The HHS website contains enforcement results by year beginning in 2003 for review.

Improved privacy and security provisions to HIPAA were included in parts of the **American Recovery and Reinvestment Act** (ARRA) when President Obama signed it into law on February 17, 2009. These parts of the law are known as the HITECH Act.

Table 10.1. Summary of HIPAA security standards

| Standards | Sections | Implementation Specifications (R)=Required,(A)=Addressable |
|---|---|---|
| **Administrative Safeguards** | | |
| Security Management Process | 164.308(a)(1) | Risk Analysis (R) |
| | | Risk Management (R) |
| | | Sanction Policy (R) |
| | | Information System Activity Review (R) |
| Assigned Security Responsibility | 164.308(a)(2) | (R) |
| Workforce Security | 164.308(a)(3) | Authorization and/or Supervision (A) |
| | | Workforce Clearance Procedure (A) |
| | | Termination Procedures (A) |
| Information Access Management | 164.308(a)(4) | Isolating Healthcare Clearinghouse Function (R) |
| | | Access Authorization (A) |
| | | Access Establishment and Modification (A) |
| Security Awareness and Training | 164.308(a)(5) | Security Reminders (A) |
| | | Protection from Malicious Software (A) |

(continued)

Table 10.1. Summary of HIPAA security standards (*Continued*)

| Standards | Sections | Implementation Specifications (R)=Required,(A)=Addressable |
|---|---|---|
| **Administrative Safeguards** | | |
| | | Log-in Monitoring (A) |
| | | Password Management (A) |
| Security Incident Procedures | 164.308(a)(6) | Response and Reporting (R) |
| Contingency Plan | 164.308(a)(7) | Data Backup Plan (R) |
| | | Disaster Recovery Plan (R) |
| | | Emergency Mode Operation Plan (R) |
| | | Testing and Revision Procedure (A) |
| | | Applications and Data Criticality Analysis (A) |
| Evaluation | 164.308(a)(8) | (R) |
| Business Associate Contracts and Other Arrangement | 164.308(b)(1) | Written Contract or Other Arrangement (R) |
| **Physical Safeguards** | | |
| Facility Access Controls | 164.310(a)(1) | Contingency Operations (A) |
| | | Facility Security Plan (A) |
| | | Access Control and Validation Procedures (A) |
| | | Maintenance Records (A) |
| Workstation Use | 164.310(b) | (R) |
| Workstation Security | 164.310(c) | (R) |
| Device and Media Controls | 164.310(d)(1) | Disposal (R) |
| | | Media Re-use (R) |
| | | Accountability (A) |
| | | Data Backup and Storage (A) |
| **Technical Safeguards(see § 164.312)** | | |
| Access Control | 164.312(a)(1) | Unique User Identification (R) |
| | | Emergency Access Procedure (R) |
| | | Automatic Logoff (A) |
| Audit Controls | 164.312(b) | (R) |
| Integrity | 164.312(c)(1) | Mechanism to Authenticate Electronic Protected Health Information (A) |
| Person or Entity Authentication | 164.312(d) | (R) |
| Transmission Security | 164.312(e)(1) | Integrity Controls (A) |
| | | Encryption (A) |

Source: 45 CFR 160, 162, 164.

### The St. Rita's Healthcare System Case Study

Val convened the regular meeting of the EIM team. She was happy to announce that Wayne and Shelia had been appointed by Joan Morton as permanent members of the team.

"I thought I knew HIPAA security until I went through and read all of its parts in the regulation text at the HHS website," said Monte. "It seems almost overwhelming."

"HIPAA security is a big job," responded Wayne "and that is why I'm thankful that we're pursuing a DG program at St. Rita's. I can see the benefits for both security and privacy implementation and monitoring through a formal organization of data stewards."

"I certainly now understand the need for both a security and a privacy officer," said Fred. "Although privacy and security are clearly related, I can definitely see the differences between them. HIPAA Privacy Rules apply to all PHI no matter if it is paper, electronic, or other media, whereas HIPAA Security applies to ePHI."

"And HIPAA Privacy has so many standards on uses and disclosures of PHI; so many responsibilities with release of information and tracking releases," added Denise. "But I can see where we have to coordinate both security and privacy."

"Precisely," said Wayne. "Shelia and I work closely together and we work with other compliance officials at St. Rita's including legal counsel, risk management, and human resources. HIPAA must appear seamless to our end users. For example, HIPAA training here at St. Rita's encompasses both privacy and security. And recently, we've implemented one HIPAA hotline for both security and privacy issue resolution. In this way end users don't need to think about whom they should contact for help. It's one hotline. We make the decision where to triage the issue once it is received."

After finishing their discussion on HIPAA security, Wayne got started on an overview of security planning and management, integrating into his presentation how HIPAA security regulations applied. Wayne started with a listing of strategies typically used and then led into the security organization and security plan.

## Developing a Data Security Program

Healthcare organizations must have protections in place to safeguard their information assets. Like protection of any other business asset, data security should fulfill the needs or requirements of the following:

- Stakeholders' needs: Includes privacy and confidentiality needs of patients, clients, providers, employees, suppliers, business associates, and stakeholders. Stakeholders are the legitimate owners of the data about them.
- Government and accreditor requirements: Includes complying with government regulations or accreditation requirements.
- Business needs: Consists of protection of proprietary data, intellectual property, and business data about customer or partner relationships or other data used for competitive advantage, business development, or business planning.
- Operational needs: Involves the legitimate access to carry out business operations (DAMA 2010).

The development of a data security program meets these needs. Although data security programs among organizations vary due to organization size, criticality of data, information infrastructure, and regulatory mandates, the following is a set of steps that organizations commonly use to protect both their information and information system. Taken together, these form a data security program:

1. Establish a security organization
2. Develop an organization security plan
3. Conduct risk analyses and assessments
4. Establish access controls
5. Implement physical and management controls
6. Implement software application controls
7. Develop a disaster recovery and business continuity plan

8. Implement network controls
9. Implement employee security awareness

The following sections cover each of these steps and their relationship to compliance with HIPAA Security Rule standards.

## Security Organization

The first and most fundamental step in developing a data security program is to establish a security organization that is responsible for managing all aspects of computer security. The assignment of responsibility for security management is part of the HIPAA administrative safeguards. Organizations must document data security authority and responsibilities throughout the organization. Each CE must identify a security official who has been assigned security responsibility by the organization for the development and implementation of policies and procedures required by the HIPAA Security Rule. The organization must have a process in place for creating, maintaining, and overseeing the development of security policies and procedures, conducting risk analysis, risk management, development of a sanction policy, and review of information system activity.

To be effective, top management must charter, support, and fund a security organization. Top executives need to assign responsibility and authority in the organization. The security organizational structure varies among enterprises. In a small clinic practice, for example, the security organization structure may consist of a staff member who is assigned security responsibilities by the clinic executive team. This individual may be supported by a privacy and security team made up of key personnel who help carry out security responsibilities. Outside consultants and security professionals may also support the security officer and team.

Larger organizations may establish an office, division, or department of information systems security. In this arrangement, the security office usually is headed by a **chief information security officer** (CISO), also called a **chief security officer** (CSO), who is responsible for coordinating the development and implementation of security policies and who may also be responsible for managing security information technology (IT) operations. The CISO may report directly to the organization CEO or the CIO or other executive officer. The CISO has a team of individuals who help carry out the duties of the information systems security office (ISSO) such as security administrator, security analysts, and program analysts.

No matter the size of the organization, a typical list of security officer job responsibilities includes:

- developing and maintaining information security policies, procedures, and control techniques to address system security planning;
- managing the identification, implementation, and assessment of common security controls;
- ensuring personnel with significant responsibilities for system security plans are trained;
- assisting senior agency officials with their responsibilities for system security plans; and
- identifying and coordinating common security controls for the agency (NIST 2006, 5).

Besides appointing someone to the CISO position and staffing the ISSO, the security organization should include an advisory or policy-making group. This group is often called the information security committee. This committee usually works with the CISO to evaluate the organization's security needs, develop an enterprise security plan, establish security policy, and ensure everyone is following all organizational information security policies. Organizational reporting of the information security committee varies among organizations. For example, some organizations may accomplish oversight in collaboration with compliance. Another approach may be to align this function with risk management (McMillan 2010).

## Security Plan

Development of a **security plan** is an essential component for successful security. Without a comprehensive approach that brings together a coordinated set of strategies and tactics, effective security is unlikely. The information systems security committee usually develops the security plan, while the ISSO administers it. Although the formats of information systems security plans vary widely, a security plan includes the following actions at minimum:

- Evaluation of information assets
- Evaluation of security risk
- Protection mechanisms

- Detection mechanisms
- Incident response and recovery
- Monitoring and maintenance

HIPAA security administrative safeguards include these basic security plan components. For example, risk assessment, risk management, and information system activity review are all required HIPAA implementation specifications.

## Evaluation of Information Assets

One of the first steps in developing a data security plan is identifying information assets. You cannot protect what you do not know you have. Identifying information assets should result in a resource inventory. The inventory should include a listing of each resource and the following information for each resource: responsible individual, creators and users, and individual responsible for maintaining and controlling the use of the resource. Each resource should have an assigned value. Frequently, the security committee determines this by using a guide similar to Federal Information Processing Standard 199 security categorization for determining information asset value as shown in table 10.2 (NIST 2006, 20). Items organizations should consider in valuing an asset include, among others, determining cost of recreating the information, cost of unavailability, cost of disclosure, and cost of inability to recreate the information.

Table 10.2. Federal information processing standard 199

| | POTENTIAL IMPACT | | |
|---|---|---|---|
| *Security Objective* | LOW | MODERATE | HIGH |
| Confidentiality<br>Preserving authorized restrictions on information access and disclosure, including means for protecting personal privacy and proprietary information.<br>[44 U.S.C., SEC. 3542] | The unauthorized disclosure of information could be expected to have a **limited** adverse effect on organizational operations, organizational assets, or individuals. | The unauthorized disclosure of information could be expected to have a **serious** adverse effect on organizational operations, organizational assets, or individuals. | The unauthorized disclosure of information could be expected to have a **severe or catastrophic** adverse effect on organizational operations, organizational assets, or individuals. |
| Integrity<br>Guarding against improper information modification or destruction, and includes ensuring information non-repudiation and authenticity.<br>[44 U.S.C., SEC. 3542] | The unauthorized modification or destruction of information could be expected to have a **limited** adverse effect on organizational operations, organizational assets, or individuals. | The unauthorized modification or destruction of information could be expected to have a **serious** adverse effect on organizational operations, organizational assets, or individuals. | The unauthorized modification or destruction of information could be expected to have a **severe or catastrophic** adverse effect on organizational operations, organizational assets, or individuals. |
| Availability<br>Ensuring timely and reliable access to and use of information.<br>[44 U.S.C., SEC. 3542] | The disruption of access to or use of information or an information system could be expected to have a **limited** adverse effect on organizational operations, organizational assets, or individuals. | The disruption of access to or use of information or an information system could be expected to have a **serious** adverse effect on organizational operations, organizational assets, or individuals. | The disruption of access to or use of information or an information system could be expected to have a **severe or catastrophic** adverse effect on organizational operations, organizational assets, or individuals. |

Source: NIST 2006.

Once a resource has been assigned by the security team to a security category, appropriate security measures can be assigned for the resource. While a security program should address all information assets, the reality is that trade-offs often need to be made. Categorization of the information resource, threat probability assessment, and determination of risk helps make trade-off decisions.

## Evaluation of Security Risk and Vulnerability

Risk management begins by conducting a **risk analysis.** This includes assessing security threats, security vulnerabilities, and the likely impact should the system expose a vulnerability. A **security threat** is anything that can exploit a security vulnerability. Vulnerability is a weakness or gap in security protection. And risk is the intersection between threat, vulnerability, likelihood, and impact.

Identifying security threats, determining how likely it is that any given threat may occur, and estimating the impact of an untoward event are all parts of a risk assessment (Johns 2010). Among the threats to security are human, technical, environmental, and natural threats. Table 10.3 provides a sample template for assessing security threats. The table lists the threat, examples of the threat, the level of likelihood that a threat may occur, and its probable impact. In a real situation, the threat matrix is likely to be several pages long. Organizations may use several different methodologies to carry out a threat analysis. Calculations of the threat risk based on unintentional occurrences such as power failures or data-entry error are usually based on the probability of the specific event occurring. Calculations of risk for intentional risk such as fraud or theft are usually based on such factors as the attractiveness of a system to a perpetrator and the degree of system vulnerability (Johns 2010).

Table 10.3. Sample security threat listing template

| Likelihood = Low-Medium-High \| Impact = Confidentiality-Integrity-Availability | | | | |
|---|---|---|---|---|
| **Human Threat** | | | | |
| **Threat** | **Consideration** | **Example** | **Likelihood L-M-H** | **Impact C-I-A** |
| Data-entry error | Daily transactions<br>System complexity<br>User training | Entering incorrect values<br>Incorrect spelling<br>Omitting data | H | I |
| Fraud or theft | Patient Data<br>Employee Data<br>Financial Data<br>E-commerce<br>Disgruntled employee | Copying Social Security number<br>Copying credit card number<br>Copying demographic data | | |
| Sabotage | | | | |
| Impersonation | | | | |
| Improper disposal | | | | |
| Improper release of information | | | | |
| **Technical Threat** | | | | |
| Eavesdropping | | | | |
| Hardware failure | | | | |
| Unauthorized software | | | | |
| Installation error | | | | |
| System errors | | | | |
| **Environmental Threat** | | | | |
| Electromagnetic interference | | | | |
| Water leaks | | | | |
| Air conditioning failure | | | | |

(continued)

Table 10.3. Sample security threat listing template (*Continued*)

| Likelihood = Low-Medium-High \| Impact = Confidentiality-Integrity-Availability | | | | |
|---|---|---|---|---|
| **Human Threat** | | | | |
| **Threat** | **Consideration** | **Example** | **Likelihood L-M-H** | **Impact C-I-A** |
| Physical cable cuts | | | | |
| Power fluctuation | | | | |
| Internal fire | | | | |
| | | | | |
| **Natural Threat** | | | | |
| External fire | | | | |
| Hurricane | | | | |
| Tornadoes | | | | |
| Earthquake | | | | |
| Flood | | | | |



Before implementing security solutions it is necessary for the security team to identify the organization's security vulnerabilities. This is normally done by developing a formal **security test and evaluation** (ST&E) plan. The plan documents specific criteria the system under study must meet. These include criteria for management, operational, and technical controls. **Management controls** focus on management of information systems and management of risks. **Operational controls** are implemented by people, not systems. **Technical controls** are executed by the information system. Table 10.4 provides a list of the controls normally found in each category (NIST 2006).

Table 10.4. Listing of security controls by control class

| CONTROL CLASS | CONTROL |
|---|---|
| **Management** | Risk Assessment |
| **Management** | Planning |
| **Management** | System and Services Acquisition |
| **Management** | Certification, Accreditation, and Security Assessments |
| **Operational** | Personnel Security |
| **Operational** | Physical and Environmental Protection |
| **Operational** | Contingency Planning |
| **Operational** | Configuration Management |
| **Operational** | Maintenance |
| **Operational** | System and Information Integrity |
| **Operational** | Media Protection |
| **Operational** | Incident Response |
| **Operational** | Awareness and Training |

(continued)

Table 10.4. Listing of security controls by control class (*Continued*)

| CONTROL CLASS | CONTROL |
|---|---|
| **Technical** | Identification and Authentication |
| **Technical** | Access Control |
| **Technical** | Audit and Accountability |
| **Technical** | System and Communications Protection |

Source: NIST 2006.

Usually, a set of tests are applied by the security team to the system to see if it meets the established criteria. These include operational, penetration, vulnerability, and system tests. Once threat and vulnerability identification is complete, then risks can be assessed and corrective action can be put into place by the organization.

## Protection, Detection, and Response

Table 10.4 lists several protection mechanisms that organizations should include for implementation in a security plan. HIPAA security provisions include all of these and this textbook discusses them as well. Appendix B contains a review of specific HIPAA Security Rule standards.

### Awareness Training – Operational Control

An essential control included in a good security program is an employee **security awareness program**. As discussed earlier, employees are often responsible for threats to data security. Consequently, employee awareness is a particularly important tool in reducing security breaches.

The organization should offer a formal program that educates every new employee on the confidential nature of patient and organization-related data. The program should inform employees about the organization's security policies and the consequences of failing to comply with them. Ordinarily, the organization should give each employee a copy of its security policies as they relate to his or her job function. It should also require every employee to sign a yearly confidentiality statement. Finally, because data security is such an important part of everyone's job, employees should receive periodic security reminders.

### Risk Management Program – Management Control

Another strategy in protecting the organization's data is to establish a risk management program. **Risk management** encompasses the identification, management, and control of untoward events. Risk management programs are essential if healthcare facilities are to comply with the Fair and Accurate Credit Transaction Act (FACTA) to identify, detect, and respond to "**red flags**" that may signal the presence of identity theft. Red flags that sound an alert of potential identity theft consist of five categories:

- Alerts, notifications, or warnings from a consumer reporting agency
- Suspicious documents such as an altered identification
- Suspicious personally identifying information such as a suspicious address that does not exist or that belongs to someone else in the business's accounts
- Unusual use of, or suspicious activity relating to a covered account
- Notices from customers, victims of identity theft, law enforcement authorities, or other businesses about possible identity theft in connection with an account

Healthcare entities must take steps to prevent, detect, and mitigate activities that address both external and internal incidents. Well-conceived risk management programs help prevent, detect, and mitigate security breaches, including identify theft.

### Incident Detection – Technical Control

Once a healthcare facility is aware of a possible threat, it is important to detect if a threat or incident has occurred. **Incident detection** methods identify both accidental and malicious events. Detection programs monitor the information systems for abnormalities or a series of events that might indicate that a security breach is occurring or has occurred. There are a variety of analytic detection tools available for this purpose.

**Incident Response Plan and Procedures – Operational Control**

When an organization identifies a security incident, it must coordinate a response to mitigate the incident. An **incident response** plan includes management procedures and responsibilities to ensure a quick and effective response to specific types of incidents. For example, in some instances the plan may call for a "watch and warn" response that includes monitoring and notification of an incident to the designated authority but takes no immediate action. In other instances an organization may institute a "repair and report" response. This type of response may be used in the case of a computer virus attack. A third type of response is to "pursue and prosecute" which includes monitoring and minimizing the attack, collecting evidence, and involving a law enforcement agency. This last example might be used in instances of suspected identity theft.

Regardless of the specific response, all response plans must include seven activities. These include documenting the event, determining that an untoward security event has occurred or is occurring, notifying the appropriate people of the security incident, containing the incident, assessing the scope of damage, removing the cause of the incident, and recovering the system (Pipkin 2000).

**Access Controls – Technical Control**

Establishing **access controls** is a fundamental security strategy. Basically, it means being able to identify which employees should have access to what data. The general practice is that employees should only have access to data they need to do their jobs. For example, an admitting clerk and a healthcare provider do not need access to the same kinds of data.

Determining what data to make available to an employee usually involves identifying classes of information based on the employee's role in the organization. Thus, the organization determines what information an admitting clerk, for example, needs to know to do his or her job. Thereafter, every individual who works as an admitting clerk has access to the same information.

Every job role in the organization is identified, usually by a multi-disciplinary team, along with the type of information required to perform it. This is often referred to as role-based access. Although there are other types of access control strategies, role-based access is probably the one healthcare organizations use most often (appendix B presents detailed information on identification, authentication, and authorization associated with access control).

**Physical Controls – Operational Control**

**Physical access controls** are safeguards that protect physical equipment, media, or facilities. For example, doors leading to the areas that house mainframes and other principal computing equipment should have locks on them. In addition, personal computers and terminals should have locks to guard against theft. Positioning computer terminal screens so confidential data are not exposed to public view is another physical control.

**Administrative Controls – Management Control**

**Administrative controls** include policies and procedures that address the management of computer resources. For example, one such policy might direct users to log off the computer system when they are not using it. Another policy might prohibit employees from accessing the Internet for purposes that are not work related.

**Software Application Controls – Technical Control**

Another security strategy is to implement **application controls.** Application controls are important because they perform automatic checks that preserve data confidentiality and integrity. These are controls contained in the application software or computer programs. One common application control is password management. It involves keeping a record of end users' identifications and passwords and then matching the passwords to each end user's privileges. Password management ensures that end users can access only the information for which they have permission.

Another type of application control is the edit check. Edit checks help to ensure data integrity by allowing only reasonable and predetermined values to be entered into the computer.

The audit trail falls within the family of software controls. The audit trail is a software program that tracks every single access to data in the computer system. It logs the name of the individual who accessed the data, the date and time, and the action taken (for example, modifying, reading, or deleting data). Depending on the organization's policy, audit trails are reviewed periodically or on predetermined schedules by designated security team members. Audit trail reviews are a critical source to help detect security breaches.

**Network Controls – Technical Control**

Another important strategy for guarding against security breaches is implementing **network controls.** Healthcare organizations use a variety of networks to transmit healthcare data today, and the data must be protected from intruders and corruption during transmission. With widespread Internet use, network controls also are essential to prevent the threat of hackers. Examples of network controls include data encryption, implementation of firewalls, network segmentation, and implementation of virtual private networks.

**Business Continuity Plan – Operational Control**

What happens when an organization's computer systems are damaged or destroyed by an intentional or unintentional event, or a natural disaster such as a flood, tornado, or hurricane? Even though such an event may be unlikely to occur, organizations must be prepared in the event that one does.

Organizations develop a **business continuity plan** (BCP) to handle an unexpected computer shutdown caused by an intentional or unintentional event or during a natural disaster. An example of an intentional event is a computer shutdown caused by hackers. A shutdown due to a software error is usually classified as an unintentional event. Examples of natural disasters include floods, hurricanes, and tornadoes.

Sometimes the BCP is also called contingency and disaster planning. The BCP typically includes policies and procedures to help the business continue operation during the unexpected shutdown or disaster. It also includes procedures the business can implement to restore its computer systems and resume normal operation after the disaster.

The BCP is based on information gathered during the risk assessment and analysis discussed above. The risk assessment includes the probability of an unexpected shutdown. Using this information, organizations develop the BCP based on the following steps:

1. Identifying the minimum allowable time for system disruption
2. Identifying alternatives for system continuation
3. Evaluating cost and feasibility of each alternative
4. Developing procedures required for activating the plan (Johns 2010)

An important part of the BCP is planning how to return the computer system to normal operation and ensuring the availability and accuracy of data after a disaster. Restoring system integrity and ensuring all data are recovered requires all parts of the system be verified by the security team after the disaster has occurred. Usually organizations bring up one system or one component of a system at a time and verify that processes are working correctly.

The typical contents of a BCP include:

- *Assigning responsibility for development and implementation of the plan:* This includes identifying the responsibilities of the security management team, the emergency operation team, and the damage assessment team and how all teams are coordinated.
- *Determining how a disaster is identified:* This includes the definition of disaster and its identification, notification procedures, identification of disaster cause, and communication procedures.
- *Putting in place a recovery plan:* For example, outlining the recovery organization and staffing, and ensuring the organization has vendor contracts and backup plans, plans to recover data affected by the disaster, and alternate-site contracts.
- *Testing the plan:* A plan is only as good as its implementation. The organization must test the BCP periodically to ensure all parts of the plan, from disaster identification to recovery work, run smoothly (Johns 2001).

**Data Quality Control Processes – Operational Control**

Ensuring data quality is an essential part of any data security program. Among these dimensions are: accuracy, accessibility, comprehensiveness, consistency, currency, definition, granularity, precision, relevancy, and timeliness.

Responsibility for ensuring data quality is shared by many organization stakeholders. For example, data item definition may be the responsibility of the data administrator or those in charge of the data dictionary. Depending on the type of data, determining data granularity may be the responsibility of various department heads or clinical managers. Data accuracy begins with any individual who enters or documents data.

Monitoring and tracking systems that ensure data quality are part of a data security program. A formal data quality management program should address all the dimensions of data quality. Aspects of such a program are discussed in chapter 11.

Data accessibility, consistency, and definition are three data quality dimensions often addressed using computer tools. Data accessibility means that users can easily obtain the data. Computer tools monitor unscheduled computer downtime, determine why failures occurred, and provide data to help minimize future problems.

Data consistency means data do not change no matter how often or in how many ways they are stored, processed, or displayed. Data values are consistent when the value of any given data element is the same across applications and systems. Procedures are usually developed by a technical team to monitor data periodically to ensure they are consistent as they move through computer processes or from one system to another.

Data definition means data are defined by the organization. Every data element should have a clear definition and a range of acceptable values. Data definitions and their values are usually stored in a data dictionary.

## The St. Rita's Healthcare System Case Study

By working with Wayne and Shelia, the EIM team came to a better understanding of the complexities of data security and privacy and that both these areas should be included in any DG program. The primary agenda item for the meeting was to identify broad governance functions for data security and privacy. Val split the team into two groups. Each group engaged in brainstorming for 30 minutes to develop a list of DG functions specific to data security and privacy. Afterwards, the two groups shared and compared their lists and developed an initial draft of DG.

# Applying Data Governance

The team agreed that while data privacy and security are related, they are distinct functional areas. Therefore "privacy" was added to "data security" in the column title on the EIM Functional Chart (table 10.5). Broadly these DG functions include:

- Identifying and classifying sensitive data across enterprise systems
- Developing data security and privacy policies and standards
- Aligning governance, compliance, security, privacy, and technology to meet compliance and regulatory requirements
- Assessing risk and identifying controls to manage risk
- Performing data security and privacy audits and reporting findings
- Developing and implementing data privacy and security awareness and training
- Working with other stakeholders to assure compliance with regulatory, accreditation, and other requirements

Table 10.5. DG deliverables by EIM function

| Data Governance | Data Architecture Management | Metadata Management | Master Data Management | Content Management | Data Security and Privacy Management | Business Intelligence Management | Data Quality Management | Terminology and Classification Management |
|---|---|---|---|---|---|---|---|---|
| Identify mission and scope | Develop and maintain data models | Develop policies, procedures, and standards | Identify master and reference data requirements | Develop roadmap for content management | Identify and classify sensitive data across enterprise systems | | | |
| Establish goals and success measures | Develop, maintain, and evaluate data model policies and standards | Ensure metadata meets functional requirements | Develop policies, procedures, and standards for management of master data | Develop policies and procedures for content management | Develop data security and privacy policies and standards | | | |
| Put in place DG structure, processes, and communications plan | Define roles, responsibilities, and accountabilities for data architecture management | Develop and maintain appropriate metadata schema | Establish master data definitions, validation, and verification levels for master data quality | Apply taxonomies, thesauri, ontologies, and other content management classifications | Meet compliance and regulatory security and privacy requirements | | | |

(continued)

Table 10.5. DG Deliverables by EIM function (*Continued*)

| Data Governance | Data Architecture Management | Metadata Management | Master Data Management | Content Management | Data Security and Privacy Management | Business Intelligence Management | Data Quality Management | Terminology and Classification Management |
|---|---|---|---|---|---|---|---|---|
| Secure funding | Develop, maintain, and evaluate policies and standards for requirements analysis | Ensure metadata capture, maintenance, distribution, and integration | Ensure master and reference data meet regulatory requirements, including lineage history and security | Develop policies and procedures that ensure legal and regulatory mandates are met | Assess risk and identify controls to manage risk | | | |
| Establish decision rights | Develop and maintain data artifacts and standards | Ensure metadata security | Establish audit procedures and standards for master data | Establish standards and audit procedures | Perform data security and privacy audits and report findings | | | |
| Identify accountabilities | Establish quality control program and metrics for data architecture management | Develop and implement quality controls for metadata | Identify stakeholders and establish decision rights and accountabilities | Implement stewardship processes over the content management life cycle | Develop and implement data privacy and security awareness and training | | | |

## Part of the Team: Topics for Discussion and Action

1. The EIM team reviewed the HIPAA privacy provisions. The team agreed that while data security and privacy are related, each is a distinctly separate function. Wayne and Shelia said they work closely together and coordinate their activities. Review the HHS's guidance materials on HIPAA privacy available on their website. Compare HIPAA privacy provisions to HIPAA security provisions listed in appendix B. Make a list of the security and privacy provisions on which you believe Shelia and Wayne might work most closely together.

## Advanced Concepts

1. Review the guidance materials on HIPAA privacy provisions on the HHS's website. Identify opportunities for synergy and coordination with data security and how these could be translated into DG to reduce repetition and enhance both security and privacy. Develop a proposal to the EIM team that includes your recommendations for achieving better effectiveness and efficiency through coordination of DG functions and governance for these two areas.
2. This chapter provided the components of a data security plan. Conduct a review of the literature and identify the customary components for a data privacy plan. Assess the similarities and differences between a data security plan, as outlined in this chapter, and a data privacy plan. Develop an annotated outline for a healthcare data privacy plan, taking into account HIPAA and other requirements.
3. Conduct a search of the Privacy Rights Clearinghouse database of healthcare breaches from 2005 until the present at their website. Develop graphs or charts reflecting data security breach statistics that you could use in a presentation to executives and managers at St. Rita's to inform them of data security status. What would be your overriding message to these managers in three to five bullet points?

## References

45 CFR 160, 162, 164: HIPAA Administrative Simplification. 2013 (Mar. 26).

45 CFR 164.304: Definitions. 2009 (Aug. 4).

Anderson, M. 2011. The Costs and Implications of EHR System Downtime on Physician Practices. The AC Group, Inc. http://www.himss.org/files/HIMSSorg/content/files/Stratus%20White%20Paper%20Effect_of_Downtime_on_Physician_Practices.pdf.

Balwin, G. 1999 (October). Information age requires strategic plans. *Health Data Management*.

Blumberg, S. 2013 (October 19). Hospice of Chesapeake shut down computer after security break. *Maryland Gazette*. http://www.capitalgazette.com/maryland_gazette/news/money/hospice-of-chesapeake-shut-down-computer-system-after-security-break/article_c5f6ddd3-c82d-5684-85ea-99eb61329140.html.

Brewin, B. 2009 (March 24). Officials criticize defense's 'unreliable' health record system. Nextgov. http://www.nextgov.com/health/2009/03/officials-criticize-defenses-unreliable-health-record-system/43412/.

Charette, R.N. 2013 (September 3). IT hiccups of the week: Sutter Health's $1 billion EHR system crashes. *IEEE Spectrum*. http://spectrum.ieee.org/riskfactor/computing/it/it-hiccups-of-the-week-sutter-healths-1-billion-ehr-system-crash.

CISCO. 2013 (January 30). Press Release: Cisco annual security report: Threats step out of the shadows. http://newsroom.cisco.com/release/1133334.

CSI/FBI Computer Crime and Security Survey. 1997 (spring). *Computer Security Issues and Trends*.

CSI/FBI Computer Crime and Security Survey. 2005. Computer Security Institute. San Francisco, CA

DAMA. 2010. *The DAMA Guide to the Data Management Body of Knowledge*. Bradley Beach: Technics Publications.

Department of Health and Human Services. 2003 (January 17). Press Release: New rule protects patient privacy, secures health information. http://www.hhs.gov/news/press/2013pres/01/20130117b.html.

Department of Health and Human Services. 2013 (January 25). Modifications to the HIPAA Privacy, Security, Enforcement, and breach notification rules under the Health Information Technology for Economic and Clinical Health Act and the Genetic Information Nondiscrimination Act; Other modifications to the HIPAA rules. *Federal Register* 78(17): 5556–5702.

Dick, R., E. Steen, and D. Detmer, eds. 1997. *The Computer-Based Patient Record: An Essential Technology for Health Care*, revised ed. Washington, D.C.: National Academy Press.

Farley, H.L., K.M. Baumlin, A.G. Hamedani, D.S. Cheung, M.R. Edwards, D.C. Fuller, N. Genes, R.T. Griffey, J.J. Kelly, J.C. McClay, J. Nielson, M.P. Phelan, J.S. Shapiro, S. Stone-Griffith, and J.M. Pines. Quality and safety implications of emergency department information systems. *Annals of Emergency Medicine* 62(4):399–407.

FEMA. 2014. Disaster Declarations by Year. https://www.fema.gov/disasters/grid/year.

Gostin, L.O., J. Turek-Brezina, M. Powers, and R. Kozloff. 1995. Privacy and security of health information in the emerging health system. *Health Matrix: Journal of Law-Medicine* 3:18.

Filkins, B. 2013. SANS Inaugural Healthcare Survey. *SANS Institute InfoSec Reading Room*. http://www.sans.org/reading-room/whitepapers/analyst/inaugural-health-care-survey-34855.

iHealthBeat. 2014 (June 2). Healthcare Organizations Across the U.S. Report Data Breaches. http://www.ihealthbeat.org/articles/2014/6/2/health-organizations-across-the-us-report-data-breaches.

Johns, M. 2010. Information Security. Chapter 17 in *Health Information Management Technology: An Applied Approach*, 3rd ed. Edited by M.L. Johns. Chicago: AHIMA Press.

Johnson, E. M. Data Hemorrhages in the Health-Care Sector. Hanover, NH. Dartmouth College; 2009.

Kirsch, M. 2013 (January 11). Unlike EMRs, patient charts never crash. *Medpage Today's KevinMD.com*. http://www.kevinmd.com/blog/2013/01/emrs-paper-charts-crash.html.

McMillan, M. 2010. IT Security Governance. Chapter 1 in *Information Security in Healthcare Managing Risk*. Edited by T.W. Herzig. Chicago: HIMSS.

National Institute of Standards and Technology (NIST). 2006 (February). Guide for Developing Security Plans for Federal Information Systems. http://csrc.nist.gov/publications/nistpubs/800-18-Rev1/sp800-18-Rev1-final.pdf.

National Institute of Standards and Technology (NIST). 2008. An Introduction Resource Guide for Implementing the Health Insurance Portability and Accountability Act (HIPAA) Security Rule. *NIST Special Publication 800-66 Revision 1.*

Office of Civil Rights. 2013 (July 11). Press Release: WellPoint pays HHS $1.7 million for leaving information accessible over Internet. http://www.hhs.gov/news/press/2013pres/07/20130711b.html.

Pipkin, D.L. 2000. *Information Security: Protecting the Global Enterprise*. Upper Saddle River: Prentice Hall.

Ponemon Institute LLC. 2009. Business Case for Data Protection Study of CEOs and other C-level Executives. http://edocumentsciences.com/wp-content/uploads/2010/03/Business-Case-for-Data-Protection.pdf.

Ponemon Institute, LLC. 2012. Third Annual Benchmark Study on Patient Privacy and Data Security. http://lpa.idexpertscorp.com/acton/attachment/6200/f-0033/1/-/-/-/-/file.pdf.

Privacy Rights Clearinghouse. 2012. California Medical Privacy Fact Sheet C4: Your Prescriptions and Your Privacy. https://www.privacyrights.org/fs/fsC4/CA-medical-prescription-privacy.

Privacy Rights Clearinghouse. 2012 [2]. California Medical Privacy Fact Sheet C2: How Is Your Medical Information Used and Disclosed – With and Without Consent? https://www.privacyrights.org/fs/fsC2/CA-medical-uses-disclosures.

Privacy Rights Clearinghouse. 2005. Chronology of Data Breaches 2005–Present. http://www.privacyrights.org/data-breach.

Redspin. 2013 (February). Breach Report 2012: Protected Health Information. http://www.redspin.com/docs/Redspin_Breach_Report_2012.pdf.

Redspin. 2014 (February). Breach Report 2013: Protected Health Information (PHI). https://www.redspin.com/docs/Redspin-2013-Breach-Report-Protected-Health-Information-PHI.pdf.

Rouse, M. 2010. Data Breach. http://searchsecurity.techtarget.com/definition/data-breach.

Russell, Matthew. 2011. Permanent record: Electronic records aid in the aftermath of Joplin tornado. *Journal of AHIMA* 82(9): 34–37.

U.S. Congress, Office of Technology Assessment. 1993. *Protecting Privacy in Computerized Medical Information*, OTA-TCT-576. Washington, DC: U.S. Government Printing Office.

Verhulst, S. 2006. Background Issues on Data Quality. http://www.markle.org/health/markle-common-framework/connecting-professionals/t5.

Wells, J. 2000 (August 10). Errant E-Mails Violate Privacy of Kaiser Members. *San Francisco Chronicle*. http://www.sfgate.com/health/article/Errant-E-Mails-Violate-Privacy-of-Kaiser-Members-2710295.php..

# Chapter 11

# Business Intelligence and Big Data

**Business intelligence** (BI) is a set of technologies and processes that use data to understand and analyze business performance (Davenport and Harris 2007, 7). In healthcare, this definition extends to assessing healthcare delivery, patient care, and outcomes as well as business performance. BI processes and technologies extract, identify, and analyze data to report current conditions or to predict future views of healthcare operations (HIMSS 2014). Among the goals of BI are to improve processes and performance, lower costs, and create value. Both economic and political drivers make BI a critical function for healthcare organizations. Current research finds that companies that use data-driven decision making or BI outperform their competitors (Brynjolfsson et al. 2011).

Increases in data liquidity in healthcare have reached a tipping point where the power of big data can help the industry address problems such as quality of care and escalating costs (Kayyali et al. 2013). **Big data** provide the fuel for BI activities. The term big data has various definitions, but it is generally agreed that it describes the concept of large volumes of data that are complex, diverse, and timely (Kimball and Luisi 2013). The large data volume requires advanced and unique data storage, management, analysis, and visualization technologies (Chen et al. 2012). With the diffusion of electronic health records (EHR), claims and cost data, pharmaceutical data, data from sophisticated medical instruments, and other data resulting from the application of associated and supporting information technologies, healthcare lays claim for partly contributing to big data.

The ability to analyze such a wealth of data using advanced analytical techniques has enormous potential for improving healthcare delivery and patient outcomes and lowering costs. Big data analytics provides the opportunities to uncover previously "hidden" information in the form of identifying trends and new insights, as well as drilling down into specific information about market, customer, provider, or patient segments. Some examples of such analyses include

- Research to determine which treatments for which patients are the most clinically helpful and cost effective, reducing the incidents of both overtreatment and under-treatment
- Implementing clinical decision support systems for prediagnosis and mining the literature and other data sources for suggesting optimal treatment options that meet a specific patient's needs
- Analytics to identify and optimize sources of variability and waste
- Simulations to map processes and physical flows to reduce delays in healthcare delivery
- Dashboards and scorecards for publishing performance data to increase transparency
- Patient profiling to proactively identify individuals who need specific care (Manyika et al. 2011)

While big data analyses are enormously promising, the underlying problems of semi-structured data, unstructured data, and lack of processes to manage data represent barriers in achieving the goals it sets. This chapter examines BI and big data in the context of healthcare enterprise information management (EIM) and specifically focuses on topics that can help you to:

- Differentiate among types of data and their sources
- Describe BI and big data

- Explain the continuum of BI activities
- Describe BI architectures
- Practice data governance (DG) principles related to BI

## The St. Rita's Healthcare System Case Study

Linda and Fred were ready to start working with a new member of the EIM team to examine BI functions and how they related to a total EIM program. Susan had been asked to join the team because of her background in data analytics. Before coming to St. Rita's, Susan worked in analytics for a healthcare consulting firm, focusing on marketing analytics. At St. Rita's she worked for the chief financial officer and was responsible for decision support for that business unit. Susan was thrilled to be asked to join the EIM team and fully supported the EIM concept.

"I'm so happy to be a part of a very future-oriented project," Susan shared with Linda and Fred. "We need an integrated approach to analytics and data management, and I'm glad to see this effort developed here at St. Rita's."

"I'd like to pick your brain, Susan," Fred said. "It seems like BI and data analytics are tough to get your arms around, like the other functional areas of EIM that we've examined. Just looking at the amount of data, its diversity, lack of standardization, and poor integration among our current systems has me wondering, how do we start?"

"My experience," replied Susan, "is that the best approach is to zero in on what I call 'low hanging fruit' to develop a roadmap, building the organization's analytic capabilities around key strategic areas. Increasing BI capacity is an iterative process. Start with cleaning up and making sure the transaction data are good. Then, proceed and assess what it is that the organization really wants to achieve from analytics. Of course, there has to be top management support for any analytics initiative, and we should have in place both analytics technology and a knowledgeable analytics staff."

"Sounds like you've lived the story," noted Linda. "I think this will be an interesting assignment."

With that, the three team members developed a list of tasks and made assignments to delve into issues relating to BI. They decided to look broadly at what constitutes healthcare data, then focus on internal organizational data and finalize their research by reviewing categories of external data that may be used by a healthcare organization like St. Rita's.

# Data and Healthcare Organizations

Healthcare data are voluminous and diverse. The types of data can be sliced and diced in many different ways. For example, there are data about people who receive healthcare, providers who deliver healthcare services, and communities (for example, counties and states) and groups (for example, adolescents, mothers, and babies) that concern health behaviors, diseases, and injuries. Besides these, there are non-profit and other organizations focused on specific disease entities, and research organizations that collect health and healthcare data. A major source of health and healthcare data are state and federal governments and third party payers of healthcare services such as insurance companies. Each of the data sets collected about or by these groups has its own idiosyncrasies related to purpose, use, data definition, data structure, and data quality. Given this, these groups often cannot use the wealth of data available for comparison purposes or for integrating or analyzing data across domains in a meaningful way. The key to this issue is that organizations must know the data's use, structure, and definition before using it for reporting or analytic purposes.

Besides data relating to healthcare delivery, hospitals, healthcare systems, clinics, and related organizations also create and maintain significant amounts of data relating to business operations. This includes data to support day-to-day activities, management-oriented tactical data, and data that support the organization's strategic decisions. Some of the data is structured, but much of it is unstructured, uncategorized, and stored in reports, policies, procedures, contracts, and other business records that mostly reside in paper, digital, and hybrid data silos.

Clinical data and its management receive a lot of focus in healthcare organizations, and rightly so, but an EIM program must encompass management of all organizational data. Focusing on the quality, security, retrieval, and use of any one type of data at the expense of others does not result in efficient and effective information management. Organizations must build into their BI systems the connection and relation between different types of data (clinical, administrative, and operational) and the processes they support. For example, the correlation between staffing data and patient outcomes is important for determining optimal staffing patterns. The relation between supply chain data, patient outcomes, and cost offers yet another important opportunity for BI investigation.

Data consists of either primary or secondary data sources. In the context of records management, a **primary data source** is a record an individual creates at about the same time as the event he or she is describing. Clinical records such as operative reports, nursing notes, and physician orders are examples of primary sources. **Secondary data sources** are data that are taken from a primary record and used for a purpose different than the original use. In healthcare, secondary data are frequently entered into registries and databases by HIM professionals, analysts, or other professional staff.

## Primary Data Sources

Primary data sources include clinical, administrative, and operational data. Healthcare professionals frequently create, capture, use, store, and archive these data in uncoordinated ways, creating silos of data. Thus, integration of these data for BI purposes becomes a challenge. Below is an overview of some of these primary data sources to give a perspective of the expanse and variety of data organizations must manage and consider for BI purposes.

### Clinical Primary Data

Creation of clinical documentation forms a preponderance of data in any healthcare delivery organization. These primary data sources include documents and reports generated by humans and machines and exist in multiple types of media.

Examples of human-generated content include operative, patient history, and physical examination reports that a clinician usually dictates, and then is transcribed into a digital format, typically in a word-processed document. Depending on the sophistication of the organization's EHR system, digital documents such as these can be automatically captured and stored in an archive and integrated into the EHR. In other instances, a paper document may be printed from the digital source and, using a document imaging or an electronic document management system (EDMS), scanned and archived on digital media and integrated with an EHR system. In most cases, an automated process adds metadata to the document that identifies its document type. In some cases the metadata may include content headings, but for the most part, the content in these kinds of records is highly unstructured. As discussed in chapter 9, unstructured content presents challenges for data search, identification, retrieval, and analysis. Content management techniques such as using taxonomies, thesauri, and ontologies are necessary before applying BI technologies and analysis to these kinds of records.

A **point-of-care** (POC) charting system is a data capture strategy that provides structure to record content. These types of clinical documentation systems allow providers (physicians, nurses, and therapists) to enter data at the time when patient care is delivered. Among the documentation types used by POC are patient history, physical examination, and clinical notes. These systems structure data entry by using drop-down menus, checklists, templates, and other **structured data entry techniques** that constrain data capture into a common format or vocabulary. A purpose of structured data entry is to reduce variability in terminology, allowing for standardization. An outcome of this type of data entry is the ability to better identify, search, retrieve, and compare data.

The content captured through structured data entry is only as good as the degree to which it represents the concepts and context being documented by the end user. There is debate regarding structured data entry techniques and if they are sufficient for capturing the richness of clinical encounters content (AMA 2013). For example, if a physician's entry is limited by structured data entry in a standard EHR, the entry may omit clinically significant information that an unstructured dictated report contains (Resnik et al. 2008). More advanced techniques using unstructured text and coded data to create what is referred to as a structured narrative are in early development stages (Johnson et al. 2008). To produce a structured narrative, the gross structure of the record, such as sections, fields, and headings, is marked up by the system. Then the system applies natural language processing (NLP) to the record to identify concepts, modifiers, and relationships among the content, and these are subsequently identified using standardized codes. The resultant codes enable linkage to content, other events, information reuse, and are easier to use for analytics.

Other types of clinical documentation, such as clinical orders, medications, and laboratory reports are more amenable to structured entry. Physicians and other qualified providers use **computerized provider order entry** (CPOE) to enter medication, treatment, and other patient care orders directly into the computer in a structured format. These systems use structured data entry techniques but also include decision support capabilities such as prompts, alerts, and reminders associated with the order. For example, a CPOE system might alert the physician to a contraindication related to a drug order, such as a patient's drug allergy or potential interaction with another currently prescribed medication. Some research found CPOE associated with increased patient safety and quicker patient treatment through reduced turnaround times between time of order entry and time of treatment (Steele and DeBrow 2008).

Another example of a primary data source is machine data capture and entry. For example, automated laboratory instruments, called autoanalyzers, directly report results of clinical laboratory tests to computer systems which store them. Diagnostic images, such as x-rays, mammograms, and CT scans, are provided directly from automated systems into picture and archiving communication systems (PACs) as image reports. The images themselves are one part of an imaging report; the other is a physician's narrative interpretation of the image. The same concerns identified with structuring narrative text in a physical examination also apply to machine data capture and entry. For example, even though laboratory values are discrete data, the results are often produced by the system as a print file and not stored in a data repository (a transactional database, described later in the chapter) as structured data (Amatayakul 2012).

### Administrative and Operational Primary Data

**Administrative data** are important to the operation, performance, and financial evaluation of a healthcare organization. Administrative and operational data refer to data that pertain to operations of the organization. These can include financial management, human resource management, materials management, and facilities management data.

Financial primary data range from invoices, healthcare claims, expense statements, sales receipts, profit and loss statements, and balance sheets to financial policies and procedures. Human resource primary data include employee evaluations, job descriptions, letters, memos, attendance records, benefits records, and disability documents. Materials management primary records comprise purchasing records, inventory records, materials receiving documents, and inventory distribution records. Facilities management primary data consist of contractor and vendor contracts, vendor directory, equipment inventory, staffing schedules, and certificates of insurance.

Similar to clinical information systems, there are systems that automate many of these processes. For example, human resource management systems have the ability to automate several functions including payroll, time and attendance records, benefits administration, training documentation, and performance appraisal. **Enterprise resource planning** (ERP) systems track the status of business commitments, purchase orders, and supplies. A large part of ERP systems is managing the master data related to master supply items, managing inventory, streamlining ordering, tracking items and expiration dates, and capturing charges. Automated facilities management software includes functions ranging from tracking and setting up preventative equipment maintenance to generating service requests.

## Secondary Data Sources

Secondary data sources, as noted earlier, are data collected or extracted from a primary data source and used for purposes other than their original intended use. For example, the primary purpose for creating an emergency department record is to deliver patient care and document care rendered by the staff. Data extracted from emergency department records for a trauma registry are an example of secondary data. Secondary data sources are frequently maintained in registries, databases, or indexes. Healthcare organizations maintain a number of secondary data sources including internal and external secondary data.

### Internal Secondary Data

Internal secondary data are frequently data an HIM professional or other authorized staff abstracts from a primary record and enters into registries, indexes, and databases. Historically, organizations needed these secondary sources because primary data sources were in paper format, making it difficult to identify, retrieve, aggregate, and analyze data. For example, trying to locate the data of all patients who had an acute myocardial infarction during a specific period without the aid of an index or registry would require the daunting task of searching through thousands of paper health records. The answer to this dilemma in the paper world was to extract and store a small set of pertinent and structured data from primary sources to make it easier to retrieve and aggregate data for analysis purposes. Even though today a significant percentage of primary source data is digital, extraction of data for secondary use is still common, particularly for unstructured data. Until better methods are available for content, metadata, and master data management for identifying and retrieving data, organizations will continue to use a variety of secondary data sources.

Common internal secondary data sources include **disease and operation indexes**, and physician indexes. Typically, these indexes include a health record number, demographic information, admission and discharge dates, physician identifier, and International Classification of Diseases (ICD) diagnostic and procedural codes. Today, these indexes are normally generated as a byproduct of the integration of diagnostic and procedural encoding systems with EHR systems. These types of indexes allow retrieval of patient records by diagnosis and procedural codes or physician identifier. From these records analysts can generate descriptive statistics, such as length of stay by gender, age, and diagnosis and can make comparisons among groups of patients by diagnosis or procedure or physician.

Healthcare institutions may also maintain a number of registries. Registries differ from indexes because they usually contain more extensive and descriptive information and require abstracting unstructured data manually from the patient health record and other sources. Some examples of common registries are trauma, cancer, birth defects, diabetes, implant, transplant, and immunization registries. Abstracted unstructured data are usually collected by analysts and put in a structured format in an electronic database or paper form. Figure 11.1 provides a sample of the discrete data a healthcare institution may collect for an immunization registry. Because registries include structured data, they are a good source for analytic activities.

Figure 11.1. Example of structured content for an immunization registry

Patient last name: ____________________
Patient first name: ____________________
Patient middle name: ____________________
Patient's sex: ____________________
Patient's birthdate and country of birth: ____________________
Mother's last name: ____________________
Mother's first name: ____________________
Mother's middle name: ____________________
Mother's maiden name: ____________________
Vaccine type: ____________________
Vaccine manufacturer: ____________________
Vaccination date: ____________________
Vaccine lot number: ____________________



## External Secondary Data

Hospitals and other healthcare delivery organizations rely on and use secondary data from a number of sources. Among these are population-based data from public health agencies, pharmaceutical data, and data from federal government entities such as the Centers for Medicare and Medicaid Services (CMS), the Centers for Disease Control and Prevention (CDC), the National Center for Health Statistics (NCHS), and the Agency for Healthcare Research and Quality (AHRQ). An excellent site for a description of and access to a number of publically available federal data sets is the Research Data Assistance Center sponsored by the University of Minnesota. This site describes over 40 data sets that are available for research and benchmarking use.

In addition to these, healthcare organizations may also use any number of secondary data sources for comparison purposes. Some of these are aggregate data from primary data sources while others fall into the category of reference data or benchmarking data. Besides secondary sources that are of a clinical nature, other data sets are used for administrative decision making and evaluation such as marketing, performance, and financial benchmarking. A sample of these is provided in figure 11.2.

Figure 11.2. Examples of data sets used for decision making and benchmarking

- **Medicare Provider Analysis and Review** (MedPAR). The data source contains data from claims for services provided to beneficiaries admitted to Medicare-certified inpatient hospitals and skilled nursing facilities (SNF). MedPAR data is useful for tracking inpatient history and patterns or outcomes of care over time and for studying chronic disease prevalent in elderly populations such as cancer, heart disease, and diabetes. Data of death information is appended and can be used for mortality studies.
- **Outpatient Standard Analytic File** (SAF) and **Outpatient Prospective Payment System (OPPS) Data**. The outpatient SAF contains all institutional outpatient claims filed on the UB-04 form. The OPPS file contains only those claims paid under the prospective payment system (PPS).
- **National Practitioner Databank** (NPDB). The NPDB is a comprehensive database of the professional credentials of healthcare practitioners, healthcare entities, providers, and suppliers that includes data on medical malpractice payments, adverse licensure actions, and certain other professional review actions.
- National Ambulatory Care Surveys. Consists of two surveys. One is **The National Ambulatory Medical Care Survey** (NAMCS) which is designed for gathering objective, reliable information about the provision and use of ambulatory medical care services in the United States. The second is **The National Hospital Ambulatory Medical Care Survey** (NHAMCS) which is designed to collect data on the utilization and provision of ambulatory care services in hospital emergency and outpatient departments and in ambulatory surgery centers. The data sets for the results of both surveys are available for download at the CDC website.
- **Healthcare Cost and Utilization Project** (HCUP). HCUP is composed of multiple databases that include the largest collection of longitudinal hospital care data in the United States. Organizations can use the data to evaluate cost and quality of health services, medical practice patterns, access to healthcare programs, and treatment outcomes.
- **Hospital Compare.** Hospital Compare reports on 94 measures of hospital quality of care for heart attack, heart failure, pneumonia, and prevention of surgical infections.
- The **Leapfrog Group**. The Leapfrog Group collects and distributes data through the Leapfrog Hospital Survey. This is a voluntary program and any hospital is eligible to report data. The group reports data from the survey in the form of a scorecard on the Leapfrog website.

### *The St. Rita's Healthcare System Case Study*

Linda, Susan, and Fred met in the IT conference room and shared the information each had gathered thus far on BI. "I didn't realize the volume and variety of data that exists for potential analytic purposes," said Linda after Susan's wrap up on healthcare data.

"I only scratched the surface, but I think this provides the EIM team with a big-picture view of the analytic challenges at St. Rita's," responded Susan.

"I keep recalling your advice to us, Susan, that the best first step is to zero-in on developing a plan to build the organization's analytic capabilities over time around key strategic areas," Fred observed.

"That's a key takeaway we must emphasize when we give our presentation to the entire team," Linda added.

"This is a good introduction to what we've found," Fred said. "I'll go next and share what I've put together on the continuum of BI functions. I think it fits perfectly with an iterative approach to developing BI capabilities."

## Data for Decisions

The primary purpose of BI is to take raw data and change it into active information for the purpose of decision making that enables effective action and supports establishing and achieving business goals (Rajteric 2010). A key success to BI is good data management practice that ensures availability, access, and the means to extract good data as well as using methods for analysis that supplies useful information. These aspects of BI are examined in this section.

## Decision Making Levels

"Good data" refers to the quality of the data and its "fitness" for supporting a variety of decision levels. BI functions must accommodate the continuum of decision-making levels from those that are operational and day-to-day to those that are strategic, look far into the future, and are complex and risky. Decisions made along the continuum have separate data needs and are examined below. To realize the usefulness of BI functions, it is necessary to understand what type of data organizations need to make decisions and how these relate to organizational levels of decision making. Figure 11.3 provides a typical representation of decision-making levels within an organization.

Figure 11.3. Continuum of decision making levels

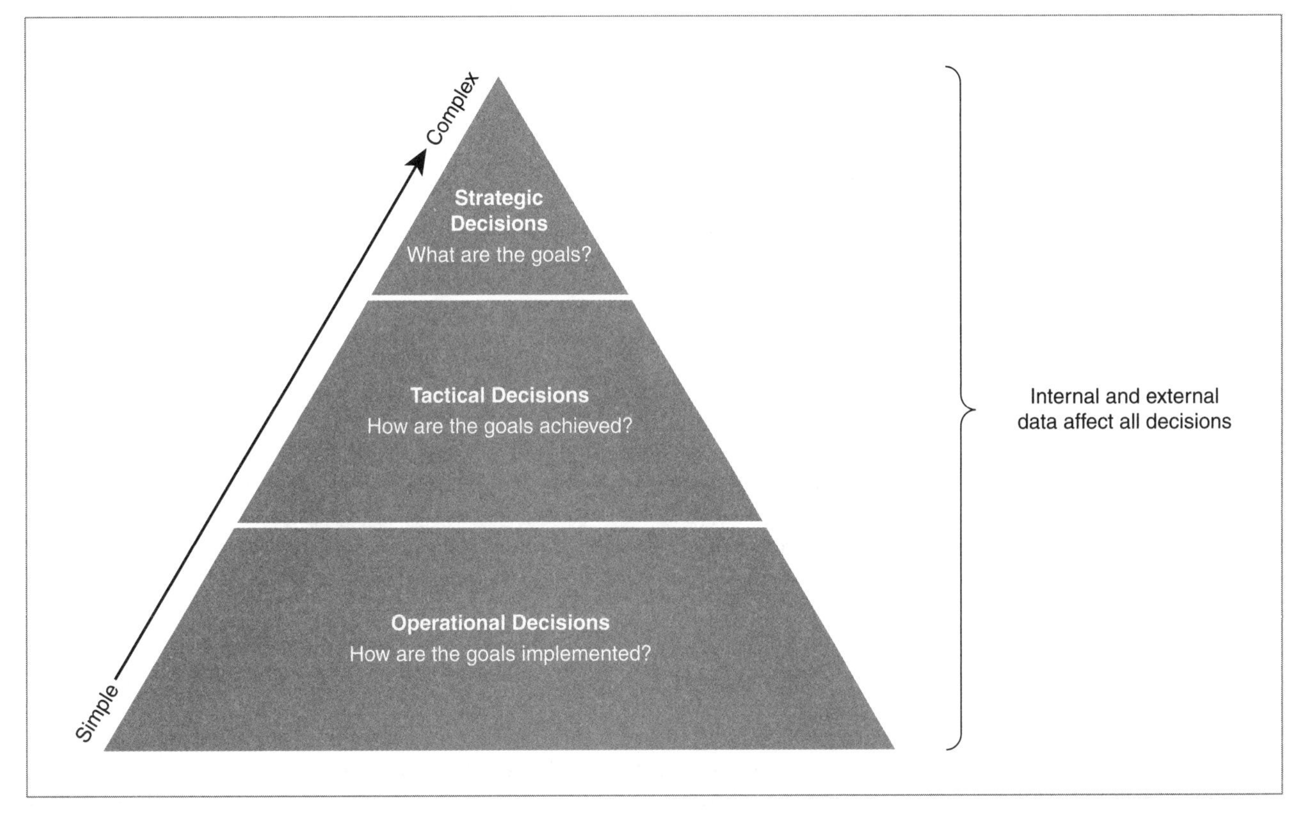




As expressed in figure 11.3, at the top of the pyramid are decisions that set the strategic direction of the organization. These decisions require complex data analysis of external and internal data.

In **strategic decision making,** executives make decisions about the strategic direction of the organization and set the goals they want to achieve. Strategic goals are futuristic and determine the long range direction of an organization. An example of a strategic goal for a healthcare system might include expanding the current market to a wider geographic area.

Setting strategy involves complex decision making. Organizations require advanced analytical techniques and predictive models to analyze the volume and diversity of data to gain insights and knowledge for making complex decisions. Internal as well as external information is necessary for strategic decisions. Information that provides knowledge about key marketplace drivers and competitors offers a broad picture of the environmental landscape and pinpoints current status of internal operations. These provide the foundation for strategic decision making. Usually, information at this level is aggregated by analysts and provides summary, predictive, and trend data.

**Tactical decision making** is the next level in the decision pyramid. The type of information needed for tactical decisions is different than information required at strategic decision-making levels. At the tactical level, organizations develop plans to determine how they will achieve their strategic direction. Decisions at this level are made within business units. For instance, communications and marketing, patient-care services, information technology, health information management (HIM), and finance may be viewed as business units. From a tactical decision-making standpoint, these units are concerned with what approaches should be implemented within their units to achieve the organization's strategic goals. If the strategic goal is to increase performance through data-driven decision making, then each of these units would adopt approaches to further that goal. The HIM unit might use benchmarking data and historical operational data to assess its ICD coding productivity and capacity, or it might use operational data and predictive modeling to determine staffing skill set and staffing number depending on increases or decreases in patient mix and patient days. Information commonly used for tactical decisions includes descriptive and inferential analyses and comparative data. Processes are monitored by the manager using dashboards, which are described later in this chapter. Organizations use key performance indicators to compare their current state with their strategic goals.

**Operational decision making** involves the day-to-day or routine decisions that keep the organization running. Operational decisions are frequently codified in procedures or business rules. Making decisions on requests for release of patient information, assigning a primary diagnosis code, determining how to triage a patient in the emergency department, and making daily nursing staff decisions are examples of operational decisions. While some operational decisions are determined solely by business rules, others rely on a combination of business rules and current data, usually in the form of reports and descriptive data. For example, a business rule might state that when the occupancy rate exceeds a certain percentage for a unit, additional nursing staff must be available to the unit. The data for this operational decision requires current data on percentage of occupancy by unit, current nursing allocation, and a listing of available personnel who could be assigned to the unit. Operational decisions such as this are becoming increasingly automated.

## Access and Reporting

At the most foundational level, BI includes access to data and the ability to analyze that data. There are a variety of tools for assisting end users in accessing data and standard reports, designing their own reports, and performing a variety of analyses. Individual users have different needs for data access, analysis, presentation, and visualization. For BI to be effective, BI tools should accommodate individual user needs. There are a variety of ways to access and use data including static reports, ad hoc reports, dashboards, scorecards, embedded BI, interactive fixed reports, and write-back reports.

- **Static reports**: Reports with a fixed layout with data variables defined by a business analyst or report designer. Users generate these reports on request, then they automatically refresh periodically, or embed in an application program.
- **Ad hoc reports**: Reports generated by manipulation and exploration of data by analysts and produced on an as-needed basis by them. Ad hoc reports are usually used one time to answer a single, specific question.
- **Dashboard**: Produces reports focusing on operational information. A data visualization function displays the current (real time) status of pre-defined metrics and key performance indicators for an enterprise or business unit on a single screen. A dashboard can include both static and interactive reports, graphs, charts, and illustrations.
- **Performance scorecard**: Report focusing on long-term operational, tactical, or strategic goals. A data visualization function displays progress over time in meeting specific goals.
- **Scoreboard**: Report which combines dashboard and performance functions on one screen.
- **Embedded BI:** Reports, dashboards, scorecards, and alerts are embedded into application programs and integrated into work flow so that end users do not have to access separate BI programs for each report.
- **Interactive fixed reports**: Reports having a fixed design with data variables defined by a business analyst or report designer. They usually provide general information with dynamic drill-down, slicing, dicing, and filtering functions. The end user generated these on request or they refresh periodically.
- **Write-back reports**: Interactive reports directly linking to the data warehouse that allow modification of the data.

The variety of report types requires careful planning so end users have the right tool (report) to support their work. For example, front line workers might have static reports or embedded BI reporting available to them, but not ad hoc reporting functions. Figure 11.4 provides an illustration of the relationship of use between report category and decision type.

Figure 11.4. Frequency of use of BI reports by decision type

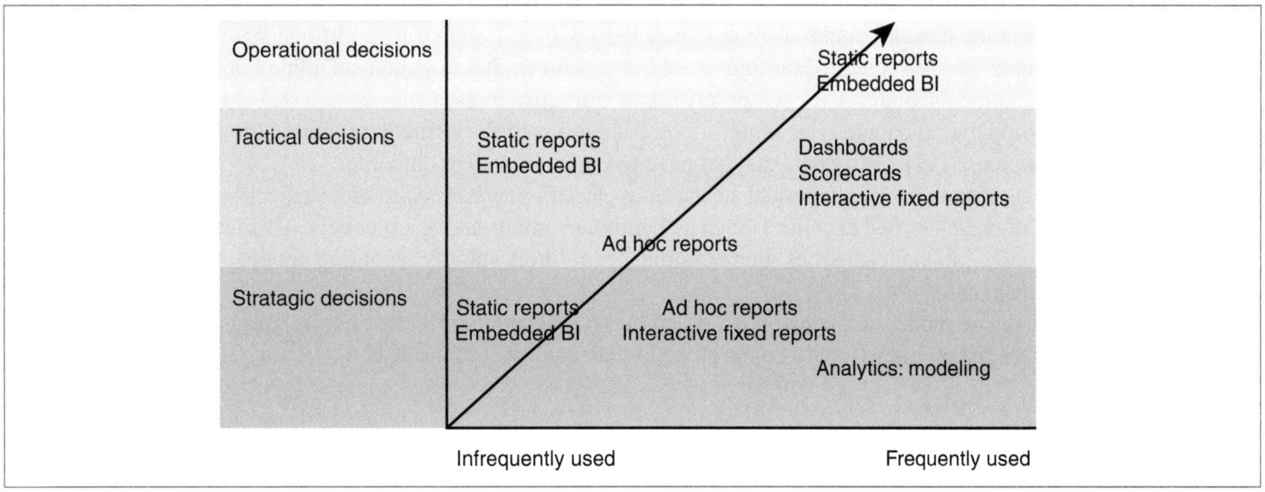

Operational decisions
Static reports
Embedded BI
Tactical decisions
Static reports
Embedded BI
Dashboards
Scorecards
Interactive fixed reports
Ad hoc reports
Stratagic decisions
Static reports
Embedded BI
Ad hoc reports
Interactive fixed reports
Analytics: modeling
Infrequently used
Frequently used

©Merida L. Johns

## Analytic Approaches

The definition of analytics may vary in the marketplace and among BI vendors. Analytics in the context of BI is defined as "the extensive use of data, statistical and quantitative analysis, explanatory and predictive models, and fact-based management to drive decisions and actions" (Davenport and Harris 2007, 7). There is a difference between reports and analytics, however. Organizations use the reports noted earlier most frequently for tactical and operational decision making. Those reports are based on specific questions like

- What is the current status?
- What happened?
- What are the problems or bottlenecks?
- What requires action?

Analytics, on the other hand, extract knowledge from large data sources (rather than humans posing direct queries) and answer strategic questions like

- Why is this happening?
- What if these trends continue?
- What will happen next?
- What's the best outcome?

A process called **data mining** helps answer these questions. Data mining involves applying artificial intelligence, machine learning, and statistics to large data sets to discover patterns in the data. There are two principal models in data mining: descriptive and predictive. **Descriptive analytics** describes patterns in data that were previously unknown, for example, answering the question "Why is this happening?" **Predictive analytics** uses data with known results to develop a model to explicitly predict values, for example answering the question "What will happen next?"

Finding patterns in data is interesting but not necessarily useful. For example, a healthcare system may find at two of its clinics upper middle-class patients who live in the same zip code frequently use the clinics. This is an interesting finding, but what should the healthcare system do with this knowledge? Should it open more clinics in that zip code? Should it open similar clinics in other zip codes with the same patient demographic? Or, should it tap into an entirely different market, say, of middle-class people, where clinics are not available? Without further information about market saturation or the presence of other clinics in zip codes where upper middle-class people live or work, the healthcare system cannot make an informed decision. Predictive analytics provides additional information to help make these kinds of decisions. Examples of types of descriptive and predictive analytics include

- **Anomaly detection**: Identifies outliers or unusual cases in a supposed homogeneous set of data. For example, an analyst could develop a model of typical medical claims and, using anomaly detection, identify cases that do not fit the model. These outliers could potentially identify medical claims fraud.

- **Association learning**: Association rules are "if/then" statements. Association rules are developed by examining a data set for frequent if/then (association) patterns. Using other statistical analyses such as determining how frequently the items appear in the database and how many times the associations are true, an if/then statement is developed by the system or an analyst. Association learning is used in recommendation systems. Online book sellers use this type of analytics to recommend additional book purchases to their customers.
- **Cluster detection**: Divides data into meaningful groups based on the information found in the data set. For example, clustering might be used to identify patients that have the same treatment outcomes.
- **Classification**: Uses an existing categorical structure to classify new cases into the categories. The computer learns from a large set of pre-classified examples, such as legitimate emails and spam emails. This learning is then applied to classify new cases into the categories. For example, spam filters classify incoming emails into a legitimate email category and a spam category.
- **Regression**: Predictive models are constructed based on several variables. For example, using a variety of variables, a model for patient risk mortality could be developed by an analyst (Furnas 2012).

# Business Intelligence Maturity Models

Most BI efforts take years to fully develop. This is due to many factors, some of which include lack of continuous executive support for BI development, poor strategy, data quality and integration barriers, data complexity, absence of technological infrastructure, and development costs (Manos 2014). The development of BI is often explained by a **maturity model** that describes the successive steps of growth and development of BI technologies and processes along a continuum that goes from simpler to more complex functions and technologies. A maturity model is a framework an organization uses to compare its capabilities to the stages of development of a process, in this case BI development. Different phases are identified within a maturity model, each consisting of key processes.

Implementing BI is not an easy undertaking. Not only are there technical challenges, but there are cultural and organizational challenges as well. Comparing against a maturity model helps organizations assess where they are in the BI continuum from technical and organizational views, how they can improve, and answers the following questions:

- Where in the organization is most of the reporting and business analysis done today?
- Who uses business reports, analysis, and success indicators?
- What drives BI in the organization?
- Which strategies for developing BI are in use today?
- What business value does BI bring (Rajteric 2010, 50)?

There are several BI maturity models available. Many of these have been developed by vendors, consultants, and recognized experts in the field. Given this, the perspective expressed in some models often mirrors the preferences or viewpoints of the authors, while others are research-based. While none of the models are perfect, they do provide a starting point for an organization to evaluate its position or readiness for BI (Rajteric 2010).

As an example, the TDWI Business Intelligence Maturity Model has six stages including

- *Prenatal Stage.* Focus on departmental and operational system-produced static reports. There is lack of customization to meet manager's needs.
- *Infant Stage.* Managers develop their own data sets stored in spreadsheets and desktop databases, resulting in fragmented data sources, metrics, and rules throughout the organization. This prevents a consistent view of the total organization.
- *Child Stage.* Interactive reporting tools are implemented by the organization, and analytical systems are put in place with ad hoc reporting. The system has the capacity to analyze trends and historical data. The emphasis is understanding past business actions.
- *Teenager Stage.* Analysts in separate departments oversee BI management for their departments under the direction of a BI program manager. They use a common data model and platform for BI with a centralized data warehouse. This allows analysts the ability to perform analysis on an enterprise-wide level. Departmental dashboards are implemented with key performance indicators. Interactive reporting and analysis is available to managers throughout the organization.
- *Adult Stage.* BI becomes a central driving force of operations. Dashboards help monitor processes while key performance indicators evaluate current status against strategic goals. BI management becomes centralized. Common data warehouse architecture is integrated in real time to data sources. Language and metric rules are standardized. Use of prediction and modeling tools is introduced. A separate BI team reports directly to executive management.

- *Sage Stage.* There is centralized management of the data warehouse for all enterprise data, with federated management and development in business units. Business units are empowered to deliver BI capabilities and services. BI is embedded in core processes and becomes an integral part of achieving business strategy and capitalizing on market opportunities (Eckerson 2007).

Another maturity model separates BI evolution into three phases (Chen et al. 2012). In the first phase, data are predominately in a structured format, collected by legacy systems, and stored in relational databases. This phase is further developed by using data warehouses and designing and using smaller, specialized databases, called data marts, and by tools for converting and integrating enterprise-wide data. Functionalities include database query, online analytical processing (OLAP), and simple reporting tools and graphics. Scorecards and dashboards are also implemented. Statistical analysis, data mining techniques, and predictive modeling are used, as well.

While the first phase focuses on structured data, the second evolutionary phase moves into using unstructured and web-based content for BI analysis. This phase requires mature techniques in text mining, web mining, and social network analyses. The third phase takes BI to a higher level that adds mobile and sensor-based content to the data sources for BI analysis. The richness of knowledge in the healthcare sector achieved with BI in the third phase is promising for improving patient outcomes and care coordination and advancing innovation. Specifically, big data from genomics, EHRs, and health and patient social media will likely have the greatest impact in human genomics, healthcare decision support, and patient community analysis (Chen et al. 2012).

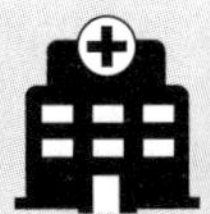

**The St. Rita's Healthcare System Case Study**

"Super job," said Susan at the BI sub-team's next meeting. "I think you nailed the high points. Using a maturity model is a good foundation for developing a roadmap of next steps. I wonder, though, how thorough these maturity models are and if they are appropriate to use at St. Rita's?"

"Glad you brought that up, Susan. I found some good academic research that essentially said all the models are somewhat lacking because each comes from a specific perspective. One researcher suggested reviewing all models and then using a 'mix-and-match' approach to arrive at a model that fits the organization's needs [Rajteric 2010]. But that is probably premature to do right now," said Fred.

"I found your information on the analytics portion particularly instructive," commented Linda. "I'm not a numbers geek, so this overview was helpful. Thanks for not getting too far into the weeds with it. What it pointed out to me is that analytics is more than reports. There is a tremendous amount of planning necessary to match the right data to the right people and right type of decision making. And there has to be a well thought out strategy to analytics. It's just not fishing around to find interesting patterns. It has to be purposeful," Linda added.

"OK, your turn, Linda," said Fred. "I want to learn more about the data life cycle and architecture and technology that we need to put in place for BI."

# Business Intelligence Data Life Cycle

The BI data life cycle is a four-stage process: data acquisition, data cleaning, data organization and storage, and data maintenance (Davenport and Harris 2007). Linda decided to use this framework to organize a presentation to Fred and Susan because it naturally coincided with life cycle concepts associated in other areas the EIM team studied and because it is relatively straightforward and easy to understand.

## Data Acquisition

The BI data life cycle begins with **data acquisition**, or, the creation or procurement of data. For example, will data be used for strategic, tactical, or operational decision making? This initial choice determines not only what data to collect, but also how to technically manage and deliver it. Once the organization chooses general categories of decision making it wants BI to support, then it must address additional questions. For instance, if BI is deployed for tactical decision making, the question posed may be, "What domains or functional areas, such as patient-care services, marketing, finance, or others, should we include in the effort?" Drilling down further, the next question is, "What are the specific BI goals for each of the functional areas?"

Addressing these questions leads to identifying the necessary data sources to support the BI goals. These might include internal transaction data residing in relational databases, master data and reference data sources, unstructured data residing in digital files, or external data sources.

## Data Cleansing and Transformation

It has been said that the lion's share of the work in any BI effort is the preparation and processing of the data (DAMA 2010, 230). Data quality issues abound in both internal and external data sources, and remain one of the biggest challenges to BI efforts across all industries (Gartner 2008). **Data cleansing** is defined as the process of checking internal consistency and duplication, as well as identifying outliers and missing data in data sources. It involves correcting and enhancing the values of individual data elements, including the enforcement of standards (DAMA 2010, 231). Specifically, data cleansing includes detecting and removing data that is out of date, incorrect, incomplete, or redundant. Organizations spend between 25 and 30 percent of a BI effort on initial data cleansing (Davenport and Harris 2007, 164).

Data problems exist in data sources for a variety of reasons, such as misspellings, missing data, incomplete data, and incorrect data. Data quality problems are compounded when multiple data sources need to be integrated for BI purposes. Not only do data problems exist in each system, but when combined from multiple sources, the sources often include redundant data, contradicting records, and data that are represented differently. BI activities usually need multiple data sources. Therefore, the data problems can be extensive.

To identify data problems, organizations use **discrepancy detection** methods. Metadata can identify discrepancies. If the data values do not fit the attributes of the metadata, then there is a potential data problem. For example, if a data value exceeds the maximum range of an attribute, it likely indicates a data quality problem. Descriptive summaries of the data are also used to identify data problems. Descriptive summaries of the data are developed by using measures of central tendency such as mean, median, and mode, and statistical techniques that analyze a data source.

After identifying data problems, routines, referred to as **data transformations**, can be used to fill in missing values, smooth incorrect attribute values, identify and remove outliers, and resolve inconsistencies (Han et al. 2006). This is referred to as transformation of the data. Data transformations are made using commercial tools, extract-transform-load (ETL). However, taking care to ensure the transformations do not introduce additional errors is essential. Many times, the analytic team must develop specific scripts based on their knowledge about the data source being used to transform the data.

## Data Integration

Usually, organizations use multiple data sources in data mining and BI. The data sources need to be integrated, but this is not necessarily an easy task because of differences in naming attributes and data models, and redundancies in instances of entities. Therefore, there are several issues to address before integrating data from multiple data sources. One of these has to do with entity identification issues (Han et al. 2006). **Entity identification** matches data with the right entity and entity attributes. Varying gender descriptions are an example of attribute value differences. For instance, one data source represent gender numerically using 1, 2, and 3, while another source represents gender as M, F, and U, and yet another source represents the same attribute as Male, Female, and Unknown. Such differences must be reconciled before beginning data integration.

**Attribute redundancy** is another problem. This is where a data source may have multiple records for the same entity. Redundancies in the master patient index are examples of this problem. As discussed in chapter 8, there are various ways to identify and rectify record redundancies. Using various statistical techniques such as correlations can help resolve the issue.

Another integration concern is detecting and resolving value conflicts. **Value conflicts** happen when multiple data sources use different metrics as data values. An example of a potential value conflict is the use of pounds versus kilograms. The following is a summary of transformation processes.

- *Smoothing:* Techniques to identify trends in the data and remove data that deviate from the trend or pattern. Data smoothing is used to predict trends. As an example, a healthcare administrator might use smoothing to predict the trend in outpatient visits over a period of time.
- *Aggregation:* Summary (or aggregation) operations are applied to the data. For example, an analyst may aggregate inpatient claims to compute monthly and annual amounts.

- *Generalization:* Higher-level concepts replace primitive (or, raw) data using concept hierarchies. For example attributes, such as specific ICD codes, can be generalized to higher-level concepts or an attribute such as age can be mapped to higher-level concepts like child, adolescent, or adult.
- *Normalization:* Attribute data are scaled to fall within a small, specified range. For example, the salaries and ages of five employees might be normalized to fall within a range of 0 to 1. Normalization improves the performance of data mining algorithms and provides results that are easier to interpret.
- *Attribute reconstruction:* New attributes are constructed and added from the given set of attributes to help the mining process (Han et al. 2006, 70). This technique, for example, is often used to protect sensitive attributes for privacy purposes.

## Data Reduction

Large, complex data require enormous processing power for analysis. The solution is compressing or reducing data, yielding an approximate set of data that maintains the integrity of the original data set. This is called **data reduction**. Data mining on the reduced set of data produces results equally as good as mining on the original data sources. There are various techniques to accomplish reduction.

## Data Repositories

After identifying, extracting, cleansing, and transforming data, they need to be maintained in a repository. Normally this is the data warehouse. A **data warehouse** is a special type of database that has a single data model optimized for data analytics and extracts and stores selected data from one or more operational databases for the purpose of analytics decision support. Typically, data in a data warehouse are historical in nature. The characteristics of a data warehouse are explained further here:

- **Subject-oriented**: The data warehouse is organized around major subjects, such as customer, supplier, product, and sales. In the case of healthcare, the subjects might include patient, provider, insurer, and so on.
- **Integrated**: A data warehouse is constructed by integrating multiple heterogeneous sources, such as relational databases, flat files, and on-line transaction records. Data cleansing and integration ensure consistency in naming conventions, encoding structures, and attribute measures.
- **Time-variant**: Data are stored to provide information from a historical perspective (for example, the past 5 to 10 years). Every key structure in the data warehouse contains, either implicitly or explicitly, an element in time (such as a time stamp). The data warehouse is a historical record of snapshots in time.
- **Nonvolatile**: A data warehouse is always a physically separate store of data transformed from the application found in the operational environment. Due to this separation it does not require transaction processing, recovery, or concurrency controls. It usually only requires two data operations: initial loading of data and access of data (Han and Kamber 2006, 106).

Operational databases differ from data warehouses. The major task of an operational database is to perform online transactions and queries. It processes the day-to-day transactions that keep a business running. Hospital examples of operational systems include making a patient appointment, registering a patient, ordering a medication, assigning a bed, scheduling an operating room, and processing a claim. Operational systems are referred to as **online transaction processing** (OLTP) systems. Transaction databases usually have relational or hierarchal database designs. A data warehouse, in contrast, focuses on data analysis and not day-to-day operations. The database design of a data warehouse is typically a star or snowflake model and is a subject-oriented design. Data warehouse systems are referred to as **online analytical processing** (OLAP) systems.

Data marts, as noted earlier, support a specific business unit or functional area. A data mart can be a separate repository or a partitioned section of the data warehouse. Typically, data marts contain predetermined analysis that managers use to further probe in different ways.

A **metadata repository**, a specialized database for storing metadata, is essential to a data warehouse. In this context, metadata repositories store metadata that describe data warehouse objects. Metadata include data names and definitions as well as timestamps for extracted data and identification of the data source of extracted data. Specifically, the metadata repository should include

- A description of the data warehouse schema (data model), view, dimensions, hierarchies and derived data definitions, as well as data mart locations and content
- Operational metadata which include data lineage, currency of data, and monitoring information
- Algorithms used for summarization

- Mapping from the operational environment to the data warehouse which includes source databases and their contents, gateway descriptions, data partitions, data extraction, cleaning, transformation rules and defaults, data refresh and purging rules, and user authorization and access control
- Data related to system performance such as indexes and profiles that improve data access and retrieval performance and rules for the timing and scheduling of refresh, update, and replication cycles
- Business metadata, which include business terms and definitions, and data ownership information (Han and Kamber 2006, 134)

# Business Intelligence Architecture

There are two predominant architecture models for BI. They are the model developed by Ralph Kimball, called the **Kimball Method**, and the model developed by Bill Inmon and Claudia Inhoff, called the **Corporate Information Factory** (CIF). The approaches differ in their philosophies, design, and implementation. The Kimball Method, often referred to as a "bottom-up" approach, suggests starting with several data marts to serve the needs of specific business units and then to "virtually" integrate these data marts. While this approach may provide quick returns from a departmental viewpoint, it also is problematic because redundant and siloed data marts easily develop. Thus, data consistency throughout the enterprise is potentially lost.

The CIF proposes starting with a single, centralized enterprise-wide data warehouse. Feeding data from the centralized data warehouse to satellite and dependent data marts serves the needs of specific business units. This is often referred to as a "top-down" approach. This approach uses a relational database for structuring the data. The centralized approach provides an enterprise-wide view of the data and diminishes data inconsistency throughout the enterprise, but it is a complex undertaking usually taking several years to implement. The CIF is described in figure 11.5.

Figure 11.5. Schematic of BI architecture

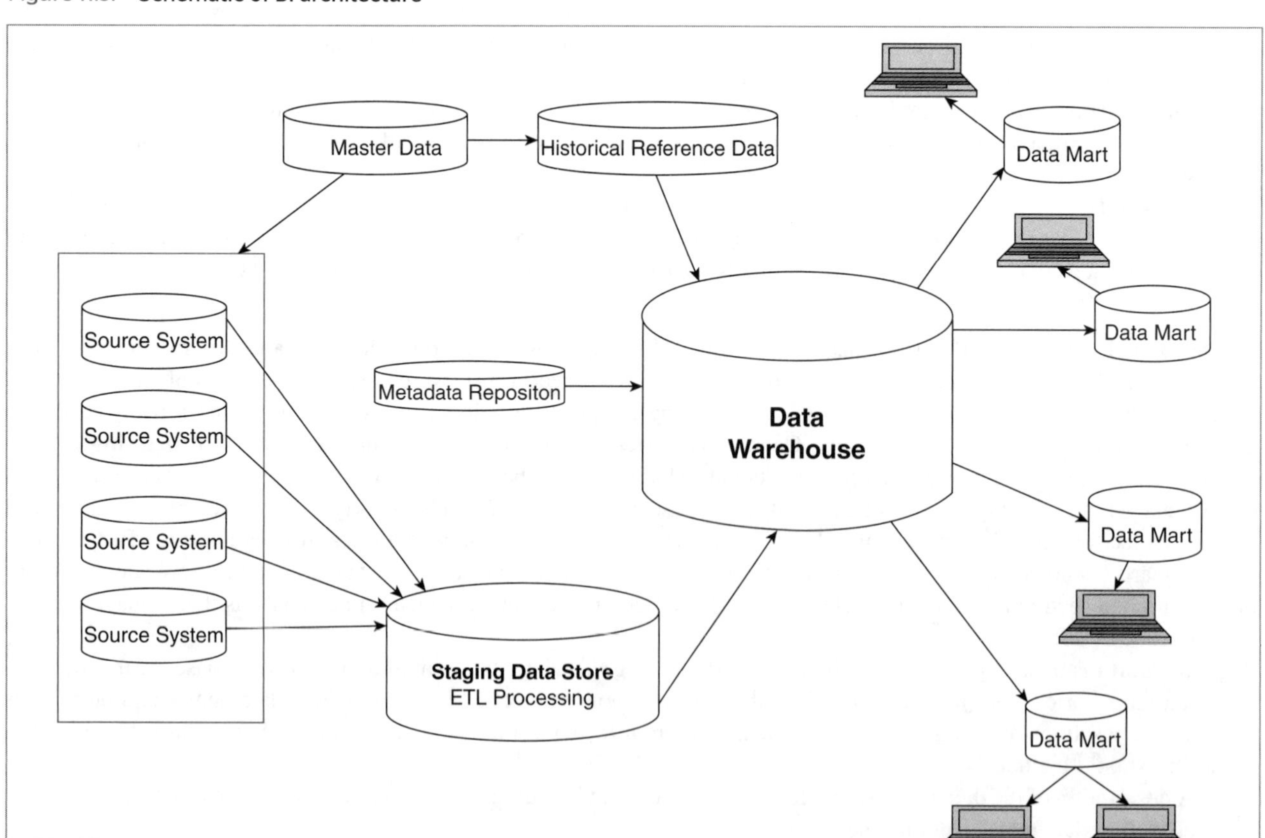

Here, data are extracted from the operational source systems into a **staging area** where the data are "prepped" or prepared for use and placement in a centralized data warehouse. The staging area functions include data extraction and data cleansing from each data source, data integration from the various data sources, and data aggregation. As noted earlier, these processes taken together are referred to as ETL.

Specific domain data are loaded into data marts from the centralized data warehouse to support the needs of a specific business unit. Data marts in this model may be physical storage areas separate from the data warehouse, or they may be defined by a semantic layer on top of the data warehouse to provide a data mart view to specific business units. Three other repositories are associated with a centralized data warehouse. These include the master data repository, the historical reference data repository, and a metadata repository. The master data repository contains the organization's master data, such as patient, vendor, and provider data, while the historical reference data repository contains reference data. Access to these repositories provides a method for helping to ensure the consistency and data quality in the data warehouse. Both of these are examined in chapters 6 and 7.

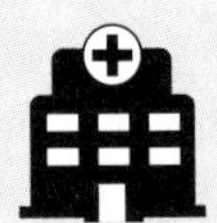

### The St. Rita's Healthcare System Case Study

Susan and Fred applauded Linda on her review of BI lifecycle and architecture. "This clears up a lot for me," said Fred. "I get the big picture of the data warehousing process, how data are extracted from source systems, like human resources, finance, materials management, and patient care and then go to a staging repository where the data are cleansed, transformed, and integrated before passing on into the data warehouse. Your descriptions of transaction system and a data warehouse are also good. The data warehouse is a snapshot in time, processing lots of data for making non-routine decisions."

"An important point you emphasized, Linda, was how other domains within EIM support the BI effort," Susan offered. "For example, the enterprise data model is important for identification of entities, and business metadata are important in several ways, but particularly in data cleansing. Master data are essential too, because they are considered source records."

"A critical element is that strategy has to come before action," added Linda. "One point that was repeated throughout the literature I read was that BI development is an iterative process. Organizations should not bite off more than they can chew. The BI effort needs to be developed incrementally and it's got to be built on a strong business case and most importantly end user needs."

Linda, Fred, and Susan then went to work on identifying DG activities associated with BI.

## Applying Data Governance

Linda, Fred, and Susan broadly identified BI DG functions as the following and included these in the EIM deliverable chart (table 11.1):

- Assess organizational and stakeholders needs
- Develop and implement BI roadmap to meet organizational goals
- Develop accountability and reporting structure
- Define BI architecture
- Develop policies, procedures, and standards ensuring data security and quality and oversight of the BI data lifecycle
- Develop and maintain schema and metadata

Table 11.1. DG deliverables by EIM function

| Data Governance | Data Architecture Management | Metadata Management | Master Data Management | Content Management | Data Security and Privacy Management | Business Intelligence Management | Data Quality Management | Terminology and Classification Management |
|---|---|---|---|---|---|---|---|---|
| Identify mission and scope | Develop and maintain data models | Develop policies, procedures, and standards | Identify master and reference data requirements | Develop roadmap for content management | Identify and classify sensitive data across enterprise systems | Assess organization and stakeholder needs | | |
| Establish goals and success measures | Develop, maintain, and evaluate data model policies and standards | Ensure metadata meets functional requirements | Develop policies, procedures, and standards for management of master data | Develop policies and procedures for content management | Develop data security and privacy policies and standards | Develop BI roadmap to meet organization goals | | |
| Put in place DG structure, processes, and communications plan | Define roles, responsibilities, and accountabilities for data architecture management | Develop and maintain appropriate metadata schema | Establish master data definitions, validation, and verification levels for master data quality | Apply taxonomies, thesauri, ontologies and other content management classifications | Meet compliance and regulatory security and privacy requirements | Develop accountability and reporting structure | | |
| Secure funding | Develop, maintain, and evaluate policies and standards for requirements analysis | Ensure metadata capture, maintenance, distribution, and integration | Ensure master and reference data meet regulatory requirements, including lineage history and security | Develop policies and procedures that ensure legal and regulatory mandates are met | Assess risk and identify controls to manage risk | Develop policies, procedures, and standards for data security and quality, and monitor them | | |
| Establish decision rights | Develop and maintain data artifacts and standards | Ensure metadata security | Establish audit procedures and standards for master data | Establish standards and audit procedures | Perform data security and privacy audits and report findings | Define BI architecture | | |
| Identify accountabilities | Establish quality control program and metrics for data architecture management | Develop and implement quality controls for metadata | Identify stakeholders and establish decision rights and accountabilities | Implement stewardship processes over the content management life cycle | Develop and implement data privacy and security awareness and training | Develop and maintain schema and metadata | | |

## Part of the Team: Topics for Discussion and Action

1. The EIM team will have to develop a business case for BI activities at St. Rita's. To help them do this, develop a preliminary business case draft. The business case should include the following elements:
   a. Description of BI
   b. Drivers for conducting BI
   c. Anticipated benefits of BI
   d. Case examples that demonstrate benefits of BI

## Advanced Concepts

1. The EIM team discussed the importance of evaluating St. Rita's current position in regard to a BI maturity model. However, all agreed that no current BI maturity model is perfect. One of the first steps

in addressing the BI functions within the EIM program at St. Rita's is to assess current maturity and capability. Review the article by Rajteric titled "Overview of Business Intelligence Maturity Models" in the *Journal of Contemporary Management Issues* Volume 15, Number 1. After review of the author's assessments, develop a draft maturity model that incorporates what you believe are the best elements from all the evaluated models. Explain how St. Rita's can use the maturity model you developed to assess their capability and maturity.

## References


Amatayakul, M. 2012. *Electronic Health Records A Practical Guide for Professionals and Organizations*, 5th ed. Chicago: AHIMA Press.

American Medical Association (AMA). 2013. Testimony of the American Medical Association: Implementation and Usability of Certified Electronic Health Records. *Health IT Policy Committee's Workgroups on Certification/Adoption and Implementation.* July 23. http://www.healthit.gov/archive/archive_files/FACA%20Hearings/2013/2013-07-23%20Standards%3A%20Implementation,%20Meaningful%20Use,%20and%20Certification%20%26%20Adoption%20WGs,%20%20Implementation%20%26%20Usability%20Hearing/ama_usabilitytestimony_0.pdf.

Brynjolfsson, E., L.M. Hitt, and H.H. Kim. 2011. Strength in Numbers: How Does Data-Driven Decisionmaking Affect Firm Performance? http://ssrn.com/abstract=1819486 or http://dx.doi.org/10.2139/ssrn.1819486.

Chen, H., R. Chiang, V. Storey. 2012. Business intelligence and analytics: From big data to big impact. *Management Information Systems Quarterly* 36(4): 1165–1188.

DAMA. 2010. *The DAMA Guide to the Data Management Body of Knowledge*. Bradley Beach: Technics Publications, LLC.

Davenport, T., J. Harris. 2007. *Competing on Analytics: The New Science of Winning*. Boston: Harvard Business School Press.

Eckerson, W.W. 2007. Beyond the Basics: Accelerating BI Maturity. *TDWI Monograph Series.* http://download.101com.com/pub/tdwi/Files/SAP_monograph_0407.pdf.

Furnas, A. 2012 (April 3). Everything you wanted to know about data mining but were afraid to ask. *The Atlantic.* http://www.theatlantic.com/technology/archive/2012/04/everything-you-wanted-to-know-about-data-mining-but-were-afraid-to-ask/255388/.

Gartner. 2008 (January 22). Press Release: Gartner says organisations must establish data stewardship roles to improve data quality. http://www.gartner.com/newsroom/id/589207.

Han, J., and M. Kamber. 2006. *Data Mining: Concepts and Techniques*, 2nd ed. San Francisco: Morgan Kaufmann.

HIMSS. 2014. Healthcare IT News Index. http://www.healthcareitnews.com/directory/business-intelligence-bi.

Johnson, S.B., S. Bakken, D. Dine, S. Hyun, E. Mendonca, F. Morrison, T. Bright, T. Van Vleck, J. Wrenn, and P. Stetson. 2008. An electronic health record based on structured narrative. *Journal of the American Medical Informatics Association* 15(1): 54–64. http://www.ncbi.nlm.nih.gov/pmc/articles/PMC2274868/.

Kayyali, B., S. Van Kuiken, and D. Knott. 2013. The big-data revolution in US healthcare: Accelerating value and innovation. McKinsey & Company. http://www.mckinsey.com/insights/health_systems_and_services/the_big-data_revolution_in_us_health_care.

Kimball, S. and J. Luisi. 2013 (February 1). Architecture Made Easy, Part 14: Big Data and Data Administration: Data Modeling in the World of BigData. The Data Administration Newsletter. http://www.tdan.com/view-articles/16837.

Manos, D. 2014 (February 21). BI adoption pace slowed by skills gap. *Healthcare IT News.*

Manyika, J., M. Chui, B. Brown, J. Bughin, R. Dobbs, C. Roxburgh, A. Hung Byers. 2011 (June). Big data: The next frontier for innovation, competition, and productivity. *McKinsey Global Institute.* http://www.mckinsey.com/insights/business_technology/big_data_the_next_frontier_for_innovation.

Ponniah, P. 2010. *Data Warehousing Fundamentals for IT Professionals,* 2nd ed. Hoboken: John Wiley & Sons, Inc.

Rajteric, I.H. 2010. Overview of business intelligence maturity models. *Management: Journal of Contemporary Management Issues* 15(1): 47–67.

Resnik, P., M. Niv, M. Nossal, A. Kapit, and R. Toren. 2008. Communication of Clinically Relevant Information in Electronic Health Records: A Comparison between Structured Data and Unrestricted Physician Language. Proceedings of the Computer-Assisted Coding Conference, Perspectives in Health Information Management. http://perspectives.ahima.org/PDF/Finished/bok1_044316.pdf.

Steele, A.M. and M. DeBrow. 2008. Efficiency Gains with Computerized Provider Order Entry. In: Henriksen, K., J.B. Battles, M.A. Keyes, and M.L. Grady, eds. *Advances in Patient Safety: New Directions and Alternative Approaches (Vol. 4: Technology and Medication Safety).* Rockville,MD: Agency for Healthcare Research and Quality. http://www.ncbi.nlm.nih.gov/books/NBK43766/.

# Chapter 12

# Data Quality Management

"Beyond people themselves, the foundation of any company is the knowledge used to conduct business" (Dravis 2008, 12). The combined characteristics of data quality, such as data accuracy, completeness, consistency, currency, and timeliness, create trusted information. Making policy, developing strategic and operational plans, and essentially carrying out day-to-day company operations require trusted information. Without trusted information, the efficiency, effectiveness, productivity, and competitiveness of companies and organizations in any business sector severely diminish. A major concern confronting organizations across all business sectors today is the degree to which their data is trustworthy.

Historically, data quality issues have challenged organizations. More than 25 percent of critical data in Fortune 1000 companies include incomplete, inaccurate, or duplicate data, costing companies hundreds of billions of dollars a year (Swartz 2007). Another estimate puts the costs of poor quality business information at a staggering $250 billion (English 2009). The sheer size of the data explosion across business sectors only compounds these problems.

Like Fortune 1000 companies, healthcare enterprises suffer from data quality problems. A number of studies have linked poor quality data with medical errors and poor quality of care (Markle 2006). Replacing paper medical records with electronic health records (EHRs) has not been a cure-all for data quality issues (IOM 2011). With pressure on healthcare enterprises and providers to adopt and implement EHRs within short time constraints, red flags have surfaced about data quality issues.

Various proprietary and open source frameworks and models exist for assessing, measuring, and managing data quality efforts. While each of these differs in some respects, most have a common cyclical process that includes assessment, measurement, and improvement, and emphasizes a focus on data consumers, users, and data governance (DG) processes. Even though all the enterprise health information management (EHIM) domains incorporate data quality as a goal, a coordinating framework for how to assess data quality across the enterprise is required. This ensures data quality is handled uniformly throughout the organization. Frameworks provide definitions, standards, and guiding principles for data quality that apply across the enterprise with the expectation that they be appropriately incorporated into each EHIM domain of practice. The emphasis of this chapter is on data quality assessment as a distinct EHIM domain, but one whose functions should be woven into the fabric of all other EHIM domains. This chapter covers topics that will help you to:

- Assess the state of data quality
- Define data quality dimensions
- Explain methods for data quality management and assessment
- Practice data governance principles applied to data quality activities

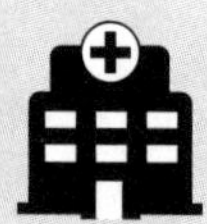

## The St. Rita's Healthcare System Case Study

Shelia and Bob volunteered to study data quality assessment methods for the EIM team. Shelia brought a compliance perspective to data quality. "Patient safety is the primary driver for data quality, but compliance and regulatory concerns are certainly drivers, too," Shelia remarked at the EIM team meeting. "Regulatory oversight is very complex. Healthcare organizations must comply with a myriad of laws and regulations such as Medicare, Medicaid, Stark, ERISA, and HIPAA, and those related to tax, finance, and environmental protections. Auditing and reporting are key components in a compliance program, and these activities are dependent on good data," Shelia explained.

"That sure brings in another perspective," said Shirlee. "I always think of the importance of quality data in the day-to-day operations for delivering patient care, so what you are saying really helps me get a handle on the diverse impact of data quality."

"But, if data quality is good in the first place, then shouldn't it remain good for downstream processes like reporting?" asked Monte.

"Generally, that would be correct," responded Bob. "However, data sometimes get corrupted as they move through a system, and we have to be alert to that possibility. Data quality assessment needs to consider quality throughout the data life cycle. Ensuring quality throughout the data life cycle is the challenge that intrigues me," Bob added.

The EIM team was thrilled that Shelia and Bob would be at the helm of data quality assessment and would report their findings at the next EIM meeting.

Shelia and Bob decided the best place to start was to find out the status of healthcare data quality. Knowing more about problems with healthcare data quality will help them get a better perspective on the size and breadth of the issues involved in the process.

# The State of Data Quality

The state of data quality in patient healthcare records has been studied for many decades, going as far back as the first hospital standardization efforts in the United States by the American College of Surgeons (ACS) in 1911. Due to the poor quality of record keeping, one of the five standards established by the ACS for hospital standardization addressed quality record-keeping systems:

> …accurate and complete records [should] be written for all patients and filed in an accessible manner in the hospital—a complete case record being one which includes identification data; complaint; personal and family history; history of present illness; physical examination; special examinations such as consultants, clinical laboratory, x-ray, and other examinations; provisional or working diagnosis; medical or surgical treatment; gross or microscopical pathological findings; progress notes; final diagnosis; condition on discharge; follow-up; and, in case of death, autopsy findings. (American College of Surgeons 2011)

Throughout the intervening years, multiple studies consistently raised concerns about the quality of data in patient healthcare records. A study in 1971 found up to 20 percent of patient medical records were missing data. In up to 80 percent, the patient record and the verbal content of the physician-patient encounter disagreed (Tufo and Speidel 1971). Throughout the years, several more studies have documented the poor state of data quality and similar results (Dick et al. 1991). More recently, in 2011, there was a call for greater oversight by public and private sectors to protect Americans from potential medical errors associated with the use of information technologies (IOM 2011). While EHRs provide many benefits, they also raise ethical concerns regarding the risks associated with developing, using, and maintaining both institutional and provider-based EHRs (Kopola and Mitchell 2011).

Although multiple studies find data quality issues in healthcare data, the results of these are not easily comparable. One reason is the research community has not developed or adopted a consistent taxonomy of data quality, thus there are inconsistent and overlapping descriptions of data quality dimensions which make results incomparable. For example, one study may use the terms "completeness," "correctness," "consistency," and "currency" to describe data quality dimensions, while another may use similar, but different terms such as "availability," "believability," "validity," and "accuracy." A second issue that arises is the varying methods for assessing data quality. In general, most healthcare data quality studies relied on methods with a minimal empirical or theoretical basis. In other words, these studies cannot be generalized or repeated by other researchers (Weiskopf and Weng. 2013).

Collecting and analyzing unintended consequences and errors generated by EHRs that have potential safety concerns is ongoing. For example, one event describes an EHR where medical assistants can easily confuse entering kilograms versus pounds for the weight of pediatric patients. This has potentially significant adverse outcomes since these data feed the dosing module (PDR Secure 2012). Another example is when a hospital discovered that interface and data exchange problems between the hospital and the laboratory caused electronic test results to attach to the wrong patient records (ONC 2009).

Because health records are longitudinal (spanning an individual's lifetime) patient information crosses the continuum of care, multiple providers, and other stakeholders. Incorrect data, therefore, have a ripple effect. Once in the electronic system, caregivers and others may not detect or be able to correct them in downstream systems that receive the data. For instance, a dosing error initially made in a physician office system and subsequently transferred into an inpatient electronic system may go undetected; correcting it at the source may not necessarily mean anyone will correct it in downstream systems.

Studies show that errors in EHR data are introduced in a variety of ways. These include programming errors, incomplete interfaces between systems, preprogrammed order sets that have not been thoroughly vetted, poor user interface design, and wrong information incorporated into the software (Gardner 2010). EHRs can also encourage providers to "copy and paste" clinical data which can introduce errors into the system, particularly when data relating to one patient is inadvertently included in another's electronic record. Another criticism of EHR systems is that they support "automatic behavior" rather than careful reasoning and analysis (Terry 2012).

Besides the patient care perspective, data quality also has implications for derived datasets used for a variety of reporting purposes such as public health and disease registries. Looking at data quality from the standpoint of datasets compiled from the EHR for research purposes, the quality of EHR data is highly variable (Weiskopf and Weng 2013).

## Data Quality Dimensions

There are many descriptions of data quality. The American Health Information Management Association (AHIMA) describes data quality as having the following dimensions:

- **Data accuracy:** The extent to which the data are free of identifiable errors
- **Data accessibility**: Data items that are easily obtainable and legal to access with strong protections and controls built into the process
- **Data comprehensiveness:** All required data items are included, ensuring the entire scope of the data is collected with intentional limitations documented
- **Data consistency:** The extent to which the healthcare data are reliable and the same across applications
- **Data currency:** The extent to which data are up-to-date; a datum value is up-to-date if it is current for a specific point in time, and it is outdated if it was current at a preceding time but incorrect at a later time
- **Data definition:** The specific meaning of a healthcare-related data element
- **Data granularity:** The level of detail at which the attributes and values of healthcare data are defined
- **Data precision:** Data values should be strictly stated to support the purpose
- **Data relevancy:** The extent to which healthcare-related data are useful for the purposes for which they were collected
- **Data timeliness:** A concept of data quality that involves whether the data is up-to-date and available within a useful time frame; timeliness is determined by the manner and context in which the data are being used (AHIMA 2012)

Others, however, have defined the dimensions of data quality differently. In one instance, an exhaustive literature review of 95 clinical research studies discussing data quality assessment resulted in five substantively different dimensions of data quality, which are listed below:

- Completeness: Is a truth about a patient present in the EHR?
- Correctness: Is an element that is present in the EHR true?
- Concordance: Is there agreement between elements in the EHR, or between the EHR and another data source?

- Plausibility: Does an element in the EHR makes sense in light of other knowledge about what that element is measuring?
- Currency: Is an element in the EHR a relevant representation of the patient state at a given point in time (Weiskopf and Weng 2013)?

Another definition of the data quality dimensions is found in The Data Quality Vector (DQV) which takes into account the shifting nature of biomedical data (for example, its use for different purposes such as clinical care and research). The purported value of the model is that it provides a standard for developing data quality algorithms for evaluating biomedical data. The following are the model's nine data quality dimensions:

- Completeness: The degree to which relevant data is recorded
- Consistency: The degree to which data satisfies specified constraints and rules
- Duplicity: The degree to which data contains duplicate registries representing the same entity
- Correctness: The degree of accuracy and precision where data is represented with respect to its
- real-world state
- Timeliness: The degree of data temporal stability
- Spatial stability: The degree to which data is stable among different populations
- Contextualization: The degree to which data is correctly or optimally annotated with the context in which it was acquired
- Predictive value: The degree to which data contains proper information for specific decision-making purposes
- Reliability: The degree of reputation of the stakeholders and institutions involved in the acquisition of data (Saez et al. 2012, 723)

The Canadian Institute for Health Information (CIHI) Data Quality Framework applies a consistent set of processes that focus on data quality priorities, assess data quality, and produce standard documentation. The framework has three components: a data quality work cycle, a data quality assessment tool, and documentation about data quality. In this framework, data quality is defined as the following five dimensions:

- Accuracy: The accuracy dimension refers to how well information in or derived from the data holding reflects the reality it was designed to measure.
- Timeliness: Refers primarily to how current or up-to-date the data is at the time of release, by measuring the gap between the end of the reference period to which the data pertains and the date on which the data becomes available to users.
- Comparability: The comparability dimension refers to the extent to which databases are consistent over time and uses standard conventions (such as data elements or reporting periods), making them comparable to other databases.
- Usability: Determines the ease with which a data holding's data may be understood and accessed.
- Relevance: Relevance reflects the degree to which a data holding meets the current and potential future needs of users (CIHI 2009, 6).

An example of data quality dimensions used outside of healthcare is in a US Department of Transportation (DOT), Federal Highway Administration white paper (Ahn et al. 2008). The report looks at data quality within the context of transportation operations and management. The report uses a framework for data quality measurement for the DOT to assess data quality. It includes the following six dimensions:

- Accuracy: The measure or degree of agreement between a data value or set of values and a source assumed to be correct
- Completeness: The degree to which data values are present in the attributes that require them
- Validity: The degree to which data values satisfy acceptance requirements of the validation criteria or fall within the respective domain of acceptable values
- Timeliness: The degree to which data values or a set of values are provided at the time required or specified
- Coverage: The degree to which data values in a sample accurately represent the whole of that which is to be measured
- Accessibility: The relative ease with which data can be retrieved and manipulated by data consumers to meet their needs (DOT 2004)

One of the most complete assessments of data quality is one that views data quality from the dimensions of data content and data presentation quality (English 2009, 180–182). Data quality is as much about content quality as it is about how data are presented.

In the first quality dimension, **data content quality** represents the raw data used to produce information. Here, content quality includes the following:

- Definition conformance: Data values are consistent with the definition of the attribute with which the value is associated.
- Existence: Each process or decision has all the information it requires (a record exists for every entity).
- Completeness: Each process or decision has all the information it requires (each data that should have a value has a full value stored).
- Validity: There are three dimensions to data validity including **value validity** where a value is within a specified range of values, **business rule validity** where data conform to business rules, and **derivation validity** where a derived value is produced according to a specified calculation formula.
- Accuracy: The data value correctly represents the real-world object or event. There are two possible dimensions to accuracy. One is accuracy to reality and the other is accuracy to a surrogate source. This latter dimension refers to data received from a source outside of the organization that is demonstrated to be a reliable source.
- Precision: Data values are correct to the right level of granularity.
- Non-duplication: There is only one record in a given data store that represents a single real-world object or event.
- Source quality and security warranties or certifications: The source of information guarantees the quality of information it provides.
- Equivalence of redundant or distributed data: Data about an object or event in one data store is semantically equivalent to data about the same object or event in another data store.
- Concurrency of redundant or distributed data: Concurrent queries to data about an event or object in a redundant or distributed data store produce the same result.
- Currency: The age of the data is correct for the user's purpose or purposes.

Besides these data content characteristics, there are several characteristics of **data quality presentation**. These include

- Availability: Data are accessible when they are needed
- Accessibility timeliness: The characteristic of retrieving or having data when needed by a process or user
- Presentation media appropriateness: Data are presented in the right technology media
- Relevance: The data are the right kind that add value to the task being performed
- Presentation standardization: Formatted data is presented consistently in a standardized way across different media, such as computer screens, reports, or manually prepared reports
- Presentation clarity: Data are presented in a way that clearly communicates the truth of the data and includes clear labels, footnotes, or other explanatory notes and links

The above examples are just a few among the scores of data quality descriptions. Such variations make it difficult to compare the results of data quality assessment from various sources. Specifically in healthcare, adopting a consistent taxonomy of EHR data quality is necessary to integrate work on data quality assessment from within healthcare and other fields, as well as adopting systematic, empirically driven, statistically based data quality assessment methods (Weiskopf and Weng 2013).

## The St. Rita's Healthcare System Case Study

"I never realized how many interpretations there are for the dimensions of data quality," said Shelia when she and Bob got together to compare the results of their data quality reviews. "I definitely see how problems can arise with comparability of data quality results."

"Right," Bob agreed. "And the quality dimensions are only one issue. Another issue involves the metrics used in assessments and how the evaluations are conducted. For example, various approaches possibly use different algorithms or calculations to arrive at data quality measurements."

"That's where standardization within an organization is so important," Shelia stated. "Think about the impact on the company if business units within the same organization used different assumptions and different dimensions and measures for data quality. The company ends up essentially comparing apples and oranges and won't have a good understanding of its level of data quality."

"Precisely," answered Bob. "For a while there I was thinking that data quality could be totally contained within all the other EIM disciplines, such as metadata and master data management, or even by business units themselves. But I see now that data quality must be an enterprise-wide effort, with standards and methods the entire organization follows. At St. Rita's, we need to define what we consider the dimensions of data quality to be. We have to develop standard metrics and a standard process for data quality measurement throughout the organization."

"And what happens when other organizations don't use the same dimensions and metrics as St. Rita's?" pondered Shelia. "It means," she concluded, "that our data quality estimates are not comparable to other organizations, and the issues raised by this variability could be significant for data exchange with other organizations."

With these insights, Shelia and Bob proceeded to plan out how to evaluate actual models for data quality management and assessment. After a cursory review of the literature, they determined that they needed a consistent set of criteria to benchmark the models against each other.

For consistency and comparison purposes, Shelia and Bob developed the following as a guide for assessing each model:

- **Framework**: The concepts, beliefs, theories, assumptions, or expectations that provide the foundation for the model
- **Key processes:** Principal activities performed to realize the framework
- **Measurement:** The basis or standard of comparison used to assess data quality
- **Governance:** How authority, accountability, and control for data quality is designed
- **Implementation:** How governance, key processes, and measurement are implemented

With this outline in hand, Sheila and Bob launched their investigation of several data quality management models.

# Methods for Data Quality Management and Assessment

Similar to the variability of dimensions of data quality, there are several approaches and interpretations for data quality management and assessment. Three models for data quality assessment are examined here, including the AHIMA Data Quality Management Model, The CIHI Data Quality Framework, and the GS1 Data Quality Framework 3.0. The former two models are healthcare-related, and the last one is for data quality assessment in global supply chains.

While there are differences among the approaches, and some are more detailed than others, there are similarities between the three models. All of the models espouse that **fitness of use** is a key characteristic of data quality. In other words, data quality is predicated and evaluated on how well the needs of the data consumers are being met. Making data quality an enterprise-wide value and developing an organizational culture of data quality is another important aspect of each model. DG is viewed as a required coordinating feature for the success of any data quality program in all models.

## AHIMA Data Quality Management Model

The AHIMA Data Quality Management (DQM) model integrates the ten data quality dimensions defined by AHIMA with four data quality management functions which are a continuum in the life cycle of data. The model provides a general list of criteria to apply within each of the four data quality management functions, but does not address specific implementation or governance processes (AHIMA 2012).

### Framework

The AHIMA DQM views data quality management as a continuous quality improvement effort carried out on an enterprise-wide level. The model is based on the assumption that "data quality begins when EHR applications are planned." Although not explicitly stated, the intent is that organizations should apply the model to electronic healthcare information, as opposed to the application to other information domains, such as administrative, research, or other data.

The model defines data quality management as the business processes that ensure the integrity of an organization's data during collection, application (including aggregation), warehousing, and analysis. The model uses the Agency for Healthcare Research and Quality's definition of a quality measure as "a mechanism to assign a quantity to quality of care by comparison to a criterion" (AHIMA 2012). Although not stated in the model, one could presumably interpret this definition, when applied to data rather than to patient care, as meaning a mechanism to assign a quantity to quality of data by comparison to a criterion.

The model is based on ten data quality dimensions and four data quality management functions, also referred to as domains (AHIMA 2010). The ten quality dimensions are listed earlier in this chapter. The four data quality management functions include

- Application: The purpose for the data collection
- Collection: The processes by which data elements are accumulated
- Warehousing: Processes and systems used to archive data and data journals
- Analysis: The process of translating data into information utilized for an application

Achieving the ten data quality dimensions is predicated on the management of each of these four functions (see figure 12.1).

Figure 12.1. **AHIMA DQM model**

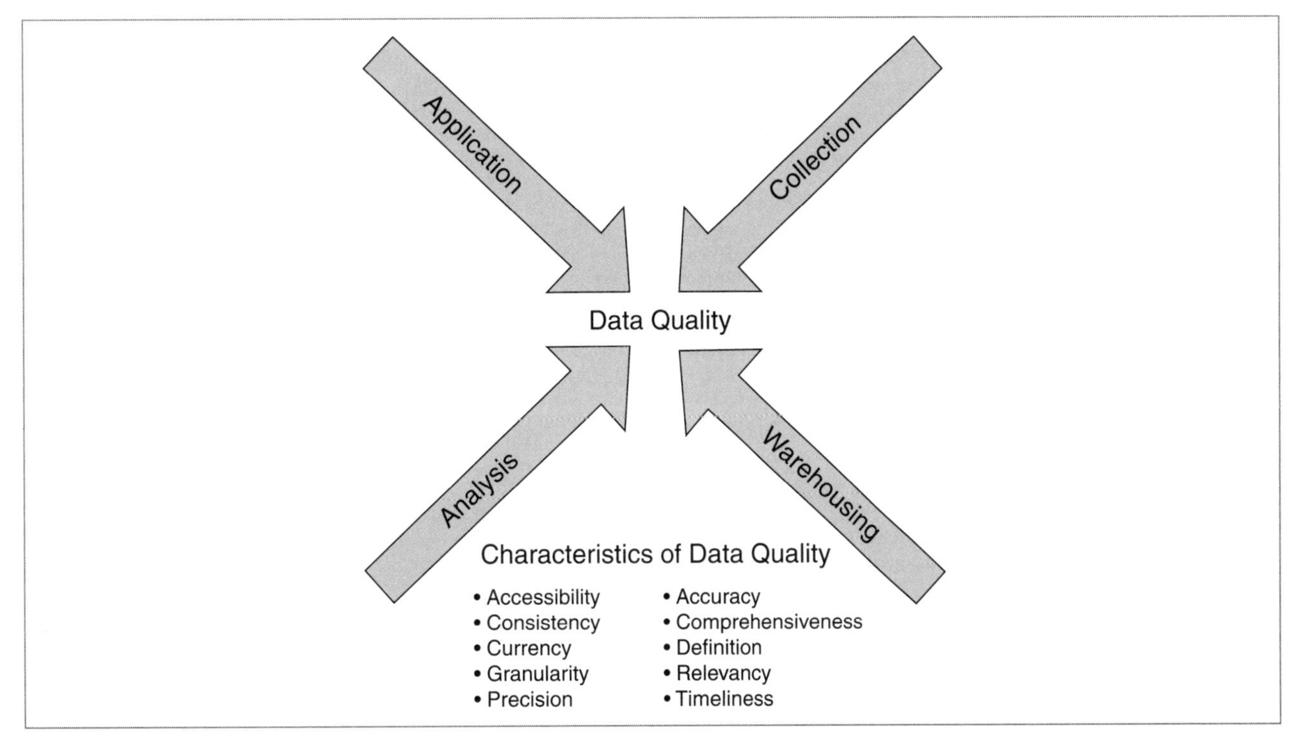


Source: AHIMA 2012.

## Key Processes

AHIMA developed the DQM model to illustrate the different data quality challenges. The intersection between the dimensions and the functions is considered to represent data quality challenges (table 12.1). Each cell in table 12.1 contains examples of each characteristic within each domain. Some of these examples could be interpreted as measurement criterion while others are illustrations of key processes, although not a complete set of processes. For example, key processes identified from table 12.1 include

- Determining the application's purpose
- Establishing appropriate education and training
- Applying appropriate edits
- Establishing data ownership and guidelines for who may access or modify data or systems
- Taking data inventory to facilitate access

Table 12.1. AHIMA DQM model domains and characteristics

| Characteristic | Application | Collection | Warehousing | Analysis |
|---|---|---|---|---|
| **Data Accuracy**<br>The extent to which the data are free of identifiable errors. | To facilitate accuracy, determine the application's purpose, the question to be answered, or the aim for collecting the data element.<br>Use standard acceptable values where available. Where possible, implement value flags and constraints.<br>For example, data entry of height into EHRs should flag or highlight very small (less than 12 inches) or very tall (over seven feet) heights. | Ensuring accuracy involves appropriate education and training along with timely and appropriate communication of data definitions to those who collect data. The applications should constrain entry to allowable values where possible.<br>For example, data accuracy ensures a patient height cannot be entered erroneously as five inches when it is in fact 50 inches. In addition to a primary data error, this impacts any calculated fields such as body mass index (BMI). | To warehouse data, put in place appropriate edits to ensure accuracy, such as basic field length checks.<br>Also, generate error reports related to transfers to and from the data warehouse.<br>All data warehouses should have a correction and change management policy to track any changes. | To accurately analyze data, ensure the algorithms, formulas, programming, and translation systems are correct.<br>For example, make sure the encoder assigns correct codes and the appropriate DRG for the codes entered.<br>Continual data validation is important to guarantee each record or entry within the database is correct. |
| **Data Accessibility**<br>Data items that are easily obtainable and legal to access with strong protections and controls built into the process. | The application and legal, financial, process, and other boundaries determine which data to collect. Ensure that collected data are legal to collect for the application.<br>For example, recording the date of birth and race in the EHR is appropriate and should only occur once with verification. Then the values should roll forward. | When developing the data collection instrument, explore methods to access needed data and select the best, most economical method. The amount of accessible data may increase through system interfaces and integration of systems.<br>For example, the best and easiest method to obtain demographic information may be from an existing system. Another method may be to assign data collection by the expertise of each team member. For example, the admission staff collects demographic data, the nursing staff collects symptoms, and the HIM staff assigns codes.<br>Data entry should undergo a cost-benefit analysis process to determine which method provides the best data most efficiently. | Technology and hardware impact accessibility. Establish data ownership and guidelines for who may access or modify data or systems. Inventory data to facilitate access.<br>In the EHR it may be advisable to establish data ownership or governance at the data element level, especially reused data. For example, allergies are recorded by many different clinicians and come in many forms. Who defines what an allergy is? How does this impact the use of allergies in the EHR, especially for clinical decision support? | Access to complete, current data ensures accurate analysis and data mining. Otherwise, results and conclusions may be inaccurate or inappropriate.<br>For example, using the Medicare case mix index (CMI) alone does not accurately reflect total hospital CMI. Consequently, strategic planning based solely on Medicare CMI may not be appropriate. |
| **Data Comprehensiveness**<br>All required data items are included. This ensures the entire scope of the data is collected with intentional limitations documented. | Clarify how the data will be used and identify end users to ensure complete data are collected for the application. Include a problem statement and cost-benefit or impact study when collected data increases.<br>For example, in addition to outcome, it may be important to gather data that impact outcomes. | Achieve cost-effective comprehensive data collection via interface to or download from other automated systems.<br>Data definition and data precision impact comprehensive data collection (see these characteristics below). | Warehousing includes managing relationships of data owners, data collectors, and data end users to ensure all are aware of the available data in the inventory and accessible systems. This also helps to reduce redundant data collection. | Make sure all pertinent data impacting the application are analyzed in concert.<br>This is especially important when using EHR clinical decision support. Incomplete data can result in underreporting a numerator or denominator. |
| **Data Consistency**<br>The extent to which the healthcare data are reliable and the same across applications. | Data are consistent when the value of the data is the same across applications and systems, such as the patient's health record number. In addition, related data items should agree.<br>For example, data are inconsistent when it is documented that a male patient had a hysterectomy. | Using data definitions, extensive training, standardized data collection (procedures, rules, edits, and processes), and integrated or interfaced systems facilitate consistency.<br>Static data should be moved between users. For example, once definitively establishing date of birth, age at the time of treatment should be calculated, not entered by a user who might make an error. | Warehousing employs edits or conversion tables to ensure consistency. Coordinate edits and tables with data definition changes or data definition differences across systems. Document edits and tables.<br>When new data are loaded, check it against existing data for consistency. For example, is someone reporting a different race for a patient? | Analyze data under reproducible circumstances by using standard formulas, scientific equations, programming, variance calculations, and other methods. Compare "apples to apples."<br>Thoroughly document any data manipulation, aggregating or otherwise. For example, how is BMI calculated and has the formula been checked? |

(continued)

Table 12.1. AHIMA DQM model domains and characteristics (*Continued*)

| Characteristic | Application | Collection | Warehousing | Analysis |
| --- | --- | --- | --- | --- |
| **Data Currency**<br>The extent to which data are up-to-date; a datum value is up-to-date if it is current for a specific point in time. It is outdated if it was current at a preceding time yet incorrect at a later time. | The appropriateness or value of an application changes over time.<br>In EHRs up-to-date guidelines and algorithms are imperative. For example, acceptable blood pressure ranges have lowered, as have target HbA1C levels. | Data definitions change or are modified over time. Document these so current and future users know what the data mean. Make these changes in accordance with data governance policies and practices. Further, they must be communicated in a timely manner to those collecting data and to the end users. | To ensure current data are available, warehousing involves continually validating systems, tables, and databases. The dates of warehousing events should be documented. | The availability of current data impacts the analysis of data.<br>For example, analyzing the long-term incidence or prevalence of disease requires data in a different timeframe than when trying to track a disease outbreak for biosurveillance purposes.<br>Validating data from various fiscal and calendar years should also be considered. |
| **Data Definition**<br>The specific meaning of a healthcare-related data element. | The application's purpose, the question to be answered, or the aim for collecting the data element must be clarified to ensure appropriate and complete data definitions.<br>Does the system use the Office of Management and Budget (OMB) standard for race and ethnicity? If not, what are the definitions and acceptable values? | Clear, concise data definitions facilitate accurate data collection.<br>For example, the definition of patient disposition may be "the patient's anticipated location or status following release or discharge." Acceptable values for this data element should also be defined. The instrument of collection should include data definitions and ensure the application limits data collection to the allowed values. | Warehousing includes archiving documentation and data. Consequently, data ownership documentation and definitions should be maintained over time. Inventory maintenance activities (purging, updates, and others), purpose for collecting data, collection policies, information management policies, and data sources should be maintained over time also. | For appropriate analysis, display data needs to reflect the purpose for which the data were collected. Appropriate comparisons, relationships, and linkages need to be shown. |
| **Data Granularity**<br>The level of detail at which the attributes and values of healthcare data are defined. | A single application may require varying levels of detail or granularity.<br>For example, census statistics may be utilized daily, weekly, or monthly depending upon the application. Census is needed daily to ensure adequate staffing and food service. However, the monthly trend is needed for long-range planning.<br>Similarly, lab test results trend at various levels of detail. | Collect data at the appropriate level of detail or granularity.<br>For example, the temperature of 100° may be recorded. The granularity for recording outdoor temperatures is different from recording patient temperatures. If patient Jane Doe's temperature is 100°, does that mean 99.6° or 100.4°?<br>Appropriate granularity for this application dictates recording the data to the first decimal point while appropriate granularity for recording outdoor temperatures may not require it. | Warehouse data at the appropriate level of detail or granularity.<br>For example, exception or error reports reflect granularity based on the application. A spike (exception) in the daily census may show little or no impact on the month-to-date or monthly reports. | Appropriate analysis reflects the level of detail or granularity of the collected data.<br>For example, a spike (exception) in the daily census resulting in immediate action to ensure adequate food service and staffing may have no impact on analysis of the census for long-range planning. Of particular note for analysis is the impact of any rounding which might be done for numerical data. |
| **Data Precision**<br>Data values should be strictly stated to support the purpose. | The application's purpose, the question to be answered, or the aim for collecting the data element must be clarified to ensure data precision.<br>What level of detail is needed for data collection purpose? Are age ranges or four US regions sufficient? | To collect data precise enough for the application, define acceptable values or value ranges for each data item.<br>For example, limit values for gender to male, female, and unknown; or collect information by age ranges or allow more detailed collection to fully meet the needs. | Are warehouses receiving and storing all data elements being transferred from the source system? | If the precision of the data has been altered in the analysis, is the process understood and well documented? |
| **Data Relevancy**<br>The extent to which healthcare-related data are useful for the purposes for which they were collected. | The applications purpose, the question to be answered, or the aim for collecting the data element must be clarified to ensure relevant data. | To better safeguard relevancy, complete a pilot of the data collection instrument to validate its use. A "parallel" test may also be appropriate, completing the new or revised instrument and the current process simultaneously. Communicate results to those collecting data and to the end users. Facilitate or negotiate changes as needed across disciplines or users. | Establish appropriate retention schedules to ensure availability of relevant data. The application defines relevancy.<br>It may be appropriate for warehouses to subset data related to its relevancy for certain uses. | For appropriate analysis, display data to reflect the purpose for which the data were collected. This is defined by the application. Show appropriate comparisons, relationships, and linkages. |

(continued)

Table 12.1. AHIMA DQM model domains and characteristics (*Continued*)

| Characteristic | Application | Collection | Warehousing | Analysis |
|---|---|---|---|---|
| **Data Timeliness**<br><br>Concept of data quality that involves whether the data is up-to-date and available within a useful time frame. Timeliness is determined by how the data are being used and their context. | The application defines timeliness.<br><br>For example, patient census is needed daily to provide sufficient day-to-day operations staffing, such as nursing and food service. However, the organization needs annual or monthly patient census data for strategic planning.<br><br>In the EHR, vitals may be taken once per visit for ambulatory care patients, but every 15 minutes or more often for critically ill patients. | Timely data collection is a function of the process and collection instrument.<br><br>In the EHR, system performance plays an important role in data timeliness. Data display should be sub-second and data entry should occur instantaneously. | Warehousing ensures data are available per information management policy and retention schedules.<br><br>For EHR or clinical data warehouses, is the data updated concurrently or does it occur in a batch process? | Timely data analysis allows for the initiation of action to avoid adverse impacts. For some applications, such as allergy-drug or drug-drug interactions, timely may be seconds. For others, such as the prevalence of a disease over time, it may be years. |

Source: AHIMA 2012.

## Measurement

Figure 12.2 contains a checklist for the AHIMA DQM model that outlines basic assumptions in data quality management for healthcare professionals to follow. Healthcare professionals can use this as a set of criteria for the measurement of data quality (figure 12.2).

Figure 12.2. Checklist to assess data quality management efforts

Use the checklist below to assess overall data quality management efforts within an organization or for an application.

**Application**

The purpose for data collection.

- The application's purpose, the question to be answered, or the aim for collecting the data is clear
- Boundaries or limitations of data collected are known and communicated
- Complete data are collected for the application
- Value of the data is the same across applications and systems
- The application is of value and is appropriate for the intent
- Timely data are available

**Collection**

The process by which data elements are accumulated.

- Education and training is effective and timely
- Communication of data definitions is timely and appropriate
- Data source provides most accurate, most timely, and least costly data
- Data collection is standardized
- Data standards exist
- Updates and changes are communicated appropriately and on a timely basis
- Data definitions are clear and concise
- Data are collected at the appropriate level of detail or granularity
- Acceptable values or value ranges for each data element are defined; edits are determined
- The data collection instrument is validated
- Quality (for example, accuracy) is routinely monitored
- Meaningful use is achieved via the evaluation of EHR data

(continued)

Figure 12.2. Checklist to assess data quality management efforts (*Continued*)

| Warehousing and Interoperability |
|---|
| Processes and systems used to archive data and data journals.<br>• Appropriate edits are in place<br>• Data ownership is established<br>• Guidelines for access to data and systems are in place<br>• Data inventory is maintained<br>• Relationships of data owners, data collectors, and data end users are managed<br>• Appropriate conversion tables are in place<br>• Systems, tables, and databases are updated appropriately<br>• Current data are available<br>• Data and application journals (data definitions, data ownership, policies, data sources, and so on) are appropriately archived, purged, and retained<br>• Data are warehoused at the appropriate level of detail or granularity<br>• Appropriate retention schedules are established<br>• Data are available on a timely basis<br>• Health information exchange is achieved as a result of EHR interoperability |
| **Analysis** |
| The process of translating data into information used in an application.<br>• Algorithms, formulas, and translation systems are valid and accurate<br>• Complete and current data is available<br>• Data impacting the application are analyzed in context<br>• Data are analyzed under reproducible circumstances<br>• Appropriate data comparisons, relationships, and linkages are displayed<br>• Data are analyzed at the appropriate level of detail or granularity |

Source: AHIMA 2012.

### Implementation

The model does not recommend specific implementation steps.

### Governance

The model is predicated on the belief that the healthcare industry needs DG programs to help manage the growing amount of electronic data. DG is described as "the high-level, corporate, or enterprise policies and strategies that define the purpose for collecting data, the ownership of data, and the intended use of data" (AHIMA 2012). The outgrowth of governance functions and stewardship is that health information use and management is compliant with jurisdictional law, regulation, standards, and organizational policies. The model does not address how to structure governance or how to assign or define roles, authority, and accountabilities (AHIMA 2012).

## Canadian Institute for Health Information Data Quality Framework

The following analysis is based on the CIHI Data Quality Framework (CIHI 2009). CIHI is a secondary data collection organization. It is an independent, non-profit corporation that links federal, provincial, and territorial governments with non-governmental health-related groups in Canada. As a secondary data collection organization, its data quality challenges are compounded by ensuring best practices not only in internal data handling, but also data handling from external source systems. Because the model addresses both internal and external data, its application is useful for healthcare organizations that are concerned with integration of external data into their data stores.

## Framework

The CIHI Data Quality Framework aligns with the Institute's corporate strategy which is found in a six-point plan aimed at prevention, early detection, and resolution of data issues. The six points are to

- foster a data quality culture;
- strengthen data quality infrastructure and capacity;
- cultivate the data supply chain;
- enhance external data quality collaboration;
- promote communication and provide consultation; and
- initiate the fast-track priority projects fund (CIHI 2009).

The framework is an approach for applying consistent processes to data flow that focus on data quality priorities, assessing the data quality of a data holding, and producing standard data-holding documentation. Like the AHIMA model, CIHI views data quality management as a continuous improvement activity. The framework's main components include (figure 12.3)

- A data quality work cycle
- A data quality assessment tool
- Documentation about data quality

Figure 12.3. Representation of CIHI data quality framework

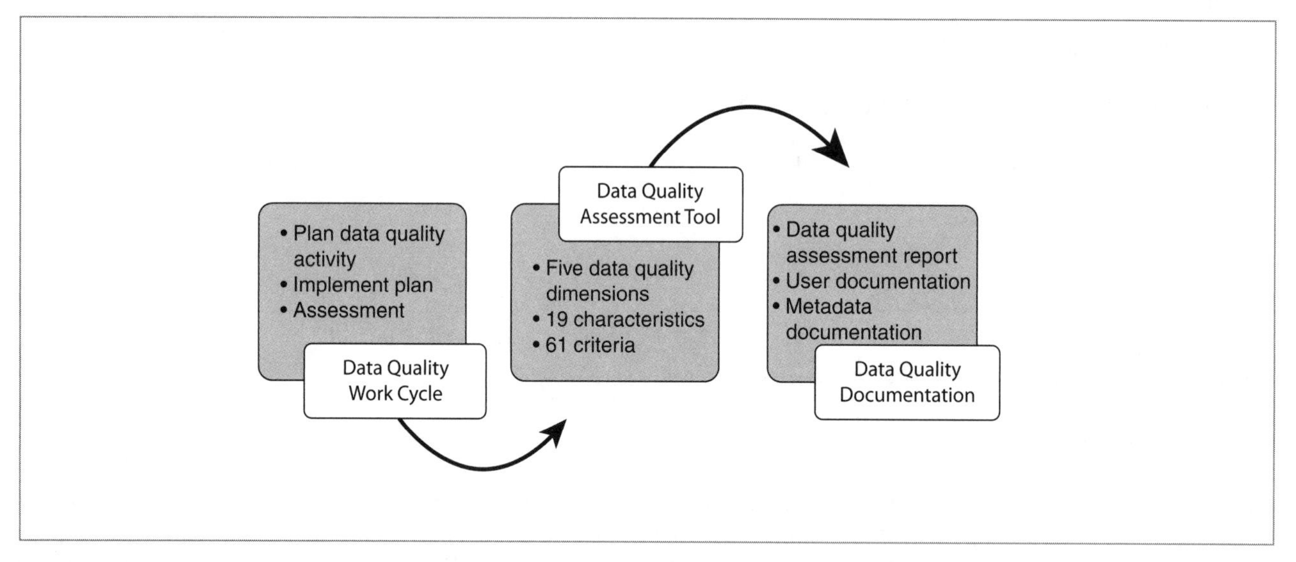




The framework defines data quality in the context of "fit for use," meaning that if the data satisfies data consumers' needs then it is fit for use. To be fit for use, data must meet three data quality dimensions. These include utility, objectivity, and integrity. Utility is defined as the usefulness of data or information for its intended users. Objectivity is defined as data or information that is accurate, reliable, and unbiased and is presented in an accurate, clear, and unbiased format. Integrity is described as the security or protection of data or information from unauthorized access or revision. Essential management functions for deriving high data quality include identifying the root causes of information defects, error-proofing information processes, identifying information quality requirements, and controlling information processes.

## Key Processes

The first component of the framework is the data quality work cycle. Within the work cycle are three key processes or activities. The first of these is planning a data quality activity. This step includes identifying and planning for the activities necessary to prepare and prioritize the processes required for a data holding (database, dataset, and so on) that ensure data quality. The second key process is implementing. Implementing includes developing the processes needed to implement the plan. For example, this might include collecting data, monitoring incoming records, and so on. The final key process is assessment. Assessment entails evaluating the quality of the data and determining whether the desired objectives of the plan were achieved. If the desired outcomes are not achieved, the cycle is repeated by the data quality team until they are attained. Thus, the cycle is iterative in nature.

### Measurement

An assessment tool is a core component of the framework. The tool examines five dimensions of data quality that include accuracy, timeliness, comparability, usability, and relevance. Each dimension is divided into 19 related characteristics, and each characteristic is further made up of 61 criteria. In the majority of cases, each criterion is rated as met, unmet, unknown, or not applicable. In cases where this rating is not used, other predetermined ratings are applied by analysts, such as minimal or none, moderate, significant, or unknown. The ratings provide consistent measures that allow comparisons among data holdings and between data years within a holding.

### Implementation

Implementation of the data quality effort is carried out through the documented cyclical process of planning, implementation, and documentation, which is an essential part of the framework. Planning includes identifying and prioritizing quality issues and identifying the processes needed to address them. Implementation includes putting into operation the processes identified to assess a specific data quality issue. Measurement processes described above are part of the implementation process.

Once measurement is completed, an action plan is developed to address any data quality issues identified. The action plan includes recommendations (strategy), a timeline, the staff responsible for completing remediation, and a target date for completion.

Documentation is the third key process of the framework. Three types of documentation about a data holding's quality are produced. These include

- Data quality assessment reports which are internal CIHI reports that summarize the results of the data quality assessment for a data holding
- Data quality documentation for users, or documentation provided to users of the data holding (for example, external to CIHI)
- Metadata documentation, which is a detailed documentation about the data holding

Implementing policies and procedures that enumerate the purpose, content, and format for each documentation type, process of review and sign-offs, and publication is essential.

### Governance

Data quality is a corporate priority and is part of the CIHI culture. Every staff member is responsible for data quality regardless of job position or business department. Senior management provides the overall direction for the data quality program. A data quality council is composed of managers and users of respective data holdings, meets monthly, and reports to the senior management team. Each area responsible for a data holding is assigned specific data quality functions including analyzing and evaluating their data and data processes, identifying data quality issues, preparing plans to address identified issues, identifying ways to improve data holdings, conducting special studies, and preparing data quality documentation. A dedicated department provides tools, methodological support, assistance with conducting special studies, and other support to all program areas in carrying out data quality efforts (CIHI. 2009).

## GS1 Data Quality Framework 3.0

GS1 Data Quality Framework 3.0 is a non-healthcare example. The GS1 framework was developed by GS1, a not-for-profit organization dedicated to the design and implementation of standards for demand and supply chains globally and across business sectors. Adopting new methods in healthcare in areas such as management, quality assessment, and information technology and systems is largely informed by tapping into the knowledge base and experiences of other industry segments. Exploring the GS1 framework illustrates how data quality management is approached in another industry.

The GS1 framework was developed to improve the quality of data within the end-to-end global supply chain. The framework is grounded in the belief that suppliers of data have a responsibility to provide timely and good-quality data and in return, recipients of data must have the internal processes and procedures in place to protect the integrity of data they synchronize with their trading partners (GS1 2010b). The framework is a voluntary, sector-neutral, standardized solution.

## Framework

The framework includes the following four components:

- Data quality management system: This provides guidance for organizations in establishing, maintaining, and improving processes and activities related to the management of information and data quality of their master data output. It is a series of documented, periodically-reviewed procedures that an organization implements to ensure quality data.
- Self-assessment tools: These tools provide organizations with the means to perform a self-assessment against the key elements of the data quality management system. The organization can then use the results of the self-assessment as a gap analysis tool for prioritizing improvement areas.
- Product inspection procedure: This is a standardized approach used to inspect the characteristics of trade items and compare them to their master data.
- Reference documentation: Provides additional information on any of the three other components.

## Key Processes

There are 12 key processes of the Data Quality Management System:

- Secure top management commitment: Senior management must demonstrate its commitment to the data quality effort. Commitment is evidenced by, among other things, senior management's involvement in establishing data quality goals, providing program resources, appointing a program coordinator, and holding the program accountable for meeting goals.
- Appoint responsible managers: A principal manager should be appointed by top management who has the total backing and empowerment from the CEO of the organization and has the authority, resulting from rank, seniority, or both to influence managers and others of all levels and function.
- Inaugurate data quality awareness programs: Data quality awareness program(s) should be implemented by the organization on an enterprise-wide level that helps build a culture of data quality awareness and responsibility.
- Provide training: Staff require specific data quality training commensurate with their job responsibilities. Data quality training should be an integral part of the data quality plan and effort.
- Create data quality management processes: This comprises the implementation and operational plan. The specific plan should address how the data quality objectives established by senior management will be achieved by the organization. This includes development of policies, procedures, and standards.
- Create data quality management documentation: Processes should be established by the organization to ensure documentation of all data quality program policies, procedures, and standards, as well as materials such as training manuals, records (for example, meeting minutes and action plans), reports, and communications.
- Develop processes for document control: After creating data quality program documentation, it must be controlled. Control includes managing the creation, approval, distribution, revision, storage, and disposal of the various types of documentation the program generates.
- Implement and operate the program: The data quality program should be implemented to meet the goals of the program. Assigning authority and responsibilities, activating communication channels, and monitoring processes ensure the data quality program meets goals and policy objectives.
- Perform internal data quality audit: Regularly conducted audits ensure the program continues to meet strategic objectives and goals. Audits should evaluate both performance of the data quality management program and data output.
- Management review: An initial management review should be conducted after the system has been in operation between three to six months to ensure adequacy and effectiveness. The review should assess opportunities for improvement, identify necessary changes, and include items such as audit reports, feedback from users and stakeholders, status of prevention and corrective actions, and so on.
- Conformity assessment (optional): This entails an assessment to determine if the program is meeting all legal, regulatory, or contractual obligations related to data quality or data quality activities.
- Continual improvement: Organizations should have in place continuous improvement programs related to the data quality program which link to other areas such as metadata management and master data management.

## Measurement

The framework recommends the development of a series of objective, parametric measures expressed as key performance indicators (KPI). The organization should periodically monitor these to verify the actual accuracy of the data.

## Implementation

Implementation guidelines for executing the 12 key processes are provided in a detailed 31-page implementation guide. Essentially implementation is a serial execution of the 12 key processes. Specific tasks are attached to each process in the implementation guide (figure 12.4)

Figure 12.4. **GS1 Data Quality Framework 3.0 12 key processes**

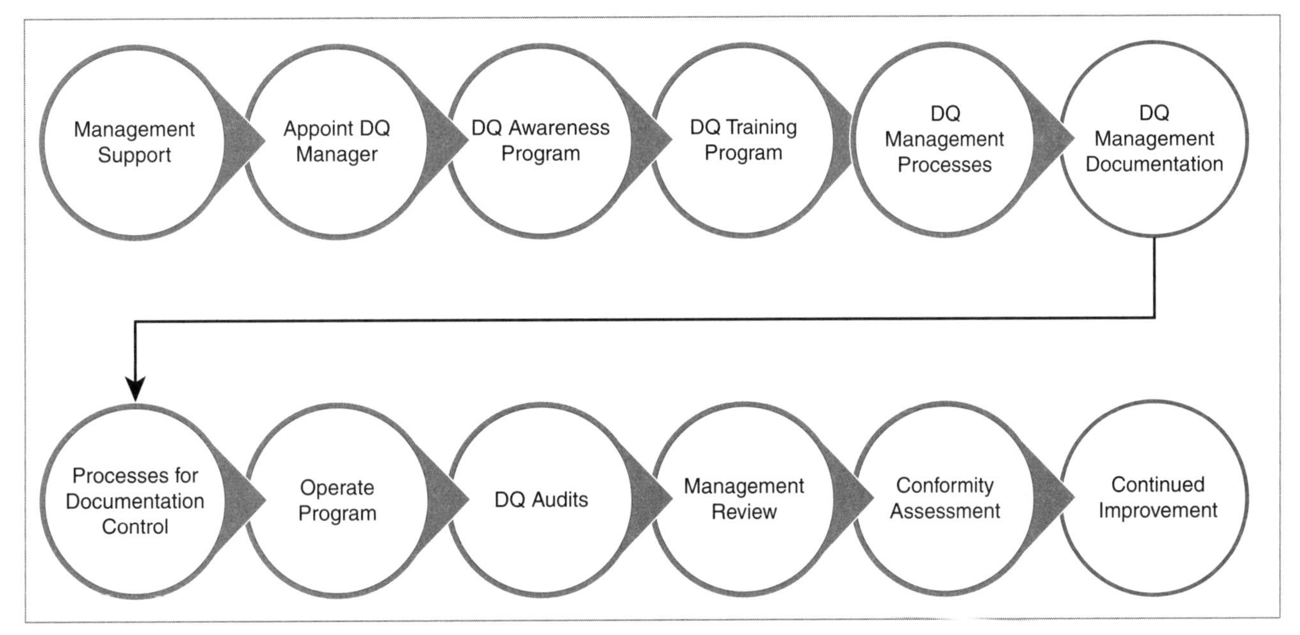




## Governance

An essential premise of the framework is that the data quality management program must have the full backing of the organization's CEO. He or she demonstrates support by establishing data quality goals for the enterprise, appointing a senior level data quality manager to coordinate the program with responsibility for instituting processes for the data quality program, and using appropriate oversight authority. Data quality is an important strategic objective and all staff have responsibility for data quality depending on their job role and position (GS1 2010b).

### The St. Rita's Healthcare System Case Study

"This has been a great learning experience," said Shelia when she and Bob met to compile their presentation to the EIM team. "After reading how detailed some of these models are, I think we have a very long road to travel here at St. Rita's in addressing data quality."

"I wholeheartedly agree with you, Shelia," Bob responded. "For the most part, what I've seen in practice is abdicating data quality to the technical staff. Most places have not taken on a consistent, formalized, and comprehensive effort on the level that we've seen in these frameworks. Here at St. Rita's, we have not cultivated data quality as a corporate value. While we do have some data quality training, it is spotty at best. And certainly data quality has not been elevated to a top strategic priority emanating from the CEO. The CIHI and GS1 models are very specific about the need for senior management visibility in this effort."

"I'm very enthusiastic to be part of the presentation to the EIM team on this topic," Shelia remarked. "The imperative is to make data quality a top priority and not just in terms of the revenue cycle and diagnostic coding. I'm eager to implement data quality from a broader perspective that pays big dividends to patients and all data consumers. I can't wait to get started on this initiative."

Shelia and Bob began to assemble their slide deck and outlined the DG activities they thought they should align with data quality management.

## Applying Data Governance

Governance and data quality management are closely aligned. Arguably, one cannot exist without the other. Governance is important in establishing standards, policies, and procedures for implementation on an enterprise-wide basis. Without governance, it is impossible to consistently evaluate data quality or assess and contrast the degree of data quality among different organizational business units. All the models reviewed in this chapter speak to the importance of a formalized structure of governance in carrying out data quality management activities. Specifically these activities include the following and are reported in table 12.2:

- Develop a data quality framework, and assign roles, responsibilities, and accountability for data quality
- Define data quality requirements and metrics
- Establish data quality policies, procedures, and standards
- Develop and promote data quality awareness
- Establish processes for assessing and measuring data quality
- Report, correct, resolve, and manage data quality issues

Table 12.2. DG deliverables by EIM function

| Data Governance | Data Architecture Management | Metadata Management | Master Data Management | Content Management | Data Security and Privacy Management | Business Intelligence Management | Data Quality Management | Terminology and Classification Management |
|---|---|---|---|---|---|---|---|---|
| Identify mission and scope | Develop and maintain data models | Develop policies, procedures, and standards | Identify master and reference data requirements | Develop roadmap for content management | Identify and classify sensitive data across enterprise systems | Assess organization and stakeholder needs | Develop DQ framework; establish DQ roles and responsibilities | |
| Establish goals and success measures | Develop, maintain, and evaluate data model policies and standards | Ensure metadata meets functional requirements | Develop policies, procedures, and standards for management of master data | Develop policies and procedures for content management | Develop data security and privacy policies and standards | Develop BI roadmap to meet organization goals | Define DQ requirements and metrics | |
| Put in place DG structure, processes, and communications plan | Define roles, responsibilities, and accountabilities for data architecture management | Develop and maintain appropriate metadata schema | Establish master data definitions, validation, and verification levels for master data quality | Apply taxonomies, thesauri, ontologies and other content management classifications | Meet compliance and regulatory security and privacy requirements | Develop accountability and reporting structure | Establish and implement DQ policies, procedures, and standards | |

(continued)

Table 12.2. DG deliverables by EIM function (*Continued*)

| Data Governance | Data Architecture Management | Metadata Management | Master Data Management | Content Management | Data Security and Privacy Management | Business Intelligence Management | Data Quality Management | Terminology and Classification Management |
|---|---|---|---|---|---|---|---|---|
| Secure funding | Develop, maintain, and evaluate policies and standards for requirements analysis | Ensure metadata capture, maintenance, distribution, and integration | Ensure master and reference data meet regulatory requirements, including lineage history and security | Develop policies and procedures that ensure legal and regulatory mandates are met | Assess risk and identify controls to manage risk | Develop policies, procedures, and standards for data security and quality, and monitor them | Develop and promote data quality awareness | |
| Establish decision rights | Develop and maintain data artifacts and standards | Ensure metadata security | Establish audit procedures and standards for master data | Establish standards and audit procedures | Perform data security and privacy audits and report findings | Define BI architecture | Establish processing for assessing and measuring DQ | |
| Identify accountabilities | Establish quality control program and metrics for data architecture management | Develop and implement quality controls for metadata | Identify stakeholders and establish decision rights and accountabilities | Implement stewardship processes over the content management life cycle | Develop and implement data privacy and security awareness and training | Develop and maintain schema and metadata | Report, correct, resolve, and manage DQ issues | |

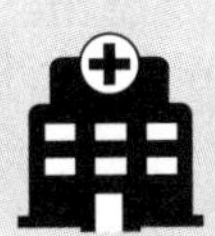

## The St. Rita's Healthcare System Case Study

The EIM team was revved up at the end of the day. Their meeting was about to begin and everyone was in a great mood; they were finally able to see how the pieces of the jigsaw puzzle fit together. "I'm getting it," said Linda. "When we first started, I have to admit I sure didn't understand the outcome or how important EIM was for St. Rita's."

"Here, here," Monte chimed in. "I was pretty disillusioned going into this because I thought the data problems were just too great to handle, and we couldn't do anything about them. But now I really have some hope. I can see that through a collaborative DG strategy and structure we can make headway. It's a really good feeling."

When all the team arrived, Shelia and Bob shared the information they gathered on data quality management. Similar to the other presentations there was a lot of new material, and it took a few moments to assimilate it all.

"Comments and takeaways?" asked Val.

Shirlee jumped right in. "I never gave dimensions of data quality a thought before now. I had my own interpretation of data quality, which I admit was pretty narrow. But now I see why it's important to nail down what we really mean by data quality. If we can't define it, then we can't measure it."

"Great takeaway," added Linda. "And what is surprising to me is how many models there are for evaluating data quality. My big takeaway is that you can't compare apples and oranges, and that's exactly the situation we will be in if we don't identify the data quality dimensions like you said, Shirlee, and if we don't have a standard and systematic method for data quality evaluation."

"I have to say," began Shelia, "my biggest takeaway is the critical piece of building a culture of data quality and embedding that value in everyday work. And, part of that piece is really focusing on the needs of the data consumer, our end users. If we plan our information systems well, with good requirements that support the job task, we will have fewer data problems."

"Isn't it interesting," interjected Bob "how it all goes back to where we started with data engineering, one of the first EIM functions?"

## Part of the Team: Topics for Discussion and Action

1. The EIM team's discussion focused on the need for a standard taxonomy to use to qualify the dimensions of data quality. Without such a taxonomy, comparability of data quality measurements are meaningless across the organization. The team put development of the taxonomy in the "parking lot" to be addressed at a future date. To help the team take this item out of the parking lot, do the following:
   a. Prepare a matrix that compares and contrasts the quality dimensions cited in this chapter
   b. Assess similarities among the approaches
   c. Identify important differences among the approaches
   d. Based on your assessments, prepare a draft taxonomy for the EIM team on the dimensions of data quality. Include your justifications of why each of the dimensions you suggest should be included in the taxonomy.

## Advanced Concepts

1. Shelia and Bob reported on only three data quality management and assessment frameworks. While these are a good start for illustration purposes, it would be good if the EIM team had a larger sample to evaluate key similarities and differences among models. Conduct a literature review and identify at least two other frameworks or models. Evaluate these against the criteria Shelia and Bob developed. List the insights gained from this exercise. What are the similarities? What new information have you identified to help St. Rita's develop their own framework?
2. Several approaches to data quality assessment have been presented in this chapter. Given the variety of approaches and what each has to offer and building off the taxonomy developed as The Part of the Team exercise, develop a concept paper for a data quality assessment and measurement model for St. Rita's. Include in the concept paper the following:
   a. Executive summary
   b. How data quality will benefit St. Rita's
   c. Data quality taxonomy for St. Rita's
   d. Proposed method for data quality assessment at St. Rita's
   e. Implementation steps for data quality assessment at St. Rita's
   f. Key actions, resources, and a five-year plan for data quality at St. Rita's

## References

AHIMA. 2012. Data Quality Management Model (Updated). *Journal of AHIMA* 83(7): 62–67.

Ahn, K, H. Rakha, and D. Hill. 2008. Data Quality White Paper. U.S. Department of Transportation. Report Number FHWA-HOP-08-038. http://ops.fhwa.dot.gov/publications/fhwahop08038/pdf/dataqual_whitepaper.pdf.

American College of Surgeons. 2011. The 1919 Minimum Standard Document. http://www.facs.org/archives/minimumhighlight.html.

Dravis, F. 2008. White Paper: Enterprise Information Management: Strategy, Best Practices and Technologies on Your Path to Success. Baseline Consulting Group. http://www.sap.com/netherlands/solutions/sapbusinessobjects/pdf/Whitepaper_Baseline_Consulting_Enterprise_Information_Management.pdf.

CIHI. 2009. The CIHI Data Quality Framework. http://www.cihi.ca/CIHI-ext-portal/pdf/internet/data_quality_framework_2009_en.

Dick, R., E.B. Steen, and the Institute of Medicine, eds. 1991. *The Computer-Based Patient Record: An Essential Technology for Health Care*. Washington, DC: National Academy Press.

English, L.P. 2009. *Information Quality Applied: Best Practices for Improving Business Information, Processes and Systems*. Indianapolis: Wiley Publishing, Inc.

Gardner, E. 2010. Danger. *Health Data Management* 18(8): 30–34.

GS1. 2010a (May). Data Quality: An introduction to the role and value of data quality in organisations. http://www.gs1pa.org/pdf/importanciadatos.pdf.

GS1. 2010b (October). Data Quality Framework Version 3.0 Issue 2. http://www.gs1.org/gdsn/dqf/data_quality_framework.

Institute of Medicine. 2011. *Health IT and Patient Safety: Building Safer Systems for Better Care*. Washington, D.C.: The National Academies Press. http://www.iom.edu/Reports/2011/Health-IT-and-Patient-Safety-Building-Safer-Systems-for-Better-Care/Press-Release.aspx.

Kopola, B. and M.E. Mitchell. 2011. Use of digital health records raise ethics concerns. *Journal of Nursing Administration's Healthcare Law, Ethics, and Regulation* 13(3): 84–89. https://www.nursingcenter.com/pdf.asp?AID=1213590.

Markle Foundation. 2006 (April). The Connecting for Health Common Framework: Background Issues on Data Quality. http://www.markle.org/sites/default/files/T5_Background_Issues_Data.pdf.

Office of the National Coordinator (ONC). 2009. Understand Unintended Consequences: Example 14: System Integration Problems. http://www.healthit.gov/unintended-consequences/content/example-14-system-integration-problems.html.

PDR Secure. 2012 (January). The EHR Event Newsletter. http://hosted-p0.vresp.com/250140/15426f2a90/ARCHIVE.

Sáez, C., J. Martínez-Miranda., M. Robles, and J.M. García-Gómez. 2012. Organizing data quality assessment of shifting biomedical data. *Studies in Health Technology and Informatics* 180: 721–725.

Swartz, N. 2007. Gartner Warns Firms of Dirty Data. *Information Management Journal* 41(3): 6.

Terry, K. 2013 (January 13). EHRs linked to errors, harm, AMA says. *Information Week*. http://www.informationweek.com/healthcare/electronic-health-records/ehrs-linked-to-errors-harm-ama-says/d/d-id/1102259?.

Tufo, H. M., J. Speidel. 1971. *Problems with Medical Records*. Lippincott-Raven Publishers.

United States Department of Transportation. 2004 (September 15). Traffic Data Quality Measurement: Final Report. 3.0 Framework for Data Quality Measurement. http://ntl.bts.gov/lib/jpodocs/repts_te/14058_files/index.htm.

Weiskopf, N., C. Weng. 2013. Methods and dimensions of electronic health record data quality assessment: Enabling reuse for clinical research. *Journal of the American Medical Informatics Association* 20(1): 144–151.

# Chapter 13

# Terminology and Classification Systems Management

In contrast to other industries, there are different drivers, imperatives, and implementation issues involving enterprise information management (EIM) in healthcare. The first eight electronic health information management (EHIM) domains are consistent, in most respects, with EIM models developed by others (chapter 4). The ninth and last domain, terminology and classification systems, is a significant differentiator among the models.

The need for standardized nomenclatures (language) and classification systems in healthcare has long been acknowledged. A nomenclature is a list of acceptable or approved terminology. On the other hand, a classification organizes like or related terms or entities in a systematic way (Moriyama et al. 2011, 13). As early as 1839, William Farr in the first Annual Report of the Registrar-General of England and Wales noted that a disease nomenclature was of equal importance in death registration as weights and measures in the physical sciences.

Adoption of standard nomenclatures and classification systems in healthcare is important for several reasons. They are critical in order to merge or compare data from a variety of often dissimilar data sources in order to produce comparable statistics about population health, disease processes, treatment outcomes, and productivity measures. They are essential for exchanging meaningful and usable data within and among organizations for healthcare delivery, research, administrative purposes, and payment for healthcare services. The Institutes of Medicine (IOM) underscores the importance of standardization:

> If health professionals are to be able to send and receive data in an understandable and usable manner, both the sender and the receiver must have common clinical terminologies for describing, classifying, and coding medical terms and concepts. Use of standardized clinical terminologies facilitates electronic data collection at the point of care; retrieval of relevant data, information, and knowledge; and reuse of data for multiple purposes (for example, disease surveillance, clinical decision support, patient safety reporting). No single terminology has the depth and breadth to represent the broad spectrum of medical knowledge; thus a core group of well-integrated, non-redundant clinical terminologies will be needed to serve as the backbone of clinical information and patient safety systems. (Aspden et al. 2004, 37–38)

While a large number of nomenclatures and classification systems have been developed, the lack of resources on how to properly use these has resulted in a slow adoption rate (Cimino 2010). On the other hand, as more electronic clinical information systems are developed, organizations are using standard nomenclatures and classification systems to a greater degree, although many times, not to their full potential. Most of these are specialized and do well in supporting a specific intended use. But when attempting to compare and evaluate for equivalence from one nomenclature, classification system, or data set to another, a separate problem related to data sharing and interoperability emerges. One approach for solving this predicament is to create data maps from one system to another that facilitate the reuse of data (McBride et al. 2006).

Thus, the focus of this chapter is to shed light on two equally important priorities. The first is to build awareness of the breadth of existing nomenclatures, classifications, and data sets and the potential benefits they offer in creating useful information through standardization. The second is to address how cartography or data mapping can help solve the conundrum created by using a variety of specialized nomenclatures and classifications that perform well for their intended purpose but are not readily amenable for data sharing or merging. Specifically, this chapter covers topics that will help you to:

- Explain the history of terminologies and classifications in healthcare
- Assess the types of terminologies and classifications used in healthcare
- Use healthcare data standards and data sets
- Apply data mapping principles
- Practice data governance principles applied to terminology and classification management

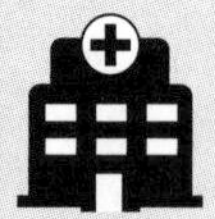

### The St. Rita's Healthcare System Case Study

Denise and Shirlee volunteered to study the last EIM function: terminology and classification management. Denise had experience in the subject, and Shirlee had always been fascinated with the topic since a brief brush with the nomenclature SNOMED a few years ago. "OK, Denise, where do we begin?" asked Shirlee.

"It's always good to start with the foundations," replied Denise. "The history of how classifications started in the middle ages is really captivating. When I was in London last year, I had an opportunity see an exhibit on the bills of mortality. The one published in 1665 was particularly moving because there were so many deaths due to the plague and high infant mortality. During peak epidemics, these hand bills, listing the number of deaths for each week and their associated causes, were published weekly and posted in public places around the city. It was sort of the "Internet" of its day and forerunner, although exceedingly primitive, of population statistics that public health departments publish today."

"Our next target ought to be examining the profusion of terminologies and classification systems that exist. I think you will be surprised, Shirlee, to see the cornucopia of these. While each has a good purpose, the number of these present real problems for data exchange," Denise added.

Denise and Shirlee worked out their game plan and decided that Shirlee would focus on the historical aspects and Denise would compile a beginning list of terminologies and classifications.

## Terminologies and Classifications in Healthcare

Frequently, the terms terminology, nomenclature, vocabulary, and classification are used interchangeably and misconstrued. Because of the subtleties among them, it is often difficult to get complete agreement on the definitions for these concepts (Palkie 2013). For discussion purposes in this chapter, the following are explanations of each:

- A **terminology** is a set of terms representing a system of concepts.
- A **vocabulary** is a collection of words or phrases with their meanings, that is, a dictionary of those terms.
- A **nomenclature** is a recognized system of terms that follows pre-established naming conventions.
- A **classification** is a system that arranges or organizes like or related entities (Giannangelo 2013, 3).

## History of Terminology and Classification Systems

In healthcare, professionals use terminologies primarily to capture clinical information. To accomplish this purpose, terminologies are highly detailed and have substantial granularity but at the same time lack reporting rules and guidelines. Classifications, on the other hand, are intended for secondary data use, including quality of care measurement, reimbursement, statistical and public health reporting, operational and strategic planning, and other administrative functions (AMIA and AHIMA Terminology and Classification Policy Task Force 2006).

Both terminologies and classifications have a long history in medicine going back to the Middle Ages, beginning with parish authorities registering births and deaths in Italian city-states. In sixteenth century London, the systematic collection of the number of births and deaths was documented in bulletins (bills). These were called London's bills of mortality. The bills were first introduced as a way to systematically record plague deaths. Local parish clerks collected the information in London parishes and submitted the data for weekly publication. Over time, the bills became more sophisticated, and in 1629, officials segregated deaths by sex and added additional causes of death (Byrne 2012).

In 1662, John Graunt used the London bills of mortality to compile the *Natural and Political Observations of the Bills of Mortality*, an attempt to classify diseases for statistical purposes (Jones 1945). From the data in the bills, Graunt created mortality tables, re-categorized the causes of death, and sought explanations from the previously disorganized data, such as endemic disease patterns and their causes. His contribution created the disciplines of population-based epidemiology and modern nosology (Chute 2000).

The development of healthcare terminologies has been evolutionary. This is no more evident than in the developmental path of the **Standardized Nomenclature of Diseases (SND)** which ushered in the modern era of clinical descriptions in 1929 and eventually led to the development of the Systematized Nomenclature of Medicine Clinical Terms (SNOMED CT) released in 2002 and used today. This evolutionary path included SND, the Standard Nomenclature of Diseases and Operations (SNDO), the Systemized Nomenclature of Pathology (SNOP), SNOMED (medicine), SNOMED II, SNOMED International, SNOMED RT, and SNOMED Clinical Terms (Chute 2000).

The development of clinical classifications has taken an evolutionary path similar to medical terminologies. The **International Classification of Diseases (ICD)** began as the Bertillon Classification of Causes of Death in 1893. The classification, also used as a standard nomenclature and for the statistical study of disease, underwent revision approximately every 10 years under the auspices of the International Statistical Institute. In 1948, the World Health Organization (WHO) became responsible for maintaining the ICD. The classification is in its 10th edition, and the WHO is currently revising it, with expected completion of the 11th edition in 2017. As of 2015, more than 100 nations used the system to report morbidity and mortality data (WHO 2014).

The National Center for Health Statistics (NCHS) developed a clinical modification of ICD-9 called ICD-9-CM to use in the United States. This modification provides more diagnostic and procedure detail to classify morbidity and mortality data and surgical procedures. Healthcare professionals use ICD-9-CM to classify inpatient diagnoses and procedures as well as use it as the basis for reporting healthcare delivery services for reimbursement purposes.

The development of terminologies and classifications continues today. A single, comprehensive standard medical terminology which would improve the automated flow of clinical information, however, does not exist (Open Clinical 2005). In the United States, the **Unified Medical Language System (UMLS)** project began in 1986 to aid health professionals and researchers in retrieving and integrating information from a variety of sources and for users to link disparate information systems. Today there are in excess of 100 different vocabularies and classifications compiled in the UMLS. Table 13.1 provides a listing of some these vocabularies and classifications in use today. The following sections provide an overview of a few of the more predominant ones in the United States.

Table 13.1. Governance of various terminology systems in the United States

| Name of Terminology | Owner | Governance Process |
|---|---|---|
| Alternative Billing Concept (ABC) Codes | Foundation for Integrative Healthcare | Terminology development is coordinated through the Foundation for Integrative Healthcare (FIHC) and its practitioner association constituents (called member associations). |
| Clinical Care Classification | Virginia Saba | Terminology updates are vetted through an Advisory Board. |
| Current Dental Terminology (CDT) | American Dental Association (ADA) | ADA manages and provides staff to coordinate the technical review and revision process. A Code Revision Committee is composed of representatives from the ADA, America's Health Insurance Plans, the Blue Cross/Blue Shield Association, Centers for Medicare & Medicaid Services (CMS), Delta Dental Plans Association, and National Purchaser of Dental Benefits. |

(continued)

Table 13.1. Governance of various terminology systems in the United States (*Continued*)

| Name of Terminology | Owner | Governance process |
|---|---|---|
| Current Procedural Terminology (CPT) | American Medical Association (AMA) | AMA oversees a CPT editorial panel that is responsible for development and maintenance. The Panel is composed of 15 physicians and two non-physician healthcare professionals appointed by the AMA Board of Trustees. |
| Diagnostic and Statistical Manual (DSM ) | American Psychiatric Association (APA) | APA Division of Research manages the DSM revision process. |
| Global Medical Device Nomenclature (GMDN) | GMDN Agency | The GMDN, located in the United Kingdom, is a not-for-profit corporation. It is responsible for maintaining the GMDN and providing access to the GMDN. |
| Healthcare Common Procedure Coding System (HCPCS) Level II Codes | CMS | The CMS HCPCS Workgroup is responsible for development and maintenance. |
| International Classification of Diseases for Oncology (ICD-O) | World Health Organization (WHO) | WHO Collaborating Centres govern development and maintenance. |
| International Classification of Diseases – 10th Revision (ICD-10) | WHO | WHO Collaborating Centres govern development and maintenance. |
| International Classification of Diseases, 10th Revision, Clinical Modification (ICD-10-CM) | National Center for Health Statistics (NCHS) | NCHS governs development and maintenance. |
| International Classification of Diseases, 10th Revision, Procedure Coding System (ICD-10-PCS) | CMS | The Division of Acute Care within the Center for Medicare Management of CMS governs development and maintenance. ICD-10-PCS was developed by 3M HIS under a CMS contract. |
| International Classification of Diseases, 9th Revision, Clinical Modification (ICD-9-CM) | NCHS and CMS | NCHS governs development and maintenance of ICD-9-CM diagnoses; the Division of Acute Care within the Center for Medicare Management of CMS governs development and maintenance of ICD-9-CM procedures; American Health Information Management Association (AHIMA), American Hospital Association (AHA), CMS, and NCHS (known as the Cooperating Parties) are responsible for developing official coding guidelines for proper use of ICD-9-CM codes. |
| International Classification of Functioning, Disability, and Health (ICF) | WHO | WHO Collaborating Centres govern development and maintenance. |
| International Classification of Primary Care | Wonca International Classification Committee | World Organization of Family Doctors governs development and maintenance. |
| Logical Observation Identifiers Names and Codes (LOINC) | Regenstrief Institute | Regenstrief Institute and LOINC Committee govern development and maintenance process. The LOINC Committee is composed of representatives from a number of organizations representing both the public and private sectors. |
| MEDCIN | Medicomp Systems | Medicomp Systems is responsible for maintenance and development. |
| Medical Dictionary for Regulatory Activities (MedDRA) | International Conference on Harmonization of Technical Requirements for Pharmaceuticals for Human Use (ICH) and Maintenance and Support Services (MSSO) | MedDRA MSSO serves as the repository, maintainer, and distributor of MedDRA as well as the source for the most up-to-date information regarding MedDRA and its application within the biopharmaceutical industry and regulators. The MSSO includes a group of internationally based physicians who review all proposed subscriber changes and provide a timely response directly to the requesting subscriber. |

(continued)

Table 13.1. Governance of various terminology systems in the United States (*Continued*)

| Name of Terminology | Owner | Governance process |
|---|---|---|
| NANDA | NANDA International | NANDA International is responsible for development and maintenance. |
| National Drug File Reference Terminology (NDF-RT) | U.S. Department of Veterans Affairs, Veterans Health Administration (VA) | Ongoing development and maintenance is supported under the VA's Enterprise Reference Terminology project. |
| National Drug Code (NDC) | Food and Drug Administration (FDA) | The Center for Drug Evaluation and Research within the FDA is responsible for ongoing development and maintenance. |
| Nursing Interventions Classification (NIC) | University of Iowa | University of Iowa College of Nursing, Center for Nursing Classification and Clinical Effectiveness is responsible for ongoing development and maintenance. |
| Omaha System | Karen Martin | Karen Martin is responsible for ongoing development and maintenance with updates and feedback from the Omaha System users group. |
| Perioperative Nursing Data Set | Association of Perioperative Registered Nurses (AORN) | AORN is responsible for ongoing development and maintenance. |
| RxNorm | National Library of Medicine (NLM ) | NLM is responsible for ongoing development and maintenance. |
| Systematized Nomenclature of Dentistry (SNODENT) | ADA | The Advisory Committee on Dental Electronic Nomenclature, Indexing, and Classification (ACODENIC) processes requests for modifications, and Council on Dental Benefit Programs has final approval. ACODENIC is composed of representatives from all of the recognized dental specialty organizations, payers, and the ADA. |
| SNOMED CT | International Health Terminology Standards Development Organisation (IHTSDO) | Owned, maintained, and distributed by IHTSDO, a nonprofit standards organization governed by 27 international members. |
| Universal Medical Device Nomenclature System (UMDNS) | ECRI Institute | ECRI Institute, a non-profit designated evidence-based practice center, governs ongoing development and maintenance. |

Source: Terminology and Classification Task Force 2007; and LaTour et al. 2013.

## Terminologies and Classifications Used for Administrative and Statistical Reporting

It could be argued that terminologies were initially developed for administrative purposes and statistical reporting. Certainly, the early initiatives in the Middle Ages and in sixteenth century London of tracking deaths due to plague epidemics were for these purposes. "The raw number of plague deaths, as well as trends up or down, also gained importance as civic authorities were required to judge whether the summer would bring a handful of cases or an epidemic that would empty the city and crash its economy" (Byrne 2012, 38). Thus, population statistics in the sixteenth century were as important and used for the same reasons as they are today.

Today, terminology and classification systems support a variety of administrative functions from classifying morbidity and mortality information to developing population and epidemiology statistics. These statistics subsequently inform health policy, public health planning, and healthcare delivery services development. The statistics support other functions as well. Among these are determining outcomes of patient care, monitoring resource utilization, measuring quality, safety, and appropriateness of care, analyzing provider practices, performing clinical research and clinical trials, and substantiating reimbursement for healthcare services. The next sections describe five commonly used systems.

## International Classification of Diseases, Ninth Revision, Clinical Modification

*Summary:* Introduced in the United States in 1979, ICD-9-CM is a modification of *The International Classification of Diseases, Ninth Revision* developed by the WHO. The NCHS developed the modification for use in the United States to provide morbidity data and introduce a volume for classification of procedures. Since 1983, healthcare organizations, government agencies, and insurance companies have used coded data using ICD-9-CM as the basis for determining reimbursement for healthcare services.

*Content:* Three volumes comprise ICD-9-CM. Volume 1 is a tabular list of chronological codes for diseases, injuries, and supplementary classifications. Volume 2 is an alphabetic index of terms and corresponding codes for diseases, injuries, and external causes of injury and poisoning, and also includes a table of drugs and chemicals. Volume 3 classifies procedure codes and includes both an alphabetical index of terms and a tabular list of codes. Diagnosis codes are made up of three to five characters.

*Structure:* For diagnosis codes, the structure is three characters to the left of a decimal point, and up to two additional digits to the right. All characters are numbers except for the beginning character for codes in the supplementary classifications. For instance, code 492.21 represents obstructive chronic bronchitis with (acute) exacerbation. An example of a code from a supplementary classification is E928.6, representing an external cause of an injury due to environmental exposure to harmful algae and toxins.

Procedure codes have at least three digits, with a maximum of four digits. Two digits are placed to the left a decimal, and one or two additional digits are placed to the right. For example, 37.11 represents cardiotomy.

*Governance:* The NCHS governs development and maintenance of ICD-9-CM diagnoses.

The Division of Acute Care within the Center for Medicare Management of CMS governs development and maintenance of ICD-9-CM procedures. AHIMA, AHA, CMS, and NCHS (known as the cooperating parties) are responsible for developing official coding guidelines for proper use of ICD-9-CM codes.

## International Classification of Diseases, Tenth Revision, Clinical Modification/Procedure Coding System

*Summary:* Scheduled to replace ICD-9-CM beginning October 1, 2015, *The International Classification of Diseases, Tenth Revision, Clinical Modification (ICD-10-CM)* and *The International Classification of Diseases, Tenth Revision, Procedure Coding System (ICD-10-PCS)* are clinical modifications of the WHO's ICD system. While the purpose of ICD-10-CM remains the same as ICD-9-CM, it contains a substantial increase in content as opposed to its predecessor.

*Content:* ICD-10-CM and ICD-10-PCS are used for different purposes: ICD-10-CM for diagnosis coding and ICD-10-PCS for inpatient procedure coding. ICD-10-CM contains more than 68,000 diagnosis codes as compared to approximately 13,000 diagnosis codes in ICD-9-CM. The additional content allows for greater specificity in code assignment, expanded use of injury codes, and provides for the identification of laterality information (for example, side of body affected). Like ICD-9-CM, there is both a tabular chronological list of codes and an alphabetical list of terms and their corresponding codes.

ICD-10-PCS replaces volume 3 of ICD-9-CM and contains approximately 87,000 procedure codes as compared to about 4,000 procedure codes of its predecessor.

*Structure:* ICD-10-CM codes consist of three to seven characters with three characters placed to the left of a decimal, and up to four characters to the right. The first character is alphabetic, the second character is numeric, and characters three through seven are alphabetic or numeric. Alphabetic characters are not case sensitive. An example is code S93.401A which represents "Right ankle sprain, initial encounter."

ICD-10-PCS codes have a multi-axial, seven-character, alpha-numeric structure. The position of each character has a specific meaning. For example, reading the code for dilation of right femoral artery with intraluminal device, open approach, 047K0DZ, from left to right, the positions represent the following:

- First position: section
- Second position: body system

- Third position: root operation
- Fourth position: body part
- Fifth position: approach
- Sixth position: device
- Seventh position: qualifier

*Governance:* The NCHS governs development and maintenance of ICD-10-CM diagnoses, and the Division of Acute Care within the Center for Medicare Management of CMS governs development and maintenance of ICD-10-PCS procedures. The AHIMA, AHA, CMS, and NCHS (known as the cooperating parties) are responsible for developing official coding guidelines for proper use of ICD-10-CM codes.

## Current Procedural Terminology

*Summary:* The **Current Procedural Terminology (CPT)** describes medical services and procedures performed by physicians and other healthcare providers. The terminology contains no diagnosis codes. It is used for reimbursement purposes to report physician services, non-physician services (for example, therapy), and surgical services performed in hospital outpatient departments and ambulatory surgery centers. The data are also used for trending and planning, benchmarking, and evaluating patient care services.

The system was introduced in 1966 by the AMA and is published annually. In 1983, CMS adopted CPT as the standard for physician and hospital outpatient service coding for Medicare reimbursement. With implementation of HIPAA code set standards, CPT, in combination with the HCPCS (addressed in the following section), became the only acceptable system for reporting services in these outpatient settings.

*Content:* CPT is composed of several types of codes. Category I codes are five-digit numeric codes that describe procedures and services performed by physicians and other healthcare providers. There are six main sections within the Category I codes. These include evaluation and management codes, anesthesia codes, surgery codes, radiology codes, pathology and laboratory codes, and medicine codes. CPT also provides supplementary codes. These include Category II, Category III, and CPT Modifiers. Category II focuses on performance management and contains optional codes. Professionals use these codes for specific services or test results that are agreed upon by the Performance Measures Advisory Group (PMAG) for contributing to positive health outcomes and quality patient care. Category III codes are for emerging technology procedures or services. Codes in this category are for data collection purposes to substantiate widespread usage of an emerging procedure or service. Medical coders can report CPT Modifiers along with many Category I codes to report additional information, such as bilateral and multiple procedures.

*Structure:* Category I codes are five-digit numeric codes that may also have two-digit character modifiers. Most of the modifiers are numeric, but some are alphanumeric. Category II codes are composed of five characters: four numbers and an alphabetic fifth character, capital letter F. Category III codes are composed of five characters: four numbers, and an alphabetic fifth character, capital letter T.

*Governance:* CPT is a registered trademark of the AMA. AMA oversees a CPT editorial panel that is responsible for development and maintenance.

## Healthcare Common Procedure Coding System

*Summary:* The **Healthcare Common Procedure Coding System (HCPCS),** also referred to as the **National Codes**, was introduced in 1983 by CMS to report services and supplies not covered by CPT codes for reimbursement purposes. HCPCS contains two sections, called levels. Level I contains CPT codes as published by the AMA. Level II contains codes that represent products, supplies, and services not included in CPT. HCPCS codes are used for reimbursement purposes for services to both Medicare and Medicaid patients.

*Content:* Level II codes are divided into 17 sections. These sections contain procedure codes primarily for non-physician services such as for enteral and parenteral therapy, chemotherapy, and drug abuse treatment services. HCPCS also includes a table of drugs that describes administered drugs.

*Structure:* Level II codes consist of five-digit alphanumeric codes beginning with an alphabetic character (A through V, excluding S), followed by four numeric characters.

*Governance:* The CMS HCPCS Workgroup is responsible for developing and maintaining the classification.

## National Drug Codes

*Summary:* The **National Drug Codes (NDCs)** serve as product identifiers for human drugs and biologics. The NDC is the HIPAA standard medical data code set for reporting drugs and biologics for retail pharmacy transactions. NDC numbers are included in the Medicare Part D data, which CMS collects from transactions between pharmacies and Medicare Part D sponsors.

*Content:* The NDC includes prescription drugs and selected over-the-counter and homeopathic products.

*Structure:* Each drug is assigned a unique 10-digit, 3-segment number. The first segment is the labeler or vendor code, the second segment is the product code, and the third segment is the package code. The FDA assigns a code to each labeler. The product code is assigned by the firm and identifies a specific strength, dosage form, and formulation for a particular firm. The package code is also assigned by the firm. It identifies package size.

*Governance:* The Center for Drug Evaluation and Research within the FDA is responsible for ongoing development and maintenance of the NDCs.

# Other Terminologies and Classifications

Described here are other terminologies and classifications commonly used for clinical purposes today in the United States.

## Systematized Nomenclature of Medicine Clinical Terms

*Summary:* **SNOMED CT** is a controlled medical terminology with comprehensive coverage of diseases, clinical findings, etiologies, procedures, and outcomes. A controlled terminology means "the content of the terminology is managed with careful quality assurance procedures in place to ensure that the terminology is structurally sound, biomedically accurate, and consistent with current practice" (Foley 2010, 115). SNOMED is based on SNOP. The College of American Pathologists published the first edition of SNOMED in 1974. Since that time, SNOMED has gone through different versions. IHTSDO first released SNOMED CT in 2002 and revises and updates the international version twice a year. The general purpose of SNOMED CT is to index, store, and retrieve information about a patient in an electronic health record (EHR). Unlike a classification, SNOMED CT is designed to uniquely identify clinical information consistently and in great detail.

*Content:* SNOMED CT is a comprehensive terminology containing terms about diseases, findings, procedures, body structures, and pharmacy products. It contains over 300,000 active concepts with unique meanings and formal logic-based definitions organized into hierarchies.

*Structure:* Unlike classifications that organize codes in a hierarchical model by body system (for example, ICD), SNOMED CT codes are based on underlying medical concepts. The basic structural elements of SNOMED CT are concepts, descriptions, hierarchies, attributes, and relationships.

*Governance:* The IHTSDO is responsible for maintaining and distributing SNOMED CT.

## Logical Observation Identifiers, Names and Codes

*Summary:* The **Logical Observational Identifiers, Names and Codes (LOINC)** provides a set of universal identifiers for laboratory and clinical observations and is the generally accepted exchange standard for laboratory results. The purpose of LOINC is to provide a universal code system that facilitates exchange, pooling, and processing of results. LOINC was developed at the Regenstrief Institute, Inc., a nonprofit, medical research organization associated with Indiana University. LOINC development began in 1994, and Regenstrief released the latest version, 2.46, in December 2013. Healthcare organizations use LOINC in their EHR systems as a clinical reference terminology to capture data for problem lists and patient assessments at the point of care (Palkie 2013).

*Content:* LOINC has essentially two parts: the laboratory portion and the clinical portion. The laboratory portion includes the content for clinical laboratory specimen testing such as microbiology, chemistry, allergy, and toxicology testing. The clinical portion includes terms, for example, relating to radiology testing, ultrasound, and vital signs.

*Structure:* A LOINC code consists of a numerical identifier with a check digit separated by a dash. There is no embedded meaning in a LOINC code. An example of a LOINC code is 718-7 which refers to the hemoglobin level. LOINC codes are assigned in order. The structured LOINC name is composed of six axes: component, property measured, timing, system, scale, and method. The component refers to the substance being measured, evaluated, or observed, such as sodium or glucose. The property measured refers to the characteristic of the analyte being measured, observed, or evaluated, such as mass or substance concentration. Timing refers to the interval of time over which the observation or measurement is, such as 12 hours, 24 hours, or a specific point in time. System refers to the context or specimen type such as serum, urine, or whole blood. Scale describes the scale used for the measurement or observation such as quantitative, ordinal, or nominal. Method is an optional axis and used only if it affects the interpretation, such as in the case of different normal ranges or test sensitivity.

*Governance:* The Regenstrief Institute and LOINC Laboratory and Clinical Committees govern the development and maintenance process. The LOINC Committee is composed of representatives from a number of organizations representing both the public and private sectors. Funding sources include the Regenstrief Foundation and the NLM.

## Terminology and Classification Challenges

The multiplicity of terminologies and classifications in healthcare presents several challenges. While terminologies and classifications are extremely useful for their intended purpose, obvious challenges arise when translating one terminology to another. This is especially evident when comparing statistics gathered using one classification to those gathered using another system, or when a computer application using one terminology must exchange information with another application that employs a completely different terminology.

First, the life cycle of terminologies and classifications is complex. Given the examples described in this chapter, the differences in life cycle management among these makes the process of translation and data exchange among them difficult. For example, updates are not synchronous and development methods are not standardized. Further complicating the issue is that many of these are proprietary, and the development and maintenance of the terminologies are hampered by prohibiting open publication of content (AMIA and AHIMA 2006).

Another challenge for the individual organizations using these is the lack of business process automation across organizations or departments for updating or maintaining terminologies. Once organizations use terminologies and classifications, they then must deal with issues for maintaining and updating these for the variety of computer applications that use them. A matrix of four healthcare organizations showing the multiple tools an organization must use to deal with interoperability issues appears in table 13.2. (AMIA and AHIMA 2006).

Table 13.2. Terminology services and tools in four organizations

| Service | CUMC[2] | IHC[3] | Mayo[4] | VAMC[5] |
|---|---|---|---|---|
| Terminology Development/Editing/ Maintenance | MED | 3M HDD | LexGrid | Apelon TDE/SDS Maint. App. |
| Terminology Browser | MED | IHC Search | LexGrid | Apelon DTS/SDS Maint. App. |
| Terminology Mapping | MED (1:1 only) | IHC Match | LexGrid | Apelon TermWorks |
| Concept-based Indexing and Retrieval | Infobutton Manager | IHC Infobutton | LexGrid | VETS/SDS Read-Only APIs |
| Terminology Import | MED | 3M HDD | LexGrid | VETS |
| Terminology Export | MED | 3M HDD | LexGrid | VETS/Database Replication |

(continued)

Table 13.2. Terminology services and tools in four organizations (*Continued*)

| Service | CUMC[2] | IHC[3] | Mayo[4] | VAMC[5] |
|---|---|---|---|---|
| Natural Language Processing | MedLEE | IHC NLP | UIMA/LexGrid | |
| Clinical Terminology Server[1] | MED (word completion only) | 3M HDD | LexGrid | VETS |

[1]Word normalization, word completion, target terminology specification, spelling correction, lexical matching, term completion, semantic locality, term composition, and term decomposition.

[2] At Columbia University Medical Center of New York Presbyterian Hospital, terminology services are supported through the Medical Entities Dictionary (MED), the Infobutton Manager, and the Medical Language Extraction and Encoding (MedLEE) system. The MED, a concept-oriented terminology, serves as the institutional data dictionary and uses a semantic network model that includes a classification hierarchy. MED-related applications support browsing, development, editing, and maintenance of the MED as well as terminology import and export. Terminology server functionality of the MED is limited. The Infobutton Manager is built upon the foundation of semantic relationships in the MED and provides context-specific links to information resources from within the clinical information systems, for example, at the time of order entry or when viewing laboratory results. MedLEE provides natural language processing for a variety of functions including decision support. These tools provide a rich foundation upon which to build a broader set of terminology services throughout the enterprise.

[3] At Intermountain Healthcare, the run time services, terminology database, and basic import and export programs are based on the Healthcare Data Dictionary (HDD) application provided by 3M Healthcare. The initial design of the software was described by Roberto Rocha (see "Designing a Controlled Medical Vocabulary Server: The VOSER Project," *Computers and Biomedical Research*, 1994). Intermountain has built search programs and terminology matching programs that extend the original HDD functionality. Intermountain wrote its own Infobutton technology, but it is based largely on the model created by Cimino at Columbia. Natural language processing software has been created by Peter Haug and associated researchers at Intermountain.

[4]At Mayo Clinic, production terminology services remain largely done through vendor products (e.g., GE/IDX/LastWord). However, the research community is fully supported by LexGrid (http://informatics.mayo.edu). NLP tools were developed in collaboration with IBM and mounted on the Unstructured Information Management Architecture, though the entire suite remains open source. The LexGrid tools underpin vocabulary maintenance and support at HL7, the National Cancer Institute's Biomedical Informatics Grid, and the CDC Public Health Information Network.

[5]At the Department of Veterans Affairs, Apelon is used for clinical terminology, but administrative terminology is homegrown. Terminology services are provided by a combination of VA-developed and commercial products. Currently, clinical and administrative (nonclinical) terminology are modeled, maintained, and deployed separately. Clinical terminology is modeled and maintained in the Apelon Terminology Development Environment. The VA-developed VHA Enterprise Terminology Services (VETS) tools allow analysts to review and deploy terminology to VA sites as well as provide a real-time terminology server. Development and utilization of the terminology services are still in the early stages. Administrative terminology is developed and maintained in the VA-developed solution called Standard Data Service (SDS) maintenance application. SDS data is stored in a central Oracle database. Applications access the data via read-only APIs, and cache the data locally in either Oracle or Cache databases. Nightly replication keeps the databases in sync, should any changes occur in the SDS central database. Synchronization with Legacy files will be achieved through HL7 messaging.

Source: AMIA and AHIMA 2006

The landscape is also complicated by the many governing bodies determining what system to adopt and implement. Just knowing what terminologies and classifications exist, what they are used for, when they were adopted and implemented, when they were updated, and who maintains them is a challenging task for organizations (AMIA and AHIMA 2006).

## The St. Rita's Healthcare System Case Study

"OK, Denise, now my head is really spinning," exclaimed Shirlee. "How does one ever keep all of the classifications, vocabularies, and terminologies straight?"

"Well that *is* the problem," replied Denise. "And, we just skimmed the surface. There are terminologies for nursing, primary care, dental care, clinical drugs, and many, many more. As we found out in our research, the NLM's UMLS contains over 100 vocabularies used in medicine and health."

"OK, for the regular hospital, how is all this handled? What does a hospital like St. Rita's do about working with all these terminologies and classifications?" asked Shirlee.

"This is why the American Medical Informatics Association (AMIA) and AHIMA convened a special task force on terminology and classification policy to study this issue. The task force made several recommendations to address fragmented governance, proprietary licensing, and uncoordinated release times. There are efforts underway by groups such as the NLM, the Healthcare Information Technology Standards Panel (HITSP), the Consolidated Health Informatics Initiative (CHI), and others to help ensure interoperability among terminologies and classifications," Denise replied.

"The United States can't be the only country encountering these problems. How are other countries handling this issue?" asked Shirlee.

"Other countries are addressing the issue in various ways; Australia, Canada, and the United Kingdom are among them. The AMIA-AHIMA task force provides an overview of these efforts." Denise then shared a copy of the report with Shirlee. [You can view the report in the student workbook for this text.]

"This is extremely helpful," said Shirley as she skimmed the report. "The report outlines the challenges that I instinctively thought were issues. And, the task force makes some excellent recommendations. We should include a copy of the report in the briefing materials we give to the EIM committee. But how are these issues handled today?"

"Efforts have moved forward in trying to deal with some of these issues," Denise replied. "Specifically, federal initiatives in health IT standards adoption that have been spurred by legislation such as HIPAA, the Health Information Technology for Economic and Clinical Health Act (HITECH), and meaningful use that require data exchange. It would be good to look at the status of these and see how much progress the feds are making. Let's look at both data set standards and data interchange standards to get a feel for how they are approaching interoperability among information system applications. That may help shed additional light on how they're addressing terminologies," Denise suggested.

# Data Set Standards

A **data set** is defined as a list of recommended data elements with uniform definitions that are relevant for a particular use. Data sets are used to encourage uniform data collection and reporting. Data sets include both a description of the data elements in the data set and definitions for those elements. The data element definitions may include element attributes such as allowable values and length. Figure 13.1 provides a listing of common data sets in the United States. To illustrate what constitutes a data set and how to use them, the next sections cover the Uniform Hospital Discharge Data Set (UHDDS) and the Uniform Ambulatory Care Data Set (UACDS).

Figure 13.1. Examples of commonly used data sets in the United States

Common US data sets

- Healthcare Effectiveness Data and Information Set (HEDIS)
- Uniform Hospital Discharge Data Set (UHDDS)
- Uniform Ambulatory Care Data Set (UACDS)
- Minimum Data Set for Long-Term Care and Resident Assessment Protocols (MDS 3.0)
- Outcomes and Assessment Information Set (OASIS)
- Data Elements for Emergency Department Systems (DEEDS)
- Inpatient Rehabilitation Facility-Patient Assessment Instrument (IRF-PAI)
- Functional Independence Measures (FIM)
- End Stage Renal Disease (ESRD) data sets
- Transplant data through United Network for Organ Sharing (UNOS)
- Mental Health National Outcome Measures (NOMS)
- Drug and Alcohol Services Information System (DASIS)
- Essential Medical Data Set
- Meaningful Use Requirements

Source: LaTour, et al. 2013

## Uniform Hospital Discharge Data Set

The **Uniform Hospital Discharge Data Set (UHDDS)** is a core set of data elements adopted by the U.S. Department of Health, Education, and Welfare in 1974 that acute care short-term stay hospitals collect on all discharges (Giannangelo 2010). The UHDDS is one of the oldest data sets in use in the United States. Promoting the standardization of health information through uniform minimum data sets was an ambitious project that was taken on through the leadership of the National Committee on Vital and Health Statistics (NCVHS) in 1970. Until this time, vital statistics in the United States were limited to uniform data in birth and death certificates, and did not apply to a wide range of other health data. The development of healthcare data sets beyond the limited scope of birth and death certificates was viewed as a critical advance in gathering data for vital and health statistics.

The purpose of the NCVHS efforts in establishing standard data sets was to achieve comparability in health data collected by federal agencies, states and localities, the private sector, and the international community. The first Uniform Hospital Abstract Minimum Data Set was recommended by the NCVHS in 1972 after extensive field test and study. While not endorsed by the Department of Health, Education, and Welfare (DHEW) as departmental policy until 1980, several key national organizations in the private sector endorsed it (Kanaan 1999). Since 1980, the UHDDS has gone through several revisions.

The Uniform Bill 04 (UB-04), the Medicare and Medicaid claim form, is a major vehicle for collecting UHDDS data elements. UHDDS definitions were incorporated into the rules and regulations by the federal government for implementing the federal inpatient prospective payment system based on diagnosis related groups (DRGs). The current version of the UHDDS appears in figure 13.2.

Figure 13.2. UHDDS data elements

| Data Element | Definition or Descriptor |
|---|---|
| 01. Personal identifier | The unique number assigned to each patient within a hospital that distinguishes the patient and his or her hospital record from all others in that institution. |
| 02. Date of birth | Month, day, and year of birth. Capture of the full four-digit year of birth is recommended. |
| 03. Sex | Male or female |
| 04. Race and ethnicity | 04a. Race<br>American Indian/Eskimo/Aleut<br>Asian or Pacific Islander<br>Black<br>White<br>Other race<br>Unknown<br>04b. Ethnicity<br>Spanish origin/Hispanic<br>Non-Spanish origin/Non-Hispanic<br>Unknown |
| 05. Residence | Full address of usual residence<br>Zip code (nine digits, if available)<br>Code for foreign residence |
| 06. Hospital identification | A unique institutional number used across data collection systems. The Medicare provider number is the preferred hospital identifier. |
| 07. Admission date | Month, day, and year of admission |
| 08. Type of admission | Scheduled: Arranged with admissions office at least 24 hours prior to admission<br>Unscheduled: All other admissions |
| 09. Discharge date | Month, day, and year of discharge |
| 10. & 11. Physician identification<br>• Attending physician<br>• Operating physician | The Medicare unique physician identification number (UPIN) is the preferred method of identifying the attending physician and operating physician(s) because it is uniform across all data systems. |
| 12. Principal diagnosis | The condition established, after study, to be chiefly responsible for occasioning the admission of the patient to the hospital for care. |

(continued)

Figure 13.2. Continued

| Data Element | Definition or Descriptor |
|---|---|
| 13. Other diagnoses | All conditions that coexist at the time of admission or that develop subsequently or that affect the treatment received or the length of stay. Diagnoses that relate to an earlier episode and have no bearing on the current hospital stay are to be excluded. |
| 14. Qualifier for other diagnoses | A qualifier is given for each diagnosis coded under "other diagnoses" to indicate whether the onset of the diagnosis preceded or followed admission to the hospital. The option "uncertain" is permitted. |
| 15. External cause- of-injury code | The ICD-9-CM code for the external cause of an injury, a poisoning, or an adverse effect (commonly referred to as an E code). Hospitals should complete this item whenever there is a diagnosis of an injury, a poisoning, or an adverse effect. |
| 16. Birth weight of neonate | The specific birth weight of a newborn, preferably recorded in grams. |
| 17. Procedures and dates | All significant procedures are to be reported. A significant procedure is one that is:<br>• Surgical in nature, or<br>• Carries an anesthetic risk, or<br>• Carries a procedural risk, or<br>• Requires specialized training.<br><br>The date of each significant procedure must be reported. When more than one procedure is reported, the principal procedure must be designated. The principal procedure is one that is performed for definitive treatment rather than one performed for diagnostic or exploratory purposes or is necessary to take care of a complication. If two procedures appear to be principal, the one most closely related to the principal diagnosis should be selected as the principal procedure. The UPIN must be reported for the person performing the principal procedure. |
| 18. Disposition of the patient | • Discharged to home (excludes those patients referred to home health service)<br>• Discharged to acute-care hospital<br>• Discharged to nursing facility<br>• Discharged home to be under the care of a home health service (including a hospice)<br>• Discharged to other healthcare facility<br>• Left against medical advice<br>• Alive, other; or alive, not stated<br>• Died<br><br>All categories for primary and other sources are:<br>• Blue Cross/Blue Shield<br>• Other health insurance companies<br>• Other liability insurance<br>• Medicare<br>• Medicaid<br>• Workers' Compensation<br>• Self-insured employer plan<br>• Health maintenance organization<br>• CHAMPUS<br>• CHAMPVA<br>• Other government payers<br>• Self-pay<br>• No charge (free, charity, special research, teaching)<br>• Other |
| 19. Patient's expected source of payment | Primary source<br>Other sources |
| 20. Total charges | All charges billed by the hospital for this hospitalization. Professional charges for individual patient care by physicians are excluded. |

Source: LaTour et al. 2013

## Uniform Ambulatory Care Data Set

The **Uniform Ambulatory Care Data Set (UACDS)** is a data set also developed by NCVHS consisting of a minimum set of patient- or client-specific data elements to be collected in ambulatory care settings. The purpose of the UACDS is to collect and report standardized ambulatory data. The UACDS is recommended by the NCVHS for use in any ambulatory care facility. Unlike the UHDDS, however, the UACDS has not been published into federal regulations. However, the UACDS is incorporated into forms for Medicare outpatient billing. The UACDS data elements and definitions appear in figure 13.3.

Figure 13.3. UACDS data elements

| Data Element | Definition/Descriptor |
|---|---|
| Provider identification, address, type of practice | Provider identification: Include the full name of the provider as well as the unique physician identification number (UPIN). Address: The complete address of the provider's office. In cases where the provider has multiple offices, the location of the usual or principal place of practice should be given. Profession:<br>• Physician, including specialty or field of practice<br>• Other (specify) |
| Place of encounter | Specify the location of the encounter:<br>• Private office<br>• Clinic or health center<br>• Hospital outpatient department<br>• Hospital emergency department<br>• Other (specify) |
| Reason for encounter | Includes, but is not limited to, the patient's complaints and symptoms reflecting his or her own perception of needs, provided verbally or in writing by the patient at the point of entry into the healthcare system or in the patient's own words recorded by an intermediary or a provider at that time. |
| Diagnostic services | All diagnostic services of any type. |
| Problem, diagnosis, or assessment | Describes the provider's level of understanding and the interpretation of the patient's reasons for the encounter and all conditions requiring treatment or management at the time of the encounter. |
| Therapeutic services | List, by name, all services done or ordered:<br>• Medical (including drug therapy)<br>• Surgical<br>• Patient education |
| Preventative services | List, by name, all preventative services and procedures performed at the time of encounter. |
| Disposition | The provider's statement of the next step(s) in the care of the patient. At a minimum, the following classification is suggested:<br>1 No follow-up planned<br>2 Follow-up planned<br>• Return when necessary<br>• Return to the current provider at a specified time<br>• Telephone follow-up<br>• Return to referring provider<br>• Refer to other provider<br>• Admit to hospital<br>• Other |

Source: NCVHS 1992.

## Interoperability and Data Interchange Standards

**Interoperability** means the ability of two or more systems or components to exchange information and use the information they have exchanged (ONC 2013, 1). With growth in the use and complexity of health information systems, data interchange standards that support interoperability among information systems are critical for supporting healthcare delivery services, administrative decision and policy making, and research and data collection activities for public health and other functions. Some of the data silo problems facing St. Rita's are the result of the lack of such standards.

There are different levels of interoperability. These include basic, function, and semantic interoperability. **Basic interoperability** refers to the ability of one computer system to send and receive a message from another computer system. **Functional interoperability** means there is a common message syntax between two computer systems that allow them to interpret the message format, but not the meaning of the data being exchanged. **Semantic interoperability** means the data within the message can be interpreted between computer systems (NCVHS 2000).The healthcare industry has faced the challenge of interoperability for decades, in fact, since the introduction of health information technology (HIT) systems. The frustration concerning the lack of standards is reflected in a General Accounting Office report entitled "Automated Medical Records Leadership Needed to Expedite Standards Development" submitted to the U.S. Senate in 1993:

> The current inability to share medical information electronically stems largely from the lack of comprehensive standards for automated medical records. Such standards provide the foundation needed to support automated medical records and electronic data-sharing. These standards would allow hospitals to streamline operations by facilitating data transfer both among departments within a hospital and among different hospitals. In addition, standards would facilitate data transmission between outpatient and inpatient facilities. They would also permit data transmission to insurers who pay patients' bills; organizations that perform quality reviews; and institutions that perform health outcomes and effectiveness research, such as the tracking of health outcomes associated with new drugs and medical devices. (GAO 1993, 4)

Over the past 25 years, the call for standards has been heeded, and significant progress and foundational work has been achieved by the industry in general (AMIA and AHIMA 2006). While more work remains, a recent report from the Office of the National Coordinator (ONC) shows that hospital electronic health information exchange grew substantially between 2008 and 2012 (Furukawa et al. 2013). Findings showed that 58 percent of hospitals exchanged information with providers outside their organization in 2012, a 41 percent increase since 2008. The results also revealed that hospitals exchanging information with hospitals outside their organization more than doubled during the study period, and ranged from 39-55 percent depending upon the type of clinical information exchanged. Much of this is the result of government policies and initiatives to expand the use of EHRs and the exchange of information through regional health information organizations (HIOs).

However, the report also showed a gap in exchange among non-affiliated entities. For example, while 40 percent of hospitals electronically sent laboratory and radiology data to providers outside their organization, only 25 percent of hospitals could exchange medication lists and clinical summaries outside their organization. An ONC analysis of data from the 2011 National Ambulatory Medical Care Survey Electronic Health Record Supplement revealed that only 31 percent of physicians electronically exchanged clinical summaries with other providers (ONC 2013).

Gaps and challenges in the use of interoperable systems also exist across the continuum of healthcare delivery services, such as in post-acute settings, long-term care, and behavioral health. In hospitals where federal financial incentives for adopting EHRs are not available, only 6 percent of long-term acute care hospitals, 4 percent of rehabilitation hospitals, and 2 percent of psychiatric hospitals have basic EHR systems (Wolf et al. 2012). Furthermore, consumers and patients are not actively engaged in using personal health records or accessing portals to their health information.

Financial incentives and federal policy for adoption of EHR-certified systems that include interoperability appear to be making a difference. In order to close the gaps and accelerate exchange and clinical information use, the Department of Health and Human Services (HHS) developed a strategy for advancing HIE. The HHS is committed to a steady and incremental approach to accelerating health information interchange. An essential part of that strategy is moving the adoption of HIT standards forward through voluntary certification of HIT and health information exchange (HIE) products and services. To guide the strategy, the HHS identified a set of principles that provide the foundation for a comprehensive effort to accelerate HIE. The principles are organized into three categories: accelerating HIE, advancing standards and interoperability, and consumer/patient engagement (ONC 2013). These principles are provided in figure 13.4. Standards that promote interoperability among healthcare information systems are reviewed in the next section.

Figure 13.4. **HHS principles for accelerating health information interchange**

Accelerating HIE

- HHS will seek to ensure that all new regulations and guidance on existing programs enable a patient's health information to follow them wherever they access care to support patient-centered care delivery.
- HHS will implement policies that encourage HIE incrementally and could evolve from incentive and reward structures to ultimately considering HIE a standard business practice for providers.
- HHS will enable HIE where possible in support of state-led delivery and payment reform through federal and state partnerships.
- HHS will encourage interoperability across states' electronic information infrastructures, including Medicaid and State Survey Agencies and other HHS-funded enterprise systems.
- HHS agencies will collaborate with other departments in the federal government to facilitate the adoption and use of HHS HIT standards and interoperability requirements by those departments and their constituents.
- HHS will educate consumers from diverse cultural and socioeconomic backgrounds on HIE and what it means for them.
- HHS will support the privacy, security, and integrity of patient health information across all of its HIE acceleration activities.

Advancing Standards and Interoperability

- HHS will advance multi-stakeholder development of standards through the Standards and Interoperability Framework and coordination with standards development organizations such as HL7 and WEDI.
- HHS will accelerate interoperability through adoption of HIT standards through a variety of policies and programs, informed by advice from the HIT Policy Committee, HIT Standards Committee, and the NCVHS.
- HHS will, when appropriate, align HIT standards for quality measurement and improvement across Medicare and Medicaid programs.
- HHS will accelerate alignment and implementation of electronic clinical quality measures, electronic decision support interventions, and electronic reporting mechanisms.
- HHS will develop standards and policies to enable electronic management of consent and HIE among providers treating patients with sensitive health data, such as those with behavioral health conditions or HIV.
- HHS will strengthen data provenance to enhance providers' confidence in the original source of the data they receive.

Consumer/Patient Engagement

- HHS policies and programs will support appropriate patient access to their health information.
- HHS will support appropriate access to a patient's health information by family caregivers.
- HHS will make HHS standardized data available to patients wherever possible.

Source: Office of the National Coordinator 2013, 9–10.

## Standards for Interoperability

There are many types of standards needed to support interoperability. Interoperability must include not only the ability to exchange information, but also the ability to interpret and use information once it is exchanged (ONC 2013). It is possible that data exchanged from one computer to another may not be usable by the receiving computer. For example, think of data collected in a word-processed document and electronically transferred into a spreadsheet. The data can be exchanged, but it may not be readable or usable. The healthcare sector needs to establish and use standards that make both data exchangeable and usable. There are a variety of standard types needed for interoperability. Among these are structure and content standards, identifier standards, and content exchange standards (Giannangelo 2013).

**Structure and content standards** identify the data elements, data element definition, and attributes of the data element, such as data type and length. This provides a protocol for what data are exchanged and in what format the exchange is to occur. **Identifier standards** suggest methods for assigning unique identifiers to individuals including patients, healthcare providers, healthcare organizations, and vendors. **Content exchange standards** provide the specifications of the format and the sequence of data in the exchange message.

There are a profusion of standards that exist for healthcare interoperability, but they are not optimally used in all instances. Since there are hundreds of standards, the discussion of these is beyond the scope of this chapter. At present, there are efforts underway to consolidate and harmonize systems so they use consistent standards that enable interoperability. However, to establish the technical capabilities for a Certified EHR Technology to support Medicare and Medicaid EHR Incentive Programs, HIT systems must meet 43 interchange standards. The following terminology and classifications are among the required standards:

- CPT-4
- ICD-10-CM
- ICD-10-PCS
- HCPCS
- LOINC
- SNOMED CT
- RXNORM (HealthIT.gov n.d.)

**The St. Rita's Healthcare System Case Study**

"The research I did on data sets and data standards really clarified things for me," Shirlee said when she and Denise met for a brief meeting. "What was particularly helpful was finding out what is happening on the federal level. I found the information in the Standards Hub on the HealthIt.gov website really useful. The chart on the current standards that need to be met for EHR certification cleared up a lot of confusion for me."

"Yes, Shirlee, thanks for sharing this material. Although I'm fairly familiar with these from my health information management (HIM) background, there seems to be something new to learn every day. That's what makes this all so challenging," replied Denise.

"Do you think, Shirlee, that we should put together a more comprehensive listing and explanation for each of the terminologies, classifications, and standards for the rest of the team?" asked Denise.

"At some point, we are going to need something like you're suggesting from a data governance perspective (DG). But, one of the first steps is to get an inventory of what's been used already here at St. Rita's. We are a big operation, and I bet there are terminologies and classifications that departments and applications are using that we aren't even aware of. There might even be home-grown classifications they are using for internal purposes. I think this is another item for the list of DG activities," stated Shirlee.

"Good thought, Shirlee. I think we can wrap up this last function by looking at efforts that are taking place in data mapping. With your love of details, Shirlee, I think you'll like the topic," Denise said.

## Data Mapping

Data mapping projects are becoming more prevalent as the need to link disparate electronic information systems becomes increasingly critical. **Data mapping** is a process that allows data captured in one format or system to be linked or associated with data in other formats or systems. Data mapping always involves matching or linking between a source and a target (AHIMA 2013).

Data mapping is useful when data, captured in one system, need to be reused or repurposed for another computer system. There are many reasons to create data maps. In some cases, data mapping enables data exchange for healthcare delivery purposes, and in others it may support research or facilitate reimbursement, epidemiology, public health, or regulatory or accreditation data reporting (McBride et al. 2006).

In order to support these purposes, data mapping occurs between different terminologies or classification systems such as SNOMED and ICD-10-CM. Data mapping may also be needed by various groups to map data between two different versions of the same classification. This happens when updating new versions of classifications, for example linking ICD-10-CM to ICD-9-CM. Data mapping is used for administrative purposes, as well, for instance, for professional fee billing when codes are mapped to the delivery of professional services. Data mapping might also be used by systems or databases that need to exchange data but use different data element formats. For example, in one database, the date of birth element is expressed as "DOB" but in another it is defined as "BirthDate." Frequently, data mapping is required when two or more healthcare organizations consolidate and each has disparate information systems. In these instances, data mapping is used for mapping data elements between data sets. There are many types of data maps, such as

- **Standards development organization maps**. These maps are either created or adopted by a standards development organization or in cooperation between organizations. An example of this type of cooperative project is the current harmonization agreement between the IHTSDO and the WHO. These organizations are working together to develop maps between SNOMED CT and ICD-10, and link SNOMED CT and the classification codes in ICD-10 where possible.
- **Government-recognized maps**. These maps may be developed by a standards development organization or other authorized source; however, with government recognition these maps move from a voluntary standard to a government standard. Examples of this type of map are the ICD-9-CM to ICD-10-CM/PCS General Equivalence Mappings (GEMs), which were added to the HIPAA code set standards.
- **Proprietary or customized maps**. These maps are usually developed within an organization or by consultants working for them to meet their needs. In some instances they are developed as a product for purchase to meet specific needs. A proprietary map could consist of any data mapping important to achieve specific objectives. An example is local (organization-specific) terms or vocabularies mapped to standard terminologies or classifications (AHIMA 2013).

## Data Mapping Principles

If an organization decides it needs a customized map, then it must use sound data mapping processes to preserve data integrity. Frequently, organizations use this type of mapping to map disparate internal administrative or clinical applications.

Mapping begins with a source set of data to be mapped to a target set. The **source set** is the origin or data from which the mapping starts. The **target set** is the set of data for which data equivalency is trying to be established. For example, an organization may have a set of data coded in SNOMED (the source) and wants to find the equivalent codes for that data in ICD-10-CM (the target). While data mapping is simple in concept, in practice it is very complex and requires a systematic, rigorous, and well-documented process. Inaccurate mapping has unintended risks and consequences. For example, using maps for healthcare claims leads to compliance issues if the map results in incorrect code submission linked to billing for reimbursement (Hyde et al. 2013).

Before launching a data mapping project, an organization should undergo a complete requirements analysis. Developing use cases (chapter 6) helps define the map's purpose (McBride et al. 2006). Among the questions to ask when building the use case are

- How will we use the mapped data? For reimbursement, research, outcome measurements, or public health studies?
- How will we transmit the data and to what systems?
- Will we use the data to provide a selectable item within a user application, such as a dropdown list?
- Will we implement prompts for medical alerts, such as possible drug interactions or allergies based on the map?
- Will we categorize, classify, or group the mapped data into other data sets?
- Will we store the data? If yes, how?
- Where will we store the mapped data?
- How will we perform the maps? Will we use automated tools or manual review, or a combination of both (Wilson 2007)?

In data mapping, it is important to identify the source and target systems and determine the relationship of the terms between the two. For example, the following are possible relationships:

- One-to-one relationship - one term in the source system is equivalent to one term in the target system
- One-to-many relationship - one term in the source system is related to many terms in the target system
- Many-to-one relationship - many terms in the source system are related to one term in the target system
- Many-to-many relationship - both one-to-many and many-to-one relationships happen at the same time between the source and the target terminologies (Wilson 2007)

The best case is where a one-to-one or a many-to-one mapping relationship exists because these do not require an additional decision once mapping is complete. Since the source data, in either case, equates to only one code in the target system, no additional decisions must be made about how the source and target data map. Many-to-many relationships are difficult to implement and should be examined, and probably avoided for mapping by the organization.

Maps can be either unidirectional or bidirectional. In **unidirectional mapping**, the map translates only from the source to the target. In **bidirectional mapping,** mapping occurs from the source system to the target and from the target to the source. Depending on the use case requirements, relationships between the source and target may require bidirectional mapping. However, not all maps are bidirectional, for instance, a many-to-one map. Mapping from SNOMED to ICD-9-CM is a good example of a many-to-one map. The mapping between SNOMED and ICD-9-CM cannot be reversed, since there may be multiple SNOMED concepts that map to a single ICD-9-CM code and therefore one ICD-9-CM code points to several SNOMED concepts (McBride et al. 2006).

Maps are also identified as forward or reverse maps. In a **forward map**, an older version of a code set is mapped to a newer version, for example ICD-9-CM to ICD-10-CM. A **reverse map** links two systems in the opposite direction, from the newer version of a code set to an older version. In forward and backward mapping, each map produces unique results due to the disparity between the two versions of the code sets or terminologies. Therefore, it is important to know if mapping is forward or reverse since the results are dependent on the direction (AHIMA 2013).

After defining the use case for data mapping, then mapping begins. There are a number of commercial vendors that provide support and tools for automated mapping. However, the algorithms used by these tools are only as good as their fit with the defined use case. Even in the best of cases, similar to matching algorithms for master data, there needs to be human intervention or manual review to map portions of the data set that failed automated mapping and to check for validity of the data maps (Wilson 2007). When using vendor maps, it is critical to maintain an inventory of all applications where these are used in the organization. A list of maps from the vendor should be required by the purchasing organization with supporting documentation that includes a data dictionary.

When an organization elects to do an internal mapping effort, it must establish clear processes. A suggested framework appears in figure 13.5.

Figure 13.5. Suggested mapping process framework

Develop a business case. Questions to ask include

- What is the reason for the project?
- What is the expected business benefit?
- What are the expected costs of the project?
- What are the expected risks?

Define a use case for how the content will be used within applications.

- Who will use the maps?
- Is the mapping between standard terminologies or between proprietary (local) terminologies?
- Are there delivery constraints or licensing issues?
- What systems will rely on the map as a data source?

Develop rules (heuristics) to be implemented within the project.

- What is the version of source and target schema to be used?
- What is included or excluded?
- How will the relationship between source and target be defined (for example, are maps equivalent or related)?
- What mapping methodologies will be utilized by the mapping process?
- What procedures will be used for ensuring intercoder or inter-rater reliability (reproducibility) in the map development phase?
- What parameters will be used to ensure usefulness? (For example, a map from the SNOMED CT concept "procedure on head" could be mapped to hundreds of CPT codes, making the map virtually useless.)
- What tools will be used to develop and maintain the map?

Plan a pilot phase to test the rules.

- Use random samples of a statistically significant size
- Ensure reproducibility of results
- Conduct additional pilot phases until variances are resolved

(continued)

Figure 13.5. Continued

Develop full content with periodic testing throughout the process.
- Perform final quality assurance tests
- Review items unable to be mapped
- Retest if modification from the review process was implemented
- Perform quality assurance testing on the data content when software configuration is completed in development environment
- Deploy content to the production environment

Communicate with source and target system owners:
- When identifying potential issues
- When resolving issues

Map validation
- Follow the understandable, reproducible, and useable principle to develop appropriate data maps.
    - The links between data elements should be understood by the user without benefit of a user guide or lengthy manual.
    - The process to develop the data links must be straightforward enough to be reproduced so that the same results occur no matter who (human) or what (machine or software program) is creating the links.
    - The map is not valuable if it is not useable for the use case it was designed to support.
    - The validation of maps must be conducted by an entity that has not been involved with the map development or has a financial or political interest in its use.
- Additional validation reviews
    - Using authoritative sources from the standards development organization to link the codes when the map is between two official standards (for example, SNOMED CT to ICD or LOINC to CPT)
    - Drawing a statistically valid sample from the map record population to review the validity of the map results
    - Reviewing map heuristics
    - Enlisting a qualified person without access to the previous work to perform the mapping independently (blind comparison)
    - Comparing results and explaining any discordance in detail in a full report
- Perform an "in use" review and validation checks, including
    - Comparing map performance in translating the source to the target for its intended purpose (for example, does it produce the same results every time the map record is used?)
    - Assessing the concordance between software programs using the map and noting any discordance
    - Presenting a full report of findings with a qualified panel from the organization using the maps

Source: AHIMA 2013

Source and target systems change over time. Therefore, map maintenance is a continuing effort. Terminologies and classifications are good examples of such change. These systems are updated periodically or have new release dates. Consequently, a map created by an organization using a previous version of one or the other system must update its maps when new versions of the terminologies or classifications are created. When organizations use historical data for retrospective analysis, they must know what version of the classification or terminology was used during the time period the historical data were initially created.

## Equivalence Ratings

The degree of equivalence in mapping between a term in the source system and a term in the target system should be clearly described by the mapping team. **Equivalence** describes how close or distant the terms are from each other in meaning.

For example, a source code may map to one target code, but that does not mean the two codes have the exact same meaning. This often happens when mapping a terminology to a classification. To rectify this problem, map developers identify the degree of equivalence for each map and how they determined the equivalence. For clinical care maps, map developers must identify the equivalency to eliminate ambiguity about the match (AHIMA 2013). Frequently, the mapping team uses statistical algorithms to determine equivalencies and report these in match rating scales using numbers with designated values. Common equivalency terms include:

- No match, no map, no code
- Approximate match, approximate map, related match
- Exact match, exact map, equivalent match, equivalent map, equal (AHIMA 2013)

For illustrative purposes, examples of data mapping are provided in tables 13.3, 13.4, and 13.5.

Table 13.3. Single mapping between ICD and SNOMED CT with equivalent concepts in both systems

| ICD-9-CM Code | ICD-9-CM Name | Equivalence | SNOMED CT Code | SNOMED CT Name |
|---|---|---|---|---|
| 001.0 | Cholera due to vibrio cholerae | Equal | 63650001 | Cholera |
| *ICD-9-CM code 001.0 has a single relationship to a single SNOMED CT concept. The SNOMED CT concept "Cholera" (63650001) is clinically equivalent as it contains the attribute "causative agent" as Vibrio cholerae.* | | | | |
| ICD-10-CM Code | ICD-10-CM Name | Equivalence | SNOMED CT Code | SNOMED CT Name |
| A00.9 | Cholera, unspecified | Equal | 63650001 | Cholera |
| *ICD-10-CM code A00.9 also has a single relationship to a single SNOMED CT concept (6365001).* | | | | |

Source: AHIMA 2013b

Table 13.4. Two single mappings between ICD-9-CM and SNOMED CT

| ICD-9-CM Code | ICD-9-CM Name | Equivalence | SNOMED CT Code | SNOMED CT Name |
|---|---|---|---|---|
| 008.3 | Proteus (Mirabilis/Morganii) enteritis | Related | 30493003 | Intestinal infection due to Proteus mirabilis |
| 008.3 | Proteus (Mirabilis/Morganii) enteritis | Related | 36529003 | Intestinal infection due to Morganella morganii |
| *Code 008.3 has relationships to two SNOMED CT concepts. Either of the SNOMED CT codes could be properly linked to the classification. In this case it is important to consider how the resulting map affects its use.* | | | | |

Source: AHIMA 2013b

Table 13.5. Data map used by healthcare providers offering laboratory services

| Service Code | Description | CPT Code | LOINC Code | Charge |
|---|---|---|---|---|
| 123456789 | Hemoglobin Glycosylated (A1c) | 83036 | 41995-2 | $15 |
| *A map for healthcare providers that offer laboratory services is typically a proprietary map linking local data (service codes) with national standards (CPT and LOINC codes).* | | | | |

Source: AHIMA 2013b

## The St. Rita's Healthcare System Case Study

"Do I ever see DG written all over this EIM function!" Shirlee exclaimed.

"I agree," Denise replied. "As we move to reduce these data silos, participate in the regional health exchange, and meet the HITECH Act and meaningful use criteria that require us to exchange patient information among providers, data mapping is a critical integrative function. We really need to pull together our expertise in terminologies and classifications here at St. Rita's and redefine how our group functions. It isn't just about coding a patient chart for reimbursement anymore."

"What I could envision is a division responsible for managing the development and maintenance of mappings between healthcare data or code sets and classifications and terminologies, working closely with IT and our various lines of business," Shirlee observed.

"You're right on. It looks like this is another one of the topics we should place on the idea list for further discussion and evaluation by the EIM team. I wonder how many hospital systems have divisions or departments devoted to enterprise terminology management?" Denise asked.

Shirlee and Denise worked on the DG aspects of this function and prepared their slide deck for the next EIM team meeting.

## Applying Data Governance

As Shirlee and Denise observed, terminologies and classifications management requires governance on an enterprise-wide scale. Previously relegated to a focus on coding for reimbursement, the management of terminologies, classifications, and data sets are being seen by organizations from a new perspective as the needs for interoperability increase at a rapid rate. If organizations are to meet regulatory compliance and take advantage of the potential interoperability benefits, they must reinvent the way they govern, develop, implement, and maintain terminologies and classifications. They must take a fresh look and explore new, creative, and interdisciplinary approaches in how to leverage the very foundation on which they operate: the languages in which they communicate. From a DG perspective, specifically, these include and are reported in table 13.6:

- Establish policies and procedures for the development, implementation, and maintenance of terminologies and classifications
- Maintain an inventory of organization data maps
- Ensure data mapping processes and initiatives support organizational needs
- Provide oversight for data mapping efforts
- Develop and implement validation and auditing procedures for data mapping
- Resolve terminology, classification, and data set issues

Table 13.6. DG deliverables by EIM function

| Data Governance | Data Architecture Management | Metadata Management | Master Data Management | Content Management | Data Security and Privacy Management | Business Intelligence Management | Data Quality Management | Terminology and Classification Management |
|---|---|---|---|---|---|---|---|---|
| Identify mission and scope | Develop and maintain data models | Develop policies, procedures, and standards | Identify master and reference data requirements | Develop roadmap for content management | Identify and classify sensitive data across enterprise systems | Assess organization and stakeholder needs | Develop DQ framework; establish DQ roles and responsibilities | Develop policies and procedures for terminology and classification management |
| Establish goals and success measures | Develop, maintain, and evaluate data model policies and standards | Ensure metadata meets functional requirements | Develop policies, procedures, and standards for management of master data | Develop policies and procedures for content management | Develop data security and privacy policies and standards | Develop BI roadmap to meet organization goals | Define DQ requirements and metrics | Maintain an inventory of organization data maps |
| Put in place DG structure, processes, and communications plan | Define roles, responsibilities, and accountabilities for data architecture management | Develop and maintain appropriate metadata schema | Establish master data definitions, validation, and verification levels for master data quality | Apply taxonomies, thesauri, ontologies and other content management classifications | Meet compliance and regulatory security and privacy requirements | Develop accountability and reporting structure | Establish and implement DQ policies, procedures, and standards | Ensure that data mapping processes and initiatives support organizational needs |

(continued)

Table 13.6. **DG deliverables by EIM function (*Continued*)**

| Data Governance | Data Architecture Management | Metadata Management | Master Data Management | Content Management | Data Security and Privacy Management | Business Intelligence Management | Data Quality Management | Terminology and Classification Management |
|---|---|---|---|---|---|---|---|---|
| Secure funding | Develop, maintain, and evaluate policies and standards for requirements analysis | Ensure metadata capture, maintenance, distribution, and integration | Ensure master and reference data meet regulatory requirements, including lineage history and security | Develop policies and procedures that ensure legal and regulatory mandates are met | Assess risk and identify controls to manage risk | Develop policies, procedures, and standards for data security and quality, and monitor them | Develop and promote data quality awareness | Develop and implement validation and auditing procedures for data mapping |
| Establish decision rights | Develop and maintain data artifacts and standards | Ensure metadata security | Establish audit procedures and standards for master data | Establish standards and audit procedures | Perform data security and privacy audits and report findings | Define BI architecture | Establish processing for assessing and measuring DQ | Provide oversight for data mapping efforts |
| Identify accountabilities | Establish quality control program and metrics for data architecture management | Develop and implement quality controls for metadata | Identify stakeholders and establish decision rights and accountabilities | Implement stewardship processes over the content management life cycle | Develop and implement data privacy and security awareness and training | Develop and maintain schema and metadata | Report, correct, resolve, and manage DQ issues | Resolve terminology, classification, and data set issues |

## *The St. Rita's Healthcare System Case Study*

The EIM team was in a celebratory mood as it met for its last briefing meeting. It had been a long journey and they were proud of their accomplishments. Denise and Shirlee wrapped up the last functional area they studied. The team listened intently to their presentation, and by its end all of them felt the imperative for a call to action for better management of terminologies and classifications.

"What a sleeping giant," commented Monte. "This sounds like the railroads before the standard gauge was introduced. Independent companies operating railroads had different widths between their tracks. When a train loaded with cargo came to the end of the company's line, the next company's track width might be different. That meant workers had to unload all the cargo from one train and onto another so the shipment could reach its destination. In computer terms, there wasn't any throughput or interoperability without standards. Trains literally had to stop in their tracks. But economics and efficiency won the day. It looks like we are at the same point now with our healthcare computer systems."

"That's a great comparison," Linda observed. "Federal initiatives such as HIPAA and HITECH ignited the momentum. Things simply can't move forward without standards and harmonization among them."

"And talk about something that is crying for governance! I was intrigued by your comments about the potential for a division of classification and terminology management. I think there's a lot of merit into exploring this idea further," David added.

The team spent the remainder of the time discussing the implications of the AMIA-AHIMA report on healthcare terminologies, the AHIMA white paper on data mapping and its impact on data integrity, and how they could learn more specifics about some of the terminologies presented before Val initiated a short overview of next steps.

"You all have done a terrific job," Val stated. "I couldn't have had a better team to work with on this very tough topic. But, as we all know our work is not done. We need to consolidate our findings into a briefing for Joan Morton. Our charge was to report what our findings suggest about whether or not St. Rita's should establish an EIM division. Either way, we need to back up our recommendation with facts. If we recommend such a division, we need to be clear about the division's vision, mission, scope, and benefits. To carry out this work, I've scheduled a two-day offsite meeting at the end of the month. We'll be using an outside facilitator who can help us assimilate the findings and coalesce our expert opinions on the issue. But I'd like to get your ideas on initial goals for the retreat," Val continued.

The team used the remainder of the meeting to identify outcomes for the two-day retreat. These were written on flip charts and consolidated into their weekly interim report and minutes.

"Before we leave," said Val, "I'd like two volunteers to meet with me and the facilitator to put together the retreat agenda and determine logistics." Bob and Linda volunteered to work with Val in planning the retreat to be held in three weeks. The meeting adjourned and the EIM team went out for a celebratory dinner that evening.

## Part of the Team: Topics for Discussion and Action

1. Some of the EIM team members wanted to learn more specifics about the terminologies and classifications that Shirlee and Denise presented. To help the team members get more information about one of these, listen to the web presentation on LOINC presented by AMIA and available on their website. Prepare a summary of the highlights of this presentation for the team.
2. Conduct a literature search on data mapping in healthcare and identify at least three examples of different types of data mapping. Prepare a short briefing paper that includes, for each example, a summary of the source and target systems that were mapped, why the mapping was done, what type of mapping was performed, problems and issues encountered in the mapping process, and a synthesis of what you believe lies ahead for the future of data mapping in healthcare.

## Advanced Concepts

1. To be more informed about the ONC's activities in standards adoption, read the posts by Dr. Doug Fridsma, ONC's Chief Scientist, available on their website. What are the major initiatives of the ONC in standards? What challenges are they attempting to solve? How will the work of ONC potentially impact St. Rita's?
2. The EIM team has stated that terminology and classifications call out for DG. Given the broad DG functions listed in table 13.6, prepare a list of activities that fall within each function.
3. The EIM team suggested St. Rita's might benefit from a division devoted to classification and terminology management. They wondered how many other organizations have established such a division. To help the team in answering this question, develop a proposal for researching this issue and then conduct the research. Report your findings in a briefing paper to the EIM team.

## References

AHIMA. 2013. Data mapping best practices. *Journal of AHIMA* 84(11): expanded web version. http://library.ahima.org/xpedio/groups/public/documents/ahima/bok1_050536.hcsp?dDocName=bok1_050536.

American Medical Informatics Association and American Health Information Management Association Terminology and Classification Task Force. 2006 (June 27). Healthcare terminologies and classifications: An action agenda for the United States. http://library.ahima.org/xpedio/groups/public/documents/ahima/bok1_032395.pdf#xml=http://library.ahima.org/xpedio/idcplg?IdcService=GET_XML_HIGHLIGHT_INFO&QueryText=%28Terminology+and+Classification+Policy+Task+Force%29%3cand%3e%28xPublishSite%3csubstring%3e%60BoK%60%29&SortField=xPubDate&SortOrder=Desc&dDocName=bok1_032395&HighlightType=PdfHighlight.

Aspden, P., J.M. Corrigan, J. Wolcott, and S.M. Erickson. 2004. *Patient Safety: Achieving a New Standard for Care*. Washington, D.C.: The National Academies Press.

Byrne, Joseph Patrick. 2012. *Encyclopedia of the Black Death*. Santa Barbara: ABC-CLIO.

Chute, C. 2000. Clinical classification and terminology: Some history and current observations. *Journal of the American Medical Informatics Association* 7(3): 298–303.

Cimino, J. 2010. *Foreword to Health Code Sets, Clinical Terminologies, and Classification Systems*, 2nd ed., by K. Giannangelo, ed., xiii-xiv. Chicago: AHIMA Press.

Foley, M. 2010. Systematized Nomenclature of Medicine Clinical Terms. Chapter 7 in *Health Code Sets, Clinical Terminologies, and Classification Systems*, 2nd ed., by K. Giannangelo, ed., 105–126. Chicago: AHIMA Press.

Furukawa, M., V. Patel, D. Charles, M. Swain., and F. Mostashari. 2013. Hospital Electronic Health information exchange grew substantially in 2008-12. *Health Affairs* 32(8): 1346–1354 http://content.healthaffairs.org/content/32/8/1346.full?ijkey=EpCxNN/zrJIMU&keytype=ref&siteid=healthaff.

Giannangelo, K, ed. 2010. *Health Code Sets, Clinical Terminologies, and Classification Systems*, 2nd ed. Chicago: AHIMA Press.

Giannangelo, K. 2013. Healthcare Informatics Standards, Chapter 8 in *Health Information Management Concepts, Principles, and Practice*, 4th ed., edited by K.M. LaTour, S. Eichenwald-Maki, and P.K. Oachs. Chicago: AHIMA Press.

United States General Accounting Office. 1993. Automated Medical Records: Leadership Needed to Expedite Standards Development. Report to the Chairman, Committee on Governmental Affairs, U.S. Senate. http://www.gao.gov/assets/220/217903.pdf.

HealthIT.gov. Standards and Certification Regulations: Standards Hub. http://www.healthit.gov/policy-researchers-implementers/meaningful-use-stage-2-0/standards-hub.

Hyde, L. T. Rihanek, T. Santana-Johnson, R. Scichilone, C. Simmons, J. Turner, and W. Zumar. 2013. Data Mapping and Its Impact on Data Quality. http://library.ahima.org/xpedio/groups/public/documents/ahima/bok1_050525.pdf.

Jones, H.W. 1945 (January). John Graunt and his Bills of Mortality. *Bulletin of the Medical Library Association* 33(1): 3–4. http://www.ncbi.nlm.nih.gov/pmc/articles/PMC200893/.

Kanaan, S.B. 1999. The National Committee on Vital and Health Statistics 1949-1999: A History. http://www.ncvhs.hhs.gov/50history.htm.

LaTour, K.M., S. Eichenwald Maki, and P.K. Oachs, eds. 2013. *Health Information Management Concepts, Principles, and Practice*, 4th ed. Chicago: AHIMA Press.

London's Bill of Mortality (December 1664–December 1665) [Official Document], in Children and Youth in History, Item #159, http://chnm.gmu.edu/cyh/primary-sources/159. Annotated by Lynda Payne.

McBride, S., R. Gilder, R. Davis, and S. Fenton. 2006. Data Mapping. *Journal of AHIMA* 77(2): 44–48 [expanded online edition]. http://library.ahima.org/xpedio/groups/public/documents/ahima/bok1_030580.hcsp?dDocName=bok1_030580.

Moriyama I.M., R.M. Loy, and A.H.T. Robb-Smith. 2011. *History of the Statistical Classification of Diseases and Causes of Death*. Edited by H.M. Rosenberg and D.L. Hoyert. Hyattsville, MD: National Center for Health Statistics.

National Committee on Vital and Health Statistics. 1992. 1992 Revisions to UHDDS. http://www.cdc.gov/nchs/data/ncvhs/nchvs92.pdf.

National Committee on Vital and Health Statistics. 2000 (July 6). Report on Uniform Data Standards for Patient Medical Record Information. http://www.ncvhs.hhs.gov/hipaa000706.pdf.

Office of the National Coordinator. 2013 (August 7). Principles and Strategy for Accelerating Health Information Exchange (HIE). http://www.healthit.gov/sites/default/files/acceleratinghieprinciples_strategy.pdf.

Open Clinical. 2005. Medical terminologies, nomenclatures, coding and classification systems: An introduction. http://www.openclinical.org/medicalterminologies.html.

Palkie, B. 2013. Clinical Classifications and Terminologies, Chapter 15 in *Health Information Management Concepts, Principles, and Practice*, 4th ed. By K.M. LaTour, S. Eichenwald Maki, and P.K. Oachs, eds. Chicago: AHIMA Press.

Wilson, P. 2007. What mapping and modeling means to the HIM professional. *Online Research Journal: Perspectives in Health Information Management* 4(2). http://www.ncbi.nlm.nih.gov/pmc/articles/PMC2082071/.

Wolf, L., J. Harvell, and A.K. Jha. 2012. Hospitals ineligible for federal meaningful-use incentives have dismally low rates of adoption of electronic health records. *Health Affairs*, 31(3): 505–513. http://web.pdx.edu/~nwallace/AHP/HAAdopt.pdf.

World Health Organization (WHO). 2014. International Classification of Diseases (ICD): ICD-11 Frequently Asked Questions. http://www.who.int/classifications/icd/revision/icd11faq/en/.

# Part III
# Epilogue

Chapter 14

# EIM in Action

The St. Rita's enterprise information management (EIM) team put a lot of effort into investigating the concept of EIM, its benefits, and how its application might help solve St. Rita's data quality problems. But, vision without action is merely a dream. The team needed to analyze their research, recommend new ideas and improvements, and develop an action plan for achievement. They scheduled a two-day retreat for this purpose.

This chapter functions as a summative activity integrating the knowledge and perspectives in the previous chapters, wherein the St. Rita's EIM team members bring to bear their knowledge, impressions, and opinions addressing the charge given to them by St. Rita's CIO, Joan Morton:

"My instinct is that we need an office for EIM whose goals are to reduce data redundance and improve data quality, security, and ease of access. What I want is top-notch data stewardship. But this idea needs verification. I'm designating you as the EIM team to investigate the feasibility of this idea and, if realistic, identify how we might get such an effort off the ground. Your charge is to study the problems, recommend new ideas and improvements, and develop an action plan to achieve these."

The activity in this chapter is a simulation of a retreat like the one the EIM team might plan. The team addresses information and data gathered from other chapters at the retreat, laying the foundation for a comprehensive proposal of the feasibility of implementing an EIM division at St. Rita's. A draft proposal developed by the EIM team is in the student manual that accompanies this text.

The topics and activities in this chapter help you to:

- Apply key steps for planning and conducting successful retreats
- Analyze, synthesize, and evaluate the case for an EIM office at St. Rita's Hospital
- Develop a business case for EIM
- Create a proposal for the adoption of an enterprise-wide program

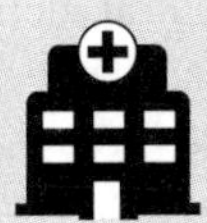

## The St. Rita's Healthcare System Case Study

The day after the EIM team wrapped up the terminologies and classification function overview, Val, Linda, and Bob met to begin planning the EIM team retreat. Val asked the retreat facilitator, Sandy, to join them at this meeting. While Sandy had no expertise in EIM or data governance (DG), it was important she understand the meeting context, its intended outcomes, and be part of planning the retreat agenda. As facilitator, Sandy was responsible for managing the meeting structure, not the content. Her role was to help the team clarify its desired outcomes and achievements by using a variety of group process techniques to keep the team focused.

"One of the first items we have to develop is the agenda," said Val. "Are we in agreement about the outcomes of the retreat?" she asked Linda and Bob.

"I looked over what the team put together at yesterday's meeting and I don't see any areas that we've missed," replied Linda. Bob was in agreement with this assessment. Val also felt the team laid out the key outcomes which were consistent with Joan's charge to the EIM team.

"OK, now that we are comfortable with what we want to achieve, how do you suggest we structure the agenda?" Val asked Sandy.

# Retreat Planning

The usual purpose of a retreat is to allow a team or group the opportunity to step away from day-to-day operational tasks and spend an extended period of time in thought, discussion, and assessment about a specific issue. The St. Rita's EIM team conducted a planning retreat. Organizations use **planning retreats** for many purposes including generating ideas or improvements, solving a specific problem, developing goals or objectives, developing action plans, or setting the strategic direction of an organization.

Good planning is the foundation for success at any retreat. The purpose and desired outcomes of the retreat need to be identified beforehand. Frequently, these are reconfirmed as one of the retreat's first agenda items. Another first agenda item is to establish criteria the group can use to measure the retreat's success. Other measures to ensure a successful retreat are to cultivate a list of participants, include a facilitator, create a room setup, and prepare the participants ahead of time.

## Retreat Participants

Determining retreat attendees is an important part of the planning process. Having the right mix of people at the table is critical. For example, if the retreat outcome is to develop a strategic objective for the organization, then executive management and the board of directors are likely participants. If the purpose is to solve an operational problem, then managers and supervisors are likely candidates as participants. Sometimes, individuals with specific expertise who are outside of an organization are asked to participate in a retreat. Because they are not tied into political or other organizational issues, such individuals provide an unbiased perspective. The St. Rita's EIM team is a defined group with a specific charge; the team members are the most likely retreat participants. EIM was Joan's priority, but she also wanted new ideas and improvements. Val, Bob, and Linda thought it would be helpful to invite some experts from outside of St. Rita's as participants. They brainstormed a list of DG and EIM experts and selected three to invite as additional retreat participants:

- a respected dean of a business school with a strong background in business intelligence and experience implementing large scale data warehouse solutions;
- an individual with a library science background who headed up an EIM effort at an academic institution; and
- a director of data governance at a large healthcare system.

## Retreat Facilitator

Adding a retreat facilitator to the planning process for the retreat contributes to the retreat's success. A neutral facilitator brings objectivity to the retreat. The facilitator may or may not have expertise in the subject matter at hand and should have no stake in the agenda issues. The facilitator should be an expert in group dynamics and processes, help groups make decisions, and develop the retreat agenda and other logistics related to the retreat. Either the facilitator or a scribe records the retreat activities, discussions, and outcomes.

## Retreat Setup

Retreats are usually held off-site in an environment that is free from the distractions of daily work. This is conducive to creative thinking, focusing on the retreat topic or objectives, and devoting sufficient structured and unstructured time to achieving retreat outcomes. The retreat site should be free from extraneous noise and have appropriate resources such as good lighting, white boards, flip charts, audio-visual equipment, break-out rooms, comfortable seats, and sufficient table space. Provide food and overnight accommodations as needed, especially if the retreat is not held in a local space.

The retreat planning team should carefully think through the retreat room setup. There may be a variety of room setups, depending on the agenda. A u-shaped table formation may be used to encourage discussion among a small number of participants. In larger groups, a classroom-style setup with breakout rooms for intensive small group work may be appropriate. Or, round tables for small group interaction may be the best choice.

## Retreat Preparation

Preparing participants for the retreat is important in setting the retreat context. Ahead of time, provide participants with the agenda and affiliated resources, such as a briefing book. A briefing book contains relevant data and information for the retreat (for example, statistics and previously compiled reports). The St. Rita's EIM team briefing book contains items such as:

- The completed table for DG deliverables by EIM functional area (table 14.1)
- EIM domains, data problems, and selected actions for St. Rita's (table 14.2)
- General articles on steps for implementing EIM

The St. Rita's EIM team briefing book is available in the student manual.

Table 14.1. DG deliverables by EIM function

| Data Governance | Data Architecture Management | Metadata Management | Master Data Management | Content Management | Data Security and Privacy Management | Business Intelligence Management | Data Quality Management | Terminology and Classification Management |
|---|---|---|---|---|---|---|---|---|
| Identify mission and scope | Develop and maintain data models | Develop policies, procedures, and standards | Identify master and reference data requirements | Develop roadmap for content management | Identify and classify sensitive data across enterprise systems | Assess organization and stakeholder needs | Develop DQ framework; establish DQ roles and responsibilities | Develop policies and procedures for terminology and classification management |
| Establish goals and success measures | Develop, maintain, and evaluate data model policies and standards | Ensure metadata meets functional requirements | Develop policies, procedures, and standards for management of master data | Develop policies and procedures for content management | Develop data security and privacy policies and standards | Develop BI roadmap to meet organization goals | Define DQ requirements and metrics | Maintain an inventory of organization data maps |
| Put in place DG structure, processes, and communications plan | Define roles, responsibilities, and accountabilities for data architecture management | Develop and maintain appropriate metadata schema | Establish master data definitions, validation, and verification levels for master data quality | Apply taxonomies, thesauri, ontologies and other content management classifications | Meet compliance and regulatory security and privacy requirements | Develop accountability and reporting structure | Establish and implement DQ policies, procedures, and standards | Ensure that data mapping processes and initiatives support organizational needs |
| Secure funding | Develop, maintain, and evaluate policies and standards for requirements analysis | Ensure metadata capture, maintenance, distribution, and integration | Ensure master and reference data meet regulatory requirements, including lineage history and security | Develop policies and procedures that ensure legal and regulatory mandates are met | Assess risk and identify controls to manage risk | Develop policies, procedures, and standards for data security and quality, and monitor them | Develop and promote data quality awareness | Develop and implement validation and auditing procedures for data mapping |
| Establish decision rights | Develop and maintain data artifacts and standards | Ensure metadata security | Establish audit procedures and standards for master data | Establish standards and audit procedures | Perform data security and privacy audits and report findings | Define BI architecture | Establish processing for assessing and measuring DQ | Provide oversight for data mapping efforts |
| Identify accountabilities | Establish quality control program and metrics for data architecture management | Develop and implement quality controls for metadata | Identify stakeholders and establish decision rights and accountabilities | Implement stewardship processes over the content management life cycle | Develop and implement data privacy and security awareness and training | Develop and maintain schema and metadata | Report, correct, resolve, and manage DQ issues | Resolve terminology, classification, and data set issues |

Table 14.2. EIM domains, data problems, and selected actions for St. Rita's case

| EIM Domain | St. Rita Data Problem | Remedy |
|---|---|---|
| **Data Architecture** | System- and application-specific data models that make data integration difficult if not impossible<br>Application systems that do not meet operational or reporting needs | Provide data model standards<br>Provide enterprise view of data through enterprise conceptual and logical data models<br>Implement formalized requirements analysis processes, and documentation |
| **Metadata Management** | Inconsistent data element names and meanings<br>Insufficient data quality checks | Implement enterprise data dictionary<br>Establish edit check standards<br>Establish metrics for data quality<br>Institute audit program |
| **Master Data Management** | Duplicate digital records in master data | Implement suite of master data management standards and practices to ensure a "single source of truth" for all organization master data |
| **Content Management** | Inability to access unstructured data in clinical and business documents for BI, research, and other purposes | Implement document management system that includes standards and processes for indexing and cataloging of data for purposes of information searching and retrieval<br>Develop an information architecture that identifies links and relationships among documents and defines the content within a document |
| **Data Security Management** | Spotty tracking of disclosures of protected health information among St. Rita's various health delivery entities | Coordinate data security management and link to other EIM functions to ensure compliance with government regulations |
| **Information Intelligence** | Inability to retrieve data in meaningful ways for executives, management, and clinicians for purposes of data analytics | Perform gap analysis between organization needs and current systems for information intelligence<br>Develop architecture for effective and efficient information intelligence |
| **Data Quality Management** | Multiple data quality issues across all systems | Develop and implement data quality standards<br>Develop and apply metrics for data quality<br>Monitor and remedy data quality issues |
| **Terminology and Classification Management** | Lack of harmonization across terminology and classification systems, making data integration and analytics difficult | Develop and implement algorithmic translations, concept representations, and mapping among clinical nomenclatures |
| **Data Governance** | No central source for resolution of data quality or other data issues<br>No central source for policy for management or monitoring data resource | Implement formal DG framework for centralization of authority and responsibility for managing the organization's data assets that includes resolution of data-related issues |

## Retreat Agenda

As with any meeting, a clear agenda is pivotal for success. The agenda must match the retreat's purpose and objectives and allocate sufficient time for each topic and activity. A principal role of the facilitator is to keep the group to the agenda timeline.

Using the agenda created by Val, Bob, and Linda, Sandy identified several group process techniques she thought would work for various sections of the agenda and noted each of these by respective topic area. The full agenda for St. Rita's EIM team is in figures 14.1 and 14.2.

Figure 14.1. Day one retreat agenda

| EIM Team Retreat Agenda | |
|---|---|
| Date - Place | |
| *Purpose: Assess EIM division options for improving data integrity issues and develop preliminary action plan* | |
| **Day One** | |
| 8:30 – 9:00 a.m. | Welcome, team building exercise, ground rules |
| 9:00 – 9:30 a.m. | Confirmation of purpose, outcomes, and criteria for success |
| 9:30 – 10:15 a.m. | Situational analysis: What is the status now? (use Nominal Group Technique)<br>• Assessment of data issues<br>• Impact of data issues<br>• Assessment of organizational needs |
| 10:15 – 10:30 a.m. | Break |
| 10:30 – 12:00 noon | Identify desired state (use Response Round Technique)<br>• What are top priorities?<br>• What are 1-, 2-, and 3-year goals?<br>• Risks if goals not achieved<br>• *Outputs:*<br>    • Vision statement<br>    • Mission statement<br>    • Values statement |
| 12:00 – 1:00 p.m. | Lunch |
| 1:00 – 2:15 p.m. | Assessment of EIM feasibility (use Subgroup Technique)<br>• What are feasible options for implementation of EIM (such as portfolio approach or other approach)?<br>    • What are benefits of each?<br>    • What are downfalls of each?<br>    • What are risks of each?<br>    • Are there risk mitigations?<br>• *Outputs:*<br>    • Draft benefit and risk assessment |
| 2:15 – 2:30 p.m. | Break |
| 2:30 – 3:30 p.m. | Prioritize and select best option (use Decision Matrix Technique)<br>• Benefit and risk assessment<br>• Select option for implementation<br>• *Outputs*<br>    • Benefit and risk assessment<br>    • Rationale for best option |
| 3:30 – 4:15 p.m. | Develop rationale, vision, and mission statements (use subgroup technique)<br>• What is the rationale for the option and how it is currently used by others to enhance operations?<br>• What are risks?<br>• What is the vision? How does this option meet the desired state vision?<br>• What is the mission? How does this option meet the desired state mission?<br>• *Outcomes*<br>    • Rationale statement, including risk assessment<br>    • Vision statement<br>    • Mission statement |
| 4:15 – 5:00 p.m. | Summary of day's work; review agenda for day two |
| 6:00 – 8:00 p.m. | Dinner |

Figure 14.2. Day two retreat agenda

| EIM Team Retreat Agenda | |
|---|---|
| Date - Place | |
| *Purpose: Assess EIM division options for improving data integrity issues and develop preliminary action plan* | |
| **Day Two** | |
| 7:45 – 8:30 a.m. | Breakfast |
| 8:30 – 10:00 a.m. | Identify function and scope of EIM approach (use Decision Matrix Technique)<br>• What functions will be performed?<br>• What is included in the scope?<br>• What is excluded from the scope?<br>• *Outcomes*<br>    • Function and scope document |
| 10:00 – 10:15 a.m. | Break |
| 10:15 – 11:30 a.m. | Determine structure and resources (use Subgroup Technique)<br>• What will be the organizational structure?<br>• How will the structure relate to existing units?<br>• What resources will be needed for this option?<br>• *Outcomes*<br>    • Proposed organizational structure and rationale<br>    • Resource requirements document |
| 11:30 – 12:30 p.m. | Lunch |
| 12:30 – 2:30 p.m. | Three-year plan and key performance indicators<br>• What are steps for years 1, 2, and 3 for implementation?<br>• What is timeline for implementation?<br>• What are resource and budget considerations?<br>• What are risks at each stage?<br>• What are key performance indicators (criteria)? |
| 2:30 – 2:45 p.m. | Break |
| 2:45 – 4:15 p.m. | Three-year plan and key performance indicators (continued)<br>• *Outputs*<br>    • Three-year implementation plan |
| 4:15 – 5:00 p.m. | Wrap up and next steps for final report to Joan Morton |



## Summary of the Retreat

Prior to the retreat, the St. Rita's EIM team had one preparatory meeting. The team was thrilled to hear from Val, Bob, and Linda that three outside experts were joining the retreat. Briefing books were distributed by the planning team so the team would have sufficient time to prepare for the retreat agenda.

The EIM team had a successful retreat in which the agenda, meeting room, and briefing materials preparation were keys to its success. The team met at a center specifically designed for retreats. It was located on the outskirts of the metropolitan area on 18 acres of forest and prairie land and included overnight accommodations and food service.

The meeting room was arranged by the facilitator in a comfortable u-shaped table format, audio-visual equipment was available, and the team made good use of the flip charts and white boards. Sandy did an excellent job of facilitation; her assistant joined as the scribe, keeping minutes and summarizing each day's events.

After the conclusion of the retreat, the team put together a proposal for Joan. Val took the retreat summary provided by Sandy, assigned each team member to author a section, and coordinated the organization of the final report. Before submitting the report to Joan, the team met one last time to sign off on it. An outline of the report is included in figure 14.3, and a draft proposal is available in the student workbook.

Figure 14.3. **Outline of final report for EIM division at St. Rita's**

**Executive Overview/Introduction**
A concise overview highlights the significant findings, situational analysis, and recommendations contained in the proposal. The executive overview sets a strong case for establishing an EIM division at St. Rita's.

**Background on Enterprise Information Management and Data Governance**
The proposal provides a rationale for EIM and DG with examples of how others currently use the functions to enhance operations. The proposal clearly outlines the definitions and functions of EIM and DG, identifies the benefits, and presents sample organizational structures. It also includes reference authority (for example, footnotes and appendix) to substantiate rationale.

**Situational Analysis**
The situational analysis cites data issues, situations, and problems at St. Rita's. The proposal provides recommendations for solving the current data crisis at St. Rita's by establishing an EIM function. The proposal cites specific examples of how EIM and DG functions can solve current problems.

**Proposal for EIM and DG**
This section provides the business case for EIM and DG and includes the following:

- Business case
- Vision and mission statement
- Scope
- Functions - Includes general discussion of functions
- Organization - Includes how the EIM department relates to other organizational areas
- Organizational placement (for example, organization chart)
- Required resources
- First-year implementation plan and key performance indicators
- Second-year implementation plan and key performance indicators
- Third-year implementation plan and key performance indicators
- Sample protocols (can be in the appendix)
- Sample policies
- Sample job descriptions (can be in the appendix)

After receiving the report, Joan asked the team for an oral briefing. Satisfied from the briefing, she scheduled a meeting with the EIM team and the members of the St. Rita's information systems strategic planning committee. This committee included the chief information medical officer, executive vice presidents, chairs of several medical specialties, and other director-level positions. Val led these briefings, assisted by the EIM team.

The team did its job well. They were prepared for these meetings and could satisfactory address every question asked of them by those in attendance. Based on the positive feedback from this meeting, Joan prepared to present a formal recommendation to establish an EIM division at St. Rita's to the St. Rita's executive team (consisting of the chief executive officer, chief financial officer, chief operating officer, chief medical officer, and chief nursing officer).

The original St. Rita's EIM team went out for a celebratory dinner after the information systems strategic planning committee briefing, but it wouldn't be the last time they were together. The final report included opportunities for all of them to contribute in various ways to the establishment of the EIM office at St. Rita's. It was likely that Denise would be appointed director of the EIM office, Val would serve as chair of the data stewardship committee, and the rest of the team would contribute as data stewards for various business areas and chair specific subcommittees of the data stewardship committee. St. Rita's was ready to take EIM into action.

## Part of the Team: Discussion and Action

1. Val, Bob, and Linda included a number of work products in the briefing book. In addition to the work products listed in this chapter, provide a list of the work products you think should be included in the briefing book.
2. How do you think adding outside experts might have helped the EIM team at their retreat? Provide specific examples for the three outside agenda participants.
3. Review the two-day agenda prepared by Val, Bob, Linda, and Sandy (figures 14.1 and 14.2). What is your critique of the agenda? Do you think it is comprehensive? Does it achieve what it is supposed to? How might you improve it?
4. In the agenda, Sandy put in a number of group process techniques to help the team come up with creative ideas and make decisions. These included the nominal group brainstorming, respond rounds, and subgroup techniques. Research these and describe how each is conducted and what the expected benefits are for them.
5. Using the draft proposal to establish an EIM division at St. Rita's in the student manual, critique the proposal and answer the following questions:

    a. Did the EIM team present a convincing business case for establishing a new EIM division at St. Rita's?
    b. Would you add anything to the team's vision and mission statements for the EIM division? Why or why not?
    c. Do you agree with how the EIM team proposed the organizational structure for the EIM division? Are there alternate structures the team could have recommended?
    d. How would you evaluate the team's recommendation for EIM implementation? Do you think this is a realistic approach? Do you think the team was too ambitious or not ambitious enough in its three-year plan?
    e. What are some challenges that may impede a smooth implementation of the EIM division at St. Rita's? What would you suggest be done to minimize these challenges?

## Advanced Concepts

1. Using the outline in figure 14.3 and the draft proposal in the student manual, prepare a formal final written proposal for establishing an EIM division at St. Rita's. What are the major differences between your final report and the draft report? What is accomplished by these differences? What are the strong points of your proposal? How do these changes make the final proposal stronger? What did you add or delete from the EIM team's proposal and why?
2. Conduct a condensed version of the EIM team's retreat. What are the key takeaways from the simulated retreat that Sandy would summarize in a report?

# Appendix A

# The Health Insurance Portability and Accountability Act

The 1996 Health Insurance Portability and Accountability Act (HIPAA) ushered in a new era of protections for health information. HIPAA represents an attempt to establish best practices and standards for health information security. Besides protections for health information, the act, also called Public Law 104-191, includes provisions for insurance reform and administrative simplification. Included in the administrative simplification provisions is a requirement for setting standards to protect health information. In February 2003, the Department of Health and Human Services (HHS) established security and privacy standards that every healthcare provider, healthcare clearinghouse, or health plan that electronically maintains or transmits patient health information had to meet. The compliance date for meeting the security regulations for all but small health plans was April 21, 2005.

In 2009, improved privacy and security provisions to HIPAA were included in parts of the **American Recovery and Reinvestment Act** (ARRA) as the Health Information Technology for Economic and Clinical Health (HITECH) Act. The HITECH Act made the most sweeping changes to HIPAA Privacy and Security Rules since initial implementation. The changes expanded many of the HIPAA requirements to business associates (BA) of covered entities that receive protected health information (PHI). In addition, penalties increased for noncompliance with the regulations based on the level of negligence with a maximum penalty of $1.5 million per violation. HITECH also made changes to strengthen breach notification requirements described later in this appendix.

To implement the statutory amendments of the HITECH Act, HHS issued final regulations on January 25, 2013, titled Modifications to the HIPAA Privacy, Security, Enforcement, and Breach Notification Rules Under the Health Information Technology for Economic and Clinical Health Act and the Genetic Information Nondiscrimination Act; Other Modifications to the HIPAA Rules. This rule is sometimes referred to as an omnibus rule because it treats several distinct matters. This omnibus rule includes four distinct rules:

1. Final modifications to HIPAA Privacy, Security, and Enforcements mandated by the HITECH Act and certain other modifications to improve the Rules
2. Final rule adopting changes to the HIPAA Enforcement Rule
3. Final rule on Breach Notification for Unsecured PHI under the HITECH Act
4. Final rule modifying the HIPAA Privacy Rule required by the Genetic Information Nondiscrimination Act (GINA) (45 CFR Parts 160 and 164).

Figure A.1 provides key highlights of the omnibus rule.

Figure A.1. Key highlights of the HITECH updates to HIPAA privacy and security requirements and breach notification

**Key highlights of the HITECH updates to HIPAA privacy and security requirements and breach notification**

- Business associates must follow the Security Rule for electronic PHI.
- BAs must have BA agreements with their subcontractors who must also follow the security rule for electronic protected health information (ePHI).
- Covered entities (CE) do not have BA agreements with BA contractors.
- Marketing for all subsidized communications where the communication encourages the recipient to purchase a product or service requires an authorization.
- Financial remuneration is defined as direct payment that comes from the third party to the covered entity who is requesting their product or service to be described.

(continued)

Figure A.1. Continued

- BAs must obtain authorizations prior to marketing.
- Grandfather clause for BA agreement transition allowing covered entities and BAs to continue to operate under existing contracts that already have a HIPAA-compliant agreement in place with varying compliance deadlines
- Sale of PHI is prohibited. Sale of PHI means that the covered entity or BA receives payment for the PHI from or on behalf of the recipient of the PHI.
- Compound authorizations for research are permitted that include informed consent for the research study as well as the use of PHI in the clinical trial.
- Authorizations for future research for use or disclosure of PHI must adequately describe the future uses or disclosure.
- Any individually identifiable health information of a person deceased more than 50 years is no longer considered PHI under the Privacy Rule.
- Covered entities are now permitted to disclose a decedent's PHI to family members and others who were involved in the care or payment for care of a decedent prior to death, unless doing so is inconsistent with any prior expressed preference of the individual that is known to the CE.
- Covered entities can disclose proof of immunization to a school where state or other law requires it prior to admitting a student. Written authorization is no longer required, but an agreement must still be obtained, which can be oral.
- Covered entities must provide the recipient of any fundraising communication with a clear and conspicuous opportunity to opt out of receiving any further fundraising communications and the individual's choice to opt out is treated as a revocation of authorization under the privacy rule.
- The Notice of Privacy Practices (NPP) must include certain new statements about the uses and disclosure of PHI.
- Requires health plans that post their NPP on their website to update the NPP on the website when material changes are made to the NPP
- Covered entities must provide individuals with an electronic copy of their PHI. Form and format of electronic copies must be in a machine-readable format
- Fees for paper and electronic copies may cover labor and supplies, but may not include a retrieval fee.
- Timeliness for responding to requests for paper and electronic records have been changed.
- The Breach Notification Rule's "harm" threshold is removed and replaced with a more objective standard.

Source: AHIMA 2013.

This appendix focuses primarily on the general provisions and modifications to the security rule. Privacy regulations are briefly outlined at the end of this appendix. The effective date for the HITECH regulations was March 26, 2013 and the compliance date was September 23, 2013, with the exception of varying deadlines for business associate agreements. As of July 27, 2009, enforcement for HIPAA security compliance was moved from the Centers for Medicare and Medicaid Services' (CMS) Office of Electronic Standards and Security to the HHS Office for Civil Rights (OCR). The HITECH Act mandates improved enforcement of the Privacy Rule and Security Rule. Enforcement of HIPAA security is taken seriously by covered entities and others who must follow HIPAA security rules. Enforcement results are available for review by year beginning in 2003 at the HHS website.

# HIPAA Privacy and Security Rules

HIPAA Privacy and Security Rules are located in Parts 160, 162, 164, and Subparts A, C, D, and E under HIPAA Administrative Simplification provisions. **Subpart A** includes the general provisions, **Subpart C** covers the security standards for the protection of ePHI, **Subpart D** includes the standards for the notification in the case of an unsecured PHI breach, and **Subpart E** covers the standards for privacy of individually identifiable health information. This appendix covers Subparts C and D in detail since these are specific to electronic data security. Figure A.2 provides the outline of these subparts as a reference tool. Key terms related to HIPAA are listed and defined in the beginning of chapter 10.

Figure A.2. Outline of HIPAA Privacy and Security Rules

**Part 164—Security and privacy**

**Subpart A—General provisions**

§ 164.102 Statutory basis
§ 164.103 Definitions
§ 164.104 Applicability
§ 164.105 Organizational requirements
§ 164.106 Relationship to other parts

**Subpart B [reserved]**

**Subpart C—Security standards for the protection of ePHI**

§ 164.302 Applicability
§ 164.304 Definitions
§ 164.306 Security standards: General rules
§ 164.308 Administrative safeguards
§ 164.310 Physical safeguards
§ 164.312 Technical safeguards
§ 164.314 Organizational requirements
§ 164.316 Policies and procedures and documentation requirements
§ 164.318 Compliance dates for the initial implementation of the security standards

**Subpart D—Notification in the case of breach of unsecured PHI**

§ 164.400 Applicability
§ 164.402 Definitions
§ 164.404 Notification to individuals
§ 164.406 Notification to the media
§ 164.408 Notification to the secretary
§ 164.410 Notification by a business associate
§ 164.412 Law enforcement delay
§ 164.414 Administrative requirements and burden of proof

**Subpart E—Privacy of individually identifiable health information**

§ 164.500 Applicability
§ 164.501 Definitions
§ 164.502 Uses and disclosures of protected health information: General rules
§ 164.504 Uses and disclosures: Organizational requirements
§ 164.506 Uses and disclosures to carry out treatment, payment, or healthcare operations
§ 164.508 Uses and disclosures for which an authorization is required
§ 164.510 Uses and disclosures requiring an opportunity for the individual to agree or to object
§ 164.512 Uses and disclosures for which an authorization or opportunity to agree or object is not required
§ 164.514 Other requirements relating to uses and disclosures of protected health information
§ 164.520 Notice of privacy practices for protected health information
§ 164.522 Rights to request privacy protection for protected health information
§ 164.524 Access of individuals to protected health information
§ 164.526 Amendment of protected health information
§ 164.528 Accounting of disclosures of protected health information
§ 164.530 Administrative requirements
§ 164.532 Transition provisions
§ 164.534 Compliance dates for initial implementation of the privacy standards

# Subpart C: Security Standards for the Protection of ePHI

Together, the HIPAA Security Rule and the Privacy Rule make up what is commonly considered HIPAA for the safeguarding of PHI. The Privacy Rule regulations (discussed later) pertain to all PHI while the Security Rule deals specifically with ePHI. Both covered entities and BAs must comply with the standards, implementation specifications, and requirements of HIPAA with respect to the ePHI of a covered entity.

HIPAA security is divided into five provisions, including:

- General rules
- Administrative safeguards
- Physical safeguards
- Organizational requirements and policies
- Procedures and documentation requirements

The details of each of these provisions are briefly described in this section. The HIPAA Security Rule explanation that follows is based upon the Security Standards Final Rule and amendments through March 26, 2013 and is available at the HHS website.

The HIPAA security provisions follow what has already been established in the information systems field as best practices for the development and implementation of good security policy and closely parallel the mechanisms for minimizing security threats that should be part of any data security plan, as discussed in chapter 10.

## General Rules

The Security Standard General Rules provide the objective and scope for the HIPAA Security Rule as a whole. They specify that covered entities must develop a security program that includes a range of security safeguards that protect individually identifiable health information maintained or transmitted in electronic form. The following provide additional detail of the General Rules.

- General requirements*:* These are requirements all covered entities and BAs must follow in their security program. For example, these include:
    - Ensuring the confidentiality, integrity, and availability of all ePHI the covered entity creates, receives, maintains, or transmits
    - Protecting PHI against any reasonably anticipated threats or hazards to the security or integrity of PHI
    - Protecting PHI against any reasonably anticipated uses or disclosure not permitted under the HIPAA Privacy Rule
    - Ensuring compliance with HIPAA security rules by workforce members
- Flexibility of approach**:** HIPAA allows covered entities and BAs to adopt security protection measures that are appropriate for each organization. Flexibility takes into consideration the organization's size and complexity, its technical infrastructure, hardware and software capabilities, security measure costs, and the probability and criticality of the potential risks to ePHI. For example, security mechanisms in complex organizations, such as a large hospital are different from those in small organizations, such as a small group practice.
- Standards*:* Security standards covered entities must comply with include the following sections in the HIPAA rule:
    - 164.308. Administrative safeguards
    - 164.310. Physical safeguards
    - 164.312. Technical safeguards
    - 164.314. Organizational requirements
    - 164.316. Policies and procedures and documentation requirements

  BAs must comply with the administrative, physical, and technical safeguards and standards for policies, procedures, and documentation requirements.
- Implementation specifications: These specifications define how to implement standards for administrative, physical, and technical safeguards. Implementation specifications are either "required" or "addressable." Covered entities and BAs must use all "required" implementation specifications. For those implementation specifications that are "addressable," the covered entity or BA must conduct a risk assessment and evaluate whether the specification is

appropriate and reasonable to its environment. If the specification is appropriate and reasonable, then the covered entity or BA should implement it. If the specification is not reasonable and appropriate, then the covered entity or BA must provide documentation as to why, and implement an equivalent alternative measure. Table A.1 provides a listing of required and addressable implementation specifications as a guide.

- Maintenance: Covered entities and BAs are required by the regulations to maintain and keep their security measures up to date. Maintenance includes review and modification of security measures, as needed, for reasonable and appropriate protection of ePHI in a changing technological environment.

Table A.1. Security standards implementation specifications

| Standards | Sections | Implementation Specifications (R)=Required,(A)=Addressable |
|---|---|---|
| **Administrative Safeguards** | | |
| Security Management Process | 164.308(a)(1) | Risk Analysis (R) |
| | | Risk Management (R) |
| | | Sanction Policy (R) |
| | | Information System Activity Review (R) |
| Assigned Security Responsibility | 164.308(a)(2) | (R) |
| Workforce Security | 164.308(a)(3) | Authorization or Supervision (A) |
| | | Workforce Clearance Procedure (A) |
| | | Termination Procedures (A) |
| Information Access Management | 164.308(a)(4) | Isolating Healthcare Clearinghouse Function (R) |
| | | Access Authorization (A) |
| | | Access Establishment and Modification (A) |
| Security Awareness and Training | 164.308(a)(5) | Security Reminders (A) |
| | | Protection from Malicious Software (A) |
| | | Log-in Monitoring (A) |
| | | Password Management (A) |
| Security Incident Procedures | 164.308(a)(6) | Response and Reporting (R) |
| Contingency Plan | 164.308(a)(7) | Data Backup Plan (R) |
| | | Disaster Recovery Plan (R) |
| | | Emergency Mode Operation Plan (R) |
| | | Testing and Revision Procedure (A) |
| | | Applications and Data Criticality Analysis (A) |
| Evaluation | 164.308(a)(8) | (R) |
| Business Associate Contracts and Other Arrangement | 164.308(b)(1) | Written Contract or Other Arrangement (R) |

(continued)

Table A.1. Security standards implementation specifications (*Continued*)

| Standards | Sections | Implementation Specifications (R)=Required,(A)=Addressable |
|---|---|---|
| **Physical Safeguards** | | |
| Facility Access Controls | 164.310(a)(1) | Contingency Operations (A) |
| | | Facility Security Plan (A) |
| | | Access Control and Validation Procedures (A) |
| | | Maintenance Records (A) |
| Workstation Use | 164.310(b) | (R) |
| Workstation Security | 164.310(c) | (R) |
| Device and Media Controls | 164.310(d)(1) | Disposal (R) |
| | | Media Re-use (R) |
| | | Accountability (A) |
| | | Data Backup and Storage (A) |
| **Technical Safeguards**(see § 164.312) | | |
| Access Control | 164.312(a)(1) | Unique User Identification (R) |
| | | Emergency Access Procedure (R) |
| | | Automatic Logoff (A) |
| Audit Controls | 164.312(b) | (R) |
| Integrity | 164.312(c)(1) | Mechanism to Authenticate Electronic Protected Health Information (A) |
| Person or Entity Authentication | 164.312(d) | (R) |
| Transmission Security | 164.312(e)(1) | Integrity Controls (A) |
| | | Encryption (A) |

Source: HIPAA 2013.

## Administrative Safeguards

**Administrative safeguards** are documented, formal practices to manage data security measures throughout the organization and include nine standards (table A.1). These safeguards require the organization to establish a security management program that includes the organization's statement of its philosophy on data security. The security management program must be responsible for creating, maintaining, and overseeing security policies and procedures development, written and formalized in a policy manual. Further, it should make a chart outlining data security authority and responsibilities throughout the organization.

The organization must conduct a thorough risk analysis of potential threats, vulnerabilities, and risks that may affect the security and privacy of PHI. Organizations must also have risk management processes in place that reduce vulnerabilities and control the risks to PHI security. Sanction policies must be in place that provide sanctions for workforce members who do not abide by the organization's privacy and security policies. The security management program must also include regular reviews of system activity including a review of system logs, audit trails, and incident reports to identify potential vulnerabilities and detect breaches. The administrative safeguards require organizations to identify and assign a security official who is responsible for required HIPAA policies and procedures development and implementation. Covered entities and BAs must, through appropriate access management processes and policies, ensure appropriate access to individually identifiable information to workforce members who need to use ePHI to perform their job duties and must prevent those who do not need it from accessing it. Furthermore, workforce security awareness and training is one of the most important strategies for ensuring data security. Both new and existing workforce members must receive appropriate security training.

A contingency plan must be developed and tested for handling unexpected or unplanned computer disruptions by covered organizations. This ensures procedures are in place to handle an emergency event, such as a power outage. The contingency plan should include provisions for data backup, data recovery, emergency mode operation, and testing and revision procedures. Organizations must perform a periodic technical and nontechnical evaluation in response to environmental or operational changes affecting the security of ePHI.

## Physical Safeguards

**Physical safeguards** include the protection of computer systems from natural and environmental hazards and intrusion, and include four general categories of controls (table A.1). These include controls for facility access, workstation use, workstation security, and device media.

HIPAA specifies that facility access controls be in place. These controls have two purposes. The first is to prohibit unauthorized access to physical hardware and the computer system. The second is to ensure the organization is allowing proper authorized access to physical resources. Employee badge controls that permit authorized personnel into the facility, locks on computer rooms, and tagging or engraving computer equipment are three examples of physical access control mechanisms. Physical safeguards must also be in place to protect a computer system from untoward physical events such as fire, flooding, and electrical malfunctions.

A workstation is defined by HIPAA as any electronic computing device (such as a laptop or desktop computer, or any other device that performs similar functions) and electronic media stored in its immediate environment. Specific workstation use controls require policies and procedures that document the proper functions workforce members may perform on workstations. For example, workforce members who use workstations that access ePHI may only use those workstations for business purposes and are required to log off the computer system when they leave their workstation. Covered entities and BAs are also required to document the physical attributes of the surroundings of a workstation or a class of workstations that access ePHI. For instance, workstations should be positioned so that unauthorized persons cannot view the computer screen. HIPAA requires safeguards to protect any workstations that access ePHI from unauthorized access. An inventory should be performed by organizations to identify any workstations that access ePHI; once identified, appropriate physical safeguards can be put in place by the organization. One example is physically locking down a workstation or laptop with a cable lock.

Other devices and media where ePHI is stored must also have physical protections. HIPAA requires policies and procedures that ensure disks, tapes, and videos are physically protected from harm or intrusion. Organizations must have policies and procedures in place that address the disposal of disks and other media, including paper reports and records that contain PHI. Policies and procedures for the removal of ePHI from media for media reuse must also be in place.

Organizations must establish controls for tracking the access, removal, and disposal of hardware and software. Using sign-out logs when anyone removes media from the secured computer location is an example. In addition, monitoring procedures must be in place to review sign-out logs and to check and evaluate audit trails. Further, the organization must have procedures to follow for creating an exact copy of ePHI before moving equipment and must have in place policies and procedures for data backup and storage.

## Technical Safeguards

**Technical safeguards** consist of five broad categories. The provisions include things covered entities and BAs can implement from a technical standpoint using computer software. These provisions include development and implementation of written policies and procedures for access controls, audit controls, data integrity, person or identity authentication, and transmission security (table A.1).

Access controls that limit access to ePHI to appropriate personnel for performance of their jobs are executed through complex software programs. Access control is usually determined by one of three techniques: context-based, role-based, and user-based access schemes. HIPAA requires organizations assign a unique name or number to individuals who have access to ePHI so the organization can track their activity while they are using any system that uses or stores ePHI. There also must be policies and procedures that allow appropriate access to ePHI in emergency situations.

Organizations execute required audit controls through software programs that monitor and maintain logs of who accessed or made an attempt to access ePHI, when the event occurred, and the type of activity that took place. Audit trails are an example of an audit control. Data integrity controls provide corroboration that ePHI has not been altered or destroyed in an unauthorized manner. Data can be altered or destroyed by technical and non-technical means. A non-technical example is an end user who inadvertently deletes a record. A technical example of alteration is when a bar code is misread by a scanning device. Data authentication can be substantiated through audit trails and system logs that track users via unique identifiers who have accessed or modified data.

The person or entity authentication standard requires organizations to implement procedures that verify a person or entity seeking access to ePHI is the one claimed. For example, an entity can be a human user of a system or another machine that has access to or transmits ePHI. Assignment of a unique identifier (such as a password) to workforce members is an example of person authentication.

The transmission security standard includes integrity controls, when deemed appropriate, for protecting ePHI from improper modification during transmission over computer networks and the use of encryption methods when ePHI is transmitted over public networks or communication systems. Encryption is a process that encodes textual material, converting it to scrambled data the receiving system must decode in order for the recipient to understand it.

## Organizational Requirements

This section includes two standards; one addresses BAs, and the other addresses requirements for group health plans. Covered entities must obtain a written contract with BAs who handle ePHI. The written contract stipulates that the BA implements HIPAA administrative, physical, and technical safeguards and procedures and documentation requirements that safeguard the confidentiality, integrity, and availability of the ePHI that it creates, receives, maintains, or transmits on behalf of the covered entity. The contract must ensure that any agent, including a subcontractor, agrees to implement reasonable and appropriate safeguards. Specifically, HIPAA requires a BA to report to the covered entity any security incident or breach of ePHI of which it becomes aware. The covered entity must authorize termination of the contract if it determines the BA violated a material term of the contract. HIPAA also requires BAs to have contracts in place that assure compliance with HIPAA rules with all subcontractors who handle ePHI. These requirements are managed via a BA agreement that is attached to the contract of services with a vendor.

Requirements for group health plans specify that plan sponsors must reasonably and appropriately safeguard ePHI they create, receive, maintain, or transmit. The Privacy Rule limits the health information that health plans, health insurance companies, and health maintenance organizations can disclose to plan sponsors. For example, this information is limited to summary health information for the purposes of obtaining premium bids from health plans for health insurance coverage, modifying, amending or terminating the plan, or for providing information on whether or not an individual is participating, enrolled, or disenrolled in the plan. Health plan documents must include requirements for a plan sponsor to

- Implement the same security measures required by the HIPAA Privacy Standard for information it creates, receives, maintains, or transmits on behalf of the health plan
- Ensure the sponsor's employees' duties are adequately separated to guarantee PHI is not used for employment or other employee-benefit decisions
- Require agents of the sponsor to provide reasonable and appropriate protection of health information provided to them by the plan sponsor
- Report any security incident of which it becomes aware to the health plan

## Policies and Procedures and Documentation Requirements

HIPAA requires covered entities and BAs have written, documented security policies and procedures. Other information about any actions, assessments, or activities associated with the HIPAA Security Rule also must be in a written format. These requirements follow accepted best practices in security management, such as developing written policies and procedures that comply with HIPAA security standards and maintaining in written form any actions, assessments, or activities concerned with the security management of an organization. An organization must retain documentation for six years from the date of its creation or the date when it last was in effect, whichever is later. It must be available to those individuals responsible for implementing security procedures. Further, it must be reviewed by the organization periodically and updated, as needed, in response to environmental or organizational changes that affect the security of ePHI.

## Subpart D: Notification in the Case of Breach of Unsecured PHI

Breach notification is Subpart D of the HIPAA Administrative Simplification Regulations. These regulations require covered entities to notify affected individuals, and require BAs to notify covered entities, following the discovery of a breach of unsecured PHI. **Breach** means the acquisition, access, use, or disclosure of PHI in any way not permitted by the HIPAA Privacy regulations which compromises the security or privacy of PHI. Protection measures must be appropriately applied to data in their various forms including data in motion, such as data moving through a network; data at rest, such as data stored in a database; data in use, such as data in the process of being created or updated; and data disposed, such as digital data being destroyed.

### Unsecured PHI

An important aspect of breach notification is knowing what constitutes unsecured PHI. Breach notification is required only in instances where there has been a breach of unsecured PHI. **Unsecured PHI** is defined as PHI that is not rendered unusable, unreadable, or indecipherable to unauthorized persons through the use of technology or methodology specified by the HHS secretary in guidance in the HITECH Law. Examples of PHI considered secure and unusable, unreadable, or indecipherable to unauthorized individuals are when PHI is encrypted following specified National Institute of Standards and Technology (NIST) publications and in cases in which PHI is stored or recorded on media that have been destroyed in a specified manner, such as by shredding if it is a paper medium or by destruction consistent with NIST specifications if it is an electronic medium.

### Exceptions to Unsecured PHI Breach

There are three exceptions to a breach of unsecured PHI. These include situations when or where:

- There is any unintentional acquisition, access, or use of PHI by a workforce member or person acting under the authority of a covered entity or BA, if the acquisition, access, or use was made in good faith and within the scope of the person's authority and does not result in further use or disclosure in a way that is not permitted under the Privacy regulations.
- There is any inadvertent disclosure by a person who is authorized to access PHI at a covered entity or BA to another person authorized to access PHI at the same covered entity or BA, or organized healthcare arrangement in which the covered entity participates, and the information received as a result of such disclosure is not further used or disclosed in a way not permitted by the Privacy regulations.
- There is a disclosure of PHI where the covered entity or BA has a good faith belief that an unauthorized person to whom the disclosure was made would not reasonably have been able to retain such information.

In situations that do not fit the exceptions, any acquisition, access, use, or disclosure of PHI in a way not permitted by the Privacy regulations is considered to be a breach unless the covered entity or BA demonstrates and documents through a risk assessment that there is a low probability the PHI has been compromised based on considering at least the following factors:

- *The nature and extent of the PHI involved, including the types of identifiers and the likelihood of reidentification.* To assess this factor, entities should consider the type of PHI involved in the impermissible use or disclosure, such as whether the disclosure involved information of a more sensitive nature.
- *The unauthorized person who used the PHI or to whom the disclosure was made* requires covered entities and BAs to consider the unauthorized person who impermissibly used the PHI or to whom the impermissible disclosure was

made. Entities should consider whether the unauthorized person who received the information has obligations to protect the privacy and security of the information.

- *Whether the PHI was actually acquired or viewed* requires covered entities and BAs to investigate an impermissible use or disclosure to determine if the PHI was actually acquired or viewed or, alternatively, if only the opportunity existed for the information to be acquired or viewed.
- *The extent to which the risk to the PHI has been mitigated.* Covered entities and BAs should attempt to mitigate the risks to the PHI following any impermissible use or disclosure, such as by obtaining the recipient's satisfactory assurances that the information will not be further used or disclosed (through a confidentiality agreement or similar means) or will be destroyed, and should consider the extent and efficacy of the mitigation when determining the probability that the PHI has been compromised (AHIMA 2013).

## Notification Requirements

Notifications are required to individuals affected by the breach, in certain circumstances to the media, and to the secretary of HHS.

- *Notifications to individuals*: When a breach has occurred, the covered entity or BA has to follow specific notification requirements. In the case of a covered entity, it must notify each individual whose unsecured PHI has been or is reasonably believed to have been accessed, acquired, used, or disclosed as a result of a breach. The covered entity must make notifications without unreasonable delay and in no case later than 60 calendar days after the breach discovery. The covered entity must write notifications describing the breach in plain language and include specific elements as specified in the implementation specifications. In those situations where a written notification is not possible, for example, if the covered entity has insufficient or out-of-date contact information for the individual, a substitute form of notice may be provided, such as a conspicuous posting for a period of 90 days on the home page of the covered entity's website.
- *Notification to the media*: For a breach of unsecured ePHI involving more than 500 residents of a state or jurisdiction, a covered entity must notify prominent media outlets servicing the state or jurisdiction. The covered entity must provide the notice without unreasonable delay and in no case longer than 60 calendar days after the discovery of the breach.
- *Notification to the secretary of HHS*: Following the breach of unsecured ePHI, a covered entity must notify the secretary of HHS by filling out and electronically submitting a breach report form. In cases where 500 or more individuals are affected by the breach, a covered entity must make this notification without unreasonable delay and in no case later than 60 days following a breach. If the breach affects fewer than 500 individuals, a covered entity may notify the secretary of HHS on an annual basis and notification is due to the secretary no later than 60 days after the end of the calendar year in which the breach occurred.
- *Breaches at or by a BA*: In those cases of a breach occurring at or by a BA, the BA must notify the covered entity following the discovery of the breach. The BA must provide the notice to the covered entity without unreasonable delay and no later than 60 days from the discovery of the breach. The BA should provide the covered entity with the identification of each individual affected by the breach as well as any information required to be provided by the covered entity in its notification to affected individuals.

# Subpart E: Privacy of Individually Identifiable Health Information

The Privacy Rule regulates the use and disclosure of PHI, whether in paper, electronic, or other form, by covered entities. It covers how a covered entity and a BA can use and disclose PHI and prohibits certain uses and disclosures, such as using genetic information for underwriting purposes or selling PHI. A complete listing of the administrative simplification text that includes the Privacy Rule can be found at the HHS website.

In summary, the Privacy Rule requirements for covered entities and BAs include the following:

- Requires covered entities to obtain a written authorization for any disclosures of PHI other than that needed to facilitate treatment, payment, or healthcare operations. In such disclosures, the covered entity or BA must make every reasonable effort to limit the disclosure to only the minimum necessary information required to achieve the purpose of the disclosure.

- Provides individuals the right to agree or object to certain uses and disclosures. For example, a listing in a hospital directory of the individual's name, the location of an individual in a healthcare provider's facility, or the individual's religious affiliation.
- Requires covered entities to provide individuals with a notice of privacy practices written in plain language that includes a description and examples of the types of uses and disclosures that do and do not require an individual's authorization.
- Provides individuals the right to request privacy protections for their PHI for certain uses and disclosures.
- Provides individuals the right to receive confidential communications of PHI.
- Provides individuals the right to request access to and copies of their PHI.
- Gives individuals the right to request the covered entity correct any inaccuracies in PHI.
- Provides individuals, with some exceptions, the right to receive an accounting of disclosures of their PHI made by a covered entity in the six years prior to the date on which the accounting is requested.
- Requires a covered entity to designate a privacy official who is responsible for the development and implementation of the privacy policies and procedures of the entity.
- Requires that documentation such as policies and procedures, communications required by the Privacy Rule, and other documentation be retained for six years from the date of its creation or the date when it last was in effect, whichever is later.

## References

AHIMA. 2013 (January 25). Analysis of Modifications to the HIPAA Privacy, Security, Enforcement, and Breach Notification Rules under the Health Information Technology for Economic and Clinical Health Act and the Genetic Information Nondiscrimination Act; Other Modifications to the HIPAA Rules. http://library.ahima.org/xpedio/groups/public/documents/ahima/bok1_050067.pdf.

45 CFR Parts 160 and 164 78(17): 55665702. Modifications to the HIPAA Privacy, Security, Enforcement, and Breach Notification Rules Under the Health Information Technology for Economic and Clinical Health Act and the Genetic Information Nondiscrimination Act. 2013 (Jan. 25).

# Glossary

## A

**Access controls:** A fundamental security strategy to identify which workforce members in a healthcare organization should have access to what data.

**Ad hoc reports:** Reports end users build on an as-needed basis to manipulate and explore data. Ad hoc reports are usually used one time to answer a single, specific question.

**Administrative controls:** Policies and procedures that address the management of computer resources in data security (for example, a policy directing users to log off the computer when they are not using it).

**Administrative data:** Data that includes demographic, emergency contact, and insurance information, and is used primarily for administrative and transaction purposes.

**Administrative information system:** A suite of applications that supports organizational strategic and operational management.

**Administrative safeguards:** Under the Health Insurance Portability and Accountability Act of 1996 (HIPAA), these are administrative actions, and policies and procedures, to manage the selection, development, implementation, and maintenance of security measures to protect electronic protected health information and to manage the conduct of the covered entity's or business associate's workforce in relation to the protection of that information (45 CFR 164.304 2013).

**Agile development:** A group of practices that emphasizes short, simple, and iterative development cycles, and when used together, are intended to shorten and improve the systems development lifecycle (SDLC).

**American Recovery and Reinvestment Act of 2009 (ARRA):** A law passed in 2009 to stimulate economic recovery and growth. The law also includes improved privacy and security provisions to the Health Insurance Portability and Accountability Act of 1996 (HIPAA). See also, HITECH.

**Anesthesia information management system (AIMS):** A system to automate the capture, storage, and presentation of data during the intraoperative period, for example, data on the type of anesthesia the provider administered, a patient's vital signs while under anesthesia, and monitors the provider used to document the data's output.

**Anomaly detection:** A type of analytics that identifies outliers or unusual cases in a supposed homogeneous set of data. For example, a model of typical medical claims could be developed and, using anomaly detection, cases that do not fit the model would be identified.

**Application controls:** Security controls contained in application software or computer programs (for example, password management).

**Artifacts:** Abstractions or models that describe the data and the relationships among data and processes.

**Association learning:** A type of analytics that uses association rules, which are developed by examining a data set for frequent if/then patterns. Also uses other statistical analyses such as determining how frequently the items appear in the database and how many times the if/then statements are true.

**Attribute:** The column in a table that describes an entity and holds specific values across records in a database. For example, date of birth, gender, name, or address might describe a PATIENT entity.

**Attribute redundancy:** A data problem where a data source may have multiple records for the same entity, for example, redundancies in the master patient index.

**Authorized Testing and Certification Body (ATCB):** Bodies authorized by the National Coordinator to test and certify that certain types of electronic health record technology are compliant with the standards, implementation specifications, and certification criteria adopted by the U.S. Department of Health and Human Services (HHS) Secretary and meet the definition of certified electronic health record (EHR) technology.

## B

**Barcode point of care:** A system that enables the use of bar code technology for identifying any individual or object.

**Basic interoperability:** The ability of one computer system to send and receive a message from another computer system.

**Bed management systems:** A system that automates the process of assigning a patient to a specific hospital care unit, taking into consideration all of the services required to support the patient's condition during hospitalization;

features include tracking bed inventory, categorizing bed requests, managing patient queues, and managing environmental services for room preparation.

**Best of suite:** A strategy for choosing information technology where an organization selects multiple core vendors for related functions, for example, one vendor for a group of related clinical applications, one for financials, and one for supply chain management.

**Best-of-breed system:** System designed to excel in a specific area, such as a laboratory information system or radiology information system, and provides extensive functionality and specialized features that best meet the needs of a clinical department or functional area. Data sharing among best-of-breed systems may be challenging, resulting in data silos and duplicated and inconsistent data.

**Bidirectional mapping:** In data mapping, where data are mapped from the source system to the target and from the target to the source.

**Big data:** The concept of large volumes of complex and diverse data.

**Breach:** Under HITECH, the acquisition, access, use, or disclosure of protected health information (PHI) in any way not permitted by the HIPAA Privacy regulations which compromises the security or privacy of PHI.

**Bus topology:** A computer network configuration where each computer connects to a common backbone or trunk through some kind of connector.

**Business associate (BA):** Under HITECH, a person who on the behalf of a covered entity creates, receives, maintains, or transmits protected health information (PHI) for a function or activity regulated by HIPAA, including claims processing or administration, data analysis, processing or administration, utilization review, quality assurance, patient safety activities, billing, benefit management, practice management, and repricing, or provides legal, actuarial, accounting, consulting, data aggregation, management, administrative, accreditation, or financial services.

**Business case:** An argument for achieving a desired outcome or benefit by implementing or changing a process or activity, or enabling stakeholder interactions; frequently an economic argument.

**Business continuity plan (BCP):** A plan to handle an unexpected computer shutdown caused by an intentional or unintentional event, or during a natural disaster, that includes policies and procedures to help the business continue operation during the unexpected shutdown or disaster, and procedures the business can implement to restore its computer systems and resume normal operation after the disaster.

**Business intelligence (BI) systems:** A set of technologies and processes that collect data from various subsystems, both clinical and administrative, and use sophisticated analysis programs to understand and analyze business performance against key indicators or measures.

**Business metadata:** Data that describes, explains, locates, or otherwise makes it easier for people who conduct an organization's day-to-day business to retrieve, use, or manage information; provides context that makes data understandable and meaningful to end users. Examples include headings such as "chief complaint," "history of present illness," and "past history," commonly found in a patient's history report.

**Business rule:** A statement that defines or constrains how someone conducts a particular aspect of a business.

**Business rule validity:** A dimension of data validity where data conform to business rules.

**Business stewards:** Recognized subject matter experts who work with data management professionals on an ongoing basis to define and control data and may serve on data steward teams.

# C

**Cardinality:** In an entity relationship diagram, how many times a parent instance occurs to a child instance; a parent-child relationship is assumed.

**Centralized metadata architecture:** A single repository that holds all the organization's metadata.

**Certification Commission for Healthcare Information Technology (CCHIT):** An independent, voluntary, private-sector initiative organized as a limited liability corporation that has been awarded a contract by the US Department of Health and Human Services (HHS) to develop, create prototypes for, and evaluate the certification criteria and inspection process for electronic health record (EHR) products.

**Certified EHR technology:** A technology that an ONC Authorized Testing and Certification Body (ATCB) has tested and certified.

**Chief executive officer (CEO):** The senior manager appointed by a governing board to direct an organization's overall long-term strategic management.

**Chief financial officer (CFO):** The senior manager responsible for the fiscal management of an organization.

**Chief information officer (CIO):** The senior manager responsible for the overall management of information resources in an organization.

**Chief information security officer (CISO):** A senior manager who heads the information security office and is responsible for coordinating the development and implementation of information security policies, and possibly for managing security information technology operations.

**Chief security officer (CSO):** *See* chief information security officer (CISO).

**Classification:** A system that arranges or organizes like or related entities. In analytics, a technique that uses an existing categorical structure to classify new cases into the categories. The computer learns from a large set of pre-classified examples, such as legitimate e-mails and spam e-mails.

**Client computer:** A network computer that accesses shared resources.

**Clinical care pathways:** Multidisciplinary, structured care plans that healthcare professionals use to implement clinical guidelines and protocols for a specific patient group, usually based on diagnosis or surgical procedure.

**Clinical data repository:** A real-time database that updates data immediately when it is entered by a person, directly from a device, or in another manner and consolidates data from different clinical source systems within an organization to present a unified view of a single patient's data.

**Clinical documentation:** A detailed account of pertinent facts, findings, and observations relating to a patient's health history, examinations, tests, treatments, procedures, and supportive care; a primary communication tool among healthcare providers that facilitates the planning and management of an individual's treatment and care over a lifetime.

**Clinical information system:** A system dedicated to collecting, storing, manipulating, and making available clinical information important to the delivery of patient care. A collection of various information technology applications that provide a centralized repository of information related to patient care across distributed locations.

**Cluster detection:** A type of analytics that divides data into meaningful groups based on the information found in the data set, for example, identifying patients that have the same treatment outcomes.

**Coexistence implementation:** A storage solution where some master data is stored along with the ability to reference other data in the source systems; also contains metadata with pointers to locations of master records and attributes.

**Collaboration tools:** Tools that enable people to create, share, and use common content, frequently used for project and program management. Examples include Microsoft SharePoint and Lotus Quickr.

**Commercial off-the-shelf software (COTS):** A ready-made software package organizations can purchase instead of developing their own; the package may or may not be customizable.

**Computer network:** A communication network consisting of a transmitter that sends data, a receiver that receives data, and a medium that connects the transmitter and receiver and provides the pathway for the transmission of the data.

**Computer Stored Ambulatory Care Record (COSTAR):** A modular medical information system used in a variety of healthcare settings for patient registration, medical records, accounts receivable, report generation, and appointment scheduling developed under the direction of Dr. Octo Barnett.

**Computer-aided software engineering (CASE):** Tools that support documentation and communication aspects of the system's development life cycle and help integrate tasks throughout the life cycle stages.

**Computer-based patient record (CPR):** A concept of maintaining health-related and patient-related data electronically, relying on multiple data sources and technologies to ensure end users can access complete and accurate data, receive alerts, reminders, clinical decision support, and links to medical knowledge.

**Computerized provider order entry (CPOE):** Systems that allow licensed individuals and those with ordering privileges to directly enter medical orders, such as medications, tests, and treatments. The system electronically routes orders to the appropriate departments and individuals for completion.

**Conceptual data model:** A high-level model consisting only of entities and their relationships, often used during the initial requirements definition stage of system development and is the precursor to development of the logical data model.

**Confidentiality:** The expectation that information an individual shares with a healthcare provider during the course of care is only used for its intended purpose.

**Consolidated implementation:** An implementation method that has each database provide its authoritative reference and master data into a single, managed master data management (MDM) data store that serves as a hub for all reference and master data for all other systems, both transaction and analytic.

**Content:** The data or information within a record that composes its intellectual substance. For example, the description of a patient's medical history, past illnesses, and current problems constitutes the intellectual substance of a patient history report.

**Content management:** The organization, categorization, and structure of data or resources so they can be stored, published, and reused in multiple ways; the tools and technologies used to capture, manage, store, preserve, and deliver content and documents related to organizational processes.

**Context:** The circumstances about a record's creation, receipt, and use (for example, how it was created, when it was created, and by whom it was created); also provides links to other records.

**Content exchange standards:** Standards that provide the specifications of the format and the sequence of data in the exchange message.

**Contingency and disaster planning:** *See* business continuity plan (BCP).

**Continuity of care record (CCR):** A content and a structure standard commonly referred to as ASTM E2369 whose purpose is to provide a snapshot in time of a patient's pertinent clinical, demographic, and administrative data and to enable electronic exchange of this data among healthcare providers.

**Controls:** Measures and functionality established for the purpose of preventing and mitigating risks.

**Coordinating stewards:** Stewards who lead and represent teams of business data stewards, serve on a data steward coordinating committee, serve as advisors to the data governance council, and work on tactical teams to draft policy, develop standards, resolve data issues, and coordinate data governance implementation.

**Corporate Information Factory (CIF):** An architecture model for business intelligence (BI) developed by Bill Inmon and Claudia Inhoff, also known as a "top-down" approach; it proposes starting with a single, centralized enterprise-wide data warehouse.

**Covered entity (CE):** As amended by HITECH, a health plan, a healthcare clearinghouse, or a healthcare provider who transmits any health information in electronic form in connection with a transaction covered by the HIPPA privacy and security rules.

**Critical care information system:** A system that provides intensive care units (ICU) with automated documentation for collection, management, and display of patient information. These systems allow direct documentation input by ICU caregivers and include patient assessments, treatment plans, caregiver notes, and flow sheets.

**Current Procedural Terminology (CPT):** Terminology developed by the American Medical Association that describes medical services and procedures performed by physicians and other healthcare providers.

# D

**Dashboards:** Reports that focus on operational information. A data visualization function displays the current (real-time) status of pre-defined metrics and key performance indicators for an enterprise or business unit on a single screen. These include both static and interactive reports, graphs, charts, and illustrations.

**Data:** Raw facts without meaning or context.

**Data accessibility:** Data items that are easily obtainable and legal to access with strong protections and controls built into the process.

**Data accuracy:** The extent to which the data are free of identifiable errors.

**Data acquisition:** The creation or procurement of data.

**Data architecture:** An integrated set of specification artifacts (models and diagrams) used to define data requirements, guide integration and control of data assets, and align data investments with business strategy; also known as data engineering and information engineering.

**Data availability:** A data quality dimension in which an organization can depend on the information system to perform exactly as expected, without error, and to provide information when and where it is needed.

**Data breach:** An incident in which an unauthorized individual(s) has potentially viewed, stolen, or used sensitive, protected, or confidential data; may involve protected health information, personally identifiable information, trade secrets, or intellectual property.

**Data cleansing:** A process that corrects inconsistency issues related to format, illegal characters, and empty fields in databases.

**Data comprehensiveness:** A data quality dimension where all required data items are included, ensuring the entire scope of the data is collected with intentional limitations documented.

**Data consistency:** A data quality dimension. The extent to which data are reliable and the same across applications.

**Data content quality:** A quality dimension that represents the raw data used to produce information and includes definition conformance, existence, completeness, and validity.

**Data currency:** A data quality dimension. The extent to which data are up-to-date; a datum value is up-to-date if it is current for a specific point in time, and it is outdated if it was current at a preceding time but incorrect at a later time.

**Data decision rights and accountabilities:** A set of actions that determines who can take what action with what data, when they can take those actions, under what circumstances, and what methods they can use.

**Data definition:** The specific meaning of a data element.

**Data dictionary:** The central repository for information about tables, attributes, and relationships which analysts, programmers, and end users can consult to understand the system.

**Data flow:** An input to or output from processes or data stores that represents data in motion and is labeled with a noun, such as patient last name and appointment date.

**Data flow diagram (DFD):** A visual process model used to model the processes, flow, and transformation of data in a system; may be developed from use cases or developed directly from the results of requirements gathering.

**Data governance (DG):** A specific enterprise information management (EIM) function that supports coordination among all other EIM functions. It is the enterprise authority that ensures control and accountability for enterprise data through the establishment of decision rights and data policies and standards that are implemented and monitored through a formal structure of assigned roles, responsibilities, and accountabilities.

**Data governance office (DGO):** A support staff dedicated to and responsible for data governance (DG). Responsibilities include providing centralized communication and archives for DG initiatives, working with stakeholders, coordinating DG initiatives, facilitating and coordinating data steward committees, task forces, and meetings, supporting the DG council, and collecting and analyzing DG metrics.

**Data granularity:** A data quality dimension. The level of detail at which the attributes and values of healthcare data are defined.

**Data integrity:** The extent that data are complete, accurate, consistent, and up-to-date.

**Data management services:** Services normally considered information technology roles such as data architects, data analysts, database administrators, data integration specialists, and business intelligence specialists.

**Data mapping:** A process that allows data captured in one format or system to be linked or associated with data in other formats or systems and always involves matching or linking between a source and a target.

**Data mart:** In data warehousing, physical storage areas or a semantic layer on top of the data warehouse for specific domain data that provides a custom view of data to specific business units.

**Data mining:** The process of applying artificial intelligence, machine learning, and statistics to large data sets to discover patterns in the data.

**Data modeling:** A technique used in requirements analysis that identifies the data about people, places, or things upon which business processes depend, and how these data are related to each other; serves as the blueprint for database development.

**Data precision:** A data quality dimension. Data values should be strictly stated to support the purpose.

**Data privacy:** Within the context of data security, defending or safeguarding access to information, for example, only those individuals who need to know information should be authorized to access it.

**Data profiling:** A key activity that applies data and statistical analysis techniques to determine the content, structure, and quality of data held in data stores, such as databases and repositories.

**Data quality management:** Processes to ensure data are meeting quality characteristics that ensure organizational success; a continuous process for defining the parameters for specifying acceptable levels of data quality to meet business needs, and for ensuring that data quality meets these levels.

**Data quality presentation:** A dimension of data quality that includes the following characteristics: availability, accessibility timeliness, presentation media appropriateness, relevance, presentation standardization, and presentation clarity.

**Data reduction:** In analytics, the process of compressing or reducing data, yielding an approximate set of data that maintains the integrity of the original data set.

**Data relevancy:** A data quality dimension. The extent to which healthcare-related data are useful for the purposes for which they were collected.

**Data security:** Protective measures and tools for safeguarding data and information.

**Data security management:** Policies and procedures that address confidentiality and security concerns of organizational stakeholders (for example, patients, providers, and employees), protect organizational proprietary interests, and comply with government and regulatory requirements while accommodating legitimate access needs.

**Data set:** A list of recommended data elements with uniform definitions that are relevant for a particular use and encourage uniform data collection and reporting; includes both a description of the data elements to be collected and definitions for those elements.

**Data stakeholders:** Individuals who have an interest or stake in organizational data, including individuals and business units who gather, compile, track, use, or are responsible for organizational data.

**Data stewards and custodians:** A network of individuals reporting directly to a specific functional unit and responsible for implementing specific enterprise information management functions pertinent to their business unit.

**Data stewardship:** A formalization of accountability; a continuum of stewardship responsibilities across the data life cycle and across the enterprise carried out by a network of data stewards.

**Data store:** An organized collection of data the organization stores for use, either electronically or manually.

**Data timeliness:** A dimension of data quality where data are up-to-date and available within a useful time frame; timeliness is determined by the manner and context in which the data are being used.

**Data transformations:** In business intelligence, routines used to fill in missing values for metadata management, smooth incorrect attribute values, identify and remove outliers, and resolve inconsistencies.

**Data warehouse:** A special type of database that has a single data model optimized for data analytics and extracts and stores selected data from one or more operational databases for the purpose of analytics decision support. Data warehouse characteristics include subject-oriented, integrated, time-variant, and non-volatile.

**Decision rights:** Rights that determine who has the authority to make data-related decisions, when they make them, and how they make them.

**Derivation validity:** A dimension of data validity where a derived value is produced according to a specified calculation formula.

**Descriptive analytics:** A data mining model that describes patterns in data that were previously unknown, for example, answering the question "Why is this happening?"

**Deterministic matching:** Also referred to as exact match logic, a simple technique for matching records where exact comparisons are made on selected data elements.

**Diagnosis-related groups (DRGs):** A prospective payment system, introduced by Medicare, that reimburses hospitals a predetermined amount based on a patient's diagnosis, the procedures the provider performed, and certain complications arising during hospitalization.

**Dietary department and management systems:** Systems that support patient nutritional assessment and management and data related to diet meal orders, cancellations and reorders, menu development, patient menu choice, and meal tracking and delivery.

**Dictionary thesaurus:** A type of thesaurus that provides all potential alternative terms for a word, makes no distinctions between terms, nor is there an indication of the preferred term, or of how broad or narrow an alternative term is. Users have to make these decisions in choosing an alternate term based upon the context in which they are going to use the term.

**Digital asset management (DAM):** The practice and domain of organizing digital files containing both the core content and associated metadata of multi-media, or rich-media items, for example, images, video, audio, graphics, web pages, and photographs.

**Discrepancy detection:** Methods used to identify data problems, such as evaluation of data against metadata and descriptive summaries of data.

**Discriminating attributes:** One of the three categories used for matching records, used to disqualify two or more similar records, rather than match them; these should be static attributes that do not normally change, such as date of birth, date of death, or gender.

**Disease and operation indexes:** A common internal secondary data source; typically includes a health record number, demographic information, admission and discharge dates, physician identifier, and International Classification of Diseases (ICD) diagnostic and procedural codes.

**Distributed metadata architecture:** An architecture in which each stand-alone data system has a corresponding stand-alone metadata system; there is no communication among systems or centralized governance, which creates metadata silos.

**Document:** Recorded information or object which can be treated as a unit, for example, filled or unfilled forms, transcribed reports, inventory lists, or notes.

**Document analysis:** A method that reviews existing policies, procedures, forms, manuals, databases, data models, and other documentation; a method used in requirements analysis.

**Duplicate records:** A record that exists for the same entity in the same database. For example, a patient, customer, or provider is assigned two or more unique identifiers.

# E

**Electronic content management:** The evolutionary successor to electronic document management systems and electronic record management systems that delivers all forms of content, including text, video, image, and audio documents or records, as well as three additional functionalities: collaboration tools, digital asset management tools, and web content management tools.

**Electronic document management (EDM):** A system used to electronically scan paper documents, creating and storing a digital image which end users can index and store for retrieval and viewing.

**Electronic health record (EHR):** An electronic record of health-related information on an individual that conforms to nationally recognized interoperability standards and that authorized clinicians and staff across more than one healthcare organization can create, manage, and consult.

**Electronic medical record (EMR):** An electronic record of health-related information on an individual that authorized clinicians and staff within one healthcare organization can create, gather, manage, and consult.

**Embedded BI:** Reports, dashboards, scorecards, and alerts are embedded into application programs and integrated into work flow so that end users do not have to access separate BI programs for each report.

**Embedded metadata:** Metadata stored in the file with the data they describe.

**Emergency department information system (EDIS):** A system that provides management and operational tools to improve emergency department (ED) performance, includes patient registration, central visualization screen for patient management, management of patient flow, monitoring patient movement throughout the ED, reporting ED room status, managing requests, and notifications for patient beds and resources.

**Encapsulation:** In object-oriented design, the concept of combining the attributes (the data) and the programming code (methods) that can operate on those data in an object.

**Enterprise content and record management (ECRM):** Expands enterprise content management (ECM) by combining electronic records management and ECM concepts; differentiates between types of content, which is generally either the intellectual substance of a document, or a record with information created or used in a business transaction or to fulfill legal obligations.

**Enterprise content management (ECM):** The management of an organization's unstructured data; includes methods for the capture, storage, retrieval, archival, and delivery of unstructured data to meet an organization's business goals.

**Enterprise data model:** A logical data model that is a representation of the logical organization of enterprise data showing overlaps between enterprise systems.

**Enterprise health information management (EHIM):** An expanded contemporary model that incorporates modern terminology, practice, and interdisciplinary theory and uses information engineering, retrieval, analysis, and policy development.

**Enterprise information management (EIM):** The set of functions used to plan, organize, and coordinate people, processes, technology, and content for managing information as a corporate asset that ensures data quality, safety, and ease of use.

**Enterprise master patient index (EMPI):** A connectivity engine that is incorporated into an application providing an index that identifies and consolidates records for each patient across an enterprise.

**Enterprise resource planning (ERP):** Systems that track the status of business commitments, purchase orders, and supplies, and manage the master data related to master supply items, managing inventory, streamlining ordering, tracking items and expiration dates, and capturing charges.

**Entity:** A person, place, thing, or event, represented by a table.

**Entity identification:** A process that matches data with the right entity and entity attributes.

**Entity-relationship diagram (ERD):** One of the most common of data modeling methods used for modeling relational databases.

**Equivalence:** In data mapping, how close or distant terms are from each other. For example, a source code may map to one target code, but that does not mean the two codes have the exact same meaning.

**Essential (business) use case:** A type of use case that describes the business process and interaction of the end user with the system without specifying any technology details.

**Executive data stewards:** Senior managers who serve on a data governance council and who are responsible for high-level decision making, including the sign-off on all data governance policies.

**External entity:** In data flow diagramming, a person, system, company, or agency outside of the organization or any individual or system unit outside of the system under discussion (SuD); the source or destination of data.

# F

**Facet taxonomy:** A type of taxonomy where multiple characteristics are assigned to one object.

**Fair and Accurate Credit Transaction Act (FACTA):** A law passed in 2003 that contains provisions and requirements to reduce identity theft.

**False negative:** In record matching, a match that fails to match records of the same individual, leaving a duplicate in the database, for example, linking two closely related people with very similar names and dates of birth who live near each other.

**False positive:** In record matching, a match of two records to one identity when the records actually belong to two individuals.

**Federated metadata architecture:** An architecture in which each data system maintains its own metadata repository but conforms to a centralized technical framework and governance structure. For example, the metadata are held with the source systems, but users can extract metadata that affect more than one system on demand for communication with other systems through the use of an integration engine and a single user interface.

**Feedback:** One of the functions of a system's operation, feedback is a control mechanism that, acting on input, allows for self-correction or maintenance. In an information system feedback consists of data.

**Financial information systems:** An umbrella of a financial systems suite that relies on data from both clinical and administrative information systems. Types of financial systems include patient and payer billing, claims management, accounts payable and receivable, collection monitoring, staff scheduling, budgeting, accounting, revenue cycle management, and facility maintenance.

**Financial master data:** One of the four classifications of master data, refers to data about business units, cost centers, and accounts, among others.

**Fitness of use:** A key characteristic of data quality that determines how well a data quality assessment model is meeting data consumers' needs.

**Flat files:** The first type of database systems where data were stored in sets of data files that application programs used. The files were composed of records that represented a specific person, place, or thing, and each record contained individual pieces of data called fields.

**Flat taxonomy:** A controlled set of categories where each object in the set has the same weight, for example, a list of states.

**Foreign key (FK):** In a relational database, an attribute used to link a column or data point in one table to the primary key column or data point in another table.

**Forward map:** A map in which an older version of a code set is mapped to a newer version, for example, ICD-9-CM to ICD-10-CM.

**Framework:** A real or conceptual structure that organizes a system or concept; a logical structure for classifying, organizing, and communicating complex activities involved in making decisions about and taking action on enterprise data.

**Functional interoperability:** A common message syntax between two computer systems that allows them to interpret the message format, but not the meaning of the data being exchanged.

**Functional requirements:** Observable tasks an information system must perform, for example, in a patient registration system, "must input patient last and first name" or "must search master patient index" or "must create a unique master person identifier."

# G

**Governance:** Establishment of policies and the continual monitoring of their proper implementation for managing organization assets to enhance the prosperity and viability of the organization; an enterprise activity.

**Governance council:** A high-level data governance board responsible for championing data governance initiatives and developing and overseeing the governance plan.

**Government-recognized maps:** Maps that may be developed by a standards development organization or other authorized source but must meet government standards. Examples include the ICD-9-CM to ICD-10-CM/PCS General Equivalence Mappings (GEMs), which were added to the HIPAA code set standards.

# H

**Health Evaluation through Logical Processing (HELP):** A health information technology system developed under the direction of Dr. Homer Warner at LDS Hospital.

**Health information exchanges (HIEs):** A federal-state collaborative initiative meant to enable and expand the secure electronic movement and use of health information among organizations using nationally recognized standards.

**Health Insurance Portability and Accountability Act of 1996 (HIPAA):** The federal legislation enacted to provide continuity of health coverage, control fraud and abuse in healthcare, reduce healthcare costs, and guarantee the security and privacy of health information; limits exclusion for pre-existing medical conditions, prohibits discrimination against employees and dependents based on health status, guarantees availability of health insurance to small employers, and guarantees renewability of insurance to all employees regardless of size; requires covered entities (most healthcare providers and organizations) to transmit healthcare claims in a specific format and to develop, implement, and comply with the standards of the Privacy Rule and the Security Rule; and mandates that covered entities apply for and utilize national identifiers in HIPAA transactions.

**Health Information Security and Privacy Collaboration (HISPC):** A multi-state collaborative initiative started in 2006 to address the privacy and security challenges presented by electronic health information exchange.

**Health Information Technology for Economic and Clinical Health Act (HITECH):** Legislation created to promote the adoption and meaningful use of health information technology in the United States. Subtitle D of the Act provides for additional privacy and security requirements that will develop and support electronic health information, facilitate information exchange, and strengthen monetary penalties. Signed into law on February 17, 2009, as part of ARRA (Public Law 111-5 2009).

**Health Level Seven (HL7):** A not-for-profit, interchange standards-developing organization dedicated to providing a comprehensive framework and related standards for the exchange, integration, sharing, and retrieval of electronic health information that supports clinical practice and the management, delivery, and evaluation of health services.

**Health maintenance organization (HMO):** Entity that combines the provision of healthcare insurance and the delivery of healthcare services, characterized by an organized healthcare delivery system to a geographic area, a set of basic and supplemental health maintenance and treatment services, voluntarily enrolled members, and predetermined fixed, periodic prepayments for members' coverage.

**Health or medical record number:** A unique identifier key to locating and retrieving all of a patient's health information, includes paper and electronic records.

**Healthcare Common Procedure Coding System (HCPCS):** A set of codes introduced in 1983 by the Centers for Medicare and Medicaid Services (CMS) to report services and supplies not covered by Current Procedural Terminology (CPT) codes for reimbursement purposes.

**Healthcare Cost and Utilization Project (HCUP):** A data set composed of multiple databases including the largest collection of longitudinal hospital care data in the United States. Organizations can use the data to evaluate cost and quality of health services, medical practice patterns, access to healthcare programs, and treatment outcomes.

**Healthcare Information Technology Standards Panel (HITSP):** An organization developed under the auspices of the American National Standards Institute (ANSI) to deal with the many issues of privacy and security as the United States Nationwide Health Information Network develops.

**Hierarchical database model:** A tree structure that first appeared as a commercial product in the mid-1960s, based on the concept of "parent" and "child" relationships where the parent table, called the root, is placed at the top of the tree and points to child tables that contain related data.

**Hierarchical taxonomy model:** A taxonomy model based on a tiered order of concepts and their relationships.

**Hospital Compare:** A data set that reports on 94 measures of hospital quality of care for heart attack, heart failure, pneumonia, and prevention of surgical infections.

**Hospital Standardization Program:** Conducted by the American College of Surgeons, the first systematic effort to establish hospital standards in the United States. The Hospital Standardization Program laid the groundwork for today's hospital standardization and accreditation programs, for example, the Joint Commission.

**Hybrid metadata architecture:** A combined architecture of a single repository and a federated system in which each data system maintains its own metadata system while the central repository accommodates critical standardized metadata extracted from source files and manually created metadata.

**Hybrid record:** A health record consisting of paper documents as well as electronic documents.

# I

**Identifier standards:** Methods for assigning unique identifiers to individuals including patients, healthcare providers, healthcare organizations, and vendors.

**Identity attributes:** One of the three categories used for matching records, identifies people, parts, products, organizations, and so on. For a patient, identity attributes include, among others, the patient's full name, key identifiers such as a Social Security number, a driver's license number, patient number, phone number, address, and e-mail address.

**Identity error:** Mismatched data in master data, including duplicate records, overlay, and overlap.

**Implementation:** The last stage of the systems development life cycle (SDLC) where an information system is deployed into the real world environment. It includes user education, putting the system into production, and transitioning ongoing support and maintenance of the system to the appropriate units of the organization.

**Incident detection:** Methods that identify both accidental and malicious data events.

**Incident response:** Management procedures and responsibilities to ensure a quick and effective response to specific types of data incidents. For example, in some instances the plan may call for a "watch and warn" response that includes monitoring and notification of an incident but takes no immediate action.

**Individually identifiable information:** A subset of health information, including demographic information collected from an individual, and: (1) created or received by a healthcare provider, health plan, employer, or healthcare clearinghouse; and (2) relates to the past, present, or future physical or mental health or condition of an individual; the provision of healthcare to an individual; or the past, present, or future payment for the provision of healthcare to an individual; and (i) that identifies the individual; or (ii) with respect to which there is a reasonable basis to believe the information can be used to identify the individual.

**Information:** Sets of data that are related and have been placed in context are filtered, manipulated, or formatted in some way, have meaning, and are useful to a particular task; also referred to as data output.

**Information governance:** An organization-wide framework for managing information throughout its life cycle and supporting the organization's strategy, operations, regulatory, legal, risk, and environmental requirements. It focuses on the proper use and application of information, concerned with the seeking and finding, creation and use, and exchange of information.

**Information management thesaurus:** A controlled list of terms linked together by semantic, hierarchical (parent-child), associative (related), or equivalence (synonymous) relationships.

**Information resources management (IRM):** The concept of managing information as a resource and integrating all information processes and computer, communication, office automation, distributed processing technologies, and selection, implementation, and operation of computer systems under a senior-level officer.

**Information security:** Protecting information and information systems from unauthorized access, use, disclosure, disruption, modification, or destruction in order to guard against improper information modification or destruction, preserve authorized restrictions on access and disclosure to protect personal privacy and propriety information, and ensure timely and reliable access to and use of information.

**Information system:** An automated system that uses computer hardware and software to record, manipulate, store, recover, and disseminate data (that is, a system that receives and processes input and provides output). An information system exists in an external environment and consists of subsystems that work toward a common goal.

**Informational privacy:** *See* privacy.

**In-house systems:** A system designed, developed, operated, and supported by a hospital's onsite staff, typically mainframe based, located in larger healthcare facilities, and frequently university-related.

**Inpatient scheduling system:** A system that supports care coordination and manages inpatient scheduling for diagnostic exams, tests, and treatments; also called inpatient flow management system.

**Input:** One of the functions of a system's operation, input initiates action by the system. In an information system input consists of data.

**Integrated:** One of four characteristics of a data warehouse where data from multiple heterogeneous sources, such as relational databases, flat files, and online transaction records are combined.

**Integrated delivery systems (IDS):** An organizational arrangement of a network of health providers that may include hospitals, physicians, and health maintenance organizations (HMO) that provides coordinated services along the continuum of care from ambulatory, acute, and long-term care and may extend across a geographical region.

**Integrated solution:** Multiple clinical and administrative applications (for example, laboratory, pharmacy, radiology, and enterprise master patient index) that use a common database and have a consistent user interface, provided by a single vendor.

**Interactive fixed report:** Reports that have a fixed design with data variables defined by a business analyst or report designer. It usually provides general information with dynamic drill-down, slicing, dicing, and filtering functions.

**Interface engine:** A software program that simplifies the development and management of interfaces by acting as a hub for data exchange; receives and exchanges messages, provides message management and verification, and performs mapping, translation, and modification of data, if needed.

**Interfaces:** Specialized software that allow computer systems to communicate with each other.

**International Classification of Diseases (ICD):** A coding and classification system which is used as a standard nomenclature for the statistical study of disease.

**Interoperability:** The ability of different information technology systems and software applications to communicate, to exchange data accurately, effectively, and consistently, and to use the information that has been changed.

**Interviewing:** A method for gathering requirements, where interviewers select appropriate subjects who use or are affected by the processes a system supports. These may include managers, end users, and other stakeholders who have an interest in system inputs, processes, or outputs.

**Iterative method:** A method that divides system development into small parts, or versions, each going through all stages of the systems development lifecycle (SDLC).

## J

**Joint application development (JAD):** A technique project teams use to study the current system and to identify the goals, objectives, and required functions of a proposed system; developed by IBM in the late 1970s to address the shortcomings and problems of requirements analysis of other methods.

## K

**Keys:** An explanatory notation that uniquely identifies each row in a database table.

**Kimball Method:** An architecture model for business intelligence (BI) developed by Ralph Kimball. Also known as a "bottom-up" approach, it suggests starting with several data marts to serve the needs of specific business units and then to "virtually" integrate these data marts.

**Knowledge:** A combination of rules, relationships, ideas, and experiences applied to information.

## L

**Laboratory information system (LIS):** Systems that support a variety of administrative and operational functions of anatomical pathology and clinical laboratory departments including workflow automation, financial and management reporting, and quality assurance.

**Location master data:** One of the four classifications of master data, refers to data about the location of the organization's customers, suppliers, and others such as postal code, latitude and longitude, geopolitical boundaries, and sales territory. In healthcare, location master data are critical from the standpoint of public health and associated surveillance of disease and health hazards.

**Logical data model:** Expands the conceptual data model by including entity attributes, primary keys, and foreign keys; also goes through a process called normalization.

**Logical DFD:** Data flow diagrams that describe the business details of a system, used in requirements analysis.

**Logical Observational Identifiers, Names and Codes (LOINC):** A set of universal identifiers for laboratory and clinical observations and generally the accepted exchange standard for laboratory results.

# M

**Managed metadata environment (MME):** An environment organizations use to organize, document, search, and retrieve digital resources; includes a metadata repository supported by data governance structure, standards, and processes.

**Management charter:** A charter developed by executive management that lays out the program's vision, justification, and expected result.

**Management controls:** Controls that focus on the management of information systems and management of risks, including risk assessment, planning, system and services acquisition, and certification, accreditation, and security assessments.

**Master data:** Data about an organization's key business entities.

**Master data management:** Managing the master data that an enterprise maintains about key business entities such as customers, employees, or patients, and reference data used to classify other data or identify allowable values for data such as codes for state abbreviations or products.

**Master entities:** The key entities upon which almost all other entities are related to or dependent upon, widely distributed across information applications, and represent a high volume of records.

**Master patient index (MPI):** An index containing unique patient identifiers (also referred to as medical or record numbers) that serve as a permanent identifier for each patient who receives services at a healthcare facility; also known as a master person index.

**Maturity model:** A framework an organization uses to compare its capabilities to the stages of development of a process.

**Meaningful use:** Specific objectives and measures that all eligible professionals and hospitals must meet to show they are using electronic health records in meaningful ways that positively affect the care of their patients.

**Medical Information Bureau (MIB):** A private company composed of about 750 member insurance companies that maintains a central database of individual medical claims and other information contributed by its member companies.

**Medicare Provider Analysis and Review (MedPAR):** A data set that contains data from claims for services provided to beneficiaries admitted to Medicare-certified inpatient hospitals and skilled nursing facilities (SNF); useful data for tracking inpatient history and patterns or outcomes of care over time and for studying chronic disease prevalent in elderly populations such as cancer, heart disease, and diabetes.

**Medical or health record number:** A unique identifier key to locating and retrieving all of a patient's health information, includes paper and electronic records.

**Medical Subject Headings (MeSH):** An information management thesaurus with a controlled vocabulary that consists of sets of terms naming descriptors in a hierarchical structure that permits searching at various levels of specificity.

**Medication administration record (MAR):** The record where a provider records all data associated with medication administration.

**Medication administration system (MAS):** A system that supports the administration of medication to patients, supported by bar coding technology.

**Medication reconciliation system (MRS):** A system that helps manage the coordination of drugs for a patient across the continuum of care to avoid medication discrepancies.

**Mesh topology:** A network computer configuration in which each device is interconnected to each other. If one device fails, the network will not go down. The World Wide Web is the most well-known example of a mesh topology.

**Metadata:** Structured data that describes, explains, locates, or otherwise makes it easier to retrieve, use, or manage an information resource.

**Metadata repository:** The physical database tables used to gather, store, and disseminate metadata.

**Metadata schemas:** Metadata elements that are grouped together to represent a particular emphasis or domain.

**Method for integrated knowledge environment (MIKE 2.0):** An open source and comprehensive methodology for enterprise information management, originally developed by a management and technology consulting company and based on the experiences of information management professionals around the world in a variety of projects.

**Migration path:** A series of coordinated and planned steps required to move a plan from one situation level to another.

**Mission statement:** A rule of engagement that helps unify and motivate stakeholders (policy makers, data owners, data stewards, and so on), keeps goals in the forefront, and holds the organization accountable for achieving the goals.

**Modality:** Refers to whether or not an instance of a child entity can exist without a related instance of a parent entity.

**Monitoring systems:** Systems that provide periodic or continuous observation of the patient or physiological functions in guiding decisions of therapeutic interventions.

**MYCIN:** A health information technology expert system spearheaded by Dr. Ted Shortliffe at Stanford University.

# N

**National practitioner databank (NPDB):** A comprehensive database of the professional credentials of healthcare practitioners, healthcare entities, providers, and suppliers that includes data on medical malpractice payments, adverse licensure actions and certain other professional review actions.

**Network controls:** A method of protecting data at rest and during transmission among information systems from unauthorized change and corruption.

**Network database model:** First developed in 1967, a database model that provides quick access to data across entities by allowing more than one parent table to share child tables; users can still access data quickly through the hierarchical tree for transaction purposes that focus on one person, place, or thing, while speeding up data access from any set of tables in the tree.

**Nomenclature:** A recognized system of terms that follows pre-established naming conventions.

**Non-functional requirements:** Standards or characteristics to which an information system must comply, rather than tasks it must perform, for example, the system "must be accessible from 0200 hours to 2400 hours seven days a week," or the system "must accommodate 1000 simultaneous users from 0700 to 2300 hours every day."

**Nonvolatile:** One of the characteristics of a data warehouse in which data are transformed and physically stored separate from the source application in the operational environment.

**Normalization:** A formal process applied to relational database design to determine which variables should be grouped in a table to reduce data redundancy.

**Nursing information system:** A computer application that supports nursing documentation for patient assessment, development of patient care plans, and documenting patient care delivery.

# O

**Object oriented database (OO):** A database developed to deal with increasingly complex data types such as graphics, engineering designs, spatial, and audio-visual data that other database types were not designed to handle; combines the concepts of the hierarchical database, encapsulation, and object-oriented programming.

**Observation:** A technique used to complement document analysis, involves systems analysts observing the work environment and learning what processes users perform, how they perform them, and what data they use to carry out the processes.

**Office of the National Coordinator for Health Information Technology (ONC):** The principal federal entity charged with coordination of nationwide efforts to implement and use the most advanced health information technology and the electronic exchange of health information.

**ONC Authorized Testing and Certification Body (ONC-ATCB):** Organizations authorized by the Office of the National Coordinator to certify electronic health record products capable of meeting meaningful use criteria.

**Online analytical processing (OLAP):** A data warehouse system that focuses on data analysis and not day-to-day operations, typically a star or snowflake model, with a subject-oriented design.

**Online transaction processing (OLTP):** Operational systems that process the day-to-day transactions that keep a business running. Hospital examples of operational transactions include making a patient appointment, registering a patient, ordering a medication, assigning a bed, scheduling an operating room, and processing a claim.

**Ontology:** A type of taxonomy with more complex relationships between terms than a thesaurus, focused on a particular domain or subject and meant to share and reuse knowledge.

**Open source framework:** Framework, usually the product of academic or other research, offered for free public use.

**Operating room management system:** A system that provides coordination of human and material resources during pre-operative, intra-operative, and post-operative phases of care; also known as perioperative information systems.

**Operational controls:** In data security, control targets implemented by people, not systems, including personnel security, physical and environmental protection, contingency planning, configuration management, maintenance, system and information integrity, media protection, incident response, and awareness training.

**Operational decision making:** The decision-making level in which an organization makes day-to-day or routine decisions that keep the organization running.

**Outpatient Prospective System Data:** A data set that contains claims paid under the prospective payment system (PPS).

**Outpatient Standard Analytic File (SAF):** A data set that contains all institutional outpatient claims filed on the UB-04 form.

**Output:** One of the functions of a system's operation, output is the end product of the system processes. In an information system, output consists of data.

**Overlap:** A situation in which a patient is issued more than one medical or health record number from an organization with multiple facilities.

**Overlay:** A situation in which a patient is issued a medical or health record number that has been previously issued to a different patient.

# P

**Parallel method:** A systems development life cycle (SDLC) implementation method where the development cycle begins with planning and analysis, and is subsequently divided by the project team into smaller sub-projects that are developed and implemented parallel with each other.

**Party data:** One of the four classifications of master data; refers to individuals or organizations, for example, employees, patients, providers, companies, and vendors.

**Performance scorecard:** A report that focuses on long-term operational, tactical, or strategic goals. A data visualization function displays progress over time in meeting specific goals.

**Person - Under HIPPA:** A natural person, trust or estate, partnership, corporation, professional association or corporation, or other entity, public or private.

**Personal health record (PHR):** An electronic record of health-related information on an individual that conforms to nationally recognized interoperability standards and that can be drawn from multiple sources while the individual manages, shares, and controls it.

**Pharmacy information system:** A system that provides decision support capabilities and online verification work lists allowing pharmacists to review, verify, and fill incoming prescription orders; should integrate with the computerized physician or provider order entry and medication administration systems, and be able to access patient demographic and key clinical information.

**Physical access controls:** Safeguards that protect physical equipment, media, or facilities, for example, locks on doors leading to the areas that house mainframes and other principal computing equipment.

**Physical data model:** A model that provides implementation details for developing the physical database, where entities are tables and attributes are fields, and metadata associated with each field are added, including descriptions such as field type and length.

**Physical DFD:** Data flow diagrams that describe the technical details of a system, used in the design stage of the systems development life cycle.

**Physical safeguards:** The protection of computer systems from natural and environmental hazards and intrusion, and include four general categories of controls: facility access, workstation use, workstation security, and device media.

**Picture archiving and communication system (PACS):** A medical imaging technology that provides storage and access to images from various modalities such as x-ray computed tomography (CT), magnetic resonance imaging (MRI), positron emission tomography (PET), mammograms, and digital radiography.

**Planning retreats:** A retreat organizations use for many purposes including generating ideas or improvements, solving a specific problem, developing goals or objectives, developing action plans, or setting the strategic direction of an organization.

**Point-of-care (POC):** A charting system that provides structure to record content; a clinical documentation system that allows providers (physicians, nurses, and therapists) to enter data at the time when patient care is delivered.

**Point-to-point interface:** An interface developed to permit communication between two systems.

**Policies:** Governing principles adopted by the organization based on best practices, industry standards, and the processes to be supported.

**Predictive analytics:** A data mining technique that uses data with known results to develop a model to explicitly predict values, for example answering the question, "What will happen next?"

**Primary data source:** A record someone created at about the same time as the event he or she is describing, for example, clinical records such as operative reports, nursing notes, and physician orders.

**Primary key (PK):** An explanatory notation that uniquely identifies each row in a database table.

**Primary users:** Healthcare professionals who deliver direct patient care, such as nurses, physicians, and therapists, and who have access to sensitive data maintained in a patient's health record.

**Primary uses of health information:** The main uses of health information, categorized into five uses: patient uses, patient care delivery uses, patient care management uses, patient care support uses, and business and legal uses.

**Privacy:** In a healthcare context, the right of individuals to limit access to information about their person. Also called informational privacy.

**Probabilistic matching:** A matching method based on the probability of error occurrence, it recognizes that a field-by-field comparison is subject to error in either matching or mismatching records. This approach takes into account both the probability of a mismatch between data values in two records that represent the same entity (for example, failing to identify records associated with the same individual), and the probability of a coincidental match between two records representing distinct entities (for example, matching records associated with different individuals).

**Probability level:** In record matching, the likelihood for record matches, usually a number that serves as a threshold, also known as the range or baseline, in determining which records match and which do not.

**Problem-Oriented Medical Information System (PROMIS):** A health information technology system championed by Dr. Lawrence Weed.

**Process:** A systematic series of actions taken to create a product or service.

**Product master data:** One of the four classifications of master data, refers to data about an organization's products and components that make up a product, product versions, pricing, and discount terms, for example, product and service identification codes, description, price, and manufacturer identification.

**Program roadmap:** The second step in the suggested seven-step life cycle for how to implement the Data Governance Institute's framework by starting in small steps and focusing their program on one specific area or activity at a time.

**Project charter:** A document that clarifies the project objectives, and identifies project scope, major milestones, risks, budget, timeline, personnel, and other resources required to complete the project.

**Project management life cycle:** Activities used to manage a project, including developing the rationale and business case for the project, prioritizing and selecting projects, identifying the project sponsor, developing the project charter, developing communication plans, establishing costs and timeline, selecting the project team members, and ensuring the project remains in scope, on budget, and on time.

**Project sponsor:** The individual responsible for oversight of the project from the business perspective.

**Proprietary framework:** A framework developed by a company that supports its own business service lines, and is not available to the public.

**Proprietary or customized data maps:** Maps developed usually within an organization or by consultants working for them to meet their needs, sometimes developed as a product for purchase to meet specific needs and can consist of any data mapping important to achieve specific objectives. An example is local (organization-specific) terms or vocabularies mapped to standard terminologies or classifications.

**Protected health information (PHI):** Individually identifiable health information transmitted by electronic media, maintained in electronic media, or transmitted or maintained in any other form or medium.

**Prototype:** A simple version of an intended system (n). To produce a simplified model of the entire system, gather input from end-user review, and then redesign the prototype based on that input (v).

**Public Law 104-191:** *See* Health Insurance Portability and Accountability Act (HIPAA).

# R

**Radio frequency identification (RFID):** The underlying technology used on the real time locator system (RTLS), fixed points throughout a building or complex are fitted with sensors that read data from the RTLS tag.

**Radiology information system (RIS):** A system that supports the workflow of departmental functions and communication within and outside the radiology department, including workflow management, materials management, charge capture, and management reporting.

**Rapid application development (RAD):** A group of information system developmental methodologies that attempt to address the long development time problem of the waterfall method, with the goal of going through the analysis, design, construction, and acceptance stages of the systems development life cycle (SDLC) quickly and getting essential parts of the system to the end user as soon as possible for their evaluation and feedback.

**Real time locator system (RTLS):** Systems that use wireless technology that identifies, determines, and tracks the location of equipment, materials, and personnel, in the case of healthcare patients, throughout a building or healthcare complex.

**Record:** Information created, received, and maintained as evidence and information by an organization or person, in pursuance of legal obligations or in the transaction of business.

**Record completion management:** A system that automates the process of ensuring a complete health record at the time of a patient's discharge from a hospital, including managing workflow, routing deficiency notices to the correct clinician for completion, and tracking record deficiencies and their completion.

**Record qualification attributes:** One of the three categories used for matching records, helps pinpoint what identification rules should apply to a record. For example, the country attribute identifies how to evaluate the structure of the attribute address, since addresses are defined differently from country to country: the system evaluates the postal code for the United States differently than the postal code for Canada.

**Red flags:** Signals of the presence of identity theft, consisting of five categories: 1) alerts, notifications, or warnings from a consumer reporting agency, 2) suspicious documents such as an altered identification, 3) suspicious personally identifying information such as a suspicious address that does not exist or that belongs to someone else in the business's accounts, 4) unusual use of or suspicious activity relating to a covered account, and 5) notices from customers, victims of identity theft, law enforcement authorities, or other businesses about possible identity theft in connection with an account.

**Reference data:** Data used to classify or categorize other data, frequently represented by codes or acronyms.

**Registration-admission-discharge-transfer (R-ADT) systems:** A system that captures patient demographic, insurance, and other administrative data at the time of registration or admission and tracks the movement of patients when there is an intra-facility transfer from one care area to another during hospitalization, and identifies the date and time the physician discharges the patients; also called patient management.

**Registry data hub:** An implementation that points to the location of the master data attributes in source systems using a metadata repository, usually only stores key identifiers and functions as a reference and links to the location of authoritative master data sources.

**Regression:** A type of analytics that constructs predictive models based on several variables. For example, using a variety of variables, a model for patient risk mortality could be developed.

**Relational database model:** First published in a series of papers by E.F. Codd and based on the concepts of relational algebra, allows users to access the database very quickly, change the database structure easily, retrieve data by simply developing complex queries, propagate data changes readily, implement data integrity effortlessly, increase data accuracy, modify and develop application programs efficiently, and use a standard query language (SQL).

**Relationships:** The connections between tables and between two entities in a database: they have two important properties: cardinality and modality.

**Repository:** A data structure where data are stored for subsequent use by multiple, disparate systems.

**Request for and release of health information management systems:** Systems that support data capture that tracks disclosure of health information (what information and to whom it was disclosed) and monitors and tracks requests from patients for their own information to ensure timely compliance with federal regulations.

**Requirements analysis:** The set of processes used for identifying what function(s) an information system must perform and how it is to provide them; the fundamental building block upon which any information system is based.

**Requisition:** An official list of requirements for a project, usually completed by the project sponsor; makes the business case for the project and includes an overview of the system purpose; the business issues, opportunities, or problems the project sponsor will address; desired functions; anticipated benefits; and departments, stakeholders, or services the project might affect.

**Results reporting:** Provides the functionality to retrieve (display) patient data related to results of clinical tests such as laboratory reports and diagnostic studies such as radiology reports; also known as results retrieval.

**Reverse map:** A map that links two systems in the opposite direction, from the newer version of a code set to an older version.

**Ring topology:** A network computer configuration in which each device connects to the network in a closed loop or ring. A unique address identifies each machine. The signal passes through each device connected to the ring in one direction.

**Risk analysis:** The first step to risk management, includes assessing security threats, security vulnerabilities, and the likely impact should the system expose a vulnerability.

**Risk management:** The identification, management, and control of untoward events.

**Rules:** A set of principles or regulations; examples include policies, requirements, standards, accountabilities, controls, and data definitions.

**Rules of engagement:** The way stakeholders (policy makers, data owners, data stewards, and so on) interact with each other.

# S

**Scoreboard:** A scorecard that combines dashboard and performance functions on one screen.

**Secondary data source:** Data taken from the primary record and entered into registries and databases. Examples include cancer registries, trauma registries, and disease and operation indexes.

**Secondary users:** Individuals or groups who do not provide direct health care services but who have access to sensitive information in a patient's health record, including researchers, pharmaceutical companies, health and life insurance companies, credit card agencies, banking companies, and the civil and criminal justice systems.

**Secondary uses of health information:** Information uses not directly related to a specific encounter, but used to influence the environment in which the patient is cared for. Secondary uses include education, accreditation, licensure, regulation, legal, research, public health, and policy-making.

**Security:** In general, the protection measures and tools for safeguarding information and information systems. HIPAA rules define security as all of the administrative, physical, and technical safeguards in an information system.

**Security awareness program:** An essential control included in a good security program that educates every new employee on the confidential nature of patient and organization-related data, and informs employees about the organization's security policies and the consequences of failing to comply with them.

**Security plan:** An essential component for successful data security that includes evaluating information assets and security risk, protection and detection mechanisms, incident response and recovery, and monitoring and maintenance.

**Security test and evaluation (ST&E):** A plan to identify an organization's security vulnerabilities, documents specific criteria the system under study must meet, including criteria for management, operational, and technical controls.

**Security threat:** Anything that can exploit a security vulnerability, or a weakness or gap in security protection.

**Semantic interoperability:** Level of interoperability where the data within the message can be interpreted between computer systems.

**Server computer:** A network computer that provides a variety of shared resources to other computers.

**Shared services:** A system that includes software applications developed by the vendor and operated on hardware at the vendor site, shared by multiple hospitals.

**Source set:** In data mapping the origin or data from which the mapping starts.

**Spiral method:** A SDLC method that incorporates features of prototyping and waterfall methods where iterative versions of a complete system are produced by the project team, with an emphasis on risk assessment at each iteration. Includes four steps: 1) identifying system objectives; 2) examining alternatives and determining risks of project failure; 3) establishing requirements and developing the software; and 4) seeking evaluation from the end user.

**Staging area:** Where data are "prepped" or prepared for use and placement in a centralized data warehouse; functions include data extraction and data cleansing from each data source, data integration from the various data sources, and data aggregation.

**Standard development organization maps:** A map either created or adopted by a standards development organization or in cooperation between organizations, for example, the current harmonization agreement between the International Health Terminology Standards Development Organisation (IHTSDO) and the World Health Organization (WHO).

**Standardization rules:** An enhancement process for structured data used in record matching; leverages the structure already associated with a specific attribute, such as an attribute's data type, length, and definition and uses equivalencies in performing the match.

**Standardized Nomenclature of Diseases (SND):** A collection of clinical descriptions created in 1929, which led to the development of the Systematized Nomenclature of Medicine Clinical Terms (SNOMED CT).

**Star topology:** A network computer configuration in which each device connects to a central hub. All of the data on the network has to pass through the hub which then forwards it to the correct destination.

**Static reports:** Reports with a fixed layout and data variables defined by a business analyst or report designer. Generated on request, they automatically refresh periodically or embed into an application program.

**Strategic decision making:** The decision-making level in which executives make decisions about the strategic direction of the organization and set the goals they want to achieve.

**Structure:** The format of the record and its relationship to the record's content. For example, headings in a patient's history, such as present illness, past illness, and so on, are related to and provide structure to the content in the record.

**Structure and content standards:** Standards that identify the data elements, data element definition, and attributes of the data element, such as data type and length; provides a protocol for what data are exchanged and in what format the exchange is to occur.

**Structured data entry techniques:** Techniques for structuring data entry such as drop-down menus, checklists, and templates, that constrain data capture into a common format or vocabulary.

**Subpart A:** A subpart of HIPAA Administrative Simplification provisions, includes the general provisions.

**Subpart C:** A subpart of HIPAA Administrative Simplification provisions, covers the security standards for the protection of electronic protected health information.

**Subpart D:** A subpart of HIPAA Administrative Simplification provisions, includes the standards for the notification in the case of an unsecured protected health information breach.

**Subpart E:** A subpart of HIPAA Administrative Simplification provisions, covers the standards for privacy of individually identifiable health information.

**Subsystems:** The elements within a system, or a system within a system.

**Subject-oriented:** A characteristic of a data warehouse where data are organized around major subjects, such as customer, supplier, product, and sales.

**System:** A group of elements that interact with each other through defined relationships to achieve a common goal or objective.

**System of record (SOR):** A computer system that is the authoritative source for data about an entity. For example, the human resources management system (HRMS) is the SOR for employee master data, the CRM system is the SOR for customer data, or the SOR for financial and product information is the enterprise resource planning (ERP) system.

**System use case:** A type of use case, provides the technology and operational details of the system and is used by the technical staff.

**Systematized Nomenclature of Medicine Clinical Terms (SNOMED CT):** A controlled medical terminology with comprehensive coverage of diseases, clinical findings, etiologies, procedures, and outcomes.

**Systems development life cycle (SDLC):** A life cycle which consists of the usual stages of development an information system goes through. Typical tasks include conducting a requirements analysis, developing process models, defining the logical data model, producing functional specifications, defining technical requirements, and constructing, testing, and implementing the new system.

## T

**Table:** A primary unit of storage that holds a group of related data, each one representing a single entity.

**Tactical decision making:** The decision-making level in which an organization develops plans to determine how it will achieve its strategic direction.

**Target set:** In data mapping, the set of data for which data equivalency is trying to be established.

**Taxonomy:** The science or technique of classification; in the context of content management, purposes are to classify objects, identify them, and help search and retrieve them.

**Technical controls:** In data security, controls that are executed by the information system, including identification and authentication, access control, audit and accountability, system and communications protection.

**Technical metadata:** Metadata used by technical information systems professionals for the design, development, implementation, and maintenance of an electronic information system; in a database environment, includes data such as table name, field name, field type, and field length.

**Technical safeguards:** Provisions that include things information systems technical professionals can implement from a technical standpoint using computer software, development and implementation of written policies and procedures for access controls, audit controls, data integrity, person or identity authentication, and transmission security.

**Technicon Medical Information System:** A health information technology model at El Camino Hospital.

**Terminology and classification management:** An enterprise information management domain unique to healthcare whose main purpose is to manage language and classification in a healthcare organization and provide a central terminology authority for the enterprise.

**Terminology:** A set of terms representing a system of concepts.

**Time-variant:** One of four data warehouse characteristics where every key structure in the data warehouse contains, either implicitly or explicitly, an element in time (such as a time stamp) and is a historical record of a snapshot in time.

**The Dublin Core:** A metadata schema consisting of a set of 15 generic elements for describing any resource type: electronic, conceptual, or real-world.

**The Leapfrog Group:** A group that conducts the Leapfrog Survey, a voluntary program in which any hospital is eligible to report data, which the group reports in the form of a scorecard on the Leapfrog website.

**The National Ambulatory Medical Care Service (NAMCS):** A survey designed for gathering objective, reliable information about the provision and use of ambulatory medical care services in the United States.

**The National Codes:** *See* Healthcare Common Procedure Coding System (HCPCS).

**The National Drug Codes (NDC):** Product identifiers for human drugs and biologics and the HIPAA standard medical data code set for reporting drugs and biologics for retail pharmacy transactions.

**The National Hospital Ambulatory Medical Care Survey (NHAMCS):** A survey designed to collect data on the utilization and provision of ambulatory care services in hospital emergency and outpatient departments and in ambulatory surgery centers.

**Threshold:** In record matching, the range or baseline used in determining which records match and which do not.

**Transaction data:** Data generated and captured by operational systems in business transactions. Examples include data related to sales (what was bought and for how much) and deliveries (what was delivered and where).

**Transaction hub implementation:** An implementation method where master data is physically stored in the master data management (MDM) hub and is used as the authoritative system of record; supports services that apply data access and update transactions to the master data in the MDM hub.

**Tuple:** A row in a table, the equivalent of a record. For example, the PATIENT table has one row (record) of data describing Patient A, another row describing Patient B, and so on.

**Turnkey:** A system consisting of software applications developed by a vendor, who then installs it on a computer system at a healthcare facility and performs the development and maintenance so healthcare organizations can "turn the key."

# U

**Unidirectional mapping:** A map that translates only from the source to the target.

**Unified Medical Language System (UMLS):** A project that started in 1986 by the National Library of Medicine to aid health professionals and researchers in retrieving and integrating information from a variety of sources and for users to link disparate information systems.

**Uniform Ambulatory Care Data Set (UACDS):** A data set developed by the National Committee on Vital Health Statistics (NCVHS) consisting of a minimum set of patient- or client-specific data elements to be collected in ambulatory care settings.

**Uniform Hospital Discharge Data Set (UHDDS):** A core set of data elements adopted by the U.S. Department of Health, Education, and Welfare in 1974 that hospitals collect on all discharges and all discharge abstract systems.

**Unsecured PHI:** Protected health information that is not rendered unusable, unreadable, or indecipherable to unauthorized persons through the use of technology or methodology specified by the HHS secretary in guidance in the HITECH Law.

**Use case:** A technique used for capturing and documenting user requirements, developed in conjunction with requirements gathering to identify and clarify the interactions between an end user and the proposed system in achieving a specific goal.

# V

**Validation and verification model (V-model):** A SDLC model that integrates testing design with all the life cycle stages, beginning at the requirements analysis stage and extending through the implementation stage.

**Value conflicts:** A data integration concern that happens when using different metrics as data values. For example, a potential value conflict is the use of pounds versus kilograms.

**Value validity:** A dimension of data validity where a value is within a specified range of values.

**Vocabulary:** A collection of words or phrases with their meanings, that is, a dictionary of those terms.

# W

**Waterfall method:** A systems development life cycle (SDLC) implementation method where development proceeds serially from one stage to the next, flowing forward like a waterfall.

**Web content management (WCM):** The process of controlling the content of a website through the use of specific management tools based on a core repository, usually include functionality for editing and versioning content, tracking media check out and check in, and cataloguing and indexing content.

**Workforce management systems:** Systems that support staffing needs assessments and workforce balance, capacity planning, and clinical staff scheduling.

**Write-back reports:** Interactive reports that directly link to the data warehouse, allows modification of the data.

# Index


## A

Abbreviations, 13
Access controls, 222
Accessing data, 223, 236–237, 249
Accessing records. *See* Record accessibility
Accreditation, 17, 25–26
Acute care settings, 12, 13–15
Ad hoc reports, 236
Administrative controls, 211, 214–215, 217, 222
Administrative data
  defined, 13
  emergency department information systems and, 49
  list of, 14–15
  mapping of, 283
  radiology information systems and, 51
Administrative information systems, 52–56
  automated diagnostic coding, 54
  bed management, 54
  business intelligence management, 54
  defined, 52
  early, 28
  financial information systems, 54
  inpatient scheduling systems, 54
  interoperability with clinical applications, 56–57
  master patient index, 55
  record completion management, 55–56
  registration-admission-discharge-transfer (R-ADT) systems, 53
  request for and release of health information management, 56
  workforce management systems, 56
Administrative metadata, 163
Administrative primary data, 232
Administrative reporting, 271–274
Administrative safeguards, 214–215, 217–218, 308–309
Affordable Care Act (ACA), 209, 273
Agency for Healthcare Research and Quality, 28, 253
Aggregation, data integration and, 240
Agile development, 113
Amendments to electronic records, 13
American College of Surgeons (ACS), 25–26, 248
American Health Information Management Association (AHIMA)
  Certification Commission for Health Information Technology (CCHIT), 32, 39
  Core Model of Practice, 63–64
  data quality description, 249
  Data Quality Management (DQM) model, 252–257
  DG framework development, 82
  health information life cycle stages, 153
  history of, 36
  practice standards of, 62
  records, defined, 191
American Recovery and Reinvestment Act (ARRA), 214, 303
Analytics for business intelligence, 237–238
Anesthesia information management system (AIMS), 47
Anomaly detection, 237
Application controls, 222
Appointment scheduling, 7–9
ARMA International, 191
Artifacts, 105, 117
Association for Information and Image Management, 189
Association learning, 238
Association of Record Librarians of North America (ARLNA), 36. *See also* American Health Information Management Association (AHIMA)
Associative entities, 133
ASTM International, 157
Attribute, 127
Attribute reconstruction, data integration and, 241
Attribute redundancy, 240
Audit trail of events, 50, 222
Australian Government Recordkeeping Metadata Standard, 163
Authorized Testing and Certification Body (ATCB), 33
Automated diagnostic coding, 54
Automated patient identification, 47
Awareness training, 221

## B

Backward mapping, 285
Bar code point of care (BPOC), 47, 50
Bar coding identification system, 31
Basic interoperability, 281
Bed management systems, 54
Benchmarking, 233–234
Best of suite, 38
Best practices
  for clinical documentation, 12–13
  for DG programs, 94
  early, 26
Best-of-breed systems, 29, 38, 182
Bidirectional mapping, 285
Big data, 69, 229. *See also* Business intelligence (BI)
Billing. *See* Reimbursement claims
Breach of security, 209–210, 311

Bus topology, 57
Business associate (BA), 208
Business case for data governance, 82, 94
Business continuity plan (BCP), 223
Business intelligence (BI), 229–246
 architecture for, 242–243
 data for decisions, 234–238
 data governance and, 243–244
 data life cycle for, 239–242
 defined, 69, 229
 healthcare organizations and, 230–234
 maturity models for, 238–239
Business intelligence (BI) systems, 54
Business metadata, 143–144, 146–148
Business rule, 151, 153
Business rule validity, 251
Business stewards, 90
Business use case, 117

# C

Canadian Health Information Management Association, 153
Canadian Institute for Health Information (CIHI) Data Quality Framework, 250, 257–259
Cardinality, 131–132
Center for Drug Evaluation and Research, 274
Centralized metadata architecture, 164
Certification
 of EHR inspection process, 39
 for medical record librarians, 36
Certification Commission for Health Information Technology (CCHIT), 32, 39
Certified EHR technology, 33, 283
Chain of custody, 51
Chief executive officer (CEO), 37
Chief financial officer (CFO), 36
Chief information officer (CIO), 37
Chief information security officer (CISO), 217
Chief security officer (CSO), 217
Classification, 238, 267, 268
Classification management, 70
Classification systems management. *See* Terminology and classification systems management
Clerks of medical records, early, 26
Client computer, 57
Clinical care pathways, 51
Clinical data repository (CDR), 38, 47
Clinical documentation, 12–13, 231–232
Clinical information systems (CIS), 46–52
 anesthesia information management system (AIMS), 47
 automated patient identification and bar coding, 47
 benefits of, 46
 clinical data repository (CDR), 47
 clinical information systems (CIS), 46
 computerized physician/provider order entry (CPOE) systems, 47–48
 critical care information systems (CCIS), 48
 defined, 46
 dietary department and management systems, 48–49
 electronic document management (EDM) systems, 49
 emergency department information system (EDIS), 49
 interoperability with administrative applications and, 56–57
 laboratory information systems (LIS), 49
 medication administration systems (MAS), 50
 medication reconciliation systems, 50
 monitoring systems, 50
 nursing information systems (NIS), 50
 operating room management systems, 50–51
 patient care pathways, 51
 pharmacy information systems, 51
 picture archiving and communication system (PACS), 52
 radiology information systems (RIS), 51
 real time locatory systems (RTLS), 51
 results reporting, retrieval, and management, 52
Clinical primary data, 231–232
Club of Record Clerks, 36
Cluster detection, 238
Codes for reimbursement, 29, 54, 272–274
Coexistence implementation, 183
Collaboration tools, 196–197
College of Healthcare Information Management Executives (CHIME), 37
Columbia University Medical Center of New York Presbyterian Hospital, 275–276
Commercial off-the-shelf software (COTS), 165
Committee on Data Standards for Patient Safety, 32
Computed tomography (CT) storage, 52
Computer code, metadata and, 146, 148
Computer networks, interoperability and, 57
Computer physical order entry (CPOE) systems, 31
Computer Stored Ambulatory Care Record (COSTAR), 28
Computer-aided software engineering (CASE) tools, 107, 115, 135–136, 153
Computer-assisted-coding (CAC), 54
Computer-based patient record (CPR) systems, 30–32
Computer-based patient records (CPRs), 7, 37–38. *See also* Electronic health records (EHRs)
Computerized physician/provider order entry (CPOE), 47–48, 232
Computers on wheels (COWs), 50
Conceptual data models, 125, 131–132
Conference on Data Systems, 126–127
Confidentiality. *See also* Data security management
 data flow and information retrieval, 8
 data security management, 69
 defined, 211
 hospital information technology (HIT) and, 31

Connectivity engines, 38–39
Consolidated implementation, 183
Consolidating healthcare organizations, 283–284
Content, 190–192
Content exchange standards, 282
Content life cycle management, 201–202
Content management, 69, 189–206. *See also* Enterprise content and record management
Content standards, 282
Context, 190–191
Context diagrams for data flow diagrams, 121–124
Contingency approach to data governance, 96–97
Contingency planning, 223
Continuity of care record (CCR), 157–160
Continuum of care, 29, 50, 55
Controlled terminology, 274
Controlled vocabularies, 57, 70, 159
Controls in data governance, 86–87
Coordinating stewards, 90
Core Model of Practice (AHIMA), 63–64
Corporate data quality management framework, 95–96
Corporate Information Factory (CIF), 242
Cost of healthcare, 3
Cost of hospital information technology, 31
Cost reduction, 32–35
Covered entity (CE), 208
Critical care information systems (CCIS), 48
Cross-referencing data, 174
Current Procedural Terminology (CPT), 159, 273
Custodians of data. *See* Data stewards and custodians
Customer relationship management (CRM) systems, 173
Customized maps, 284

# D

Dashboards, 236
Data
  administrative. *See* Administrative data
  defined, 12
  exchange of. *See* Exchange of data
  metadata, 143–170. *See also* Metadata
Data accessibility, 223, 236–237, 249
Data accuracy, 29, 249. *See also* Errors in data
Data acquisition, 239–240
Data administration (DA). *See* Enterprise information management (EIM)
Data Administration Charter, 71
Data architecture management, 105–141
  data governance and, 138–139
  decision-making for, 90
  defined, 105
  documentation techniques and tools, 117–136. *See also* Documentation techniques and tools
  electronic health information management and, 67–68
  for master data management, 182–184
  requirement analysis for, 114–117
  SDLC development methods, 109–113
  system initiation and, 108–109
  systems development life cycle and, 106–108
Data availability, 212
Data breach, 209
Data cleansing, 177, 240
Data comprehensiveness, 249
Data consistency, 223, 249
Data content quality, 251
Data currency, 249
Data custodian. *See* Data stewards and custodians
Data decision rights and accountabilities, 81, 86
Data definition, 223, 249
Data dictionaries (DDs), 133, 135–136, 164, 223
Data flow and retrieval, 7–11, 18, 121
Data flow diagrams (DFDs), 120–125
Data for decision making, 233–238
Data governance (DG), 79–104
  business intelligence and, 243–244
  case for, 81–82
  data architecture management and, 138–139
  data quality management and, 259–261
  data security management and, 224–225
  definitions and concepts of, 4, 80–81
  enterprise content and record management, 202–203
  enterprise health information management and, 70
  frameworks and methodologies of, 82–100. *See also* Frameworks of data governance
  life cycle of, 88–89
  master data management, 184–185
  metadata and, 167–168
  terminology and classification systems management and, 288–289
Data Governance Institute (DGI), 64
Data Governance Institute (DGI) framework, 82, 85–89
Data Governance Office (DGO), 88, 90
Data governance teams, 165
Data granularity, 249
Data integration, 240–241
Data integrity, 211–212, 222
Data life cycle management. *See also* Systems development life cycle (SDLC)
  business intelligence and, 239–242
  enterprise content and record management, 201–202
  enterprise health information management and, 66–67
  metadata and, 153–155
Data management. *See* Master data management
Data Management Association (DAMA), 64–65, 82, 145, 192
Data Management Association (DAMA) framework, 90–91
Data management services, 90
Data mapping, 283–287

Data marts, 241–243
Data matching, 177–181
  deterministic, 178
  probabilistic, 178–179
  standardization rules for, 178
  steps in, 179–180
  surveillance, 180–181
  validation and remediation, 180
Data mining, 237, 241
Data modeling, 130–134
Data models, 125–129
Data precision, 249
Data privacy, 211
Data profiling, 85, 176
Data quality control processes, 223
Data quality management, 247–265
  AHIMA Data Quality Management (DQM) model, 252–257
  CIHI Data Quality Framework, 257–259
  data governance and, 259–261
  defined, 70
  dimensions of, 249–251
  GS1 Data Quality Framework 3.0, 259–261
  state of, 248–249
Data quality presentation, 251
The Data Quality Vector (DQV), 250
Data reduction, 241
Data redundancy, 125, 132
Data relevancy, 249
Data repositories. *See* Repositories
Data security, 69, 207, 211
Data security management, 207–227
  access and use of patient data, 208–209
  best-of-breed systems and, 29
  data governance and, 224–225
  defined, 69
  developing program for, 216–223
  health information users and, 18
  HIPAA and, 214–215
  hospital information technology and, 31–32
  security breaches, 209–210
  security concepts, 210–212
  security threats, 212–213
  shared services and, 28
  terms used for, 208
Data security program development, 216–223
  evaluating risk and vulnerability, 219–221
  organization of, 217
  planning, 217–218
  protection, detection, and response, 221–223
Data set, 277
Data set standards
  Uniform Ambulatory Care Data Set (UACDS), 280
  Uniform Hospital Discharge Data Set (UHDDS), 278–279
Data silos
  breaking down, 38–39
  data governance and, 82
  health information system evolution and, 25, 28
  metadata and, 145, 165
Data stakeholders, 87
Data stewards and custodians
  Data Governance Institute (DGI) framework and, 87
  for metadata, 165
  Oracle best practices in data governance framework and, 94
  organization of, 71
  purpose of, 83
  types of, 90
Data stewardship, 87, 90
Data store (DS), 121
Data timeliness, 249
Data transformations, 240–241
Data warehouses, 241
Databases
  data architecture and, 105
  data warehouses, 241
  metadata and, 145, 147
  normalization of, 132–133
  prescription database companies, 209
  structures used for, 125–129
Data-information-knowledge model, 25–26
Death certificates, 13
Decision making
  business information data for, 233–236
  data governance and, 81, 86, 90, 94–95, 97–98
  levels of, 235–236
  technological influences on, 31
Decision rights, 81, 86
Defense Department, 31
Deficiencies in records, 55–56
Demographic data, 12, 13
Derivation validity, 251
Descriptive analytics, 237
Descriptive metadata, 163
Design artifacts, 105, 117
Deterministic matching, 178
Diagnosis-related groups (DRGs), 29, 37, 54
Diagnostic codes for reimbursement, 29, 54, 272–274. *See also specific types of codes*
Dictionary thesaurus, 199
Dietary department and management systems, 48–49
Digital asset management (DAM), 197
Digital images of documents. *See* Scanning documents
Digital Imaging and Communications in Medicine (DICOM) standard, 52
Digital radiography image storage, 52
Disaster planning, 223
Discrepancy detection, 240

Discriminating attributes, 179
Disease and operation indexes, 146, 233
Distributed metadata architecture, 164–165
Document, 191
Document analysis, 115
Document imaging, 193
Document management, 192–196
Document management system (DMS), 193
Documentation techniques and tools, 117–137
 CASE tools, 135
 data dictionaries, 135–136
 data flow diagrams, 120–125
 data modeling, 130–134
 data models, 125–129
 use cases, 117–1120
Domains of EHIM. *See* Enterprise health information management (EHIM) domains
Domains of practice, 63–66
Drummand Group, Inc., 39
Dublin Core metadata schema, 156–157, 163
Duplicate identifiers, 180
Duplicate records, 8, 28, 29, 55, 81
 data matching and, 177, 180

# E

Edit checks, 222
Education
 health information, use of, 17
 of medical records librarians, 36
Efficiency, 32–35
Electrical outages, 213
Electronic content management, 193
Electronic document management (EDM), 49, 193–196
Electronic document management systems (EDMS), 193–196, 231
Electronic health information systems, 45–59
 administrative information systems, 52–56. *See also* Administrative information systems
 clinical information systems, 46–52. *See also* Clinical information systems (CIS)
 data silos and, 38–39
 defined, 45
 interoperability of, 39–41. *See also* Interoperability
 system interoperability, 56–57
 vendors of. *See* Vendors of EHRs
Electronic health record (EHR). *See also* Computer-based patient records (CPRs)
 adoption rate for, 39–41
 capabilities of by stage, 40
 core functionalities, 33
 data integrity and, 211–212
 data quality and, 247
 defined, 7
 errors in, 13, 21
 hybrid health information systems and, 31–32
 incentives to use, 33, 283
 interoperability of, 32, 39, 281–283
 IOM vision for, 29–30, 37–38
 organization data silos, 38–39
 as primary data source, 231
 problem list for, 29
 vendors of. *See* Vendors of EHRs
Electronic medical record (EMR), 7. *See also* Electronic health records (EHRs)
Electronic records management (ERM), 193–196
Electronic records management systems (ERMS), 192–196
Electronic spreadsheets, 126
Electronic-based systems, 27–31
Electronic-ICU systems (e-ICU), 48
Embedded business intelligence (BI), 236
Embedded metadata, 145, 163
Emergency department information system (EDIS), 49
Employees, security breaches and, 210, 212–213
Encapsulation, 129
Encoding metadata, 156–157, 159
Enterprise content and record management (ECRM), 189–206
 classification alternatives for, 197–201
 concepts of, 190–192
 data governance and, 202–203
 defined, 189–190
 document, content, and record management, 192–196
 life cycle management of, 201–202
 tools for, 196–197
Enterprise content management (ECM), 189, 193–196
Enterprise DAM tools, 197
Enterprise data modeling, 125
Enterprise health information management (EHIM) domains, 63–70. *See also specific domains*
 business intelligence and big data, 69
 content and record management, 69
 data architecture management, 67–68
 data governance, 70
 data life cycle management, 66–67
 data quality management, 70, 247
 data security management, 69
 master data management, 68–69
 metadata management, 68
 terminology and classification management, 70
Enterprise information management (EIM), 295–302
 benefits of, 72–73
 data governance deliverables table, 297–298
 defined, 4
 implementing, 15
 organization and structure of, 71
 purpose of, 15
 retreat for planning for, 296–301. *See also* Retreat for EIM

Enterprise master patient index (EMPI), 38–39, 55
Enterprise resource planning (ERP), 232
Entity, 127
Entity identification, 240
Entity-relationship diagrams (ERDs), 130–131
Environmental threats to data, 213
EPIC, 126
Equivalence, 286
Errors in data
  best of breed systems and, 38
  data governance and, 81–82, 86–87
  data integrity and, 211–212
  data quality and, 248–249
  data security and, 212
  in electronic records, 13, 21
  interoperability of systems and, 56–57
  mismatched data, 177
  opportunities for, 10
  in paper records, 13
  preventing, 32
Essential use case (business use case), 117
Ethics, electronic records and, 248
Exact match logic, 178
Exchange of data
  early issues with, 31
  interoperability of systems and, 56–57, 281–283
Exchange standards, 18, 274, 282
Executive data stewards, 90
Executive sponsors
  of data governance frameworks, 83, 94
  of metadata management, 161
  of system initiation, 108–109
External entity (EE), 121
External secondary data, 233–234
Extraction routines, 176
Extract-transform-load (ETL), 240

# F

Facet taxonomies, 197
Facilitator of retreat for EIM, 296
Fair and Accurate Credit Transaction Act (FACTA), 221
False negative record matches, 178
False positive record matches, 178
Federal Bureau of Investigation (FBI), 210
Federal Drug Administration (FDA), 274
Federal Emergency Management Agency (FEMA), 213
Federal Information Processing Standard 199, 218
Federated metadata architecture, 164
Feedback, 23–24
Financial information systems, 28, 54
Financial master data, 173
Fitness of use, 251, 258
Flat file structure, 125–126
Flat taxonomies, 197
Food inventories, 48–49
Foreign key (FK), 128
Forward map, 285
Foundational interoperability, 56
Fragmentation of data management, 37
Framework, 82
Framework for data matching, 179
Framework of metadata schemas, 155–156
Frameworks for data quality management
  AHIMA Data Quality Management (DQM) model, 252–257
  CIHI Data Quality Framework, 257–259
  GS1 Data Quality Framework 3.0, 259–261
Frameworks of data governance, 82–100
  contingency approach to DG and, 96–97
  for corporate data quality management, 95–96
  Data Governance Institute (DGI) framework, 85–89
  Data Management Association (DAMA) framework, 90–91
  healthcare DG implementation cases, 99–100
  IBM Data Governance Council Framework and Maturity Model, 92–93
  Khatri and Brown DG framework, 94–95
  Method for an Integrated Knowledge Environment (MIKE2.0), 82–85
  non-healthcare DG implementation cases, 98–99
  Oracle best practices in governance framework, 93–94
Fraud, 210
Functional interoperability, 281
Functional requirements, 115

# G

General Accounting Office, 281
General Equivalence Mappings (GEMs), 284
Generalization, data integration and, 241
Geospatial Data Lifecycle, 67
Governance, 94
Governance council, 83–84
Government-recognized maps, 284
GS1 Data Quality Framework 3.0, 259–261

# H

Hardware
  data security and, 210, 213
  shared, 28
Health, Education, and Welfare Department, 278
Health and Human Services (HHS) Department, 33, 39, 209–210, 214, 281
Health Evaluation through Logical Processing (HELP), 28
Health Finder website, 6

Health information, 3–19
    clinical documentation, 12–13
    data flow and retrieval complexity, 7–11
    defined, 6–7
    electronic systems for, 45–59. *See also* Electronic health information systems
    enterprise solution for, 3–6
    legal and administrative documentation, 13–15
    life cycle of, 153. *See also* Data life cycle management
    managing, 61–76. *See also* Health information management (HIM)
    systems for, 21–44. *See also* History of health information systems
    uses and users of, 15–18
Health information departments, 37
Health information exchanges (HIEs)
    defined, 10
    development of, 33
    interoperability of, 281
    meaningful use criteria for, 33–35
Health information management (HIM), 61–76
    domains of EHIM, 66–70. *See also* Enterprise health information management (EHIM) domains
    domains of practice, 63–66
    EIM benefits, 72–73
    EIM organization and structure, 71
    traditional practice of, 62–63
Health Information Resource Database, 6
Health Information Security and Privacy Collaboration (HISPC), 32
Health information systems
    electronic, 45–59. *See also* Electronic health information systems
    history of, 21–44. *See also* History of health information systems
Health Information Technology for Economic and Clinical Health (HITECH) Act, 3, 33, 209, 214, 303–304
Health Insurance Portability and Accountability Act (HIPAA), 303–314
    confidentiality and, 8
    data security management and, 209–211, 214–223
    health information, defined, 6
    key terms in, 208
    National Drug Codes (NDC) and, 274
    notice of privacy practices document, 14
    Omnibus Rule of 2013, 210
    outpatient services coding and, 273
    patient rights and, 56
    purpose of, 31
    records, defined, 191
Health Level Seven (HL7), 29, 38
Health maintenance organizations (HMOs), 29
Health record numbers, 26, 55
Healthcare Common Procedure Coding System (HCPCS), 273
Healthcare Cost and Utilization Project (HCUP), 234
Healthcare DG implementation scenarios, 99–100
Healthcare Information Management and Systems Society (HIMSS)
    Certification Commission for Health Information Technology (CCHIT), 39
    HIMSS Analytics, 39–41
Healthcare Information Technology Standards Panel (HITSP), 32
Healthcare organizations, 230–234
Hierarchical database model, 126–127
Hierarchical taxonomy model, 198
HIMSS Analytics, 39
HIPAA. *See* Health Insurance Portability and Accountability Act
HIPAA Omnibus Rule, 210
History of health information management, 62–63
History of health information systems, 21–44
    current challenges, 32–35
    electronic based systems, 27–31
    electronic health records, 37–41
    hybrid environment, 31–32
    management and governance, 36–37
    paper based systems, 25–27
    systems approach, 22–25
History of terminology and classification systems management, 268–271
Hospital Compare, 234
Hospital information technology (HIT)
    adoption of, 28–29
    barriers to, 31
    management challenges of, 31–32
    recommendations for, 32
Hospital Standardization Conference (1928), 36
Hospital Standardization Program, 25–26
Human resources, 81
Hybrid health information systems, 31–32
Hybrid metadata architecture, 165
Hybrid record, 31

# I

IBM Data Governance Council Framework and Maturity Model, 92–93
iCASE tools, 135
ICD-9-CM. *See* International Classification of Diseases, Ninth Revision, Clinical Modification
ICD-10-CM. *See* International Classification of Diseases, Tenth Revision, Clinical Modification
ICSA Labs, 39
Identity attributes, 179
Identity error, 177

Identity fraud, 55
Identity theft, 210, 221
Illinois State Records Act, 191
Implementation, 107
Incident detection, 221
Incident response, 222
Inconsistent data, 125–126
Individually identifiable health information, 208
Industry needs, 28
InforGard Laboratories, Inc., 39
Information, 12, 25
Information assets, 218
Information governance, 80. *See also* Data governance (DG)
Information intelligence, 69. *See also* Business intelligence (BI)
Information management thesaurus, 199
Information resources management (IRM), 36, 64
Information security, 69. *See also* Data security
Information security committee, 217
Information systems, 22–23, 65–66
Information systems security office (ISSO), 217
Information technology (IT). *See also* Hospital information technology (HIT)
  data governance and, 85, 90
  management of, early, 36–37
  master data and, 176
Informational privacy, 210–211
In-house systems, 28
Inpatient scheduling systems, 54
Input, 23–24
Institutes of Medicine (IOM)
  clinical information system, defined, 46
  Committee on Data Standards for Patient Safety, 32
  on computer-based records, 189
  EHRs recommendations, 29–30, 37–38
  error prevention recommendations, 32
  health information, defined, 6–7
  health information users, 17
  standardization, importance of, 267
Instrument management systems (IMS), 51
Insurance. *See* Health Insurance Portability and Accountability Act (HIPAA) of 2003
Integrated data warehouses, 241
Integrated delivery systems (IDS), 29
Integrated solutions, 38
Interactive fixed reports, 236
Interface engine, 57
Interfaces, 56–57
Intermountain Healthcare, 275–276
Internal secondary data, 232–233
International Classification of Diseases (ICD), 171, 269
International Classification of Diseases, Ninth Revision, Clinical Modification (ICD-9-CM), 29, 269, 272, 284
International Classification of Diseases, Tenth Revision, Clinical Modification (ICD-10-CM), 272–273, 284
International Health Terminology Standards Development Organisation (IHTSDO), 284
International Organization for Standardization (ISO), 190, 199
Internet, 39, 57, 210, 213
Interoperability
  of computer networks, 57
  data interchange standards and, 281–283
  defined, 39, 56, 281
  hospital information technology and, 31
  interfaces for, 57
  levels of, 56–57
Intersection entities, 133
Interviewing, 115–116
Iterative method, 112

# J

Joint application development (JAD), 116

# K

Key performance indicators (KPIs), 180–181
Keys, 127–128
Khatri and Brown DG framework, 94–95
Kimball Method, 242
Knowledge, 25

# L

Laboratory information system (LIS), 49
Leapfrog Group, 234
Legal documentation, 13–17, 32
Librarian of medical records, 36, 62
Licensure, 17
Light-Weight DAM tools, 197
Location master data, 173
Logical data models, 125, 132–133
Logical DFDs, 121
Logical Observational Identifiers, Names and Codes (LOINC), 159, 171, 274–275
Long-term care facilities, 12
Lower CASE tools, 135

# M

Machine data capture, 232
Magnetic resonance imaging (MRI) storage, 52
Mammogram image storage, 52
Managed metadata environment (MME), 161
Management, 94
Management charter for metadata, 161

Management controls, 220–222
Manifest files, 163
Massachusetts General Hospital Utility Multi-Programming System (MUMPS), 126
Master data, 172–173
Master data management, 171–187
  data concepts for, 172–174
  data governance and, 184–185
  data matching and, 177–181. *See also* Data matching
  defined, 174
  EHIM and, 68–69
  identifying data for, 175
  profiling and cleansing data for, 176–177
  technical systems for, 182–184
Master entities, 172–173
Master patient index (MPI), 38–39, 52, 55, 117, 171
Maturity models, 93–94
Maturity models for business intelligence, 238–239
Mayo Clinic, 275–276
Meaningful use (MU) criteria, 33–35
Medical Information Bureau (MIB), 209
Medical record numbers, 26, 55
Medical Subject Headings (MeSH), 199–200
Medicare and Medicaid
  claim form for, 278
  diagnosis-related groups and, 29, 37
  EHR incentive programs, 283
  federal financing through, 28
  long-term care facilities and, 12
  reimbursement and, 273
Medicare Provider Analysis and Review (MedPAR), 234
Medication administration record (MAR), 50
Medication administration systems (MAS), 50
Medication reconciliation systems, 50
Meditech, 126
Menu development, 48–49
Mesh topology, 57
Metadata, 143–170
  data dictionaries and, 135
  data governance and, 167–168
  data life cycle and, 153–155
  defined, 143
  for discrepancy detection, 240
  electronic health information management and, 68
  enterprise content and record management and, 200
  existing sources of, 150–153
  planning, 161–162
  purpose and types of, 145–149
  quality of, 166–167
  schemas for, 155–160, 162–163
Metadata repositories, 145, 161, 163–166, 241
Metadata schemas, 155–160, 162–163
Metadata silos, 165
Method for an Integrated Knowledge Environment (MIKE 2.0), 64, 82–85
Microsoft Access metadata, 145, 147, 153–154
Microsoft Word metadata, 145–146
Mid-Market DAM tools, 197
Migration path, 161
Mini-computers, 28, 29
Minimum Data Set for Long-Term Care Version 2.0 (MDS 2.0), 12
Mission statement, 84
Mobile devices, 50
Modality, 131
Monitoring systems, 50
Multiphasic screening programs, 29
MYCIN expert system, 28

# N

Naming conventions, 133–134
National Alliance for Health Information Technology (The Alliance), 39
National Ambulatory Medical Care Survey (NAMCS), 234
National Center for Health Statistics (NCHS), 269
National Codes, 273
National Committee on Vital and Health Statistics (NCVHS), 32, 278–279
National Drug Codes (NDCs), 274
National Health Information Center (NHIC), 6
National health information infrastructure (NHII), 32
National health information network (NHIN), 33, 39
National Hospital Ambulatory Medical Care Survey (NHAMCS), 234
National Information Standards Organization, 145
National Library of Medicine (NLM), 6, 199
National Practitioner Databank (NPDB), 234
Natural disasters, security and, 213
Network controls, 222–223
Network database model, 126–127
Networks, computer, 57
Nomenclature, 267, 268
Non-functional requirements, 115
Non-healthcare DG implementation cases, 98–99
Nonvolatile data warehouses, 241
Normalization, data integration and, 241
Normalization of databases, 132–133
Notation styles for data flow diagrams, 121–122
Nursing homes, 12
Nursing information systems (NIS), 50

# O

Object-oriented (OO) database, 128
Observation, 115
Office of Civil Rights (OCR), 210

Office of the National Coordinator for Health Information Technology (ONC), 3, 32–33, 39, 148, 281
ONC Authorized Testing and Certification Body (ONC-ATCB), 39
Online analytical processing (OLAP) systems, 241
Online transaction processing (OLTP) systems, 241
Ontologies, 200
Open source frameworks, 82
Operating room management systems, 50–51
Operational controls, 220–223
Operational databases, 241
Operational decision making, 236
Operational primary data, 232
Oracle best practices in governance framework, 93–94
Order entry systems, 24, 47–48
Outpatient Prospective Payment System (OPPS) Data, 234
Outpatient service coding, 273
Outpatient Standard Analytic File (SAF), 234
Output, 23–24
Overlap, 177
Overlay, 177, 180

# P

Paper based systems
  errors in records and, 13
  evolution of health information systems and, 25–27
  health information management and, 62
  hybrid health information systems and, 31–32
  metadata in, 143
  scanning, 31, 49
Parallel method of SDLC, 110–111
Party data, 173
Patient care pathways, 51
Patient health information (PHI). *See* Data security management
Patient management. *See* Registration-admission-discharge-transfer (R-ADT) systems
Patient records, 7
Patient requests for health information, 16, 56
PDF files, 52
Performance scorecard, 236
Perioperative information systems, 50–51
Person, 208
Personal digital assistants (PDAs), 50
Personal health records (PHRs), 7. *See also* Electronic health records (EHRs)
Pharmacy information systems, 51
Physical access controls, 211, 222
Physical data modeling, 125, 133–134
Physical DFDs, 121
Physical safeguards, 211, 215, 309
Physician indexes, 233
Picture archiving and communication system (PACS), 52
Point-of-care (POC), 231
Point-to-point interfaces, 57
Policies, 84
Policy making, 17
Portable Document Format (PDF), 52
Positron emission tomography (PET) storage, 52
Predictive analytics, 237
Prescription database companies, 209
Primary data sources, 231–232
Primary key (PK), 128
Primary patient records, 7
Primary users, 209
Primary uses of health information, 16
Privacy. *See also* Data security management; Health Insurance Portability and Accountability Act (HIPAA)
  defined, 210–211
  health information users and, 18
  hospital information technology and, 31–32
Privacy Rights Clearinghouse, 210
Privacy Rule, 214
Probabilistic matching, 178–179
Probability level for data matching, 180
Problem list in EHRs, 29
Problem solving, 21–22
Problem-Oriented Medical Information System (PROMIS), 28, 29
Procedure codes for reimbursement, 29, 227–274
Process, 121
Product master data, 173
Profiling teams, 176
Program roadmaps, 89
Project charter, 109
Project management life cycle, 106
Project sponsors, 108–109
Project teams, 107, 109
Proprietary frameworks, 82
Proprietary or customized maps, 284
Protected health information (PHI), 208
Prototype, 112
Provider relationship management (PRM) systems, 173
Public health, 17, 39
Public Law 104-191, 214. *See also* Health Insurance Portability and Accountability Act (HIPAA)

# Q

Quality measure, 253

# R

RACI chart, 97
Radio frequency identification (RFID), 51
Radiography image storage, 52
Radiology information systems (RIS), 51
Rapid application development (RAD), 112–113
Real time locatory systems (RTLS), 51
Record, 190–191

Record accessibility
in hybrid systems, 31–32
patient requests and, 16, 56
recommendations for, 32
security and, 208–209
Record completion management, 55–56
Record linkage, 180
Record management, 69, 192–196. *See also* Enterprise content and record management (ECRM)
Record qualification attributes, 179
Red flags for identity theft, 221
Redundancy of data, 125, 132
Reference data, 171, 173–174
Regenstrief Medical Record System (RMRS), 28
Registration-admission-discharge-transfer (R-ADT) systems, 48–49, 53
Registries, 233
Registry data hub, 183
Regression, 238
Regulation, 17
Reimbursement claims
clinical documentation for, 12
diagnosis-related groups and, 29, 37, 54
diagnostic codes for, 29, 54, 272–274
Relational database model, 127
Relationships, data mapping and, 284
Reporting data, 236–237
Repositories
business intelligence and, 241–242
for clinical data, 38, 47
for metadata, 145, 161, 163–166, 241
Request for and release of health information management, 56
Requirements analysis, 107, 114–117, 284
Requirements gathering techniques, 115–117
Requisition, 108–109
Research
health information, use of, 17
multiphasic screening programs for, 29
Results reporting, 52
Retreat for enterprise information management
agenda for, 298–300
planning, 296–298
summary of, 300–301
Revenue cycle management, 37
Reverse map, 285
Rights metadata, 163
Ring topology, 57
Risk analysis, 219
Risk assessment, 113
Risk management
clinical documentation for, 12
controls in DG for, 86–87
data security and, 221
Rules, 84
Rules of engagement, 84
RxNorm, 159

# S

Safety, HIT and, 32–35
Scanning documents, 31, 49
Scheduling, 7–9, 54
Scoreboard, 236
Secondary data sources, 232–234
Secondary patient record, 7
Secondary users, 209
Secondary uses of health information, 16–17
Security awareness program, 221
Security of data. *See* Data security management
Security organizations, 217
Security plan, 217–218
Security Rule of HIPAA, 214, 217, 304–305
Security test and evaluation (ST&E), 220
Security threat, 219–220
The Sedona Conference, 145
Semantic interoperability, 57, 281
Semantics, metadata and, 163
Sequence diagram use case, 117, 120
Server computers, 57
Shared services, 28
Single vendor integrated solutions, 38
SLI Global Solutions, 39
SMART goals, 86
Smoothing, data integration and, 240
SNOMED-CT. *See* Systematized Nomenclature of Medicine Clinical Terms
Social media, security and, 213
Software
for computer-based patient records, 29
data security and, 210, 213
for document management, 194
interfaces, 57
for master data management, 182
for metadata repositories, 165
shared, 28
Software application controls, 222
Software Engineering Institute (SEI), 93
Source set, 284
Spending on healthcare, 3
Spiral method, 113
Sponsors. *See* Executive sponsors
Spreadsheets, 126
Staff management, 56
Staging area, 243
Stakeholders, metadata and, 161
Standard vocabularies, 159
Standardization
Hospital Standardization Program and, 25–26
of naming in data models, 133–134

Standardization rules, matching with, 178
Standardized Nomenclature of Diseases (SND), 269
Standards development, 281–283
Standards development organization maps, 284
Star topology, 57
State Health Information Exchange (State HIE), 33
Static reports, 236
Statistical reporting, terminologies and classifications for, 271–274
Stewards of data. *See* Data stewards and custodians
Strategic decision making, 235
Strategic policies, 84
Structural interoperability, 56–57
Structure, 190
Structure and content standards, 282
Structured data entry techniques, 231
Subject-oriented data warehouses, 241
Subsystems
business intelligence management and, 54
critical care information systems and, 48, 50–51
defined, 22–25
Surescripts, LLC, 39
Symbols in records, 13
Syntax, metadata and, 163
System, 22–23
System design, construction, acceptance, and implementation, 107
System directories, 153
System initiation, 107–109
System interoperability, 56–57
System of record (SOR), 175
System use case, 117
Systematized Nomenclature of Medicine Clinical Terms (SNOMED-CT)
continuity of care record and, 159
history of, 269
master data management and, 171
overview, 274
standards development organization maps for, 284
Systems development life cycle (SDLC)
development methods, 109–113
initiating, 108–109
managing, 106
for record management, 192
stages of, 107–108

# T

Table, 127
Tactical decision making, 235–236
Tactical policies, 84
Target set, 284
Taxonomies, 197–198
TDWI Business Intelligence Maturity Model, 238–239
Technical controls, 220–223
Technical metadata, 143–147, 163
Technical safeguards, 211, 215, 309–310
Technicon Medical Information System, 28, 29
Telemedicine, 48
Terminology, 268
Terminology and classification systems management, 267–292
for administrative and statistical reporting, 271–274
challenges in, 275–277
data governance and, 288–289
data mapping, 283–287
data set standards, 277–280
for healthcare, 268
history of, 268–271
interoperability and data interchange standards, 281–283
other types of, 274–275
Terminology differences, 46
Terminology management, 70
Textual use case, 117–119
Theft of information, 210, 212
Thesauri, 199–200
Threats to data security, 210–212
Thresholds for data matching, 180
Time-variant data warehouses, 241
Tracking data transmission, 18
Transaction data, 172
Transaction hub implementation, 183–184
Tuple, 127
Turnkey systems, 28

# U

Unidirectional mapping, 285
Unified Medical Language System (UMLS), 269
Uniform Ambulatory Care Data Set (UACDS), 280
Uniform Bill 04 (UB-04), 278
Uniform Hospital Abstract Minimum Data Set, 278
Uniform Hospital Discharge Data Set (UHDDS), 12, 278–279
Unsecured PHI, 209, 311–312
Unstructured data, 69
Updating records, 18, 125–126
Upgrading systems, 38
Upper CASE tools, 135
Use cases, 117–120, 284
Uses and users of health information, 15–18

# V

Validation and verification model (V-model) of SDLC, 110–112
Value conflicts, 240

Value statements, 88–89
Value validity, 251
Vendor maps, 285
Vendors of EHRs
  best of suite systems and, 38
  best-of-breed systems and, 29, 38
  metadata and, 153
  single vendors, 38
Veterans Administration, 31
Veterans Affairs Department, 275–276
VistA, 126
Vocabulary, 268

Waterfall method of SDLC, 109–110
Web content management (WCM), 197
Workforce management systems, 56
World Health Organization (WHO), 269, 272, 284
World Wide Web, 57
Write-back reports, 236

## X

XML coding, 156–157, 159